Rehabilita

Rehabilitation Counseling: Basics and Beyond

THIRD EDITION

Edited by

Randall M. Parker
and
Edna Mora Szymanski

pro·ed
An International Publisher
8700 Shoal Creek Boulevard
Austin, Texas 78757-6897
800/897-3202 Fax 800/397-7633
Order online at http://www.proedinc.com

An International Publisher

© 1998, 1992, 1987 by PRO-ED, Inc.
8700 Shoal Creek Boulevard
Austin, Texas 78757-6897
800/897-3202 Fax 800/397-7633
Order online at http://www.proedinc.com

Library of Congress Cataloging-in-Publication Data

Rehabilitation counseling : basics and beyond / edited by Randall M.
    Parker, Edna Mora Szymanski. — 3rd ed.
        p.   cm.
    Includes bibliographical references and index.
    ISBN 0-89079-723-4 (alk. paper)
        1. Handicapped—Rehabilitation—United States.   2. Rehabilitation
    counseling.   I. Parker, Randall M., 1940-   .   II. Szymanski, Edna.
    HV1553.R445   1997
    362.4'0486—dc21   97-10241
                                                                CIP

This book is designed in Garamond and Concorde.

Production Manager: Alan Grimes
Production Coordinator: Karen Swain
Managing Editor: Chris Olson
Art Director: Thomas Barkley
Designer: Lee Anne Landry
Reprints Buyer: Alicia Woods
Preproduction Coordinator: Chris Anne Worsham
Copyeditor: Suzi Hunn
Editor: Debra Berman
Production Assistant: Claudette Landry
Production Assistant: Dolly Fisk Jackson

Printed in the United States of America

3   4   5   6   7   8   9   10   02   01   00

Contents

Preface

The purpose of this text is to provide both a basic foundation for students beginning their journey into the profession of rehabilitation counseling and a broad-based reference for current practitioners. The contents provide a conceptual overview of the professional, historical, theoretical, research, and applied foundations of the rehabilitation counseling profession. The information presented will illuminate contemporary practices and issues, as well as point out possible future directions. The value of this book, however, will be determined by the degree to which it inspires the reader to seek further knowledge and skills. Rehabilitation counseling is an evolving, mercurial profession that depends upon the commitment of today's rehabilitation students and practitioners to embrace their professional responsibility for lifelong learning.

This third edition of *Rehabilitation Counseling: Basics and Beyond* reflects the major changes in the field of rehabilitation counseling and consequently represents a substantial update of the previous edition. For example, Chapter 1, "Philosophical, Historical, and Legislative Aspects of the Rehabilitation Counseling Profession," was updated to reflect legislative and professional developments, as was Chapter 2, "The State–Federal Vocational Rehabilitation Program."

The following chapters also were substantially updated and revised: Chapter 3, "Rehabilitation Counseling in the Private Sector"; Chapter 4, "Independent Living"; Chapter 5, "School-to-Adult Life Transition and Supported Employment"; Chapter 6, "Ethics and Ethical Decision Making in Rehabilitation Counseling"; Chapter 7, "Theoretical Foundations of the Counseling Function"; Chapter 9, "Psychosocial Impact of Disability"; Chapter 10, "Career Development of People with

Disabilities: An Ecological Model"; and Chapter 13, "Research in Rehabilitation Counseling."

Three new chapters were added to this edition: Chapter 8, "Rehabilitation Counseling Practice: Considerations and Interventions"; Chapter 11, "The Constructs and Practices of Job Placement"; and Chapter 12, "Rehabilitation Client Assessment." We believe the addition of these chapters fills critical gaps that existed in the previous edition, particularly with regard to the applied aspects of counseling, job placement, and assessment.

Editing this book over three editions has been an exceptional opportunity for us as editors. Interacting with colleagues, old and new, in producing this book has been exhilarating. Working with scholars who are secure enough in their expertise to allow us to question, comment, suggest, and occasionally cajole them about their contributions, without complaint, was highly rewarding. We trust readers similarly will recognize the collective excellence of the contributors to this volume. This book is dedicated to the contributors who have dazzled us with their knowledge and inspired us with their devotion and diligence.

We also wish to recognize the contributions of our colleagues, students, and families for their support during the writing and editing of this book. Special thanks are due to Donald Hammill and Lee Wiederholt for their kind mentoring and friendship. We are extremely grateful to Jim Patton, Alan Grimes, and the PRO-ED production staff, who deserve recognition for their expertise and patience in bringing this book to fruition. Pam Brown and Mike Duckwitz provided valuable day-to-day assistance in handling the many tasks associated with editing a book. And above all, we acknowledge our spouses, who deserve sainthood for their love and tolerance.

Randall M. Parker
Edna Mora Szymanski

Contributors

Brian Bolton, PhD
Arkansas Rehabilitation Research and
   Training Center
University of Arkansas
346 West Avenue
Fayetteville, AR 72701

Robert Brabham, PhD
Rehabilitation Counseling Program
Department of Neuropsychiatry and
   Behavioral Science
School of Medicine
3555 Harden Street Extension,
   CEB Suite B20
University of South Carolina
Columbia, SC 29203

Alfred J. Butler, PhD
University of Wisconsin–Madison
Rehabilitation Psychology and Special
   Education
432 North Murray Street
Madison, WI 53706

John Butterworth, PhD
Institute for Community Inclusion
Children's Hospital
Garner 6
300 Longwood Avenue
Boston, MA 02115

Daniel Cook, PhD
Arkansas Rehabilitation Research and
   Training Center
University of Arkansas
346 East Avenue
Fayetteville, AR 72701

Denise DeLaGarza, PhD
Rehabilitation Counselor Education
Department of Special Education, D5300
University of Texas at Austin
Austin, TX 78712

Sheila Lynch Fesko, MS
Institute for Community Inclusion
Children's Hospital
Garner 6
300 Longwood Avenue
Boston, MA 02115

Cheryl Hanley-Maxwell, PhD
Department of Rehabilitation Psychology
   and Special Education
University of Wisconsin–Madison
432 North Murray Street
Madison, WI 53706

David B. Hershenson, PhD
Rehabilitation Counseling Program
College of Education
University of Maryland
College Park, MD 20742

William M. Jenkins, EdD
Rehabilitation Counselor Education
Department of Counseling and Personnel
    Services
Patterson Building
Memphis State University
Memphis, TN 38111

Lynn Koch, PhD
Kent State University
Educational Foundations and Special
    Services
405 White Hall
Kent, OH 44242

Ross K. Lynch, PhD
Professional Rehabilitation Services, Ltd.
Rehabilitation Counseling and
    Consulting
559 D'Onofrio Drive
Suite 100
Madison, WI 53719

Ruth Torkelson Lynch, PhD
Department of Rehabilitation Psychology
    and Special Education
University of Wisconsin–Madison
432 North Murray Street
Madison, WI 53706

Kerry A. Mandeville, MS
South Carolina Vocational Rehabilitation
    Department
1410 Boston Avenue
P.O. Box 15
West Columbia, SC 29171-0015

Henry McCarthy, PhD
Louisiana State University Medical Center
School of Allied Health
Department of Rehabilitation Counseling
1900 Gravier Street
New Orleans, LA 70112-2262

Michael J. Millington, PhD
Louisiana State University Medical Center
School of Allied Health
Department of Rehabilitation Counseling
1900 Gravier Street
New Orleans, LA 70112-2262

Margaret A. Nosek, PhD
Center for Research on Women
    with Disabilities
3440 Richmond Avenue
Houston, TX 77046-3403

Laura Owens-Johnson, MS
Department of Rehabilitation Psychology
    and Special Education
University of Wisconsin–Madison
432 North Murray Street
Madison, WI 53706

Randall M. Parker, PhD
Rehabilitation Counselor Education
Department of Special Education, D5300
University of Texas at Austin
Austin, TX 78712

Jeanne Boland Patterson, EdD
6350 Verdura Way
Tallahassee, FL 32311-9368

James Schaller, PhD
Rehabilitation Counselor Education
Department of Special Education, D5300
University of Texas at Austin
Austin, TX 78712

Edna Mora Szymanski, PhD
Department of Rehabilitation Psychology
    and Special Education
University of Wisconsin–Madison
432 North Murray Street
Madison, WI 53706

Kenneth R. Thomas, EdD
Department of Rehabilitation Psychology
    and Special Education
University of Wisconsin–Madison
432 North Murray Street
Madison, WI 53706

Richard W. Thoreson, PhD
Department of Educational and
    Counseling Psychology
University of Missouri–Columbia
Columbia, MO 65201

Chapter 1

Philosophical, Historical, and Legislative Aspects of the Rehabilitation Counseling Profession

William M. Jenkins, Jeanne Boland Patterson, and Edna Mora Szymanski

Rehabilitation counseling is a challenging profession with a rich history and a promising future. Today's rehabilitation counseling graduates have more opportunities and challenges than any previous group entering the profession. The future development of the profession is, however, rooted in the foundation of the past. Thus, to the extent that professionals are unfamiliar with the history and philosophical foundation of rehabilitation counseling, they are unprepared to deal with its future challenges.

Rehabilitation counseling was once considered to be tightly bound to, if not synonymous with, the State–Federal Rehabilitation Program. This is no longer the case, however, and *the State–Federal Rehabilitation Program is now but one of a growing number of settings in which rehabilitation counselors practice.* Thus, the study of the historical foundation of rehabilitation counseling requires not only a study of the evolution of the State–Federal Rehabilitation Program, but also a study of philosophy, history, and legislation relating to people with disabilities and those who serve them. This chapter presents the following topics: (a) rehabilitation philosophy, (b) rehabilitation and related legislation, (c) rights legislation and litigation, and (d) the rehabilitation counseling profession. Interested readers can delve further into rehabilitation history by consulting E. D. Berkowitz (1979b),

Note. We gratefully acknowledge the assistance of the following individuals: Jeff Blattner, Senator Kennedy's staff; Faith Kirk, President's Committee on Employment of People with Disabilities; Larry Mars, Rehabilitation Services Administration; John Maxson, Research and Training Center on Blindness and Low Vision; and Len Perlman, legislative consultant.

Koestler (1976), Matkin (1985), Obermann (1965), Rasch (1985), Rubin and Roessler (1987), and G. Wright (1980).

Rehabilitation Philosophy

Rehabilitation has been defined as "a holistic and integrated program of medical, physical, psychosocial, and vocational interventions that empower a [person with a disability] to achieve a personally fulfilling, socially meaningful, and functionally effective interaction with the world" (Banja, 1990, p. 615). Within the context of rehabilitation counseling, *rehabilitation is defined as a comprehensive sequence of services, mutually planned by the consumer and rehabilitation counselor, to maximize employability, independence, integration, and participation of people with disabilities in the workplace and the community.* The basic philosophical tenets of rehabilitation include a recognition of the impact of disability on individuals, declarations concerning individual rights, and the suggestion of strategies to achieve the goals of rehabilitation (Maki & Riggar, 1985). Rehabilitation philosophy, which is an expression of these tenets, has remained relatively stable over time, although many changes have occurred in circumstances surrounding rehabilitation service delivery.

A study of rehabilitation philosophy over the years reveals a long history of belief in, and advocacy for, the rights of people with disabilities. Over 30 years ago, Talbot (1961) referred to rehabilitation as a way of living based on client self-awareness and fulfillment of individual capacities. More than 20 years ago, Bitter (1970) wrote that the equality of opportunity and the holistic nature and uniqueness of individuals "form a philosophical foundation for the practice of rehabilitation in America" (p. 4). Since 1959, Beatrice Wright (1959, 1972, 1983) has updated the list of basic values and beliefs that undergird rehabilitation philosophy (see Table 1.1).

Rehabilitation philosophy has been operationalized over time through various concepts and models of rehabilitation service delivery, including (a) the concept of zero-exclusion, which was initially introduced in relation to special education litigation in the 1970s, and means that no individuals should be excluded from services, regardless of the severity of their disability (Laski, 1985; Wehman, 1988); (b) ecological models of rehabilitation, which recognize the impact of environments on individuals and the importance of environmental modification (DeJong, 1979; Hahn, 1985; Szymanski, Dunn, & Parker, 1989); (c) postemployment services and supported employment (Wehman, 1988); (d) advocacy (Noble & McCarthy, 1988); (e) empowerment (Banja, 1990; Beck, 1994; Hahn, 1991; Nosek, 1988); (f) choice (Curl & Sheldon, 1992); and (g) the recognition that people with disabilities are the best judges of their own interests and are entitled to full participation in the political and economic life of their communities (DeJong, 1979). Often, rehabilitation philosophy has also influenced legislation, as is revealed by the chronology discussed in the next section.

Table 1.1
Basic Principles of Rehabilitation Philosophy

1. Every human being has an inalienable value and is worthy of respect for [her] his own sake.

2. Every person has membership in society, and rehabilitation should cultivate [her] his full acceptance.

3. The assets of people with disabilities should be emphasized, supported, and developed.

4. Reality factors should be stressed in helping the person to cope with [her] his environment.

5. Comprehensive treatment involves the "whole person," because life-areas are interdependent.

6. Treatment should vary and be flexible to deal with the special characteristics of each person.

7. Every person should assume as much initiative and participation as possible in the rehabilitation plan and its execution.

8. Society should be responsible, through all possible public and private agencies, for the providing of services and opportunities to [people with disabilities].

9. Rehabilitation programs must be conducted with interdisciplinary and interagency integration.

10. Rehabilitation is a continuous process that applies as long as help is needed.

11. Psychological and personal reactions of the individual are ever present and often crucial.

12. The rehabilitation process is complex and must be subject to constant reexamination—for each individual and for the program as a whole.

13. The severity of a handicap can be increased or diminished by environmental conditions.

14. The significance of a disability is affected by the person's feelings about the self and his or her situation.

15. The client is seen not as an isolated individual but as part of a larger group that includes other people, often the family.

16. Predictor variables, based on group outcomes in rehabilitation, should be applied with caution to the individual case.

17. Self-help organizations are important allies in the rehabilitation effort.

18. Provision must be made for the effective dissemination of information concerning legislation and community offerings of potential benefit to persons with disabilities.

19. Basic research can profitably be guided by the question of usefulness in ameliorating problems, a vital consideration in rehabilitation fields, including psychology.

20. Persons with disabilities should be called upon to serve as coplanners, coevaluators, and consultants to others, including professional persons.

Note. Principles 1 through 12, known as the Basic Dozen Principles, are from "The Current Scene," by S. G. DiMichael, 1969, in D. Malikin and H. Rusalem (Eds.), *Vocational Rehabilitation of the Disabled: An Overview,* pp. 12–13. New York: New York University Press. Copyright 1969 by New York University Press. Principles 13 through 20, printed here in changed order, are from *Physical Disability—A Psychosocial Approach* (2nd ed., pp. xi–xvii), by B. Wright, 1983, New York: Harper & Row. Copyright 1983 by Harper & Row.

Rehabilitation and Related Legislation

Legislation has affected many facets of the lives of people with disabilities; for example, it has provided for rehabilitation services, authorized financial support, guaranteed education, and promoted civil rights. Rehabilitation and related legislation has often been intertwined with legislation regarding financial support, education, and treatment of people with disabilities (Boggs, Hanley-Maxwell, Lakin, & Bradley, 1988; Laski, 1985). Thus, discussion of rehabilitation and related legislation requires an overview of a wide range of topics, including (a) the State–Federal Rehabilitation Program, (b) administration of public rehabilitation programs, (c) workers' compensation and insurance benefit systems, (d) other disability compensation programs, and (e) social security and developmental disability programs.

The State–Federal Rehabilitation Program

The rehabilitation of individuals with disabilities in the United States began with private philanthropic and voluntary charitable organizations. These groups encouraged states to establish vocational rehabilitation programs, and several such state programs were in place prior to passage of the first federal civilian rehabilitation legislation (Meyers, 1968). The sequence of legislation, culminating with the 1992 Amendments to the Rehabilitation Act of 1973, generally reflects an expansion in types of services, target disabilities, and general program capability from this early foundation. This chronology is depicted in Appendix 1.A.

Federal rehabilitation legislation had its roots in vocational education. Passage of the Smith–Hughes Act of 1917 (Public Law [P.L.] 64-347) provided federal grants to states to support vocational education and created the Federal Board for Vocational Education as the administrative agency (see Lassiter, 1972). World War I added another dimension to vocational education with the 1918 Soldier Rehabilitation Act (P.L. 65-178), which authorized vocational training and placement for veterans with disabilities (Obermann, 1965).

Civilian rehabilitation began on a federal level in 1920 with passage of P.L. 66-236, commonly referred to as the Smith–Fess Act. The intent of early civilian rehabilitation legislation was to encourage state vocational rehabilitation programs by providing grants-in-aid to state agencies that carried out approved services to citizens with disabilities. Funds were allocated to states according to population, and states were required to demonstrate financial commitment by matching their allotment on a 50–50 basis (McGowan & Porter, 1967). Early rehabilitation services were limited to *vocational* services (excluding medical, physical, and social forms of rehabilitation) and were restricted to persons with *physical* disabilities (Obermann, 1965).

Eight states had started programs of vocational rehabilitation, entirely state financed, before the Smith–Fess Act was passed, and within 18 months 34 states had become involved in the program. However, inadequate appropriations and a lack of support by many state administrative agencies made progress in the field irregular and slow for the next 15 years (Kratz, 1960). The federal government had no permanent commitment to the program; reaffirmation of the act and new appropriations had to be justified every few years.

Permanent and expanded federal financial support for vocational rehabilitation was not assured until its inclusion in P.L. 74-271, the Social Security Act of 1935 (Obermann, 1965). Major expansion of the program occurred with the Vocational Rehabilitation Amendments of 1943 (P.L. 78-113), referred to as the Barden–LaFollette Act. Emphasis was placed on the rehabilitation of people with mental retardation and mental illness, but, in actual practice, services to these individuals remained at a minimum (Thomas, 1970). A gap continued between client needs and provision of services, due to inadequate funds and facilities, as well as a lack of trained personnel. Also, funding was clearly insufficient to meet the increasing demands from the public that rehabilitation adopt "a more responsible place in dealing with the broad problems of disability among the American people" (Switzer, 1964, p. 20).

When signing the Vocational Rehabilitation Act Amendments of 1954 (P.L. 83-565), President Eisenhower stated that the law "re-emphasizes to all the world the great value which we in America place upon the dignity and worth of each individual human being" (Obermann, 1965, p. 316). The aim of the act was to assist the states "in rehabilitating . . . individuals [with disabilities] so that they may prepare for and engage in remunerative employment . . . thereby increasing not only their social and economic well-being but also the productive capability of the nation" (Vocational Rehabilitation Act Amendments, 1954, § 1).

The provisions of this act greatly increased the financial base for funding rehabilitation services. Special funding was provided for (a) extension and improvement of existing rehabilitation programs, (b) research and training programs, (c) preservice preparation of professional rehabilitation personnel (Switzer, 1969), and (d) expansion or establishment of rehabilitation facilities (e.g., workshops) and their programs (Obermann, 1965). Emphasis was placed on cooperative relationships with other agencies and organizations, both public and private (Lamborn, 1970). New types of service (i.e., work evaluation and work adjustment) serendipitously grew out of the 1954 legislation. The focus of these services was to help people who had primarily social or psychological, rather than physical, problems (Thomas, 1970).

During the early 1960s, the Kennedy administration strengthened rehabilitation services through social security and welfare provisions. Upon introduction of the antipoverty program, vocational rehabilitation techniques were recognized as particularly applicable to the antipoverty effort, and congressional committees responsible for these programs realized that a more comprehensive financial structure would be required for vocational rehabilitation to be effective in combating social disabilities (Switzer, 1969). The Vocational Rehabilitation Act Amendments of 1965 (P.L. 89-333) provided a broadened legal and financial base, ensuring continuation and growth of the programs initiated during the previous decade. It also established a National Commission on Architectural Barriers to investigate the extent of architectural barriers and what was being done to eliminate them. Reader services for people with blindness and interpreter services for individuals with deafness were also added. Section 10 allowed states to provide evaluation services within a 6- to 18-month time frame, depending on the type of disability, to determine rehabilitation potential. The recognition of "extended evaluation" was of particular value to individuals with severe disabilities who formerly would have been rejected because they were not seen as "feasible."

The Vocational Rehabilitation Act Amendments of 1967 (P.L. 90-99) authorized the establishment and operation of a National Center for Deaf-Blind Youths and Adults and funded demonstration projects for the provision of vocational rehabilitation services to "migratory agricultural workers" with disabilities and their families (§ 18). The federal share of the state–federal funding of vocational rehabilitation programs rose to 75% in 1965 and to 80% in 1968 (Rubin & Roessler, 1987).

Many problems were facing society in the early 1970s. At the same time that vocational rehabilitation had been greatly expanded, other governmental agencies had been created or broadened to render some types of rehabilitation services. There was not only a critical shortage of services but also a misdistribution of those services, with redundancies and gaps in service provision, as well as inefficiency in interprogram planning. DiMichael (1971, p. 15) viewed the coordination of services for people with disabilities as a "national issue of grave concern." Clearly, the federal and state governments needed to simplify and coordinate their programs.

Interestingly, at about this same time, government administration spokespeople were advocating stricter fiscal justification of social programs and talking of evaluating these programs with regard to their economic outcomes. A constrictive, managerial approach was instituted at both federal and state levels of vocational rehabilitation. Priority systems were again set up that emphasized serving those people with the potential to become wage earners at a minimal cost to the program. Cost accounting seemed to take precedence over humanitarian concerns; state rehabilitation agencies managed their programs based on economic considerations rather than the programs' positive impact on clients (Rusalem, 1976).

During the late 1960s and early 1970s, the Nixon administration threatened to substantially curtail the State–Federal Rehabilitation Program. An administrative memo from the Department of Health, Education, and Welfare, which was then the location of the State–Federal Rehabilitation Program, even advocated discontinuance of the program. Legislative leaders supporting rehabilitation challenged the administration to provide facts justifying such a proposal, but none were presented (Rusalem, 1976).

Contraction and restriction of the vocational rehabilitation program continued during the Nixon years (1969-1974). Training programs for rehabilitation professionals were almost phased out; funding for rehabilitation research was reduced; and programs and grant proposals had to be justified in terms of possible savings to the government rather than benefits to people. At the same time, much of the formerly centralized federal rehabilitation responsibility was distributed to a number of federal nonrehabilitation groups (e.g., the Administration on Developmental Disabilities). In addition, fiscal support for voluntary rehabilitation agencies had to be provided through funding agencies other than the State–Federal Rehabilitation Program. Rusalem (1976) stated that the rehabilitation agency administration passively accepted the new order of things, that professional organizations were generally cautious, and that only a few of the rehabilitation leaders moved to counteract the administration's plans to undermine the program. A number of rehabilitation consumer groups recognized this passivity; some helped to organize and lead grass-roots, client-directed movements against the weakening of the rehabilitation program.

In 1973 rehabilitation professionals found themselves in the middle of a confrontation between the legislative and administrative branches of government. Rehabilitation legislation became the test case for a power struggle between Congress and President Nixon. The issue was not related to the content of the proposed 1973 Rehabilitation Act, but rather to the question of "whether Congress or the President would control the development of legislation and the appropriations to finance such legislation" (Whitten, 1973, p. 2). The influence of the executive branch was brought to bear on Congress, and the act was twice vetoed before final passage in October of 1973. Over 30 organizations concerned with rehabilitation, including the National Rehabilitation Association, coordinated efforts and successfully encouraged Congress to override President Nixon's veto (Whitten, 1973).

Major gains of the Rehabilitation Act of 1973 (P.L. 93-112) included (a) provision for active participation of consumers in the development of Individualized Written Rehabilitation Programs (IWRPs), (b) establishment of a priority of services for persons with severe disabilities, (c) authorization of independent living demonstration projects and client assistance pilot projects, (d) elimination of residency requirements, (e) initiation of measures affecting federally funded programs to prevent discrimination against and to promote access for persons with disabilities, (f) provision of postemployment services, and (g) establishment of client assistance programs (CAPs) to facilitate communication between consumers and state rehabilitation agencies.

These gains were amplified by P.L. 95-602, the Rehabilitation, Comprehensive Services, and Developmental Disabilities Amendments of 1978. This legislation made independent living services a part of the State–Federal Rehabilitation Program, established the National Institute for Handicapped Research (later renamed the National Institute on Disability and Rehabilitation Research), established the National Council on the Handicapped (a broad-based advisory group, later renamed the National Council on Disability), and increased the responsibilities of CAPs.

The Rehabilitation Amendments of 1984 (P.L. 98-221) changed CAPs from discretionary, competitive grant *projects* to formula state grant *programs;* "each state was required to have a CAP in effect by October 1, 1984" (J. B. Patterson & Woodrich, 1986, p. 50). Another major contribution of P.L. 98-221 was the insertion of the word *qualified* before the word *personnel* in Title 3 (Part A, § 3) of the act. The Rehabilitation Services Administration, in the Federal Register (1985), defined qualified personnel as "personnel who have met existing State certification or licensure requirements, or in the absence of State requirements, have met professionally accepted requirements established by national certification boards" (p. 388631). However, as of this time, disputes continue within the profession over the definition of what constitutes qualified personnel (J. B. Patterson, 1992; Walker & Myers, 1988). States continue to hire persons who lack relevant preservice preparation as rehabilitation counselors (Garske & Turpin, 1992; Hershenson, 1988; Szymanski, 1991).

The Rehabilitation Act Amendments of 1986 (P.L. 99-506) expanded the purpose of the legislation to include "vocational rehabilitation and independent living, for individuals with handicaps in order to maximize their employability, independence, and integration into the workplace and community" (§ 101). In addition, the 1986 amendments (a) changed the term "handicapped individual" to "individuals with handicaps," (b) included rehabilitation engineering within the scope of vocational rehabilitation (VR) services, and (c) included a requirement that recipients of Rehabilitation Services Administration (RSA) training scholarships must "maintain employment in a non-profit rehabilitation or related agency, or in a State rehabilitation agency, on a full time basis for a period of not less than two years for each year for which assistance was received" or "repay all or part of any scholarship received, plus interest" (Title 3, Part A, § 304).

Another major contribution of the 1986 amendments was authorization for supported employment services. Special educators and advocates for people with severe disabilities (especially people with mental retardation) had been concerned that traditional, workshop-based rehabilitation services did not provide suitable employment or opportunities for community integration (Rusch, 1986; Wehman, 1988). Supported employment addressed many of these concerns with a new alternative that provided training and ongoing support for persons with severe disabilities employed in integrated settings (see Hanley-Maxwell, Szymanski & Owens-Johnson, Chapter 5, this text). An ecological orientation to assessment was recommended over traditional vocational evaluation approaches (Parker, Szymanski, & Hanley-Maxwell, 1989), and training and support on actual job sites replaced traditional work adjustment training for many clients with severe disabilities (Hanley-Maxwell & Bordieri, 1989). Supported employment has been demonstrated to be a viable alternative for individuals with severe disabilities, including multiple disabilities, such as deaf–blindness and mental retardation (Downing, Shafer, Brahm-Levy, & Frantz, 1992).

The State–Federal Rehabilitation Program continues to evolve through the influence of rehabilitation philosophy and legislation. The 1992 (P.L. 102-569) and 1993 (P.L. 103-73) Amendments to the 1973 Rehabilitation Act replaced "individuals with handicaps" with "individuals with disabilities" and "rehabilitation facility" with "community rehabilitation program." The other changes, which reflect increased access to services and greater participation by consumers, included such things as (a) *using existing consumer assessment data* to the greatest extent possible, including information provided by the family and public schools;

(b) adding to eligibility requirements a *presumption that individuals with disabilities can engage in an employment outcome* after receiving vocational rehabilitation services; (c) determining whether an applicant is eligible for VR services within 60 days of application; (d) requiring consumer *informed choice* of the employment goal, VR services necessary to reach the employment goal, and vendors providing the services and documentation of these consumer choices on the IWRP; (e) adding Section 21, which focuses on traditionally underserved minority populations; and (f) establishing consumer-controlled State Rehabilitation Advisory Councils (Rehabilitation Act Amendments of 1992; Weber, 1994).

Events in the federal political arena change rapidly, and it is difficult to predict future directions of vocational rehabilitation legislation. However, there has been a clear trend toward greater consumer involvement at all levels of the VR program, including greater empowerment of individuals with disabilities through emphasizing choice and self-determination.

Administration of Public Rehabilitation Programs

Programs authorized by federal rehabilitation legislation are administered through a variety of state and federal agencies. These administrative arrangements and some related legislation are detailed in the following paragraphs.

The Rehabilitation Services Administration

The administrative location of the State–Federal Rehabilitation Program has varied since its inception (see Appendix 1.A), beginning with the Federal Board of Vocational Education in 1920 to its present location in the Rehabilitation Services Administration of the Department of Education, Office of Special Education and Rehabilitative Services. The administrative locations of the 84 state vocational rehabilitation agencies in 50 states and territories and the District of Columbia also vary. One half of the programs are located in multiprogram agencies, one fourth are in departments of education, and the remaining agencies are independent and responsible to the governors' offices.

In 25 states, rehabilitation programs for people with blindness and low vision are administered separately from programs for people with other disabilities (Thayer, 1989). Whatever the administrative configuration, state rehabilitation agencies that serve people with blindness administer a number of programs that have been specifically legislated for this population. Some of this specific legislation, summarized in Appendix 1.A, included the following:

- The Randolph–Sheppard Act of 1936 (P.L. 74-732), which authorized people with blindness to operate vending stands in federal buildings

- The Barden–LaFollette Act of 1943 (P.L. 78-113), which established the state–federal program for individuals with blindness

- The Wagner–O'Day Act of 1938 (P.L. 75-739), which required the federal government to purchase designated products produced by people with blindness in workshops

- The Vocational Rehabilitation Act Amendments of 1965 (P.L. 89-333), which added reader services

- The Javitts–Wagner–O'Day Act of 1971 (P.L. 92-28), which retained the priority for blindness in the provision of products and added other people with severe handicaps as eligible for participation

- The Rehabilitation, Comprehensive Services, and Developmental Disabilities Amendments of 1978 (P.L. 95-602), which authorized independent living services for older individuals with blindness.

Programs for Veterans

"Veterans of wars have long constituted a special class within national populations" (Obermann, 1965, p. 137). The first national pension law that provided compensation for service-related disabilities was passed in 1776 (Obermann, 1965). Wars following the Revolutionary War resulted in additional benefit programs; however, vocational rehabilitation was first provided for by P.L. 65-178, commonly referred to as the Soldier Rehabilitation Act. Dissatisfaction with the manner in which the Federal Board for Vocational Education directed the rehabilitation program led to the creation of an independent agency, the Veterans Bureau, with P.L. 67-47 (The Sweet Bill) in 1921 (Obermann, 1965).

In 1942 and again in 1943, Representative Barden and Senator LaFollette introduced bills that were attempts "to establish a unified rehabilitation program for both civilians and veterans and to eliminate unnecessary duplication of services, personnel, and facilities" (Obermann, 1965, p. 177). Their attempts were unsuccessful, and two separate bills were passed: P.L. 78-16, which gave the Veterans Administration the authority to provide services for the vocational rehabilitation of veterans with disabilities, was signed by President Roosevelt on March 24, 1943, and P.L. 78-113, which was known as the Barden–LaFollette Act and was discussed earlier in this chapter, was signed on July 6, 1943, and contained only three references to veterans (Obermann, 1965). Today, the program for veterans with disabilities remains separate from the State–Federal Rehabilitation Program.

Workers' Compensation and Insurance Benefit Systems

The current Workers' Compensation (WC) system had its roots in the European industrial revolution, which brought with it increased disabilities and deaths of workers. Precursors of the current U.S. system developed in England and Germany in the 1880s, laying the foundation for the U.S. system that developed in the early 20th century (Matkin, 1985).

Prior to the advent of WC laws, English Common Law had allowed workers to sue their employers for injuries, but workers were required to bring their employers to court and prove that the injury resulted from the employer's negligence—a difficult, lengthy, and costly process (Obermann, 1965). The employee was rarely successful in litigation against the employer, because the employer had the "unholy trinity" of defenses against employee litigation. That meant that employees could not win compensation if an employee was 1% responsible for accident or resulting injury (Doctrine of Contributory Negligence), if the employee should have known of the danger (Doctrine of Assumption of Risk), or if the injury was caused by a coworker (Doctrine of Fellow-Servant). The current principle of WC is essentially that of "no fault": The employee receives medical treatment and some compensation for lost wages, regardless of who is to blame for the accident or injury sustained by the employee.

In 1902 Maryland became the first state to enact an insurance law that outlined benefits for the injured worker, without the worker's having to sue the employer or prove that the accident was the employer's fault. Limited to individuals who worked in mines, quarries, municipal construction, or railroads, this law was declared unconstitutional because it did not provide for a jury trial (Obermann, 1965).

In 1908 the federal government implemented a WC law that covered federal employees. This action prompted a number of states to enact laws, most of which were ultimately declared unconstitutional (Matkin, 1985). In 1911, however, 10 states enacted laws that, although similar in purpose, were not uniform and varied in "scope, benefits, system of insurance, and administration" (Obermann, 1965, p. 121). Although these initial WC laws made no provisions for vocational rehabilitation, some states that started VR programs prior to the Smith–Fess Act of 1920 had administered both WC and VR programs by the same state commission.

In 1927 the first WC law was passed in the United States for longshoremen. Difficulties, which led Congress to enact this law, resulted from the workers living at home, where they were covered under state WC laws, and working on the water, where they were subjected to maritime laws (Matkin, 1985).

Although 45 states and territories had WC laws by 1921, it was not until 1948 that all states had operational WC systems. By the 1960s it was evident that some states had excellent systems, whereas other states provided "inadequate medical, income replacement, and rehabilitation benefits" (Rasch, 1985). E. D. Berkowitz (1979a) noted that

> most states established elaborate rules defining the severity of an employee's injury, usually including four degrees of disability: permanent partial, permanent total, temporary, and death. . . . Once the injury was placed in a particular category, the employee usually received a fixed percentage of his preinjury wages, up to a maximum amount, for the period of the disability. (p. 37)

Although this approach seemed straightforward, substantial differences existed between states. For example, a permanent and total disability in New York was worth about five times what a permanent and total disability was worth in South Dakota (E. D. Berkowitz, 1979a).

Medical treatment was the major emphasis of the early WC system, but as early as 1916, rehabilitation was mentioned at the International Association of Industrial Accident Boards and Commissions' meeting as a primary goal of WC programs (M. Berkowitz, 1963). A number of states had close working relationships between WC and state agencies of the State–Federal Rehabilitation Program, and most WC clients who needed vocational rehabilitation services were referred to these state VR agencies. Exemplifying this close relationship, M. Berkowitz (1960) noted that New Jersey's state VR and WC programs were housed together and VR provided services to WC clients during the early history of both programs.

In 1970 Congress passed the Occupational Safety and Health Act (OSHA) (P.L. 91-596). OSHA was concerned with national standards for industrial safety and health; however, Section 27 created a National Commission on State Workmen's Compensation Laws to evaluate the state laws. The 1972 report of the National Commission contained 84 recommendations, 19 of which were termed "essential." Recommendations included the establishment of a medical/rehabilitation division and the provision of vocational rehabilitation services (funded by employers) to any injured worker who could benefit from such services. These and other recommendations contributed to reforms in state WC laws (Bowers & Bursinger, 1986). In fact, the commission's recommendations led a number of states to enact WC laws that required "mandatory" rehabilitation, beginning with California in 1975, followed by Georgia and Colorado in the same year, and several other states since that time (LaFon, 1988).

By 1976 at least 27 states had established WC rehabilitation (Ross, 1979). Thirteen of these programs provided direct vocational rehabilitation services to injured workers, and 14 served as referral resources, with referrals made primarily to state rehabilitation agencies (Ross, 1976). However, rising costs in the provision of rehabilitation and the insurance premiums paid by employers also led some states to eliminate the mandatory rehabilitation requirement (e.g., Washington in 1985, Colorado in 1987) (LaFon, 1988).

The history and future of rehabilitation is clearly intertwined with the history and future of workers' compensation programs. The future of workers' compensation programs is currently being written on a state-by-state basis, and it is rapidly changing.

Other Disability Programs

According to Matkin (1985), over 10% of the U.S. workforce is not covered by state or federal WC laws. These individuals fall under federal programs, individual state employers' liability acts, and tort law, which allow employees to sue their employers for damages in cases of negligence. Federal employees are covered by the Federal Employees' Compensation Act, and the Longshore and Harbor Workers' Compensation Act provides coverage for maritime workers and selected others. The Federal Employers' Liability Act, first passed in 1906 in response to the high injury rate of railroad workers, provides disability coverage for railroad workers for injuries that result from an employer's negligence (Cheit, 1961). Although more complex, the Merchant Marine Act of 1920 (Jones Act) provides similar coverage for injured seamen.

Social Security and Developmental Disabilities Programs

Social security and developmental disabilities programs are discussed together in this section because, although they are different, they are intertwined in some situations. The federal Social Security Act (P.L. 74-271), first enacted in 1935, also includes disability programs. The Social Security Administration administers the Social Security Disability Insurance (SSDI) program (Title II) and the Supplemental Security Income (SSI) program (Title XVI). SSDI provides cash benefits for individuals and their dependents who have contributed to the trust fund through tax on their earnings, whereas SSI provides a minimum income level, based on financial need, for elderly individuals and individuals with disabilities. To qualify for these programs, an individual must have a disability that prevents significant employment and is relatively permanent (Social Security Administration, 1986).

Rehabilitation programs have been supported or otherwise encouraged by social security legislation, which funded research and demonstration initiatives (Shrey, Bangs, Mark, Hursh, & Kues, 1991) and provided financial incentives (i.e., social security work incentives) for recipients of SSI or SSDI entering or returning to employment (Szymanski, 1988). Funding from the Social Security Act (specifically Medicaid funding) has also supported residential and day habilitation programs for people with mental retardation and other severe disabilities (Boggs et al., 1988).

Another area of legislation that affects many people with disabilities is developmental disabilities legislation. This legislation has been intertwined with social security and rehabilitation legislation since the 1970s. The Administration on Developmental Disabilities (ADD) was created in 1970 by P.L. 91-5176, the Developmental Disabilities Services and Facilities Construction Act. ADD currently manages four major programs: a basic state grant program; a protection and advocacy system; a university-affiliated program (UAP) for research, training, and service delivery; and a special projects program (Lakin & Bruininks, 1985). A number of ADD's programs (e.g., UAPs) have rehabilitation-oriented components, and the ADD supported employment initiative coordinated with the Office of Special Education and Rehabilitation Services' initiative to create a powerful force for systems change (Bellamy, Rhodes, & Albin, 1986).

Rights Legislation

The 1964 Civil Rights Act established protection from discrimination for women and ethnic minorities; however, people with disabilities were not protected. Not until July 26, 1990, was civil rights protection fully extended to people with disabilities. The 1990 Americans with Disabilities Act (P.L. 101-336) culminated a long series of state and federal rights legislation and litigation.

On the state level, Wisconsin prohibited discrimination against people with disabilities as early as 1967 (§ 111.31, Wisconsin Laws), and Florida guaranteed the rights of people with disabilities under Article 1, Section 2, of the state's constitution (1968), as amended in 1973. However, enabling state legislation typically was absent; that is, no provision was made for the creation of enforcement agencies and the funds to support such agencies at the time such rights were extended. For example, not until 1975 did the state of Florida create and fund an enforcement agency (i.e., Florida Commission on Human Relations), which was needed to receive and investigate complaints and to determine the validity of employment discrimination complaints filed by people with disabilities.

On the federal level, numerous advances in the rights of people with disabilities have been made through litigation and legislation. These advances include the (a) right to education, (b) right to habilitation or treatment, (c) right to legal and administrative remedies, (d) right to employment, (e) right to accessibility and accommodations, (f) right to housing, and (g) Americans with Disabilities Act (ADA).

Right to Education

The historic 1954 United States Supreme Court decision, *Brown v. Board of Education,* ruled that segregation in education was illegal (Hahn, 1989). Students with disabilities, however, were not protected against discrimination or exclusion from education until the 1970s, and full participation in education has yet to be achieved (Lipsky & Gartner, 1989). It was on the foundation of *Brown v. Board of Education,* and that of subsequent litigation and legislation, that the 1975 Education for All Handicapped Children Act (EHA) (P.L. 94-142) was framed (Gilhool, 1989; Laski, 1985). In 1990 EHA was renamed the Individuals with Disabilities Education Act (IDEA) (P.L. 101-476). The provisions of IDEA and subsequent amendments can be considered milestones in extending educational opportunities to people with disabilities. Key provisions of IDEA are (a) the guarantee of a *free* and *appropriate* public education for all students with disabilities through age 21 or completion of high school graduation, (b) a stipulation that education be provided in the *least restrictive environment,* (c) a requirement that special education and related services be provided according to the stipulations of an *Individualized Education Program* (IEP), and (d) a provision for *due process* rights for students with disabilities and their families (Podemski, Price, Smith, & Marsh, 1984).

The least restrictive environment (LRE) provision in EHA means that, according to regulation (34 C.F.R. [Code of Federal Regulations] 300.550), each public agency shall ensure that (a) to the maximum extent appropriate, children with disabilities, including children in public or private institutions or other care facilities, are educated with nondisabled children, and (b) special classes, separate schooling, or other removal of children with disabilities from the regular educational environment occurs only when the severity of the disability is such that education in regular classes with the use of supplementary aids and services cannot be achieved satisfactorily (Podemski et al., 1984).

The LRE provision is often applied in conjunction with the provisions of Section 504 of the Rehabilitation Act, which specifically stipulates that

> No otherwise qualified . . . individual [with disability] in the United States, as defined in section 7(7), shall, solely by reason of [her or] his handicap, be excluded from participation in, be denied the benefits of, or be subjected to discrimination under any program receiving Federal financial assistance. (Rehabilitation Act of 1973, § 504)

Together, the LRE provision of IDEA and Section 504 of the Rehabilitation Act afford students with disabilities—approximately 12% of all school-age children (Office of Special Education Programs, 1992)—moderate access to educational opportunities (Bruininks & Lakin, 1985; Podemski et al., 1984). However, barriers to access remain. For instance, students with mobility impairments are often unable to participate in extracurricular activities (e.g., clubs) that are critical to the educational experience, due to limited availability of special transportation (Hahn, 1989), and the curricula of integrated schools do not necessarily address the needs of students who are blind to learn braille and have access to braille materials (Bina, 1993).

Right to Habilitation or Treatment

Prior to the early 1970s, people with disabilities (especially those with developmental disabilities) were often confined to institutions in which they had no effective rights to education or treatment (Laski, 1985). In 1972 social security legislation created funding for small community-based residential programs, that is, intermediate care facilities (Boggs et al., 1988), and in 1975 developmental disabilities legislation mandated inclusion of plans for deinstitutionalization in state plans. Legal consent decrees, which resulted from litigation, forced deinstitutionalization in some areas (e.g., Willowbrook in New York, Pennhurst in Pennsylvania) (Bradley, 1985; Castellani, 1987). Thus, habilitation became legally mandated with funding contingent on compliance with specific habilitative standards (Bannerman, Sheldon, Sherman, & Harchik, 1990).

The legal mandate for habilitation, however, is subject to conflicting regulations (Boggs et al., 1988; Laski, 1985). Federal funding patterns for financial support often conflict with federal and state objectives for habilitation (Laski, 1985), and regulations of one program often constrain the intentions of another (Boggs et al., 1988). Ironically, the regulations associated with Medicaid funding of intermediate care facilities and day programs for persons with developmental disabilities discourage supported employment activities (Boggs et al., 1988; Schwartz,

1990). Although some states have used Medicaid waivers to enable Medicaid funding of supported employment for people who have been deinstitutionalized, the process is cumbersome (L. A. Majure, personal communication, September 4, 1990) and has been used by only a few states (Schwartz, 1990).

Despite the gains of the last few decades "a constitutional right to habilitation has not yet been established, [and the Supreme] Court [has] guaranteed only as much habilitation as needed to ensure freedom from unnecessary constraint" (Bannerman et al., 1990, p. 79). The right to habilitation is further complicated by its regulation, which may compromise personal liberties (e.g., the right to choice) and may inhibit or prohibit the use of natural habilitative supports (Ferguson, Hibbard, Leinen, & Schaff, 1990). Issues of choice and natural supports in habilitation and rehabilitation are likely to present major ethical dilemmas for rehabilitation counselors in the coming years (see J. B. Patterson, Chapter 6, this text).

Right to Legal and Administrative Remedies

Client Assistance Programs (CAPs) were authorized in the Rehabilitation Act of 1973 to facilitate communication between counselors and clients. In their role as ombudsmen between clients and counselors (J. B. Patterson & Woodrich, 1986), the purpose of CAPs was "to inform and advise all clients and client applicants . . . of all available benefits under this Act and upon request . . . to assist such clients or applicants in their relationships with projects, programs, and facilities providing services to them under this Act" (§ 112). The Rehabilitation, Comprehensive Services, and Developmental Disabilities Amendments of 1978 (P.L. 95-602) added to the above the phrase "including assistance in pursuing legal, administrative or other appropriate remedies to insure the protection of the rights of such individuals under this Act" (§ 105). In requiring each state to have a CAP, the 1984 Rehabilitation Act Amendments (P.L. 98-221) also required each CAP to have the ability to pursue legal and administrative remedies. As J. B. Patterson and Woodrich (1986) noted, CAPs are important because not all clients have self-advocacy skills; however, mediation procedures should be used before administrative or legal remedies. The combination of CAPs, many of which are housed in protection and advocacy agencies, and the due process provision of the EHA have helped people with disabilities pursue legal and administrative remedies when they are needed.

Right to Employment

Although the Civil Rights Act of 1964 afforded women and minorities some protection from employment discrimination, people with disabilities were given no such protection. Employers could legally discriminate against a qualified job applicant solely on the basis of disability. Not until implementation of Sections 501 and

503 of the Rehabilitation Act of 1973 was limited protection from employment discrimination given to people with disabilities.

Section 501 of the Rehabilitation Act of 1973 limited discrimination in federal employment through the establishment of an Interagency Committee on Handicapped Employees, which was charged with investigating "the adequacy of hiring, placement, and advancement practices . . . by each department, agency, and instrumentality in the executive branch of government" (87 Stat. 392). It also required affirmative action plans for each department and agency.

Section 503 of the Rehabilitation Act of 1973 limited employment discrimination by private employers who receive federal funds. It required employers with contracts or subcontracts with the federal government in excess of $2,500 to take "affirmative action to employ and advance in employment qualified" individuals with disabilities (87 Stat. 393). Although Sections 501 through 504 of the Rehabilitation Act advanced the civil rights of people with disabilities, the effect of this legislation was very limited. Only programs or facilities with federal funding were involved. Thus, discrimination in private enterprise or programs with no federal funds was still permissible. The limited applicability was compounded by limited enforcement.

Right to Accessibility and Accommodations

Section 502 of the Rehabilitation Act of 1973 established the Architectural and Transportation Barriers Compliance Board (ATBCB). The ATBCB was charged with (a) ensuring compliance with the Architectural Barriers Act of 1968 (P.L. 90-480), as amended in 1970 (P.L. 91-205); (b) investigating transportation barriers and housing needs of people with disabilities; and (c) promoting the use of the International Accessibility Symbol in all public buildings.

Technological advances broadened the meaning of accessibility, which initially focused on access issues for people who used wheelchairs (e.g., curb cuts, ramps, lifts on buses), and also led to the right of people to benefit from adaptations and accommodations. Section 508 of the Rehabilitation Act of 1973 as amended (P.L. 99-506) ensured access to computers and other electronic office equipment in places of federal employment. In 1986, Congress mandated that federal agencies were responsible for ensuring that all purchased or leased electronic office equipment be accessible to people with disabilities. The guidelines that were developed ensure that people with disabilities who use electronic equipment in federal agencies (a) can access and use the same databases and applications programs as other individuals, (b) can manipulate data and related information sources, and (c) possess the necessary adaptations to communicate with others using the same system (Staff, *NARIC Quarterly*, 1988).

P.L. 99-506 also provided for rehabilitation engineering centers and rehabilitation engineering services to VR clients, and P.L. 100-407 (The Technology-Related Assistance for Individuals with Disabilities Act of 1988) enabled people with disabilities to benefit from assistive technology. Assistive technology is "any item, piece of equipment, or product system, whether acquired commercially off the shelf, modified, or customized, that is used to increase, maintain, or improve functional capabilities of individuals with disabilities" (§ 3).

Right to Housing

The Fair Housing Amendments of 1988 (P.L. 100-430) extended to people with disabilities the same protections against discrimination already afforded to other minority groups under civil rights legislation. The amendments prohibited discrimination on the basis of handicap in the sale, rental, or other provision of housing. In addition, the amendments provided renters the right to make reasonable modifications at their own expenses and stipulated that multifamily rental units constructed in the future meet minimal standards of accessibility (President's Committee on Employment of People with Disabilities, 1988).

Americans with Disabilities Act (ADA)

On July 26, 1990, President Bush signed into law the Americans with Disabilities Act (P.L. 101-336) (President's Committee on Employment of People with Disabilities [PCEPD] and ATBCB, 1990). Finally, citizens with disabilities were given civil rights and protections that had been granted to women and minorities under the Civil Rights Act of 1964 (PCEPD & ATBCB, 1990).

ADA, which removes many of the barriers limiting full societal participation by the nation's 43 million citizens with disabilities (PCEPD & ATBCB, 1990). It is undoubtedly the most significant disability-related legislation to date. The major stipulations of ADA are summarized in Table 1.2.

The ADA enforcement jurisdiction varies by title. For Title I, which affects employment, enforcement is through the Equal Employment Opportunity Commission, the Attorney General, private right of action (e.g., lawsuits), and the remedies and procedures set forth in Title VII of the Civil Rights Act of 1964. Title II, which affects state and local governments and public transportation, is enforced by private right of action and remedies and procedures set forth in Section 505 of the Rehabilitation Act of 1973. Title III, which affects public accommodations (e.g., hotels, restaurants, retail stores), is enforced through private right to action, remedies of Title II of the Civil Rights Act of 1964, and Attorney General enforcement in pattern or practice cases. Title IV, which affects telecommunications, is enforced through private right of action and the Federal Communications Commission (Jones, 1990).

In summary, rights legislation has heralded new possibilities and opportunities for people with disabilities. Early disability policies reflected a mixture of protection and concern for individuals (e.g., by schools, hospitals), protection of society against individuals (e.g., by forced sterilization, institutionalization), pro-

Table 1.2
Key Provisions of the Americans with Disabilities Act of 1990

Title I Employment

No employer with 15 or more employees can discriminate against a qualified individual with a disability because of the disability in regard to job application procedures; the hiring, advancement, or discharge of employees; employee compensation; job training; and other terms, conditions, and privileges of employment. A "qualified" individual with a disability means an individual with a disability who, with or without reasonable accommodation, can perform the essential functions of the employment position, unless the accommodation causes an "undue hardship" for the employer. Reasonable accommodations may include such things as job restructuring, part-time or modified work, acquisition or modification of equipment or devices, and the provision of qualified readers or interpreters. [§§ 101-102]

Title II Transportation

Public entities that operate fixed-route systems that purchase or lease new or used vehicles must ensure that the vehicles are readily accessible to and usable by individuals with disabilities. When vehicles are not accessible, the entity must assure that special transportation services are available to individuals with disabilities that are of a comparable level and comparable response time to the services provided to individuals without disabilities, unless the provision of paratransit and other special transportation services imposes an undue financial burden on the public entity. In the case of intercity rail transportation, the service must have one car per train that is accessible. [§§ 222, 223, 242]

Title III Public Accommodations and Services

No individual shall be discriminated against on the basis of disability in the full and equal enjoyment of the goods, services, privileges, advantages, or accommodations of any place of public accommodation by any person who owns, leases, or operates a place of public accommodation. Public accommodations include such things as hotels and motels, restaurants and bars, theaters and auditoriums, banks, professional offices, depots, libraries, parks and zoos, social service agencies, and recreational facilities such as gyms and bowling alleys. Private clubs and religious organizations are exempt; other public entities must demonstrate that a necessary change is not "readily achieveable" in order to be in compliance. [§§ 301, 302, 307]

Title IV Telecommunications

Individuals with speech and hearing disabilities should have a rapid, efficient nationwide telephone and telecommunication system available to them. Public service announcements that are federally funded must include closed captions. [§§ 225, 711]

Title V Miscellaneous

Among the items included in this title are the issuance of guidelines for historical sites and a study of the wilderness areas and ability of individuals with disabilities to use the sites. Noted in this title was the fact that individuals who were currently using illegal drugs were not considered to be covered by the law. [§§ 504, 507, 510] ductivity enhancement (e.g., through State–Federal Rehabilitation Programs and WC programs), and benevolence (e.g., by SSI). However, the rights legislation discussed in this section demonstrated evidence of a change in focus from protection and paternalism to consideration of individual rights. Optimism must be guarded, however, because, although these laws have provided some foundation for equal opportunity for people with disabilities, their "existence . . . is hollow" (Stapleton, 1976, p. 605) unless people with disabilities and their advocates demand enforcement. Legal mandates do not, of themselves, change the attitudes of society or increase society's awareness of the individual's needs. Therein lies one of the major challenges of people with disabilities and the profession of rehabilitation counseling.

The Rehabilitation Counseling Profession

The development of the rehabilitation counseling profession has been both negatively and positively influenced by its linkage to legislation and to the State–Federal Rehabilitation Program (Emener & Cottone, 1989; Hershenson, 1988). Today, however, the State–Federal Rehabilitation Program is but one of the many settings in which rehabilitation counselors practice. Indeed, the philosophy and history of the rehabilitation movement and the State–Federal Rehabilitation Program are necessary to understand the development of the rehabilitation counseling profession. However, study of the profession of rehabilitation counseling must include a variety of additional topics: (a) history of rehabilitation counseling, (b) credentialing for rehabilitation counseling, and (c) rehabilitation counseling professional associations.

History of Rehabilitation Counseling

The rehabilitation counseling profession is one of the few professions that evolved primarily from legislation. Its path of evolution, which is discussed throughout this chapter, illustrates how rehabilitation counseling followed the sequence of steps in the professionalization process outlined by Wilensky:

(1) creation of a full-time occupation,

(2) establishment of training schools,

(3) formation of professional associations,

(4) formation of a code of ethics,

(5) further definition of the area of competence, and

(6) political agitation to protect the job territory of the occupation. (Brubaker, 1977, p. 209)

Early History

The group of rehabilitation counselors (initially termed agents or caseworkers) who were first hired to provide vocational rehabilitation services built the foundation for the new profession of rehabilitation counseling. Although most of the early agents were men, a woman (Regina Dolan) was the "first person to engage in vocational rehabilitation work as a full-time public employee," placing workers with disabilities for the Wisconsin Industrial Commission and the United States Employment Service in Milwaukee (Obermann, 1965, p. 213). Because there were no formal rehabilitation counseling training programs in these early years, agents typically came from the field of education.

By 1928, at the Fifth National Conference on Vocational Rehabilitation in Milwaukee, the "responsibilities of 'rehabilitation case workers,' and their training and supervision were extensively discussed" (Obermann, 1965, p. 253). Some of the issues that face the profession today also were evident in 1928:

> difficulties in recruiting good rehabilitation workers, problems in training them, the need for some specialized type of college training to supplement what could be taught through experience on the job, the inability to attract qualified personnel because of limited salary budgets, and political interference in selecting staff. (Obermann, 1965, p. 254)

Establishment of Rehabilitation Education

As Hershenson (1988) noted, "a national program of vocational rehabilitation was established, made permanent, and greatly expanded with no designation as to the type or qualifications of the personnel who would implement it" (p. 206). In the 1940s three programs to train rehabilitation personnel were established within different disciplines. At New York University in 1941, such a program was established within vocational education; at Ohio State University in 1944, a program was established in social work; and at Wayne State University in 1946, a program was established in special education. However, the number of programs was not greatly expanded until the Vocational Rehabilitation Act Amendments of 1954 (P.L. 83-565), which provided federal funds to colleges and universities to establish programs to train rehabilitation personnel. The Barden–LaFollette Act of 1943 (P.L. 78-113) had allowed state agencies to train, or to pay for the training of, their personnel, but did not specifically allocate federal money for this purpose (Scalia & Wolfe, 1984).

Definition of Rehabilitation Counseling

Early leaders in rehabilitation counseling were concerned with the role of the counselor (C. H. Patterson, 1957) and the education and training necessary for rehabilitation counselors (Levine & Pence, 1953; Olshansky, 1957). Consistent with then-current state–federal rehabilitation legislation, the early emphasis of rehabilitation counseling was in the vocational area. In 1961 C. H. Patterson identified the following trends in vocational rehabilitation counseling: (a) increasing specialization by services and types of clients served, (b) increasing variety of work settings for rehabilitation counselors, and (c) tendency for defining and training rehabilitation counselors as "generic" counselors.

Some early leaders, including C. H. Patterson, believed that rehabilitation counseling was a specialty of counseling rather than a separate profession. Thus, they believed that rehabilitation counselors should be psychologically trained counselors (C. H. Patterson, 1961). However, others considered rehabilitation counseling to be a separate profession (Stone, 1966) requiring separate training.

Early disparities over the profession of rehabilitation counseling are still reflected today in the parent organizations of the two professional rehabilitation counseling associations. The parent organization of the American Rehabilitation Counseling Association (ARCA) is the American Counseling Association, which is a generic professional counseling organization with specialty divisions, including ARCA, American Mental Health Counseling Association, American School Counseling Association, and so forth. The second association, the National Rehabilitation Counseling Association (NRCA), is a professional division of the National Rehabilitation Association, which includes other special interest divisions, such as independent living, vocational evaluation, and placement.

Current definitions of rehabilitation and rehabilitation counseling appear to transcend disparities regarding the relationship of rehabilitation counseling to counseling. As noted earlier in this chapter, *rehabilitation is defined as a comprehensive sequence of services, mutually planned by the consumer and rehabilitation counselor, to maximize employability, independence, integration, and participation of people with disabilities in the workplace and/or the community.* Similarly, *rehabilitation counseling is defined as "a profession that assists individuals with disabilities in adapting to the environment, assists environments in accommodating the needs of the individual, and works toward full participation of persons with disabilities in all aspects of society, especially work"* (Szymanski, 1985, p. 3). Both definitions appear to be applicable, whether one views rehabilitation counseling as a distinct profession or as a specialty within the counseling profession.

Rehabilitation Counselor Roles

The roles and functions of rehabilitation counselors have been extensively investigated (Muthard & Salomone, 1969; Rubin et al., 1984; G. N. Wright, Leahy, & Shapson, 1987), and numerous knowledge and skill areas have been identified (Leahy, Szymanski, & Linkowski, 1993). Counselors employed in different settings (e.g., state VR agencies, schools, insurance companies) interact with a number of different service delivery systems (e.g., the State–Federal Rehabilitation Program, Special Education, Workers' Compensation) and are affected by various types of legislation. Nonetheless, regardless of their employment setting, most rehabilitation counselors (a) assess client needs, (b) develop programs and/or plans to meet the identified needs, and (c) provide or arrange for the services needed by clients, which may include job placement and follow-up services. Counseling skills are a critical component of all of these activities.

Today, the specialized knowledge of disabilities and environmental factors that interact with disabilities, as well as the range of knowledge and skills in addition to counseling, differentiates the rehabilitation counselor from other types of counselors. The philosophy of rehabilitation set forth earlier in this chapter is the foundation for the practice of rehabilitation counseling in a wide and growing range of contexts. Leung (1987) suggested that the essence of professional rehabilitation counselors was

> a strong sense of professional identity, ability to function in ambiguous situations, ability to make judgments and/or decisions in not always ideal conditions or with all information in hand, capability of relating well with people with a sense of caring and empathy, yet be able to assert themselves as effective advocates. (p. 31)

This essence seems appropriate to all of the diverse contexts in which rehabilitation counselors currently practice.

Contexts of Rehabilitation Counseling Practice

As early as 1927, H. B. Cummings of the Vocational Rehabilitation Service, Federal Board of Vocational Education, noted a move toward specialization and professionalization in rehabilitation work (Obermann, 1965). Through the 1960s rehabilitation counselors worked primarily in State–Federal Rehabilitation Programs, veterans' rehabilitation programs, rehabilitation facilities, and rehabilitation hospitals. However, the settings for rehabilitation counselors expanded rapidly with the advent of preservice education programs.

In recent decades the settings of rehabilitation counseling practice have expanded dramatically, with the addition of a wide variety of agencies, including private rehabilitation and insurance companies (Lynch & Martin, 1982); substance abuse agencies (Deren & Randell, 1990; Greer, 1986); business and industry, including Employee Assistance Programs (Ellien & Wolkstein, 1987); schools (Szymanski & King, 1989); and college and university disability service offices (DiMichael & Thomas, 1985). Additional types of disabilities have also been emphasized in recent years, including mental illness (Anthony, Cohen, & Farkas, 1990), brain injuries (Corthell, 1990), substance abuse (McMahon, Glenn, & Dixon, 1994), and AIDS (Alston, Wilkins, & Holbert, 1995). Services to culturally diverse groups (Dziekan & Okocha, 1993; Smart, 1993), older individuals (Ebener, 1992), and families (Power, Dell Orto, & Gibbons, 1988) have also received increased attention.

In summary, the profession of rehabilitation counseling has evolved from its early history as a legislatively based occupation that was practiced in a limited number of settings to its current status as a profession that is practiced in diverse settings employing various service delivery systems that target a broad range of individuals. This evolution has aided and has been aided by the process of credentialing in rehabilitation counseling.

Credentialing for Rehabilitation Counseling

It is important to ensure that people with disabilities receive services from counselors with the requisite knowledge and skills. Professional initiatives to this end have taken many forms, including accreditation, certification, licensure, and registration.

Certification, licensure, and registration are ways of credentialing individuals. Accreditation, on the other hand, is a means of credentialing an institution. Certification refers to a determination that the individual possesses a set of qualifications specified by a national body, whereas licensure is granted by a state or federal agency and gives the individual permission to practice in an individual state. Licensure is commonly referred to as a *screening-out* process, whereas certification is a *screening-in* process. In the last 10 years, there has been a resurgence of both certification and licensure.

Accreditation

The accrediting body for graduate rehabilitation counseling programs is the Council on Rehabilitation Education (CORE). Incorporated in 1972, CORE is accredited by the Council for Higher Education Accreditation. The purpose of CORE accreditation of rehabilitation counselor education (RCE) programs is "to promote the effective delivery of rehabilitation services to individuals with disabilities by promoting and fostering continuing review and improvement of master's degree level RCE programs" (CORE, 1996, p. 2). The CORE standards for RCE programs address (a) the articulation and fulfillment of the RCE program's mission; (b) program curriculum; (c) the knowledge, skills, and job performance of its graduates; (d) the composition, resources, and professional involvement of its students; and (e) the program's support and resources, including architectural accessibility and faculty composition. The accreditation of rehabilitation counseling programs, an important force in rehabilitation education (Linkowski & Szymanski, 1993), assures students that a program meets nationally recognized standards and also allows program graduates to take the national certification examination without a year of supervision by a certified rehabilitation counselor (CRC).

Certification

The certification of rehabilitation counselors by the Commission on Rehabilitation Counselor Certification (CRCC) is a national process, which began in 1974, although early discussions began in 1963 (Graves, 1983). CRCC is a nonprofit independent credentialing body and a member of the National Commission for Certifying Agencies (NCCA), an independent regulatory body that oversees the certification processes of its member organizations. CRCC certifies rehabilitation counselors throughout the United States and several foreign countries. It also has a separate Canadian credentialing process.

The purpose of CRCC is to provide assurance that professionals engaged in the practice of rehabilitation counseling have met established standards at the time of entry into the profession and have maintained these standards throughout their careers (CRCC, 1994). The standards for certification are established by a commission composed of a public member (representing consumers), a member-at-large, and individuals from eight organizations, including ARCA and the NRCA. Approximately 13,000 of the estimated 18,000 to 20,000 rehabilitation counselors in the United States are certified (Leahy & Holt, 1993).

Each applicant for certification must meet educational and/or work experience requirements. NCCA requires "alternative pathways" to certification. Although the most common avenue to certification is a master's degree in rehabilitation counseling from a CORE-accredited school, individuals with certain other types of degrees may take the examination, if they have worked as rehabilitation counselors or rehabilitation educators for a specified period of time.

To become certified, rehabilitation counselors must sign a statement that they subscribe to the *Code of Professional Ethics for Rehabilitation Counselors* (see Appendix 6A in Chapter 6). They must also demonstrate knowledge of the following content areas by achieving a passing score on the national examination, which is offered twice a year (in October and April): (a) foundations of rehabilitation, (b) client assessment, (c) planning and service delivery, (d) counseling and interviewing, and (e) job development and placement. CRCs maintain their certification by (a) completing, within a 5-year period, 100 hours of acceptable continuing education intended to enhance the CRC's ability to serve clients, or (b) retaking the CRC examination. As Hedgeman (1985) noted,

> The CRC requirement is a strong part of private-for-profit rehabilitation. It is included in the Intermediate Care Facilities for the Mentally Retarded (ICF/MR) regulation. Also, it is part of the legislation specifying qualified personnel in the reauthorization of the Rehabilitation Act . . . and is being considered for licensing requirements in some states. The main benefit of certification to the counselor is that it establishes his or her identity as a professional willing to adhere to standards that benefit quality services to persons with disabilities. (p. 610)

Licensure

In 1993, 38 states had some form of counselor licensure laws (Tarvydas & Leahy, 1993). Each state establishes its own standards with respect to education, experience, and examination. Because some of these laws specifically address rehabilitation counselors, it is imperative that rehabilitation counselors become familiar with their own state licensure laws. Counselors who live in states that are considering new licensure laws should actively participate in developing legislation that protects people with disabilities and recognizes professional standards for rehabilitation counseling. Although most licensure laws are directed at counselors who provide private counseling services (e.g., mental health counseling and psychotherapy), intentionally or unintentionally other counselors may be included in the law. Rehabilitation counselors who work for the State–Federal Rehabilitation Program are generally exempt from state licensure laws.

There are three types of licensure laws: title laws, practice laws, and title and practice laws. Title laws regulate the use of the title *counselor,* whereas practice laws define and protect the counselor's *scope of practice.* Title and practice laws regulate both. Licensure laws, regardless of type, uniformly address educational requirements by delineating specific coursework or noting degrees that are acceptable. Some laws specify accreditation requirements for the graduate programs, such as those accredited by the Council for Accreditation of Counseling and Related Education Programs or CORE. Experience requirements relate to the number of years of experience in providing counseling services and generally include a specified amount of supervised experience following the graduate degree. Various examinations are employed by states; however, a number of states use the general counseling examination of the National Board for Certified Counselors.

Registration

A number of state workers' compensation laws or regulations specify the education, training, and/or credentials an individual must possess in order to provide rehabilitation counseling services to workers with disabilities (J. B. Patterson, 1987). In these states, rehabilitation counselors register with the state Workers' Compensation agency by paying a fee and providing proof of their education and/or certification. Most of these states specifically include the CRC credential for the provision of rehabilitation counseling services; however, the actual services (i.e., scope of services) that may be provided are also legislated and vary by state. Many of these states also require continuing education units, or proof that the CRC credential has been maintained, because maintenance also requires continuing professional education.

Rehabilitation Counseling Professional Organizations

An important part of being a professional is belonging to professional associations. The American Rehabilitation Counseling Association (ARCA) and the National Rehabilitation Counseling Association (NRCA) are the two primary professional associations for rehabilitation counselors. Both professional organizations began in the 1950s. As noted earlier in this chapter, the formation of ARCA and of NRCA represented differing views of the identity of rehabilitation counseling. For the early history of ARCA and NRCA, see DiMichael and Thomas (1985) and Muthard (1969).

The formation of ARCA as a division of the American Counseling Association (ACA) (previous names include the American Personnel and Guidance Association, which was followed by the American Association for Counseling and Development) represented the view of rehabilitation counseling as a specialty within the general counseling profession. This view is still reflected in the titles of the journals that ARCA members receive. The *Rehabilitation Counseling Bulletin* is the journal of ARCA, and the *Journal of Counseling and Development* is the journal of the parent organization, ACA.

The formation of NRCA as a division of the National Rehabilitation Association (NRA) represented the view that rehabilitation counseling is a separate profession within the general field of rehabilitation. This view is reflected in the journals that NRCA members receive. The *Journal of Applied Rehabilitation Counseling* is the journal of NRCA, and the *Journal of Rehabilitation* is the journal of the parent organization, NRA.

The existence of two professional associations is frequently confusing to professionals. Thus, despite the continued existence of disparate views on the relationship of rehabilitation counseling to counseling and rehabilitation, there have been periodic discussions of merging ARCA and NRCA (see Rasch, 1979; Reagles, 1981). At this point it does not appear likely that such a merger will occur; however, the two organizations have established the Alliance for Rehabilitation Counseling, a body consisting of the leadership of the two organizations that provides for one voice when the interests of the two groups are similar (Hackett & LaForge, 1995). Thus, the organizations continue to work independently and collaboratively to promote the profession of rehabilitation counseling.

Summary

The philosophy of rehabilitation includes a recognition of the dignity and worth of people with disabilities, the value of independence and work, the importance of choice, and the responsibilities of rehabilitation professionals to adopt consumer advocacy and empowerment roles. The legislative history of rehabilitation demonstrates an evolving expression of these philosophical tenets from policies of protection and productivity to legislation that focuses on rights to education, treatment, employment, housing, legal and administrative remedies, and access.

The legislative history of rehabilitation, including the evolution of the State–Federal Rehabilitation Program, created the occupation of rehabilitation counseling, which has evolved into a profession. Today, the State–Federal Rehabilitation Program is only one of a growing number of settings in which rehabilitation counselors practice, and the profession is evolving at a rapid rate.

Historical foundations will no doubt interact with current and future events to have an impact on the future of the profession of rehabilitation counseling. The nature of this future impact will be determined, in part, by how well today's rehabilitation counselors are grounded in knowledge of their professions' history and philosophical foundations. It is a truism that those who fail to study history are doomed to repeat mistakes of the past.

Appendix 1.A
Chronology of Federal Rehabilitation Legislation and Administrative Location of the Federal Vocational Rehabilitation (VR) Program

1917   P.L. 64-347

The *Smith-Hughes Act* established the Federal Board of Vocational Education for retraining dislocated industrial workers.

1918   P.L. 65-178

The *Soldier Rehabilitation Act* authorized vocational rehabilitation services for World War I veterans.

1920   P.L. 66-236

The *Smith-Fess Act*, administered by the Federal Board of Vocational Education, authorized vocational guidance, occupation adjustment, and placement services for civilians with physical disabilities.

1933

The VR Program was located in the Office of Education, Department of the Interior.

1935   P.L. 74-271

The *Social Security Act* established the State-Federal VR program as a permanent program that could be discontinued only by an act of Congress. This action, however, did not guarantee congressional appropriations.

1939

The VR Program was located in the Federal Security Agency, Office of Education.

1943   P.L. 78-113

The *Barden-LaFollette Act* extended rehabilitation services to persons with mental retardation and mental illness and provided the first federal-state rehabilitation support for persons with blindness. The act also established the Office of Vocational Rehabilitation in the Federal Security Agency and established VR regional offices.

1953

ocational Rehabilitation was moved to the Department of Health, Education,

1954 *P.L. 83-565*

The *Vocational Rehabilitation Act Amendments* provided funding to colleges and universities for preparation of rehabilitation professionals, expanded services to persons with mental retardation and mental illness, provided rehabilitation facility expansion funds, provided funding for extension and improvement of state agencies, and authorized research and demonstration programs.

1963

The Office of Vocational Rehabilitation became the Vocational Rehabilitation Administration within the Department of Health, Education, and Welfare (HEW).

1965 *P.L. 89-333*

The *Vocational Rehabilitation Act Amendments* established a National Commission on Architectural Barriers; deleted economic need as a requirement for services; increased the federal share of federal–state programs (i.e., the matching requirement) to 75%; and added an extended evaluation, which enabled counselors to provide services for periods up to 6 or 18 months to determine eligibility for vocational rehabilitation services. Additionally, more flexibility and greater resources were provided to the federal–state program.

1967 *P.L. 90-99*

The *Vocational Rehabilitation Act Amendments* established a National Center for Deaf-Blind Youths and Adults and authorized grants to state VR agencies for pilot projects for the provision of VR services to individuals with vocational disabilities who were migratory agricultural workers and to members of their families.

1967

The Rehabilitation Services Administration (RSA) became part of Social and Rehabilitation Services in the Department of HEW.

1968 *P.L. 90-391*

The *Vocational Rehabilitation Amendments* further increased the federal share of federal–state programs to 80% and continued the expansion of the program.

1973 *P.L. 93-112*

The *Rehabilitation Act of 1973* introduced the Individual Written Rehabilitation Program (IWRP) and postemployment services, established a priority of services to persons meeting the federal definition of severe handicaps, provided special consideration for public safety officers injured in the line of duty, authorized demonstration projects for independent living rehabilitation in six locations (including Berkeley, San Antonio, and New York City), established client assistance pilot projects, eliminated any residency requirements for services, mandated consumer involvement in state agency policy development, stressed program evaluation, and initiated legislation to prohibit discrimination against and to provide access to persons with disabilities in federally funded programs (§§ 501–504).

1974 P.L. 93-651

The *Rehabilitation Act Amendments of 1974* extended the authorizations of appropriations in the Rehabilitation Act of 1973 for a year, transferred the Rehabilitation Services Administration to HEW, strengthened the Randolph–Sheppard Act (referred to as the Randolph–Sheppard Act Amendments of 1974), and provided for the convening of a White House Conference on "Handicapped Individuals."

1975

Reorganization of HEW placed RSA in the Office of Human Development Services.

1978 P.L. 95-602

The *Rehabilitation, Comprehensive Services, and Developmental Disabilities Amendments of 1978* expanded the quality and scope of reader services for individuals with blindness and interpreter services for people with deafness; established independent living services as part of the federal–state rehabilitation program, including independent living services for "older blind individuals"; provided VR services grants to American Indian tribes located on federal and state reservations; established the National Institute of Handicapped Research (later renamed the National Institute on Disability and Rehabilitation Research), Rehabilitation Research and Training Centers, Comprehensive Rehabilitation Centers, and the Helen Keller Center for Deaf–Blind Youths and Adults; and established the National Council on the Handicapped (later renamed the National Council on Disability).

1979

The Cabinet-level Department of Education was created, and RSA was located in its Office of Special Education and Rehabilitative Services.

1984 P.L. 98-221

The *Rehabilitation Amendments of 1984* established Client Assistance Programs in each state and inserted the word "qualified" before personnel for training programs in the act.

1986 P.L. 99-506

The *Rehabilitation Act Amendments of 1986* stipulated in § 101 (a)(7)(B) that rehabilitation services be delivered by qualified personnel; added the definition of supported employment to the act, established supported employment as an acceptable goal for rehabilitation services, and provided funding for state-supported employment programs; added rehabilitation engineering services as a VR service; added scholarship "payback" requirements to the RSA training programs; and gradually decreased the federal share of federal–state programs from 80% to 75%.

1992 P.L. 102-569

The *Rehabilitation Act Amendments of 1992* advanced the cause of consumer empowerment by increasing client choice of employment objectives, providers, and services with a statement by the consumer on the IWRP; established consumer-controlled State Rehabilitation Advisory Councils; established a presumption of eligibility that individuals could benefit from VR services, unless the agency could demonstrate otherwise; expanded services to include transition services, on-the-job services, other personal assistance services, and supported employment as a basic service; enhanced access to traditionally underserved minority populations; increased accountability measures; limited the time period for determining eligibility to 60 days from application; and directed Client Assistance Programs to include individual and systemic advocacy.

1993   P.L. 103-73

The *Rehabilitation Act Amendments of 1993* made technical corrections or "amendments" to the Rehabilitation Act Amendments of 1992.

Appendix 1.B
Sources of Additional Information

**American Rehabilitation Counseling
  Association**
5999 Stevenson Avenue
Alexandria, VA 22304
800/545-ARCA

**Commission on Accreditation of
  Rehabilitation Facilities**
101 North Wilmot Road, Suite 500
Tucson, AZ 85711
602/748-1212

**Commission on Rehabilitation
  Counselor Certification**
1835 Rohlwing Road
Rolling Meadows, IL 60008
847/394-2104

Council on Rehabilitation Education
1835 Rohlwing Road
Rolling Meadows, IL 60008
847/394-1785

**National Rehabilitation Counseling
  Association**
8807 Sudley Road, #102
Manassas, VA 22110-4719
703/361-2077

**The President's Committee on
  Employment of People with
  Disabilities**
1111 20th Street, NW, Suite 636
Washington, DC 20036-3470
202/653-5044 (voice)
202/653-7386 (TDD)

References

Alston, P., Wilkins, L., & Holbert, D. (1995). Rehabilitation counselor attitudes toward working with clients with AIDS. *Journal of Applied Rehabilitation Counseling, 26*(3), 26–29.

Americans with Disabilities Act of 1990, 42 U.S.C. § 12101 *et seq.*

Anthony, W., Cohen, M., & Farkas, M. (1990). *Psychiatric rehabilitation.* Boston: Boston University, Center for Psychiatric Rehabilitation.

Architectural Barriers Act of 1968, 42 U.S.C. § 4151 *et seq.*

Banja, J. D. (1990). Rehabilitation and empowerment. *Archives of Physical Medicine and Rehabilitation, 71,* 614–615.

Bannerman, D. J., Sheldon, J. B., Sherman, J. A., & Harchik, A. E. (1990). Balancing the right to habilitation with the right to personal liberties: The rights of people with developmental disabilities to eat too many doughnuts and take a nap. *Journal of Applied Behavior Analysis, 23,* 79–89.

Barden–LaFollette Act of 1943, 29 U.S.C. § 31 *et seq.*

Beck, R. (1994). Encouragement as a vehicle to empowerment in counseling: An existential perspective. *Journal of Rehabilitation, 60*(3), 6–11.

Bellamy, G. T., Rhodes, L. E., & Albin, J. M. (1986). Supported employment. In W. E. Kiernan & J. A. Stark (Eds.), *Pathways to employment for adults with developmental disabilities* (pp. 129–138). Baltimore: Brookes.

Berkowitz, E. D. (1979a). The American disability system in historical perspective. In E. D. Berkowitz (Ed.), *Disability policies and government programs* (pp. 16–74). New York: Praeger.

Berkowitz, E. D. (Ed.). (1979b). *Disability policies and government programs.* New York: Praeger.

Berkowitz, M. (1960). *Workmen's compensation.* New Brunswick, NJ: Rutgers University.

Berkowitz, M. (1963). *Rehabilitating the disabled worker: A platform for action.* Washington, DC: Department of Health, Education, and Welfare, Vocational Rehabilitation Administration.

Bina, M. (1993). Do myths associated with schools for students who are blind negatively affect placement decisions? *Journal of Visual Impairment and Blindness, 87,* 213–215.

Bitter, J. A. (1970). *Introduction to rehabilitation.* St. Louis: Mosby.

Boggs, E. M., Hanley-Maxwell, C., Lakin, K. C., & Bradley, V. J. (1988). Federal policy and legislation: Factors that have constrained and facilitated community integration. In L. W. Heal, J. I. Haney, & A. R. N. Amado (Eds.), *Integration of developmentally disabled individuals into the community* (2nd ed., pp. 245–271). Baltimore: Brookes.

Bowers, C., & Bursinger, K. L. (1986). A history and overview of the workers' compensation system. *Journal of Private Sector Rehabilitation, 1,* 83–86.

Bradley, V. J. (1985). Implementation of court and consent decrees: Some current lessons. In R. H. Bruininks & K. C. Lakin (Eds.), *Living and learning in the least restrictive environment* (pp. 81–96). Baltimore: Brookes.

Brubaker, D. R. (1977). Professionalization and rehabilitation counseling. *Journal of Applied Rehabilitation Counseling, 8,* 208–217.

Bruininks, R. H., & Lakin, K. C. (Eds.). (1985). *Living and learning in the least restrictive environment.* Baltimore: Brookes.

Castellani, P. (1987). *The political economy of developmental disabilities.* Baltimore: Brookes.

Cheit, E. F. (1961). *Injury and recovery in the course of employment.* New York: Wiley.

Civil Rights Act of 1964, 42 U.S.C. § 2000 *et seq.*

Corthell, D. (Ed.). (1990). *Traumatic brain injury and vocational rehabilitation.* Menomonie: University of Wisconsin–Stout, Research and Training Center.

Commission on Rehabilitation Counselor Certification. (1994). *Guide to rehabilitation counselor certification.* Rolling Meadows: IL: Author.

Council on Rehabilitation Education. (1996). *Accreditation manual for rehabilitation counselor education programs.* Rolling Meadows, IL: Author.

Curl, R., & Sheldon, J. (1992). Achieving reasonable choices: Balancing the rights and responsibilities of consumers with those of rehabilitation counselors. *Rehabilitation Education, 6,* 195–205.

DeJong, G. (1979). Independent living: From social movement to analytic paradigm. *Archives of Physical Medicine and Rehabilitation, 60,* 435–446.

Deren, S., & Randell, J. (1990). The vocational rehabilitation of substance abusers. *Journal of Applied Rehabilitation Counseling, 21*(2), 4–6.

Developmental Disabilities Services and Facilities Construction Act of 1970, 84 Stat. 1316, 1325.

Developmental Disabilities Services and Facilities Construction Act Amendments of 1978, 92 Stat. 3003–3017.

DiMichael, S. G. (1969). The current scene. In D. Malikin & H. Rusalem (Eds.), *Vocational rehabilitation of the disabled: An overview* (pp. 5–27). New York: New York University Press.

DiMichael, S. G. (1971). Dimensions in coordinating rehabilitation services. *Journal of Rehabilitation, 37*(1), 14–16.

DiMichael, S. G., & Thomas, K. R. (1985). ARCA's journey in professionalism: A commemorative review on the 25th anniversary. *Journal of Counseling and Development, 63,* 428–435.

Downing, J., Shafer, M., Brahm-Levy, A., & Frantz, M. (1992). Supported employment for individuals with dual sensory impairments and mental retardation: Current practice and future challenges. *Journal of Vocational Rehabilitation, 2*(1), 28–38.

Dziekan, K., & Okocha, A. (1993). Accessibility of rehabilitation services: Comparison by racial-ethnic status. *Rehabilitation Counseling Bulletin, 36,* 183–189.

Ebener, D. (1992). The influence of negative perceptions of aging on the delivery of rehabilitation services: Implications for rehabilitation counselor education. *Rehabilitation Education, 6,* 335–340.

Education for All Handicapped Children Act of 1975, 20 U.S.C. § 1400 *et seq.*

Ellien, V., & Wolkstein, E. (Eds.). (1987). Rehabilitation in business and industry [Special issue]. *Rehabilitation Education, 1*(2/3).

Emener, W. G., & Cottone, R. (1989). Professionalization, deprofessionalization, and reprofessionalization of rehabilitation counseling according to criteria of professions. *Journal of Counseling and Development, 67,* 576–581.

Fair Housing Amendments of 1978, 102 Stat. 1619 (as codified at 42 U.S.C. § 360 *et seq.*).

Federal Employer's Liability Act of 1906, 34 Stat. 232, 45 U.S.C. § 51 *et seq.*

Federal Register. (1985, September 23). Rules and Regulations. *50*(184), 388631-388632.

Ferguson, P. M., Hibbard, M., Leinen, J., & Schaff, S. (1990). Supported community life: Disability policy and the renewal of mediating structures. *Journal of Disability Policy Studies, 1*(1), 9-35.

Florida Constitution (1973), art. 1 § 2.

Garske, G., & Turpin, J. (1992). Minimum training and experience qualifications for entry level rehabilitation counselors: A national survey. *Rehabilitation Education, 6,* 341-354.

Gilhool, T. K. (1989). The right to an effective education: From Brown to P.L. 94-142 and beyond. In D. K. Lipsky & A. Gartner (Eds.), *Beyond separate education: Quality education for all* (pp. 243-253). Baltimore: Brookes.

Graves, W. H. (1983). Rehabilitation counselor certification: The path toward professional recognition. *Journal of Applied Rehabilitation Counseling, 14*(4), 24-28.

Greer, B. (1986). Substance abuse among people with disabilities: A problem of too much accessibility. *Journal of Applied Rehabilitation Counseling, 18*(1), 34-38.

Hackett, J., & LaForge, J. (1995, September/October). The alliance for rehabilitation counseling. *Professional Report, 36,* 6.

Hahn, H. (1985). Changing perception of disability and the future of rehabilitation. In L. G. Perlman & G. F. Austin (Eds.), *Social influences in rehabilitation planning: Blueprint for the 21st century* [A report of the ninth Mary E. Switzer Memorial Seminar] (pp. 53-64). Alexandria, VA: National Rehabilitation Association.

Hahn, H. (1989). The politics of special education. In D. K. Lipsky & A. Gartner (Eds.), *Beyond separate education: Quality education for all* (pp. 225-241). Baltimore: Brookes.

Hahn, H. (1991). Alternative views of empowerment: Social services and civil rights. *Journal of Rehabilitation, 57*(4), 20.

Hanley-Maxwell, C., & Bordieri, J. E. (1989). Purchasing supported employment: Evaluating the service. *Journal of Applied Rehabilitation Counseling, 20*(3), 4-11.

Hedgeman, B. S. (1985). Rehabilitation counselor certification. *Journal of Counseling and Development, 63,* 609-610.

Hershenson, D. B. (1988). Along for the ride: The evolution of rehabilitation counselor education. *Rehabilitation Counseling Bulletin, 31,* 204-217.

Individuals with Disabilities Education Act of 1990, 20 U.S.C. § 1400 *et seq.*

Javitts-Wagner-O'Day Act of 1971, 41 U.S.C. §§ 46-48, 48a-48c.

Jones, E. C. (1990). ADA: What's next. *Worklife, 3*(2), 26-27.

Koestler, F. (1976). *The unseen minority.* New York: American Foundation for the Blind.

Kratz, J. A. (1960). Vocational rehabilitation, past, present and future in the United States. In C. H. Patterson (Ed.), *Readings in rehabilitation counseling* (pp. 25-30). Champaign, IL: Stipes.

LaFon, R. H. (1988). The past, the present and the future: How can we avoid the pitfalls and realize the potential of vocational rehabilitation? *Journal of Private Sector Rehabilitation, 3,* 75-84.

Lakin, K. C., & Bruininks, R. H. (1985). Contemporary services for handicapped children and youth. In R. H. Bruininks & K. C. Lakin (Eds.), *Living and learning in the least restrictive environment* (pp. 3-22). Baltimore: Brookes.

Lamborn, E. (1970). The state-federal partnership. *Journal of Rehabilitation, 36*(5), 10–15.

Laski, F. J. (1985). Right to habilitation and right to education: The legal foundation. In R. H. Bruininks & K. C. Lakin (Eds.), *Living and learning in the least restrictive environment* (pp. 67–79). Baltimore: Brookes.

Lassiter, R. A. (1972). History of the rehabilitation movement in America. In J. G. Cull & R. E. Hardy (Eds.), *Vocational rehabilitation: Profession and process* (pp. 1–58). Springfield, IL: Thomas.

Leahy, M., & Holt, E. (1993). Certification in rehabilitation counseling: History and process. *Rehabilitation Counseling Bulletin, 37,* 71–80.

Leahy, M., Szymanski, E., & Linkowski, D. (1993). Knowledge importance in rehabilitation counseling. *Rehabilitation Counseling Bulletin, 37,* 130–135.

Leung, P. (1987). Rehabilitation counselor education or rehabilitation technical training. *Rehabilitation Education, 1,* 29–33.

Levine, L. S., & Pence, J. W. (1953). A training program for rehabilitation counselors. *Journal of Rehabilitation, 19*(1), 16–17.

Linkowski, D., & Szymanski, E. (1993). Accreditation in rehabilitation counseling: History and current context and process. *Rehabilitation Counseling Bulletin, 37,* 81–91.

Lipsky, D. K., & Gartner, A. (Eds.). (1989). *Beyond separate education: Quality education for all.* Baltimore: Brookes.

Lynch, R. K., & Martin, T. (1982). Rehabilitation counseling in the private sector: A training needs survey. *Journal of Rehabilitation, 48*(3), 51–52, 73.

Maki, D. R., & Riggar, T. F. (1985). Rehabilitation counseling: Orientations to practice. *Journal of Applied Rehabilitation Counseling, 16*(3), 2.

Matkin, R. E. (1985). *Insurance rehabilitation.* Austin, TX: PRO-ED.

McGowan, J. R., & Porter, T. L. (1967). *An introduction to the vocational rehabilitation process.* Washington, DC: U.S. Department of Health, Education, and Welfare; Rehabilitation Services Administration.

McMahon, B., Glenn, M., & Dixon, S. (1994). Prologue to the special issue on drugs and alcohol: Resource center on substance abuse prevention and disability—Bridging the gap. *Rehabilitation Counseling Bulletin, 38,* 84–92.

Merchant Marine Act of 1920, 46 U.S.C. § 802 *et seq.*

Meyers, J. K. (1968). The prophetic mission of rehabilitation: Curse or blessing. Statement. *Journal of Rehabilitation, 34*(1), 23–33.

Muthard, J. E. (1969). The status of the profession. In D. Malikin & H. Rusalem (Eds.), *Vocational rehabilitation of the disabled: An overview* (pp. 275–308). New York: New York University Press.

Muthard, J. E., & Salomone, P. R. (1969). The roles and functions of the rehabilitation counselor. *Rehabilitation Counseling Bulletin, 13*(1-SP), 81–168.

Noble, J. H., & McCarthy, C. M. (1988). Organizational accommodation and rehabilitation values. In S. E. Rubin & N. M. Rubin (Eds.), *Contemporary challenges to the rehabilitation counseling profession* (pp. 15–29). Baltimore: Brookes.

Nosek, M. A. (1988). Independent living and rehabilitation counseling. In S. E. Rubin & N. M. Rubin (Eds.), *Contemporary challenges to the rehabilitation counseling profession* (pp. 45–60). Baltimore: Brookes.

Obermann, C. E. (1965). *A history of vocational rehabilitation in America.* Minneapolis: T. S. Denison.

Occupational Safety and Health Act of 1970, 29 U.S.C. § 651 *et seq.*

Office of Special Education Programs (1992). Statistical data. *Education of the Handicapped, 18*(15).

Olshansky, S. (1957). An evaluation of rehabilitation counselor training. *Vocational Guidance Quarterly, 5,* 164-167.

Parker, R. M., Szymanski, E. M., & Hanley-Maxwell, C. (1989). Ecological assessment in supported employment. *Journal of Applied Rehabilitation Counseling, 20*(3), 26-33.

Patterson, C. H. (1957). Counselor or coordinator? *Journal of Rehabilitation, 23*(3), 13-15.

Patterson, C. H. (1961). Trends in vocational rehabilitation counseling. *Rehabilitation Counseling Bulletin, 5,* 59-67.

Patterson, J. B. (1987). Certified rehabilitation counselors (CRC). *Journal of Applied Rehabilitation Counseling, 18*(4), 45-47.

Patterson, J. B. (1992). Graduate-level preparation of rehabilitation counselors. *Journal of Vocational Rehabilitation, 2*(4), 28-34.

Patterson, J. B., & Woodrich, F. (1986). The client assistance projects: 1974-1984. *Journal of Rehabilitation, 52*(4), 49-52.

Podemski, R. S., Price, B. J., Smith, T. E., & Marsh, G. E. (1984). *Comprehensive administration of special education.* Rockville, MD: Aspen.

Power, P., Dell Orto, A., & Gibbons, M. (Eds.). (1988). *Family interventions throughout chronic illness and disability.* New York: Springer.

President's Committee on Employment of People with Disabilities. (1988). *The Fair Housing Amendments: Legislative history.* Washington, DC: Author.

President's Committee on Employment of People with Disabilities and U.S. Architectural and Transportation Barriers Compliance Board. (1990). *Americans with Disabilities Act (ADA) in Brief.* Washington, DC: Authors.

Randolph–Sheppard Act of 1936, 20 U.S.C. §§ 107, 107a-f.

Rasch, J. D. (1979). The case for an independent association of rehabilitation counselors. *Journal of Applied Rehabilitation Counseling, 10*(4), 171-176.

Rasch, J. D. (1985). *Rehabilitation of workers' compensation and other insurance claimants.* Springfield, IL: Thomas.

Reagles, K. W. (1981). Perspectives on the proposed merger of rehabilitation organizations. *Journal of Applied Rehabilitation Counseling, 12*(2), 75-79.

Rehabilitation Act of 1973, 87 Stat. 355, 29 U.S.C. § 701 *et seq.*

Rehabilitation Act Amendments of 1974, 89 Stat. 2.

Rehabilitation Amendments of 1984, 98 Stat. 2489.

Rehabilitation Act Amendments of 1986, 100 Stat. 1808.

Rehabilitation Act Amendments of 1992, 106 Stat. 4344.

Rehabilitation Act Amendments of 1993, 107 Stat. 718.

Rehabilitation, Comprehensive Services, and Developmental Disabilities Amendments of 1978, 92 Stat. 2955.

Ross, E. M. (1976). *Workmen's compensation rehabilitation: A study of the rehabilitation of injured workers in the United States and member jurisdictions of the International Association of Industrial Accident Boards and Commissions.* Des Moines, IA: The Associations.

Ross, E. M. (1979). Legislative trends in workers' compensation rehabilitation. *Journal of Rehabilitation, 45*(3), 20-23, 70.

Rubin, S. E., Matkin, R. E., Ashley, J., Beardsley, M., May, V. R., Onstott, K., & Puckett, F. (1984). Roles and functions of certified rehabilitation counselors. *Rehabilitation Counseling Bulletin, 27,* 199-224, 238-245.

Rubin, S. E., & Roessler, R. T. (1987). *Foundations of the vocational rehabilitation process* (3rd ed.). Austin, TX: PRO-ED.

Rusalem, H. (1976). A personal recent history of vocational rehabilitation in America. In H. Rusalem & D. Malikin (Eds.), *Contemporary vocational rehabilitation* (pp. 25-46). New York: New York University Press.

Rusch, F. R. (Ed.). (1986). *Competitive employment strategies and issues.* Baltimore: Brookes.

Scalia, V. A., & Wolfe, R. R. (1984). Rehabilitation counselor education. *Journal of Applied Rehabilitation Counseling, 15*(3), 34-38.

Schwartz, P. (1990). *Medicaid waiver funding.* Unpublished manuscript, University of Wisconsin-Madison, Department of Rehabilitation Psychology and Special Education.

Shrey, D. E., Bangs, S. A., Mark, L. S., Hursh, N. C., & Kues, J. R. (1991). Returning social security beneficiaries to the workforce: A proactive disability management model. *Rehabilitation Counseling Bulletin, 34,* 257-273.

Smart, J. (1993). Level of acculturation of Mexican Americans with disabilities and acceptance of disability. *Rehabilitation Counseling Bulletin, 36,* 199-211.

Smith-Fess Act (Vocational Rehabilitation of Persons Disabled in Industry Act of 1920), 41 Stat. 735.

Smith-Hughes Act (Vocational Education Act of 1917), 20 U.S.C. § 11 *et seq.*

Social Security Act of 1935, 49 Stat. 620.

Social Security Administration. (1986). *Disability evaluation under social security* (SSA Publication No. 05-10089). Washington, DC: Author.

Soldier Rehabilitation Act of 1918, 40 Stat. 617.

Staff. (1988, Fall). Section 508 ensures technological access for all. *NARIC Quarterly, 1*(3), 1, 19.

Stapleton, M. (1976). Rights to equality for disabled persons under federal and state law. *Rehabilitation Counseling Bulletin, 19,* 597-606.

Stone, J. B. (1966). Counseling and rehabilitation counseling. *Rehabilitation Counseling Bulletin, 10,* 127-133.

Switzer, M. E. (1964). The public program today. *Journal of Rehabilitation, 30*(5), 20-24.

Switzer, M. E. (1969). Legislative contributions. In D. Malikin & H. Rusalem (Eds.), *Vocational rehabilitation of the disabled: An overview* (pp. 39-55). New York: New York University Press.

Szymanski, E. M. (1985). Rehabilitation counseling: A profession with a vision, an identity, and a future. *Rehabilitation Counseling Bulletin, 29,* 2-5.

Szymanski, E. M. (1988). Rehabilitation planning with social security work incentives: A sequential guide for the rehabilitation professional. *Journal of Rehabilitation, 54*(2), 28-32.

Szymanski, E. M. (1991). The relationship of level of rehabilitation counselor education to rehabilitation client outcome in the Wisconsin Division of Vocational Rehabilitation. *Rehabilitation Counseling Bulletin, 35,* 23-37.

Szymanski, E. M., Dunn, C., & Parker, R. M. (1989). Rehabilitation of persons with learning disabilities: An ecological framework. *Rehabilitation Counseling Bulletin, 33,* 38-53.

Szymanski, E. M., & King, J. (1989). Rehabilitation counseling in transition planning and preparation. *Career Development for Exceptional Individuals, 12*(1), 3-10.

Talbot, H. S. (1961). A concept of rehabilitation. *Rehabilitation Literature, 22,* 358-364.

Tarvydas, V., & Leahy, M. (1993). Licensure in rehabilitation counseling: A critical incident in professionalization. *Rehabilitation Counseling Bulletin, 37,* 92-108.

Technology-Related Assistance for Individuals with Disabilities Act of 1988, 29 U.S.C. § 2201 *et seq.*

Thayer, D. (Ed.). (1989). *Annual report of the Rehabilitation Services Administration on federal activities related to the Administration of the Rehabilitation Act of 1973, as amended.* Washington, DC: U.S. Department of Education, Office of Special Education and Rehabilitative Services, Rehabilitation Services Administration.

Thomas, R. E. (1970). The expanding scope of services. *Journal of Rehabilitation, 36*(5), 37-40.

Veteran's Bureau Act of 1921, 42 Stat. 147.

Vocational Rehabilitation Act of 1918. (P.L. 65-178).

Vocational Rehabilitation Act of 1920, 41 Stat. 735.

Vocational Rehabilitation Act Amendments of 1943, 57 Stat. 374.

Vocational Rehabilitation Act Amendments of 1954, 68 Stat. 652.

Vocational Rehabilitation Act Amendments of 1965, 79 Stat. 1282.

Vocational Rehabilitation Act Amendments of 1967, 81 Stat. 250.

Vocational Rehabilitation Act Amendments of 1968, 82 Stat. 298.

Wagner-O'Day Act of 1938, 41 U.S.C. §§ 46-48.

Walker, M. L., & Myers, R. W. (1988). A counter proposal: Defining the qualified rehabilitation professional. *Rehabilitation Education, 2,* 49-57.

Weber, M. (1994). Towards access, accountability, procedural regularity and participation: The Rehabilitation Act Amendments of 1992 and 1993. *Journal of Rehabilitation, 60*(3), 21-25.

Wehman, P. (1988). Supported employment: Toward zero exclusion of persons with severe disabilities. In P. Wehman & M. S. Moon (Eds.), *Vocational rehabilitation and supported employment* (pp. 3-14). Baltimore: Brookes.

Whitten, E. B. (1973). Rehabilitation in 1973: A reassessment. *Journal of Rehabilitation, 39*(3), 2, 43.

Wisconsin Laws. (1967). § 111.31.

Wright, B. (Ed.). (1959). *Psychology and rehabilitation.* Washington, DC: American Psychological Association.

Wright, B. (1972). Value-laden beliefs and principles for rehabilitation psychologists. *Rehabilitation Psychology, 19,* 38-45.

Wright, B. (1983). *Physical disability—A psychosocial approach* (2nd ed.). New York: Harper & Row.

Wright, G. N. (1980). *Total rehabilitation.* Boston: Little, Brown.

Wright, G. N., Leahy, M. J., & Shapson, P. R. (1987). Rehabilitation skills inventory: Importance of counselor competencies. *Rehabilitation Counseling Bulletin, 31,* 107–130.

Chapter 2

The State–Federal Vocational Rehabilitation Program

Robert Brabham, Kerry A. Mandeville, and Lynn Koch

Vocational rehabilitation, as practiced in the State–Federal Vocational Rehabilitation (VR) Program, may be defined from the standpoint of three salient elements: philosophy, services, and service delivery. The underlying philosophy of the program recognizes that Americans live in a work-oriented society, that people with disabilities should be employed in accordance with their abilities, and that through productive activity each citizen with a disability makes a contribution to society. This philosophy is implemented through the provision of rehabilitation services, which are intended to enable individuals with physical, mental, or emotional disabilities to become gainfully employed (Institute of Rehabilitation Issues, 1975). The State–Federal VR Program serves people with a wide range of disabilities. In 1990, the largest categories of rehabilitant disabilities were orthopedic impairments (20.8%), mental illness (16.2%), and mental retardation (14.1%) (Rehabilitation Services Administration [RSA], 1991).

The description of the State–Federal VR Program presented in this chapter incorporates a philosophical premise, a listing of component services, and an emphasis on the rehabilitation process leading to the achievement of an employment outcome. The last of these elements, the rehabilitation process, serves as the primary focus of this chapter because it is the dynamic by which the program achieves its goals. Therefore, understanding and implementing the rehabilitation process is the task faced by all new rehabilitation professionals.

More than any other rehabilitation professional, the counselor is the personification of the rehabilitation process. Accordingly, in this chapter, explanations of significant aspects of the rehabilitation process are presented from the perspective of the counselor through the presentation of the following topics: (a) structure and purpose of the State–Federal VR Program, (b) the case status code system, (c) the rehabilitation process leading to an employment outcome, and (d) the changing roles and functions of rehabilitation counselors within the State–Federal VR Program. Independent living, another central element of the Rehabilitation Act of 1973, is extensively covered by Nosek (Chapter 4, this text).

The Structure and Purpose of the State–Federal VR Program

In principle, the program is founded on the following two assumptions:

> First, every member of a democratic society has an inherent right to the opportunity to earn a living and make a contribution to society; second, society has the corresponding obligation to equalize, as best it can by special services, the . . . opportunity [of people with disabilities] to earn a living equivalent to the opportunity possessed by nondisabled members of society. (McGowan, 1969, p. 113)

Over the course of approximately 75 years, the grant-in-aid State–Federal VR Program has undergone a number of title changes and has passed through several administrative structures. Currently, the program is conducted by the U.S. Department of Education's Rehabilitation Services Administration (RSA) under the legal authority of the Rehabilitation Act of 1973 and its amendments.

> The purposes of this Act are—(1) to empower individuals with disabilities to maximize employment, economic self-sufficiency, independence, and inclusion and integration into society through—(A) comprehensive and coordinated state-of-the-art programs of vocational rehabilitation; (B) independent living centers and services; (C) research; (D) training; (E) demonstration projects; and (F) the guarantee of equal employment; and (2) to ensure that the Federal Government plays a leadership role in prompting the employment of individuals with disabilities, especially individuals with severe disabilities, and in assisting States and providers of services in fulfilling the aspirations of such individuals with disabilities for meaningful and gainful employment and independent living. (Rehabilitation Act Amendments of 1992, § 2)

The U.S. Department of Education's Office of Special Education and Rehabilitative Services (OSERS) administers the State–Federal VR Programs through the RSA by providing funds, monitoring program operation, and interpreting legislative requirements for program implementation (Council of State Administrators of Vocational Rehabilitation [CSAVR], 1990; Rehabilitation Act Amendments of 1992, (§§ 3, 12). As established by the Rehabilitation Act of 1973, RSA is the principal agency for carrying out the act and, therefore, is the functioning agency for the Department of Education with respect to vocational rehabilitation. RSA also administers grants and special programs for rehabilitation counseling, rehabilitation medicine, vocational evaluation, work adjustment training, program innovation and expansion, employer development, training and development of rehabilitation personnel, and improvement and construction of rehabilitation facilities (Rehabilitation Act Amendments of 1992, § 3).

The State–Federal VR Program is implemented through state vocational rehabilitation agencies, which purchase services for and render services to persons with substantial impediments to employment for the purpose of achieving vocational rehabilitation. Nationwide conformity with respect to process and service provision is assured by the Rehabilitation Act of 1973 through a grant-in-aid mechanism whereby funding is provided to state agencies contingent on approval of their respective state plans. Funding is based on state population and per-capita income, with a federal–state matching formula entailing federal participation of 78.7% [Rehabilitation Act Amendments of 1992, §§ 7(7) and 100(a)].

The state agency can be an independent agency or a component of an education, vocational education, health, welfare, or labor agency. Currently, there are 82 state-agency VR programs, approximately one third of which serve people with blindness as well as those with other disabilities. In 25 states, people with blindness and visual impairments are served by separate state VR agencies (RSA, 1994). Further information concerning the organizational structure of state rehabilitation agencies is provided by Jenkins, Patterson, and Szymanski (Chapter 1, this text).

Regardless of the agency's administrative placement, the federal law and regulations require that the state VR agency occupy an organizational position equal to that of the other major units, that the agency be headed by a director responsible for the overall management of the program, and that the agency have its own professional staff in sufficient quantity and adequately skilled to accomplish the agency's mission. Of overriding significance, however, is the legal stipulation that the state VR agency be the only organizational unit empowered to determine client eligibility for program services and to develop jointly with the client the Individualized Written Rehabilitation Program (IWRP) [Rehabilitation Act of 1973, §§ 102(a)(5) and 102(b)(1)(A)].   *IPE – Individualized Plan for Employment*

Eligibility determination is made on a case-by-case basis. *Existing information,* which may include, for example, the consumer's report of the disability, school records, and previous professional assessments, should be used to the maximum extent possible. Eligibility for services is based solely on the following requirements (34 CFR § 361.42):

(i) A determination that the applicant has a physical or mental impairment.

(ii) A determination that the applicant's physical or mental impairment constitutes or results in a substantial impediment to employment for the applicant.

(iii) A presumption . . . that the applicant can benefit in terms of an employment outcome from the provision of vocational rehabilitation services.

(iv) A determination that the applicant requires vocational rehabilitation services to prepare for, enter into, engage in, or retain gainful employment consistent with the applicant's strengths, resources, priorities, concerns, abilities, capabilities, and informed choice.

Finally, the state VR agency must determine whether an individual is eligible for vocational rehabilitation services within 60 days after the individual has submitted an application or has otherwise requested services [Rehabilitation Act of 1973, § 102(a)(5)].

The focal document binding the relationship between the state agency and the RSA is the state plan. RSA's (1978) *Rehabilitation Services Manual* refers to the state plan as "the key legal document in this type of arrangement, which is essentially a compact or a contract, . . . which must be Federally approved as a basis for receiving Federal grant funds" (§ 501.02). Issued on a triennial basis, the state plan is written by the state VR agency and submitted for review and approval to the appropriate regional office of RSA. While serving as the basis for grant-in-aid funding, the state plan is also used by the RSA for monitoring and evaluating the state agency program. Elements of state plans include agency identification, organizational placement, leadership of a director, staff adequacy, and procedures for determining eligibility for services. State plans also must describe plans, policies, and methods for statewide studies of the needs of people with disabilities, expansion and improvement of services to persons with severe disabilities, statewide service delivery efforts, and development of an IWRP for each person declared eligible.

In the event that all persons who apply cannot be served, the state plan must explain the order in which individuals will be selected to be served, with the stipulation that individuals with the most severe disabilities will be served first. Additionally, if a state agency elects to impose a financial need criterion to the provision of services, the state plan must set forth a detailed explanation of the criterion, with the stipulation that it cannot be applied to the provision of diagnostic services, counseling and guidance, referral services, and placement (CSAVR, 1990; Rehabilitation Act Amendments of 1992). Of great significance is the matter of informed choice:

> The State plan must describe the manner in which the State unit will provide each applicant, including individuals who are receiving services during an extended evaluation, and each eligible individual the opportunity to make informed choices throughout the vocational rehabilitation process in accordance with the following requirements:
> (a) Each State unit . . . shall develop and implement written policies and procedures that enable each individual to make an **informed choice** [emphasis added] with regard to the selection of a long-term vocational goal, intermediate rehabilitation objectives, vocational rehabilitation services, including assessment services, and service providers. These policies and procedures must ensure that each individual receives, through appropriate modes of communication, information concerning

the availability and scope of informed choice, the manner in which informed choice may be exercised, and the availability of support services for individuals with cognitive or other disabilities who require assistance in exercising informed choice.

(b) In developing an individual's IWRP, the State unit shall provide the individual, or assist the individual in acquiring, information necessary to make an informed choice about the specific services, including the providers of those services, that are needed to achieve the individual's vocational goal. This information must include, at a minimum, information relating to the cost, accessibility, and duration of potential services, the consumer satisfaction with those services to the extent that information relating to consumer satisfaction is available, the qualifications of potential service providers, the types of services offered by those providers, and the degree to which services are provided in integrated settings.

(c) In providing, or assisting the individual in acquiring, the information . . . , the State unit may use, but is not limited to, the following methods or sources of information:

(1) State or regional lists of services and service providers.

(2) Periodic consumer satisfaction surveys and reports.

(3) Referrals to other consumers, local consumer groups, or disability advisory councils qualified to discuss the services or service providers.

(4) Relevant accreditation, certification, or other information relating to the qualifications of service providers. (34 CFR § 361.52)

Added to this, the Rehabilitation Act Amendments of 1992, require that the state agency seek the comments and advice of VR clients, service providers, and interested parties in formulating the state plan. By way of summary, Figure 2.1 is a graphic illustration of the State–Federal VR Program structure, its hierarchy of authority, and the relationship of its components.

The State–Federal VR Program's organizational structure provides the administrative support for the rehabilitation process, which

consists of a planned, orderly sequence of services related to the total needs of the . . . individual. It is a process built around the problems of . . . individual[s] [with disabilities] and the attempts of the vocational rehabilitation counselor to help solve these problems and thus to bring about the vocational adjustment of the . . . [individual]. The process begins with the initial case finding or referral, and ends with the successful placement [and follow-up] of the . . . individual on a job. (McGowan & Porter, 1967, p. 6)

Rehabilitation services are any goods or services necessary to render a person with a disability employable and include the following:

(1) Assessment for determining eligibility and priority for services . . .

(2) Assessment for determining vocational rehabilitation needs . . .

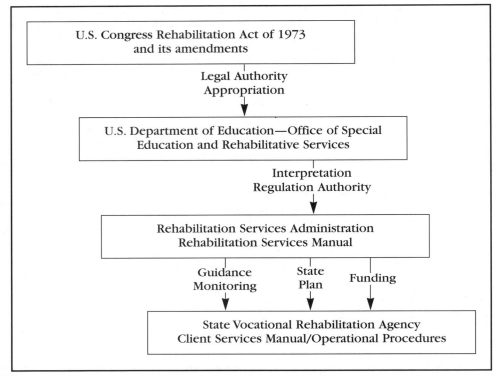

Figure 2.1. The State–Federal Vocational Rehabilitation Program.

(3) Vocational rehabilitation counseling and guidance.

(4) Referral and other services necessary to help applicants and eligible individuals secure needed services from other agencies and to advise those individuals about client assistance programs . . .

(5) Physical and mental restoration services . . . [including, but not limited to,]

(A) corrective surgery or therapeutic treatment necessary to correct or substantially modify a physical or mental condition which is stable or slowly progressive and constitutes a substantial impediment to employment . . . ,

(B) necessary hospitalization in connection with surgery or treatment,

(C) prosthetic and orthotic devices,

(D) eyeglasses and visual services . . . ,

(E) special services (including transplantation and dialysis), artificial kidneys, and supplies necessary for the treatment of individuals with end-stage renal disease, and

(F) diagnosis and treatment for mental and emotional disorders . . .;

(6) Vocational and other training services, including personal and vocational adjustment training, books, tools, and other training materials, except that no training or training services in an institution of higher education may be paid for with funds under this part unless maximum efforts have been made by the State unit and the individual to secure grant assistance in whole or in part from other sources to pay for that training.

(7) Maintenance . . .

(8) Transportation in connection with the rendering of any vocational rehabilitation service . . .

(9) Vocational rehabilitation services to family members of an applicant or eligible individual if necessary to enable the applicant or eligible individual to achieve an employment outcome.

(10) Interpreter services for individuals who are deaf and tactile interpreting services for individuals who are deaf–blind.

(11) Reader services, rehabilitation teaching services, and orientation and mobility services for individuals who are blind.

(12) Recruitment and training services to provide new employment opportunities in the fields of rehabilitation, health, welfare, public safety, law enforcement, and other appropriate public service employment.

(13) Job search and placement assistance and job retention services.

(14) Supported employment services . . .

(15) Personal assistance services . . .

(16) Post-employment services . . .

(17) Occupational licenses, tools, equipment, initial stocks, and supplies.

(18) Rehabilitation technology . . . , including vehicular modification, telecommunications, sensory, and other technological aids and devices.

(19) Transition services . . .

(20) Other goods and services determined necessary for the individual with a disability to achieve an employment outcome. [34 CFR § 361.48(a)]

Supported employment is further described by Hanley-Maxwell, Szymanski, and Owens-Johnson (Chapter 5, this text).

The Case Status Code System

To facilitate the order and coordination of the rehabilitation process, RSA established a coding system for use by state VR agencies. The process, displayed in

Table 2.1 and described in detail below, is categorized into stages indicated by two-digit codes. In 1993 the Council of State Administrators of Vocational Rehabilitation recommended a model service delivery system to streamline the VR process. This model includes the recommendation to simplify the documentation system by reducing the number of statuses in the case status code system. The proposed statuses include (a) eligibility, (b) services, and (c) outcomes. RSA has encouraged each state to develop such a simplification, but has not provided explicit guidelines. Therefore, each state may have a different system for coding cases. Despite the simplification, the full case status code system as detailed in the following section provides a clear picture of the complete VR process.

Table 2.1
Client Statuses Comprising the Vocational Rehabilitation Process[a]

Referral Processing Statuses

00   Referral—agency obtains minimal information about a potential client
02   Applicant—agency secures a document signed by the client requesting services
06   Extended evaluation

Preservice Statuses

10   IWRP development
12   IWRP completed

In-service Statuses

14   Counseling and guidance only
16   Physical and mental restoration
18   Training
20   Ready for employment
22   In employment
24   Service interrupted
32   Postemployment services

Closure Statuses

08   Closed from referral (00), applicant (02), or extended evaluation (06)
26   Closed rehabilitated
28   Closed for other reasons after the IWRP was initiated (not rehabilitated)
30   Closed for other reasons before the IWRP is initiated (not rehabilitated from Status 10 or 12)
34   Closed from postemployment services

Note. IWRP = Individualized Written Rehabilitation Program.
  [a]Application of these statuses may vary by state, in accordance with their streamlining efforts.

The Case Statuses

Status 00, Referral

This is the entry point to the VR process. A referral is any person who is known to the VR agency by letter, telephone, direct contact, and so on. The following minimum information has been provided: (a) name and address, (b) disability as reported, (c) age and sex, (d) date of referral, and (e) source of referral. This information is recorded on standard forms for statistical purposes and for the initiation of the client's case record.

Status 02, Applicant

The person's signature on a letter or agency form that requests VR services, together with the information required for Status 00, places the case in Status 02. This establishes the person as an applicant in a formal sense, which requires that he or she be informed of all decisions affecting the case. The signed document requesting services is of crucial importance, because it is the only certain basis for determining that the individual has knowledge of having been referred. Placement of the case in Status 02 is limited to 60 days (although extensions are allowed when due to unforeseen circumstances and the applicant concurs) and marks the beginning of a preliminary assessment process, the purpose of which is to determine eligibility, or the need to defer such a definitive determination and to extend the evaluation (Status 06).

Status 06, Extended Evaluation

Applicants are placed in this status when it has been determined that their disability constitutes a substantial impediment to employment, but the severity of the impairment raises significant doubts about the applicant's ability to benefit from services in attaining an employment outcome. This status requires the completion of a certificate for extended evaluation and an individualized plan outlining the evaluation and service plans needed to make the ultimate determination of eligibility (Status 10) or ineligibility (Status 08), supported by a demonstration of clear and convincing evidence that the applicant cannot benefit from VR services in terms of an employment outcome. A case may not remain in this status for longer than 18 months. In practice, this status is customarily used for applicants with severe disabilities who will require a complex combination of medical or psychological treatment and evaluation.

Status 08, Closed from Referral, Applicant, or Extended Evaluation Statuses

This status identifies all persons not accepted for VR services, whether closed from referral status (00), applicant status (02), or extended evaluation status (06). Reasons for closure are recorded according to the following categories: (1) unable to locate or contact, or moved; (2) handicap too severe or unfavorable medical prognosis (from Status 06 only); (3) refused services or further services; (4) death; (5) client institutionalized; (6) transfer to another agency; (7) failure to cooperate; (8) no disabling condition (valid only for closure from Statuses 00 or 02); (9) no vocational handicap (valid only for closure from Statuses 00 or 02); (10) transportation not feasible or available; (11) client did not meet order of selection priority; and (12) all other reasons. If closure is due to reasons 2, 8, or 9, certification of ineligibility is required, along with formal notification of the consumer. In all instances of closure, however, case record documentation must support this action.

Status 10, Individualized Written Rehabilitation Program Development

When the person is determined eligible in accordance with the legally established criteria, the case is placed in Status 10. A comprehensive case study is initiated so that the client and counselor can formulate an IWRP that will accomplish the client's vocational goal. A certificate of eligibility must be completed and be a part of the case record.

Status 12, Individualized Written Rehabilitation Program Completed

A client is placed in this status when the IWRP has been developed. The client remains in this status until at least one arrangement has been made to supply a necessary service, and the service has been initiated. In those instances where the program provides for counseling, guidance, and placement only, the client may be moved immediately after program approval into Status 14 since counseling is a continuing process.

Status 14, Counseling and Guidance Only

Counseling and guidance are to be provided to all eligible clients. This status is inappropriate for those individuals receiving physical or mental restoration or training, but is appropriate for those consumers having an IWRP entailing counseling, guidance, and placement as the only services required to prepare them for employment. In instances where restoration and/or training services may have been completed or ceased and only additional counseling, guidance, and placement are needed to accomplish employment, Status 14 is appropriate.

Status 16, Physical and Mental Restoration

If a client is receiving any physical or mental restoration services, such as medical, surgical, psychiatric, or therapeutic treatment, or is being fitted with a prosthetic appliance, the client's case is placed in this status until services are completed or terminated.

Status 18, Training

Provision of training to a client in the form of academic, business, or vocational instruction requires placement of the case in this status. Personal, social, and work adjustment training, as well as on-the-job training, are also included in this category. The training may be provided by a public or private school, a commercial or industrial establishment, a rehabilitation or other facility, an individual teacher or instructor, or correspondence. Clients' cases remain in this status until the training is either completed or terminated.

Status 20, Ready for Employment

When clients have completed the services required to prepare them for employment but have not yet been hired, their cases are placed in this status. This status is also appropriate for clients who have been formally hired but have not yet started work. Generally speaking, placement in this status signals the initiation of intensive job seeking efforts by the counselor and the client.

Status 22, In Employment

A case is placed in this status when a client has been prepared for, been placed in, and begun employment. He or she must be observed in employment for a minimum of 90 days prior to being considered Closed Rehabilitated (Status 26) to ensure adequacy of employment in accordance with the individual's needs and limitations. Cases of homemakers and unpaid family workers should be included in this status while meeting the 90-day observation criterion. Close follow-up should occur while in this status to assure successful adjustment to the job.

Status 24, Service Interrupted

If services are interrupted while a client's case is in Status 14, 16, 18, 20, or 22, the case should be moved to Status 24. Interruptions in service should be due to client unavailability or client circumstances and not to agency or counselor problems. Such cases are to be held in this status until services are resumed or the case is closed.

Status 26, Closed Rehabilitated

Clients whose cases are closed as rehabilitated must, at a minimum, have been provided services under the IWRP that contributed to an employment outcome consistent with the client's abilities, capabilities, interests, and informed choice, and in the most integrated setting. The client and the counselor must consider the employment satisfactory and agree that the client has been performing well on the job for a minimum of 90 days. Prior to case closure, however, an assessment of postemployment service needs must be conducted.

Status 28, Closed for Other Reasons After the Individualized Written Rehabilitation Program Was Initiated

Cases closed in this status must have previously been in Status 14, 16, 18, 20, 22, or 24. As such, the client must have (a) been declared eligible, (b) received appropriate diagnostic and related services, and (c) had a program for vocational rehabilitation services developed and initiated that for some reason was not completed. The reasons for closure are the same as for Status 08 (Closed from Referral, Applicant, or Extended Evaluation Statuses), except that reasons 8 (no disabling condition), 9 (no vocational handicap), and 11 (client did not meet order of selection priority) do not apply.

Status 30, Closed for Other Reasons Before the Individualized Written Rehabilitation Program Is Initiated

Clients whose cases are closed in this category are those who, although accepted for rehabilitation services, did not progress to the point of IWRP development or implementation (closures from Status 10 or 12). The reasons for closure are the same as those for closure in Status 28.

Status 32, Postemployment Services

Cases of clients served in this status must have been previously closed rehabilitated in Status 26. Cases are placed in this status to provide simple, short-term services for the purpose of maintaining, regaining, or advancing a client's employment. There is no arbitrary time limit imposed on the provision of postemployment services. The anticipated need for postemployment services must be assessed upon the formulation of the IWRP and prior to case closure in Status 26.

Status 34, Closed from Postemployment Services

Cases of clients served in Status 32 are to be closed in Status 34 upon termination or completion of postemployment services.

The case status code system illustrates the progression of the rehabilitation process. Figure 2.2 displays the dynamic relationship among the statuses and the pivotal questions upon which the process rests.

The concerted effort of many and varied professionals is usually required to move a client's case through the statuses toward the ultimate goal of employment. The VR counselor is the coordinator of a multidisciplinary team, which may include educators, therapists, physicians, and job coaches (Rubin & Roessler, 1987; Tooman, Revell, & Melia, 1988). Their role is critical to the success or failure of any given individual program.

The counselor's unique contribution begins with the synthesis of evaluative information from a variety of professional perspectives. This information is then considered in light of knowledge of the world of work and is subsequently utilized within the context of counseling to formulate a sound IWRP. Services specified in the IWRP are provided, the client is placed in appropriate employment for at least 90 days, the case is closed, and, finally, an evaluation is made of the placement and case closure.

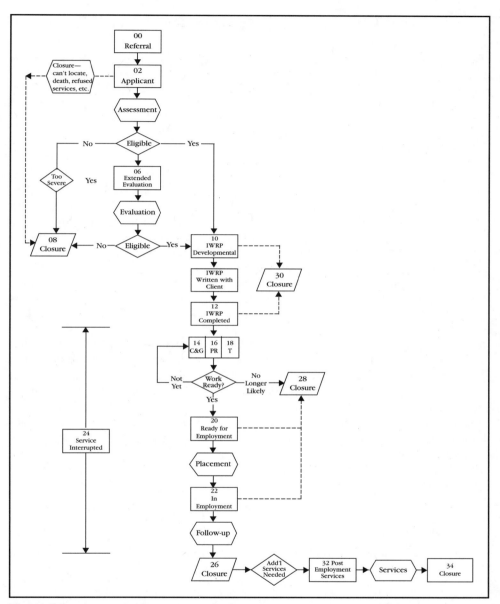

Figure 2.2. Full illustration of the complete case status code system. Application by individual states will vary in accordance with streamlining efforts. Status 14 is Counseling and Guidance Only, Status 16 is Physical and Mental Restoration, and Status 18 is Training.

The Rehabilitation Process

The essence of the rehabilitation process can be summarized by the following steps: (a) referral and preliminary investigation, (b) accumulation of client assessment data, (c) planning services, (d) service delivery, and (e) placement (McGowan, 1969).

Referral and Preliminary Investigation

The rehabilitation process begins with the referral development or case finding effort. Wright (1980) emphasized the vital importance of case finding. It affects the number of people served and the quality of services rendered because the client's attributes at the time of referral have a significant impact on the total rehabilitation process. This consideration and the fact that many persons with disabilities may not know of the program's existence demand that VR counselors cultivate and nurture strong relationships with community-based referral sources.

There are seven major categories of referral sources: educational institutions, hospitals and sanitariums, health organizations and agencies, welfare agencies, public organizations and agencies, private organizations and agencies, and individuals (Institute of Rehabilitation Issues, 1975). Cobun (1972) classified these referral sources into the following categories: (a) primary sources, which characteristically render services directly to people with disabilities in the treatment process (physicians, hospitals, schools); (b) secondary sources, which come in contact with persons with disabilities after a period of convalescence (employment service, welfare); and (c) tertiary sources, which provide few services (vendors, interested individuals). The amount of influence VR has through education and cooperation decreases progressively with each of these referral source levels.

Regardless of category or level of referral source, the state VR program is guided by the following general considerations (adapted from McGowan & Porter, 1967):

1. All persons with disabilities have the legal right to be considered for available services in light of their needs and interests.

2. Suitable referrals are those that the rehabilitation agency can serve in accordance with its objectives.

3. Referrals should be made early to assure maximum prospects for success.

4. Referral seeking should be continuous, aggressive, and comprehensive.

5. Information should be exchanged within the limits of confidentiality and services coordinated among community agencies.

6. A planned program of public relations should be developed.

The responsibility for referral development and referral source cultivation lies at the community level and falls largely to the VR counselor. The flow of referrals is dependent on the effectiveness of working relationships among community agencies and facilities. Effective relationships are manifested by written formal agreements, good interpersonal relationships of staffs, regular interagency visits, joint case staffing, joint training programs, and cooperation in public education and other community activities for people with disabilities. The relationships are enhanced by public exposure and the positive image of the rehabilitation agency and by successfully employed rehabilitation clients (McGowan & Porter, 1967).

Accumulation of Client Assessment Data

The purpose of assessment is to determine eligibility, identify problems, establish vocational direction, and ascertain service needs. Assessment may consist of a review of existing information, a preliminary diagnostic interview, sociocultural history, medical examination, psychological assessment, and vocational assessment. The different types of evaluation are usually not conducted separately; they are typically undertaken concurrently within the context of a counseling relationship.

Assessment is undertaken in two steps: first, a preliminary assessment to determine eligibility and, when requested, priority for services, and, second, a comprehensive assessment for determining vocational rehabilitation needs to be addressed in the development of the IWRP [Rehabilitation Act Amendments of 1992, § 7 (22)]. Regardless of these factors, a determination of eligibility is to be reached within 60 days unless exceptional and unforeseen circumstances beyond the control of the agency preclude doing so. The applicant must concur with any extension of time to reach such a determination (Rehabilitation Act Amendments of 1992, § 102). The scope of the evaluation process is determined by the extent and nature of the client's impairment, as well as the client's personal and social attributes.

When a client has an impairment that constitutes an impediment to employment but it is questionable that the provision of VR services will benefit the person in attaining an employment outcome, the law (Rehabilitation Act Amendments of 1992) allow for the provision of extended evaluation services for a maximum of 18 months. Extended evaluation is used with clients with severe disabilities and is a combination of ongoing evaluation and rehabilitation services. The case record for such cases requires a plan for evaluation and rehabilitation services. The plan and the client's progress are to be reviewed with the client at least once every 90 days during the extended evaluation period. If at any time during the extended evaluation period the presumption of benefit from VR services in attaining an employment outcome is confirmed, then eligibility (Status 10) should be determined. If, on the other hand, clear and convincing evidence indicates that the client cannot benefit from services in attaining an employment outcome, ineligibility should be determined (Status 08) and the client so notified (Rehabilitation Act Amendments of 1992, § 102).

Initial Interview

The assessment process begins with an initial interview, which may be conducted by a rehabilitation services technician. The initial interview can serve to identify obviously inappropriate referrals that can be redirected to appropriate agencies. Such inappropriate referrals include individuals who indicate no significant physical, mental, or emotional disability, and persons who are not interested in entering or returning to employment (Higgins, 1985).

The initial interview is the client's introduction to the agency's purpose, services, and objectives, which are explained in relation to the individual's situation. Specifically, this first contact with the client should entail the following: (a) the applicant's statement of the disability and impediments to employment, (b) a general explanation of the VR program, (c) a confirmation of the client's request for services, (d) a record of demographic information, and (e) an identification of matters requiring further evaluation (McGowan & Porter, 1967).

Medical Evaluation

A medical evaluation is often a significant element of the comprehensive assessment to determine vocational rehabilitation service needs. The major purposes of medical evaluation are to (a) review the major body systems and appraise the client's general health status, (b) determine the medical prognosis and treatment for the disabling condition(s), and (c) serve as a preliminary indicator of employment objective possibilities (McGowan, 1969). The Rehabilitation Act Amendments of 1992 [34 CFR § 361.42 (c)(1)] emphasize the use of existing medical and other information in determining eligibility for services. Such information frequently is available from the client's physician, school, or family.

When necessary, medical evaluation may be arranged by the counselor when information is needed to determine the nature and extent of the disability, as well as the prognosis and recommended treatments for the disability. In some instances the counselor may have adequate information concerning the client's medical condition and need not to refer the client for medical examinations. Throughout the course of the medical evaluation, it is the counselor's responsibility to arrange for the needed medical examinations, secure recent relevant medical records, and inform the client of the nature and purpose of the examinations. Because of the highly personal nature of medical examinations, the counselor must manage this process sensitively, tactfully, and efficiently.

The counselor should possess a thorough knowledge of health care personnel and systems, medical nomenclature, the relationship of physical and mental status to functional limitations, and the potential for physical and mental restoration. Rehabilitation counselors also need a general understanding of the role of medicine in the diagnosis, prognosis, treatment, and management of disability (Wright, 1980). With the knowledge and general understanding of medical aspects of disability, the counselor is able to fulfill the responsibilities of disability identification, management of the diagnostic assessment, determination of eligibility, and formulation of a service delivery plan (McGowan & Porter, 1967).

A valuable resource to the counselor in fulfilling these responsibilities is the medical consultant. A regularly scheduled meeting with the agency's medical consultant (a physician) may be conducted on an individual or a group basis. The functions of medical consultation are interpretation of medical terms and information, clarification and explanation of reports, confirmation of a need for additional medical evaluation, formulation of an opinion as to medical prognosis, and determination of the limiting aspects of the disability.

Medical evaluation may include a broad range of diagnostic procedures, such as medical and surgical examinations, psychiatric evaluations, dental examinations, medical specialist examinations, and various exploratory, laboratory, and X-ray procedures (McGowan & Porter, 1967).

Psychological Evaluation

Wright (1980) defined psychological evaluation as the assessment by a qualified psychologist of a client's intelligence, aptitudes, abilities, interests, adjustment, and other psychological characteristics. McGowan and Porter (1967) took a broader viewpoint, stating that psychological evaluation starts with behavioral observation during the initial interview and continues in subsequent contacts. In any case, psychological evaluation is not a discrete process; it is a blend of psychological testing, analysis of past treatment records, assessment of educational records, client self-reporting, conferences with family, and direct observation. In most cases, it is conducted to determine a client's intellectual abilities, aptitudes, interests, motivations, and personality characteristics (Bitter, 1979). Psychological evaluation may have an important bearing on eligibility determination and the creation of the IWRP.

The responsibility for determining the need for a psychological evaluation, for furnishing the psychologist with the pertinent preliminary information, and for application of the information obtained rests with the counselor. Psychological evaluation is desirable in the following instances: (a) assessment of abilities, aptitudes, achievements, interests, and personality patterns; (b) clarification of ambiguous or contradictory data regarding capacities and abilities; and (c) confirmation of suspected important talents, capacities, skills, interests, or personality traits (McGowan & Porter, 1967; also see Bolton, Chapter 12, this text).

Vocational Evaluation

A vital component of the comprehensive assessment of VR service needs is the evaluation of the individual's work tolerance and habits, aptitude for vocational training, and the need for rehabilitation technology services. This appraisal is commonly referred to as vocational evaluation. McGowan (1969) defined vocational evaluation as the culmination of the entire evaluation process; it is the "gathering, interpreting, analyzing, and synthesizing [of] all vocationally significant data, that is, medical, social, psychological, that have been collected regarding an individual and relating them to occupational requirements and opportunities" (p. 117). Hoffman (1972) provided a narrower, more technical definition, stating that vocational evaluation is "the evaluation of an individual's vocational strengths and weaknesses through the utilization of work, real or simulated" (p. 189). Which definition is applied in practice may have a significant bearing on the roles of the vocational evaluator and the counselor. Regardless of the definition used, however, the ultimate purpose should be the same: to facilitate the creation of a thorough IWRP for the achievement of a sound vocational goal.

Common methodologies of vocational evaluation are job analysis, psychometric testing, work simulation including work samples, and on-the-job tryout (Hoffman, 1972). Preliminary to these, however, are the thorough recording and studying of a client's vocational history, which is based on the premise that past performance is the best predictor of future behavior (McGowan & Porter, 1967).

Vocational evaluation has a dual focus. In one regard, it is a subjective assessment of work personality, which Wright (1980) defined as

> the configuration of responses that are revealed by the person in a productive situation. The work personality is a combination of attitudes, behavioral modes, concepts of value, incentives and capabilities; it is needed if a person is to function appropriately in a work setting. These personal qualities influence satisfactory function while choosing and preparing for a job, seeking a job, and performing it. (p. 351)

Work personality affects worker acceptance of supervision, coworker relationships, and worker reliability, all of which are crucial to successful employment (Wright, 1980).

In another sense, vocational evaluation is the objective assessment of specific skills, dexterities, interests, aptitudes, academic achievement levels, performance rates, and work tolerance. Measures of these factors help guide the client and the counselor in selecting an employment goal and the rehabilitation services necessary to reach the goal.

It should be noted that not all clients undergo a comprehensive vocational evaluation. Assessments may consist of a simple vocational history or may extend to a very technical and structured job tryout. The form and extent of vocational evaluation will vary with each client's particular needs as perceived by the counselor and the client. As with other kinds of evaluations, it is the counselor who instigates vocational assessment. The vocational evaluator depends on the counselor to furnish a specific reason for requesting the vocational evaluation, as well as for supplying any pertinent client information. Of paramount importance, however, is the counselor's responsibility for preparing the client to undergo vocational evaluation. Although usually not involved in the actual assessment, the counselor should provide supportive counseling to assist the client in maintaining a serious effort throughout the process.

Sociocultural Evaluation

Sociocultural assessment is essential to the rehabilitation process because it is neither possible nor desirable to consider clients in isolation from their sociocultural milieu. The client is the primary source of information regarding sociocultural factors. Sociocultural evaluation should, at a minimum, focus on the onset of the disability and the circumstances under which it occurred; previous medical treatment for the disability and other significant illnesses; the client's personal background, including early life, educational experience, work history, and personality and personal habits; and the client's family characteristics, including the family's cultural climate, interrelationships, and economic situation (McGowan & Porter, 1967). Obviously, many of these factors are also addressed in the medical, psychological, and vocational evaluations; this fact underscores the interconnection of thorough evaluation practice and the overriding importance of sociocultural factors in the rehabilitation of the client.

Planning Services: Individualized Written Rehabilitation Program

The formulation of an IWRP for each client determined to be eligible for services is required by the Rehabilitation Act of 1973 (§ 102). The IWRP is the central document of the rehabilitation process and is based on the findings of the assessment and is consistent with the informed choice of the client. It is developed jointly, agreed to, and signed by the counselor and the client (or, as appropriate, the client's representative) and sets forth the long-term vocational goal, the short-term objectives and corresponding services pursuant to that vocational goal, the anticipated dates for the initiation of each service, and the procedure and schedule for progress reviews.

The IWRP also sets forth the client's rights, responsibilities, extent of participation in costs, remedies, and methods of appeal; it must also allow for the expression of client views regarding the program, and how he or she was informed about and involved in choosing among alternative goals, objectives, services, providers, and methods of service procurement and provision. The IWRP must stipulate that all goods and services are provided in the most integrated settings possible and must indicate the extent to which other, comparable services and benefits are available.

The IWRP must include information regarding the availability of a client assistance program, the basis for determination of rehabilitation achievement, an assessment of the need for postemployment services, and, prior to closure as rehabilitated, plans for provision of postemployment services if indicated. A copy of the IWRP and all substantive amendments are to be provided to the client (or, as appropriate, the parent, family member, guardian, advocate, or other representative) (Rehabilitation Act Amendments of 1992, § 102).

Theoretically, the IWRP is in the process of development throughout the course of diagnostic study. Practically, however, it is completed by the counselor and the client within the context of a counseling session. The completion of an IWRP is an expression of commitment, a statement of understanding, a plan for service delivery, and a means of progress evaluation.

Service Delivery

Rehabilitation services may be any combination of goods and services that will render an eligible person competitively employed. All rehabilitation services are to be provided within the context of counseling and guidance, which is the primary function of the rehabilitation counselor (see Thomas, Thoreson, Parker, & Butler, Chapter 7; and Patterson, DeLaGarza, & Schaller, Chapter 8, this text, for further information concerning counseling). The services, whether directly provided by VR, purchased from qualified vendors, or arranged through other providers, are directed toward the achievement of the vocational goal that is in keeping with the client's career interests. Rehabilitation services are individually planned and provided in accordance with consumer needs, aptitudes, and vocational goals based on career interests.

Placement

The RSA (1978) defined job placement as

> the planning and provision of services to prepare a client for work and to assist . . . in obtaining appropriate employment. This includes development of client attitudes consistent with the job environment and reconciling problems or barriers stemming from the milieu outside the client. It is part of the counseling process directly focused on employment. (§ 1541.03)

More specifically, it entails matching clients to jobs for which they are suited by virtue of education, aptitude, skill, experience, and physical abilities (McGowan & Porter, 1967).

Placement of the client in gainful employment is recognized as the ultimate goal of all services provided clients of the State–Federal VR Program. This emphasis on employment outcome distinguishes vocational rehabilitation from most other programs (Institute of Rehabilitation Issues, 1971, p. 53). The goal of employment imposes a definitive limit to the program of services and enables VR to justify its efforts by citing obvious contributions to the economy.

Gainful employment, including self-employment, is normally thought of as being regular, reasonably permanent, and remunerated. Although the usual objective of rehabilitation services is the attainment of competitive employment, program regulations permit placement in other situations, such as self-employment, homemaking, or unpaid family worker. Regardless of the nature of the employment, it must meet several criteria. Federal regulation specifies that a client should be regarded as having achieved an employment outcome only when (a) provision of services specified in the IWRP has contributed to the achievement of the employment outcome; (b) the employment outcome is consistent with the client's strengths, resources, priorities, concerns, abilities, capabilities, interests, and informed choice; (c) the employment income is in the most integrated setting possible; (d) the individual has maintained employment for at least 90 days; and (e) after 90 days of employment, the client and rehabilitation counselor agree that the employment outcome is satisfactory and the client is performing well on the job (34 CFR § 361.56).

Placement services are built upon other preparatory VR services and are closely allied with counseling and guidance. Placement services may begin any time after eligibility is declared, but are usually provided toward the end of the rehabilitation process. The services characteristic of placement are as follows:

1. collaboration with employment services and other organizations involved in . . . [employment] assistance;
2. providing information related to employment during client assessment and IWRP development;
3. employer contact and job development;
4. task analysis and job restructuring;
5. study and interpretation of employment trends and economic forecasting;
6. individual and group instruction of clients in job seeking skills, current and potential job openings and development of a job seeking plan;
7. individual and group counseling of clients on job retention skills;
8. personal assistance in conducting job interviews;
9. consulting and advising on job adjustment and/or client/employer conflicts
10. assistance with Affirmative Action programs and projects;
11. technical assistance and consultation on the placement process;
12. assistance with and consultation on removal of architectural and transportation barriers to employment. (Rehabilitation Services Administration, 1978, § 1541.06)

Generally, the vocational rehabilitation counselor is the placement agent. The extent of a counselor's involvement is usually influenced by caseload characteristics, familiarity with the community, and agency management emphasis. In some instances, a placement specialist is used. Although use of a specialist may achieve certain efficiencies regarding employer contact, the client–counselor relationship may suffer because of the counselor's failure to participate in this critical service. By excluding the primary counselor from placement, the client may perceive a break with the preceding services (Roessler & Rubin, 1979). Regardless of which staffing pattern prevails, the ultimate responsibility for providing substantial and quality placement services rests with the VR agency (Rehabilitation

Services Administration, 1978, § 1541.07). A more detailed description of placement is provided by Millington, Butterworth, Fesko, and McCarthy (Chapter 11, this text).

Changing Roles and Functions of Rehabilitation Counselors Within the State–Federal VR Program

The preceding pages capture the essence of the State–Federal VR Program as it has existed for several decades. Despite the volumes of state and federal regulations that help define the roles and functions of rehabilitation counselors in public vocational rehabilitation systems, it must be recognized that the system is nevertheless constantly changing to meet the needs of an ever-changing population of people with disabilities.

The role of the rehabilitation counselor has been described as multifaceted, involving a variety of professional competencies and functions (Rubin & Roessler, 1995). The major knowledge domains identified as central to the roles and functions of rehabilitation counselors are (a) vocational counseling and consultative services; (b) medical and psychosocial aspects of disability; (c) individual and group counseling; (d) program evaluation; (e) case management and services coordination; (f) family, gender, and multicultural issues; (g) foundations of rehabilitation; (h) worker's compensation; (i) environmental and attitudinal barriers; and (j) assessment (Linkowski, et al., 1993).

Rehabilitation researchers have investigated the "core" competencies or generic job tasks of rehabilitation counselors that are common across work settings. The list is extensive and includes tasks such as intake, eligibility determination, vocational assessment and interpretations, plan development, vocational counseling, personal adjustment counseling, case management, job analysis, job development, placement, follow-up, and postemployment services. In general, the role of the rehabilitation counselor is described as requiring counseling, coordinating, and consulting skills (Rubin & Roessler, 1995). In addition to good written, oral, and verbal communication skills, rehabilitation counselors need skills in basic supervision, time management, budget management, and computer and technology use.

Within rehabilitation settings, including public rehabilitation agencies, the current trend in the field is toward specialization. In recent years graduates from rehabilitation counseling programs are increasingly offered opportunities to work in rehabilitation and related settings other than the state–federal system. In fact, only about 13% of recent graduates are employed by state agencies (Goodwin, 1992), although this percentage varies widely from state to state. Regardless of variation, however, state rehabilitation agencies are increasingly aware of the employment possibilities for rehabilitation counselors and are, in many instances, reacting to these changes in a variety of ways. Some of these changes are discussed, briefly, in the remainder of this chapter.

Partly in response to tighter budgets caused by minimal funding increases at best and continued increases in costs, many states are considering turning to or have already turned increasingly to private organizations (nonprofits and for-profits) to provide a host of specialized services. Much of this increased use of contractual or by-fee arrangements is focused on key specialized disability populations. A few of the major specialized services are discussed below.

Mental Health

Perry (1996) estimated that approximately 15% of adults and 12% of children will experience a psychiatric disorder in any given month. Addressing the mental health needs of such large numbers of individuals at the local community level has become a national priority. To help meet the needs of individuals with chronic, long-term mental illness, public rehabilitation agencies are increasingly aware of the important roles that rehabilitation counselors can play. Rehabilitation counselors have the knowledge and skills to function quite effectively as mental health service providers.

The mental health counselor or case manager–service coordinator functions as a member of a psychiatric treatment team that includes nurses, social workers, psychiatrists, psychologists, therapists, and psychiatric aides and technicians. Specific responsibilities vary according to setting and may include case management, treatment plan development, individual and group counseling, client advocacy, crisis intervention, and psychiatric medication monitoring. Specific counseling issues are often centered around coping and stress management skills, self-esteem, independent living skills, social functioning, vocational planning, symptoms management, and confronting social stigma and attitudinal barriers. Community mental health programs often incorporate vocational rehabilitation as a major component of mental health services.

Mental health services are provided to a diverse clientele in a vast array of settings, many often funded, at least in part, by state rehabilitation agencies, in cooperative budget agreements. Services are provided to persons experiencing stress or coping difficulties as a result of life events (e.g., divorce, natural disaster) as well as to persons with chronic mental illness. Services may be short term (e.g., crisis intervention, brief therapy) or long term (e.g., ongoing case management for persons with chronic mental illnesses). Currently, there is a need for counselors and case managers who have specialized training and skills in working with populations such as the homeless, infants and their caregivers, children, adolescents, pregnant teens, retired adults, and persons infected with the human immunodeficiency virus (HIV) (Frank, 1993; Perry, 1996). Settings that employ mental health counselors and case managers are psychiatric hospitals, general hospitals, community mental health centers, day treatment programs, residential settings, nursing homes, and schools.

Mental health is one of the fastest growing fields in the United States (Perry, 1996). An increasing emphasis is now being placed on wellness and prevention. Community mental health care is expanding while institutionalized care (e.g., hospitalization) is becoming less and less acceptable as a mode of treatment. Managed mental health care, with its emphasis on reducing costs while still providing quality services, is likely to result in the implementation of more short-term, acute care programming (Perry, 1996). Specialization is on the rise, and psychosocial rehabilitation is growing. These current trends could have a major impact on future career opportunities in mental health, including counselors in state rehabilitation agencies.

Substance Abuse Treatment

Substance abuse counselors provide services to prevent and treat substance abuse problems and alcoholism. They are employed in various settings, including hospitals, mental health centers, treatment facilities, and public agencies. The core functions of substance abuse counselors bare a striking resemblance to the core functions of rehabilitation counselors. These functions are screening, intake, orientation, assessment, treatment planning, counseling, case management, crisis intervention, education, referral, report and record keeping, and consultation (Blevins, 1993). As a result, state rehabilitation agencies increasingly are partners in substance abuse counseling services, either by being jointly funded or in paying for relatively short-term care.

Students in rehabilitation counseling who are considering a career in substance abuse treatment can increase their marketability by taking courses in the pharmacology of abused substances and group counseling (Blevins, 1993). The completion of a practicum or internship in a substance abuse program further enhances the rehabilitation counselor's marketability in this field. Many employers, including state rehabilitation agencies, encourage or require their employees to earn state certificates in substance abuse counseling (CSAC) (Goodwin, 1992). The Commission on Rehabilitation Counselor Certification (CRCC) recently approved the substance abuse counselor (SAC) specialty, which requires specific course work and acceptable supervised work experience (Cardoso, Chan, Thomas, Roldan, & Ingraham, 1996). Obtaining specialty certification can even further increase the rehabilitation counselor's marketability.

Substance abuse counseling is a field of increasing growth (Perry, 1996). The demand for prevention specialists, in particular, is expanding (Blevins, 1993). Few professionals are trained in both substance abuse and disability issues. Subsequently, rehabilitation counselors who acquire additional skills and training in substance abuse treatment appear to be in an excellent position to work in public, or private, settings.

Geriatric Rehabilitation

Historically, people generally perceived to be beyond the age of work (often 65 or 70) were not widely served in public rehabilitation settings. The logic was that older individuals, particularly those with disabilities, did not wish or need to participate in the workforce. Although there were exceptions, the number of older workers successfully rehabilitated has traditionally been quite small.

Several significant and substantial changes, however, have taken place in U.S. society over the past several decades. People over the age of 65 comprise the fastest growing segment of the U.S. population (Zola, 1989); adults in this age group are expected to represent 13% of the population by the year 2000 and 21% by 2030 (Lewis, 1989). Rapid advances in medicine and technology have resulted in a steady increase in the numbers of persons with disabilities living longer lives but with chronic disabling medical conditions. Unfortunately for many older people, their retirement incomes prove inadequate and many are forced to seek at least part-time positions to augment primary incomes. Others simply enjoy work and return to employment for broader social purposes.

The goals of geriatric rehabilitation—to maximize functional abilities, to maintain independence of older adults in their communities (Kemp, Smith, & Plowman, 1989), or to continue working—are consistent with the goals of general rehabilitation practice. As a member of a multidisciplinary team of professionals (e.g., nurses, therapists, physicians, psychologists, paraprofessionals), the geriatric rehabilitation counselor addresses the physical, psychosocial, economic, environmental, and attitudinal barriers that interfere with independent living or employment choices of the aging population. Thus, state rehabilitation agencies are serving greater numbers of elderly consumers than ever before. Specific functions of the geriatric rehabilitation counselor may consist of such activities as client advocacy, individual and group counseling, supportive counseling for family members, in-home functional and environmental assessment, coordinating and monitoring assistive technology and home restructuring services, arranging for home health care and assistance with daily living chores, discharge planning, and follow-up (Greenfield-Moore, 1993). Rehabilitation counselors can enhance their competencies by taking specialty courses in psychology, human development, and counseling that focus on the concerns of older adults. State licensure requirements should also be explored.

Employment settings for geriatric rehabilitation counselors include private and public hospitals and nursing homes, nonprofit social service organizations, government agencies, life care communities, and senior centers. Opportunities for employment in these settings are expected to expand with the population growth of people over the age of 65 (Greenfield-Moore, 1993). More than 2,000 comprehensive geriatric care management agencies are currently in operations across the United States, and this number is rapidly growing.

Employee Assistance Programs

Numerous state rehabilitation agencies are involved with Employee Assistance Programs (EAPs) offered by employers as a benefit to their employees to address and resolve issues that affect productivity in the workplace (Kiernan & McGaughey, 1992). Problems related to work satisfaction, job performance, life adjustment, stress management, alcoholism, substance abuse, financial concerns, and disability-related issues are focuses of intervention (Kiernan & McGaughey, 1992). EAP services include assessment, counseling, referral, supervisory training, management consultation, job restructuring, and follow-up (Ahrens-Jones, 1993). Such services are well within the scope of public rehabilitation agencies. Rehabilitation regulations, which specifically refer to services that contribute to "maintaining employment," clearly encourage such interventions. Because the rehabilitation profession addresses many of the concerns just described, the rehabilitation counselor is in an ideal position in a comprehensive EAP.

The benefits to employers who offer EAP services to their employees include increased employee attendance, improved productivity, and reduced job turnover (Kiernan & McGaughey, 1992). As more employers begin to acknowledge these benefits, additional EAP programs will be implemented. Therefore, opportunities in employee assistance appear to be on the rise for public rehabilitation agencies.

Private Practice or Consultation with Public Agencies

In a survey of 1,025 individuals who renewed their rehabilitation counselor certification in 1991 through the CRCC, 7% of the respondents reported their employment settings as private practice (Szymanski, Linkowski, Leahy, Diamond, & Thoreson, 1993). Some rehabilitation counselors in private practice provide comprehensive counseling, case management, and planning services. Others provide a specific service such as adjustment counseling, job development and placement, vocational assessment, career counseling, or job analysis. In specific geographic settings, or for specialized services, public rehabilitation agencies are increasingly contracting with private providers for services.

Consultation to public agencies is another service provided by rehabilitation counselors in private practice or by those in other settings. Consultation requires a variety of core rehabilitation skills, including assessment, problem solving, information synthesis, and plan development (Lynch, Habeck, & Sebastian, 1996). Consultation strategies are often targeted toward organizations or groups, but can have an impact on the lives of individuals with disabilities because they focus on change at the organizational level.

Rehabilitation consultation is provided in the legal arena, in business and industry, and in schools (Lynch et al., 1996). In the legal arena, rehabilitation consultants render expert opinions regarding the employability, placeability, earning loss, and earning capacity of individuals involved in personal injury litigation or workers' compensation settlements. Rehabilitation consultants in business and industry assist employers with developing, implementing, administering, and evaluating disability management programs. They may offer specific services such as needs assessment, ADA (Americans with Disabilities Act) compliance review, establishing policies and procedures, writing job descriptions that list essential functions, developing modified work assignments, and staff and supervisor training. Rehabilitation consultants in the schools work with a collaborative team of parents, teachers, and school professionals to facilitate transition planning at the individual and organizational level.

Additional competencies are often necessary to be effective in private practice and consultation. Time management and organizational skills, as well as an ability to be self-directed, are needed to maintain a private practice or consultation service (Berry, 1993). Advanced training in organizational and systems models, theories and techniques of consultation, marketing, and general business will enhance the rehabilitation counselor's competencies for work in these two areas (Lynch et al., 1996). The need for certified rehabilitation counselor specialty certification and licensure has been identified as critical if private practitioners and consultants are to be involved in third-party reimbursement mechanisms (Goodwin, 1992). New professionals entering the rehabilitation field should view private practice and consultation as later career options because the "crystallization of one's professional expertise and rehabilitation counseling identity" (Lynch et al., 1996, p. 195) is essential for these roles.

Summary

Vocational rehabilitation is a systematic process by which services are planned and provided in response to the special needs and abilities of eligible persons for the purpose of rendering them competitively employed. The primary purpose of vocational rehabilitation is the suitable employment of people with physical or mental impairments. This purpose permeates the entire rehabilitation process and is the foundation for all service provision.

The legal authority for the State–Federal VR Program resides in the Rehabilitation Act of 1973 and its subsequent amendments. The law is interpreted and administered by the Office of Special Education and Rehabilitative Services of the U.S. Department of Education through the Rehabilitation Services Administration (RSA), which stipulates funding mechanisms and contingencies, administrative structures, eligibility standards, and service offerings. State VR agencies determine client eligibility and deliver or arrange for rehabilitation services. Such agencies may be independent entities or parts of state-level human services agencies. The key document between the RSA and the state agency is the state plan, which sets forth matters of program operation. The state plan is subject to approval by RSA and is the standard against which state agency performance is measured.

The rehabilitation process involves a planned sequence of services related to the needs of the client for the purpose of achieving an employment outcome. It begins with case finding or referral and ends with successful job placement. It may include any variety of services and may last from a few months to several years.

The rehabilitation process may involve the efforts of many and varied professionals, but the central role is performed by the rehabilitation counselor. The counselor is directly or indirectly involved in all phases of a client's rehabilitation, and the counselor–client relationship is critical to the success of the rehabilitation process.

For all clients determined to be eligible for services, an IWRP must be developed jointly with the client. The IWRP, which is the central document of the rehabilitation process, sets forth (a) the employment goal, (b) the short-term objectives and corresponding services pursuant to the employment goal, (c) the anticipated dates for initiation of each service, and (d) the procedure and schedule for progress reviews, as well as client rights, remedies, methods of appeal, and expression of views regarding the program. The IWRP is subject to amendment as needed, but with client knowledge and participation. Copies of the IWRP and substantive amendments thereto are provided to the client.

A distinguishing feature of the State–Federal VR Program is its emphasis on the employment outcome—the placement of the client in suitable employment. Regardless of the progress a client may achieve medically, socially, or emotionally, successful vocational rehabilitation cannot be claimed until the client has maintained a suitable employment goal for at least 90 days. This orientation to outcome imposes an explicit standard of accountability on the State–Federal VR Program and is fundamental to its vitality and success as a social agency.

Finally, the changing roles and functions of rehabilitation counselors in the State–Federal VR Program, and generally across public and private vocational rehabilitation systems, offer increasing job opportunities to graduates of rehabilitation counseling graduate programs. Such opportunities exist in mental health settings, substance abuse treatment programs, geriatric rehabilitation agencies, employee assistance programs, and in a variety of private practice settings. The viability of the rehabilitation counseling profession appears secure considering the broad demand for rehabilitation professionals across diverse settings.

References

Ahrens-Jones, B. (1993). Diversity and challenge: Social work careers in employee assistance. In B. J. Morgan & J. P. Palmisono (Eds.), *Mental health and social work career direction* (pp. 99–103). Detroit, MI: Visible Ink Press.

Berry, S. J. (1993). Social work: Carving out my own special piece. In B. J. Morgan & J. P. Palmisono (Eds.), *Mental health and social work career directory* (pp. 71–75). Detroit, MI: Visible Ink Press.

Bitter, J. A. (1979). *Introduction to rehabilitation.* St. Louis: Mosby.

Blevins, G. A. (1993). Exploring a career in substance abuse counseling. In B. J. Morgan & J. P. Palmisono (Eds.), *Mental health and social work career directory* (pp. 5–9). Detroit, MI: Visible Ink Press.

Cardoso, E. D., Chan, F., Thomas, K. R., Roldan, G., & Ingraham, K. I. (1996). Substance abuse and disability: A primer for rehabilitation counselors. *Directions in Rehabilitation Counseling, 7*(11), 1–20.

Cobun, J. M. (1972). Case finding. In J. G. Cull & R. E. Hardy (Eds.), *Vocational rehabilitation: Profession and process* (pp. 177–187). Springfield, IL: Thomas.

Council of State Administrators of Vocational Rehabilitation. (1990). *Rehabilitation Act and Implementing Regulations.* Washington, DC: Author.

Council of State Administrators of Vocational Rehabilitation. (1993). *Recommendations for a model service delivery system for public vocational rehabilitation.* Washington, DC: Author.

Euler, B. (1979). Eligibility as a foundation for rehabilitation casework. *Journal of Rehabilitation, 45*(2), 52–55.

Federal Register. (1995, December 15). *60*(24), 64493.

Federal Register. (1997, February 11). *62*(28).

Frank, M. (1993). Infant mental health: An exciting, emerging field to consider. In B. J. Morgan & J. P. Palmisono (Eds.), *Mental health and social work career directory* (pp. 77–80). Detroit, MI: Visible Ink Press.

Goodwin, L. R. (1992). Rehabilitation counselor specialization: The promise and the challenge. *Journal of Applied Rehabilitation, 23*(2), 5–11.

Greenfield-Moore, W. L. (1993). Career opportunities in aging/gerontology. In B. J. Morgan & J. P. Palmisono (Eds.), *Mental health and social work career directory* (pp. 117–119). Detroit, MI: Visible Ink Press.

Higgins, P. (1985). *The rehabilitation detectives.* Beverly Hills, CA: Sage.

Hoffman, P. (1972). Work evaluation: An overview. In J. G. Cull & R. E. Hardy (Eds.), *Vocational rehabilitation: Profession and process* (pp. 188–211). Springfield, IL: Thomas.

Institute of Rehabilitation Issues. (1971). A report from the study group on placement and follow-up in the vocational rehabilitation process. *Ninth Institute on Rehabilitation Services: Placement and follow-up in the vocational rehabilitation process.* Washington, DC: U.S. Department of Health, Education, and Welfare (Rehabilitation Services Administration).

Institute of Rehabilitation Issues. (1975). *Second Institute on Rehabilitation Issues: The delivery of rehabilitation services.* Menomonie, WI: University of Wisconsin–Stout, Research and Training Center.

Kemp, B., Smith, D. B., & Plowman, V. J. (1989). Geriatric rehab program focuses on research, training, and service. *Journal of Rehabilitation, 55*(4), 9–11.

Kiernan, W. E., & McGaughey, M. (1992). Employee assistance: A support mechanism for the worker with a disability. *Journal of Rehabilitation, 58*(2), 56–62.

Lewis, K. (1989). Persons with disabilities and the aging factor. *Journal of Rehabilitation, 55*(4), 12–13.

Linkowski, D. C., Thoreson, R. W., Diamond, E. E., Leahy, M. J., Szymanski, E. M., & Witty, T. (1993). Instrument to validate rehabilitation counseling accreditation and certification knowledge areas. *Rehabilitation Counseling Bulletin, 37*(2), 123–129.

Lynch, R. T., Habeck, R., & Sebastian, M. (1996). Professional practice: Consultation. In D. R. Maki & T. F. Riggar (Eds.), *Rehabilitation counseling: Profession and practice* (pp. 183–196). New York: Springer.

McGowan, J. F. (1969). Referral, evaluation, and treatment. In D. Malikin & H. Rusalem (Eds.), *Vocational rehabilitation of the disabled: An overview* (pp. 111–127). New York: New York University Press.

McGowan, J. F., & Porter, T. L. (1967). *An introduction to the vocational rehabilitation process.* Washington, DC: U.S. Department of Health, Education, and Welfare.

Perry, P. A. (1996). *Opportunities in mental health careers.* Lincolnwood, IL: VGM Career Horizons.

Rehabilitation Act of 1973, 87 Stat. 355, 29 U.S.C. § 701 *et seq.*

Rehabilitation Act Amendments of 1992, 106 Stat. 4344.

Rehabilitation Services Administration. (1978). *Rehabilitation services manual.* Washington, DC: U.S. Department of Education, Office of Special Education and Rehabilitative Services, Rehabilitation Services Administration.

Rehabilitation Services Administration. (1991). *Annual report on federal activities related to the administration of the Rehabilitation Act of 1973 as amended.* Washington, DC: U.S. Department of Education.

Rehabilitation Services Administration. (1994). *Caseload statistics, State Vocational Rehabilitation Agencies, fiscal year 1992.* Washington, DC: U.S. Department of Education, Office of Special Education and Rehabilitative Services.

Roessler, R. T., & Rubin, S. E. (1979). Knowledge of the world of work: A necessity for rehabilitation counselors. *Journal of Rehabilitation, 45*(4), 55–58.

Rubin, S. E., & Roessler, R. T. (1987). *Foundations of the vocational rehabilitation process* (3rd ed.). Austin, TX: PRO-ED.

Rubin, S. E., & Roessler, R. T. (1995). *Foundations of the vocational rehabilitation process* (4th ed.). Austin, TX: PRO-ED.

Szymanski, E. M., Linkowski, D. C., Leahy, M. J., Diamond, E. E., & Thoreson, R. W. (1993). Validation of rehabilitation counseling accreditation and certification knowledge areas: Methodology and initial results. *Rehabilitation Counseling Bulletin, 37*(2), 109–122.

Tooman, M. L., Revell, W. G., & Melia, R. P. (1988). The role of the rehabilitation counselor in the provision of transition and supported programs. In S. E. Rubin & N. M. Rubin (Eds.), *Contemporary challenges to the rehabilitation counseling profession* (pp. 77–92). Baltimore: Brookes.

Wright, G. N. (1980). *Total rehabilitation.* Boston: Little, Brown.

Zola, I. K. (1989). Aging and disability: Toward a unified agenda. *Journal of Rehabilitation, 55*(4), 6–8.

Chapter 3

Rehabilitation Counseling in the Private Sector

Ross K. Lynch and Ruth Torkelson Lynch

In its broadest sense, rehabilitation counseling in the private sector refers to services provided on a fee-for-service basis by private rather than public employees. Public governmental agencies are legislatively mandated and tax revenue funded. In contrast, the private sector is market driven (e.g., responds to market needs) within a free enterprise system. Private sector revenues are generated from private sources (e.g., insurance, businesses, fee-paying clients) and contract or fee-for-service arrangements with public agencies or insurance funds (e.g., Social Security Administration, federal Workers' Compensation programs). Private sector rehabilitation is much broader than the more narrowly defined concept of insurance rehabilitation (contracted services funded by private insurance). Insurance rehabilitation is only one aspect of rehabilitation counseling in the private sector.

Private for-profit and private nonprofit entities are distinguished primarily by organizational structure and tax status. Even though they may differ in mission and direction, both organizational formats depend on outside funding to provide services and cover expenses. The expansion of all aspects of the private sector signals a critical evolutionary development in the rehabilitation counseling profession. Sources beyond the government recognize the value of, and are willing to pay for, the services that rehabilitation counselors can provide.

In this chapter we provide an overview of rehabilitation counseling in the private sector, particularly focusing on the array of services provided in the private for-profit sector. We address the following topics: (a) key elements and characteristics, (b) direct service delivery models in the private sector, and (c) models for professional consultation in the private sector.

Key Elements and Characteristics

Rehabilitation counseling in the private sector has evolved in response to needs generated by change in the public sector (e.g., governmental policies, legislation) as well as the private sector (e.g., business initiatives to hold down the cost of work injuries). The key elements and characteristics of rehabilitation counseling have been valued for new and expanded applications.

Development

Increased governmental emphasis on the vocational needs of industrially injured workers during the early 1970s to a large degree spawned the private for-profit rehabilitation sector (Lewis, Ramseur, & Sink, 1979). Although several factors contributed to the expansion of the private sector, a portion of the growth can be traced to federal and state rehabilitation and workers' compensation legislation (Berkowitz & Berkowitz, 1991). The public state–federal vocational rehabilitation (VR) system's mandate to prioritize services for individuals with the most severe disabilities has resulted in a large number of individuals with disabilities, in particular individuals with work-related injuries, going either unserved or underserved. The public system's administrative requirements to follow established policies and procedures (Matkin, 1995), with resulting lack of flexibility, have contributed to the demand for alternate service delivery systems. The federal government itself, through the Office of Worker's Compensation Programs (OWCP), has used the private rehabilitation sector to operate a nationwide VR system for injured workers covered under the Federal Employees Liability Act and the Longshore and Harbor Workers Act (Cheit, 1961).

Market demands for cost, efficiency, versatility, and responsiveness have been primary factors in the development and expansion of private sector services. Skyrocketing medical and compensation payments to injured workers and expenses related to catastrophic injuries have spurred insurance companies and employers to review possible ways to contain costs and to have more control over rehabilitation outcomes (particularly return to work). Job-related injuries and sickness in 1991 cost public and private employers an estimated $62 billion in workers' compensation expenditures, nearly triple the amount spent in 1980 (Larson, 1995). Some large established corporations have responded with extensive safety programs, employee support services, on-site medical departments, health promotion programs, work return transition and worker retention services, and medical case management systems (Bruyere & Shrey, 1991; Huneke, Gaiser, & Rowe, 1995; Shrey, 1990). Life care planning, disability management, head injury rehabilitation programming, and work hardening are examples of rehabilitation approaches that not only benefit individuals with disabilities but also address the concerns of employers and insurance providers.

Practice Characteristics

Facilitating return to work for injured workers covered by workers' compensation insurance is a primary activity in the private sector. Additionally, private sector counselors receive referrals to assist in vocational rehabilitation of individuals who are covered by other forms of insurance, such as automobile no-fault, medical malpractice, or long-term disability (Lynch, Lynch, & Beck, 1992). Because rehabilitation counselors have a strong knowledge and skill base in vocational assessment and career development, rehabilitation counselors in the private sector also serve as consultants in cases where loss of earnings and career disruption is at issue due to life events other than disability, such as divorce (Lynch, 1989) or employment discrimination. In all of these types of cases, private sector counselors are more likely than public sector counselors to have forensic involvement.

In addition to the above, the private sector rehabilitation counselor may receive referrals to provide direct client services (e.g., coordinating catastrophic case management services; developing life care plans; assisting the individual to return to work) and/or to prepare a comprehensive vocational assessment report (e.g., providing a vocational expert determination of loss or vocational expert testimony). Rehabilitation counselors also provide direct clinical services within private categorical programs, such as head injury rehabilitation, work hardening, outplacement counseling (i.e., assisting displaced workers), employee assistance programs, disability management and health promotion (Lynch et al., 1992). Expansion of services in the private sector is likely to continue, resulting in significant future career opportunities for rehabilitation counselors.

The growth of private rehabilitation has had a positive impact on the profession. For example, private sector practice, while fundamentally similar to public sector rehabilitation, has several characteristics that allow it to better meet needs of certain clients and referral sources: (a) small caseloads (usually 30 clients or fewer), (b) effective communication with referral sources, (c) prompt and intensive action emphasizing productivity, (d) flexible administrative and service delivery responses to new needs, and (e) effective job development and job placement based on transferable skill analysis (Berkowitz & Berkowitz, 1991; Matkin, 1995; Rasch, 1985). In short, the private sector has been innovative and represents "a new way of doing business" with particular relevance for workers' compensation and other insurance claimants.

Client Population

Although variations certainly exist, clients served in private rehabilitation settings most frequently have physical impairments of traumatic onset (e.g., work injury, motor vehicle accident) occurring during adulthood. This is a group that can experience varying emotional reactions due to resulting, often abrupt, changes in life—financial, vocational, physical, familial, social, and outlook regarding the future. Client referrals under disability and insurance plans also have been impacted by the increase in reported incidences of mental disabilities related to work (e.g., stress-related problems), an aging workforce, and the emergence of new types of injuries related to today's technological workplace (e.g., cumulative trauma disorders). Rehabilitation efforts with an adult population may be complicated as older workers are more likely to have a higher incidence of certain disabling conditions (e.g., cardiac and vascular problems), have longer recuperative periods for disability in general (Benshoff & Souheaver, 1991), and face a more difficult time with respect to employability and placeability.

Case Process

In a general sense, the rehabilitation counseling process in the private sector is similar to that followed in public rehabilitation agencies: case finding and referral processing, evaluation and assessment, plan development, service delivery and coordination, job placement, and follow-up. However, the emphasis applied to various process components tends to differ between the public and private sectors. Also, certain services rendered in the private sector are relatively unique, such as disability management and life-care planning. In general, the private sector counselor's orientation with the client is goal directed and specific, with a strong job placement emphasis. Whereas a common core of knowledge is consistent across practice settings, compared with counselors practicing in other settings, rehabilitation counselors in the private for-profit sector have rated the following areas as more important: vocational counseling and consultative services, medical and psychosocial aspects of disability, case management and service coordination, and knowledge related to workers compensation (Leahy, Shapson, & Wright, 1987; Leahy, Szymanski, & Linkowski, 1993; Lynch & Martin, 1982; Matkin, 1982). Because services are rendered on a fee-for-service arrangement, time and activities must be efficient and clearly documented, progress toward goals closely monitored, and amounts of time and resources carefully recorded for reimbursement. Differences in outcome measurement, use of retraining programs, eligibility for services, size of caseloads, population served, and promptness of service also differentiate private from public rehabilitation.

Current Issues

Private sector rehabilitation was the theme of the 1993 Switzer Memorial Seminar, a National Rehabilitation Association annual program that focuses on a different rehabilitation topic each year. The following issues and recommendations were among those identified as needs for private sector rehabilitation into the 21st century (Hansen & Perlman, 1993): (a) curriculum changes in areas of business and industry, job analysis and labor market information, compensation programs, legal and forensic issues, workplace technology and assistive technology, ergonomics, placement techniques, professional consultation techniques, and disability management; (b) expanded opportunities for communication and exchanges of information between employers, the insurance industry, and private sector rehabilitation counselors; (c) research and documentation of rehabilitation counseling effectiveness and efficiency in terms of human and dollar costs; (d) promotion of rehabilitation counselors as qualified service providers (in response to the proliferation of individuals with minimal or no rehabilitation training who are "calling themselves rehabilitation practitioners") (p. 15); and (e) endorsement of a uniform code of ethics.

In response to such concerns, rehabilitation counselor preservice education has been reevaluated over time with respect to the changing priorities and evolving knowledge and skill needs identified by Certified Rehabilitation Counselors, including those practicing in private sector settings (Leahy, Shapson, & Wright, 1987; Szymanski, Linkowski, Leahy, Diamond, & Thoreson, 1993). For example, Szymanski et al. (1993) evaluated discrepancy scores between importance and preparedness ratings on 58 knowledge areas. The results suggested a need for training in vocational services (e.g., job modification, career development, occupational and labor market information) and case management and services, particularly for counselors in state–federal and private for-profit settings. Attention has also been drawn to ethical and public image issues related to private sector growth (Hansen & Perlman, 1993; Kaiser & Brown, 1988; Patterson, 1988). Training programs are continuing to modify curricula to better address the needs of private sector rehabilitation (Council on Rehabilitation Education, 1991).

The market demand and prevalence of private sector rehabilitation agencies and the specific characteristics of services provided vary considerably from state to state and from time to time. Indeed, workers' compensation legislation, which is state specific, is particularly variable over time and greatly influences the volume and demand for private rehabilitation services. For example, California pioneered a mandatory rehabilitation component to its workers' compensation statute in 1974, and a number of other states (e.g., Minnesota, Colorado, Washington, Florida) followed with similar provisions (Berkowitz & Berkowitz, 1991). Since that time, mandatory rehabilitation under workers' compensation has been continuously reevaluated, which has led many states to repeal or radically change prior legislation. Additionally, as seen in the health care system, cost containment through establishment of mandated reimbursement rates also has had an impact on private sector practice. For example, regulation of practice in some states has extended to setting mandated hourly rates for services, which are significantly below the previously typical hourly rates (e.g., $65.00 vs. $85.00+) (Benshoff & Souheaver, 1991). In short, rehabilitation counselors must recognize that programmatic regulations and reimbursement patterns for services covered under workers' compensation insurance can vary greatly from state to state and over time.

Direct Service Delivery Models in the Private Sector

The emphasis in the private sector is geared toward returning the client to suitable work as efficiently as possible. Because most clients served in the private sector have physical impairments, it is important for counselors not only to recognize the medical and psychological factors but also to understand the situational and environmental variables encountered by the client served. A useful framework for this process was outlined by Hershenson (1990):

> (a) restore assets or skills rendered inoperative by the disabling condition (possibly by compensating for them), (b) reintegrate those aspects of the self-image that have been adversely affected by the disability, (c) reformulate those goals that the disability has made unattainable, and (d) restructure the environment to eliminate barriers and to facilitate coping. (p. 275)

Livneh (1995) condensed these components into three primary rehabilitation goals that can guide direct service delivery: "(a) reduce the cause and/or impact of disability by restoring functional capacity; (b) compensate for disability by enhancing other, nonaffected, characteristics of the person; and (c) modify environmental conditions in order to negate the impact of disability" (p. 26).

Client Variables

Individuals who incur a work-related disability have multiple concerns and issues that must be recognized by the rehabilitation counselor. Such concerns and issues include the following:

> (a) psychological, in the form of stress, fear, anger, depression, and feelings of hopelessness; (b) social, such as the loss of friendships, loss of social status, and strained family relationships; (c) physical, in terms of pain, heightened health risk factors, and reduced or impaired functional capacity; and (d) economic, such as loss of income, increased dependence on benefits, and general economic insecurity (Tate, 1992, p. 17).

Situational Variables

In addition to client variables, the rehabilitation counselor must be knowledgeable about and sensitive to the situational variables that can affect case process and outcomes. Compensation systems, employer policies and beliefs, and labor market conditions are three primary situational variables to consider.

Compensation Systems

Clients in the private sector typically receive some form of disability compensation benefits. Workers' compensation is a primary provider of disability compensation benefits. Although each state has a different workers' compensation act, all share the following attributes:

> (a) first dollar coverage with no employee deductibles or copayments; (b) provisions for replacement of lost wages (indemnity payments); (c) provisions for permanent and temporary disability payments (partial or total); (d) rights to rehabilitation (mentioned in over 44 WC acts and mandated in some); (e) access to doctor of choice (with varying restrictions); (f) unlimited medical coverage; (g) burden of proof is on employers to disprove causality, medical necessity, appropriateness of care, and disability level. (Clifton, 1995, p. 702)

The partial wage replacement benefit (i.e., Temporary Total Disability) usually continues until the client's physician (or an independent medical examiner) certifies that the injured worker has reached a healing "plateau." At that stage, if residual disability persists, the client is compensated (at a significantly reduced rate) on the basis of percentage of permanent impairment (i.e., Permanent Partial Disability) caused by the injury.

Because determinations of the length of a client's healing period and the percentage of permanent disability are often in dispute, such matters are ultimately decided by the courts. Unfortunately, the litigation process may interfere with the rehabilitation process as litigation is time-consuming and costly. According to the Workers' Compensation Research Institute's *1993 Annual Report/Research Review*, litigation added $1.5 billion to the workers' compensation bill in 1990 and this figure has been growing at an annual rate of 22% since 1981. Litigation is also often at odds with a return to independent functioning (e.g., the individual is often compensated on the basis of degree of disability manifested). By its very design, workers' compensation "has encouraged protracted medical care and discouraged attenuated treatment and early return to work" (Clifton, 1995, p. 702). Such factors may have an adverse effect on rehabilitation efforts.

In a potential litigation context, the counselor has to work with many parties, some of whom may have differing agendas. For example, the physician may treat the client passively or even resist the efforts of the rehabilitation counselor, because the physician may not fully understand the psychosociolegal implications of injury and the workers' compensation system. The compensation system itself requires that the individual continue to seek treatment because, if physician reports of appointments are not filed regularly, payments will be discontinued (Trief & Donelson, 1995). Also, the attorney may subvert the rehabilitation effort in an attempt to maximize the percentage of a permanent disability award. For example, a lawyer's recommendation for the client to keep a daily log of physical and emotional symptoms, which is intended to bolster documentation, may have a secondary effect of encouraging the individual to attend to every symptom and sensation (heightening sensitivity and anxiety about even normal variations of sensation) (Trief & Donelson, 1995). Moreover, insurance adjusters can have either beneficial or deleterious effects on the rehabilitation process, depending on their relationship with the client and knowledge of the rehabilitation process. Finally, each state has its own set of laws and rules (e.g., time frames, procedures, benefits) that may affect the rehabilitation outcome. Consequently, the counselor may often find himself or herself in the role of negotiator.

Employer Policies and Beliefs

Employer policies and beliefs are additional situational variables that have an impact on the rehabilitation process. Corporate culture (e.g., value placed on the employee, corporate social responsibility), corporate structure (e.g., size, shape, workforce composition, and degrees of centralization or bureaucratization), and corporate executive beliefs are three perspectives from which to examine employer policies regarding early return to work (Shoemaker, Robin, & Robin, 1992) and provide a basic framework for rehabilitation counselors to understand business perspectives as a situational variable. Although understanding that corporate culture and structure variables contributed to return-to-work efforts, Shoemaker et al. (1992) found that corporate executives' beliefs were the primary mitigating factor.

Labor Market Conditions

Unemployment rate, rural or urban location, size of available labor market, and employment trends (e.g., downsizing, expansion) can affect opportunities and, accordingly, return-to-work outcomes. The Americans with Disabilities Act of 1990 (ADA) is an example of legislation that has the potential to have a great impact on the labor market for individuals with disabilities. In fact, injured workers may be the ADA's principal beneficiaries because, unlike workers' compensation, which is a state-specific benefits statute, ADA is a federal civil rights statute. ADA is designed to enable an individual with a disability to gain competitive employment by breaking down attitudinal and physical barriers, and by providing "reasonable accommodation" in the workplace (Bell, 1993). Certain provisions of the ADA have particular importance for counselors working with clients covered by workers' compensation, including (a) a prohibition against preemployment medical screening, (b) confidentiality of medical information obtained through medical examinations, (c) reasonable accommodation requirements, (d) definition of disabled individuals, and (e) enforcement and remedy options (Eccleston, 1992).

Interaction of Client and Situational Variables

Support, both financial and social, to maintain disability status is a factor that may be operative when working with clients with compensable injuries. Maintaining a disability or sick role may provide primary or secondary gains, such as income, security, or avoidance of an unpleasant work situation (Tate, 1992). If a counselor believes that secondary gain or malingering is interfering with a client's rehabilitation, the counseling relationship may be strained. It is therefore important to recognize psychosocial behaviors, needs, and problems, in addition to physical functioning. With such knowledge, the rehabilitation counselor can evaluate the client more carefully and address the psychosocial needs and problems in the rehabilitation plan.

The client's perceptions regarding control and self-efficacy can also be a critical component of client–situational interaction. The workers' compensation system itself can have a negative impact on self-efficacy the longer an individual is off work. In this context, self-efficacy refers to the "personal self-judgments which influence the environments that persons choose, the activities in which they engage, and the effort and persistence they demonstrate at a task in the face of obstacles" (Mitchell, Brodwin, & Benoit, 1990).

Counseling Strategies

The choice of counseling strategies in any rehabilitation setting needs to take into account both client and situational variables for each individual. According to the model posed by Carkhuff (1971), the counseling focus might include (a) exploration—for awareness of the injured person's experience, (b) understanding—by involving the client and sharing information as clearly and explicitly as possible, and (c) taking action—to build skills and compensatory techniques for the client to use in daily functioning. This conceptualization can prove useful with a variety of private sector clients because the action component toward a functional outcome (e.g., return to work) is highly valued in the private sector. A couple of examples will illustrate this approach.

Diminished Self-Efficacy and Control

Specifying step-by-step procedures, with behavioral objectives for each step, may assist the client in becoming actively involved in his or her own rehabilitation plan. The counselor should break seemingly impossible or long-term tasks (e.g., a retraining program) into achievable, manageable units; point out the connection between job modification or retraining and successful reemployment; and facilitate client ownership of the plan by encouraging decision making (Mitchell et al., 1990). Training the client to negotiate and control symptoms (e.g., by progressively increasing task difficulty, work pacing, and/or tool or job modification) is another recommended technique for enhancing self-efficacy and control (Matheson, 1995).

Motivation

Alston (1991) proposed using Gestalt psychology exercises, such as the following, to assist injured workers to counteract ambivalence toward rehabilitation (i.e., resistance, lack of persistence):

1. Increase attachment to goals by writing down three rehabilitation goals (written goals foster ownership and involve more of the client's feeling).

2. Write down one of the goals that can be fulfilled today (makes the process current).

3. Write down the opposites of goals in Step 1 (accentuates existence of opposite needs and wants).

4. Ask injured worker to determine whether current behavior is more consistent with the positive or negative goal statements.

Case Management and Resource Coordination

In addition to direct counseling interaction, there is a tremendous demand for case management and resource coordination with private sector clients. Case management is a coordinated process in which professional case managers facilitate the most appropriate course of interventions and referrals (Donovan, 1994). Two types of case management have emerged: *fiscal,* a defensive system in the position of rationing the delivery of service, and *clinical,* an offensive system in the position of justifying the need for services (Sampson, 1994). Fiscal case managers assist clients in securing their health coverage benefits in the most cost-effective and efficient manner and determine what services the client is eligible to receive and at what cost. The primary goal of clinical case managers is to identify the individual's physical and psychological needs and to secure the services that will lead to a desired outcome. This may include assisting in maneuvering through the health care system by negotiating and advocating for services according to professional standards of care. The clinical case management model requires professional training and expertise and is very compatible with rehabilitation counseling.

The rehabilitation counselor can play a valuable leadership and case management role on the rehabilitation team, which often includes the employer, physician, attorney, client, and claims adjuster. Case managers must (a) be knowledgeable about the specific target population they are serving, (b) have effective communication skills, (c) possess good interviewing skills, (d) be knowledgeable about community programs and agencies, and (e) use effective time-management skills (Quinn, 1993). Via such competencies, the counselor attempts to facilitate cooperation and communication among the involved parties by requesting meetings, sharing reports and letters, and verifying understandings and commitments in writing. Basically, the rehabilitation counselor takes all actions necessary to facilitate the progress of a case, short of creating client dependency.

Making progress with complex cases is sometimes contingent on the counselor's negotiation and communication skills. The counselor must interact and negotiate effectively with (a) the client (e.g., getting the client to give up a disabled or injured identity), (b) the lawyer (e.g., relinquishing a permanent total disability award), (c) the insurer (e.g., making certain financial concessions), (d) the physician (e.g., giving some decision-making authority to others), and (e) the employer (e.g., negotiating accommodations in the workplace). However, the counselor's role in the negotiating process is in the behavioral, not financial, realm. The counselor should strive to enhance negotiating skills by (a) not identifying with the financial interests of the insurance carrier; (b) being as open as possible with the client; (c) helping the client make requests of the insurance carrier, employer, and treating professional, and vice versa; and (d) making an effort to create an effective rehabilitation team. If the rehabilitation counselor is a successful negotiator, his or her effectiveness in returning the client to work will be enhanced (Lynch et al., 1992).

Job Placement

As noted throughout this chapter, the primary purpose of rehabilitation counseling in the private sector is to return the client to suitable gainful employment. This is often a gradual process that, in addition to counseling, involves medical management, psychological adjustment, and, as mentioned above, negotiation by the counselor. Rehabilitation placement goals within the private sector are presented in Table 3.1. These hierarchical goals not only assist individuals to return to appropriate gainful employment in the shortest possible time but also help contain the financial cost of disability.

In planning for a return to work, the client should take joint or, preferably, primary responsibility for setting the time frame and/or goals. As adviser, the counselor may suggest, however, that the client gradually increase time at work over a period of several weeks (i.e., establish a plan consistent with work conditioning principles). Such a gradual return to work arrangement helps to reassure all parties of a reasonable alternative to the all-or-nothing dichotomy of "full return to work" (i.e., full work shift, regular duties, normal performance). Early-return-to-work strategies encourage and enable employees with injuries to return to modified duty under medical supervision (Shoemaker et al., 1992). This method, combined with thorough follow-along, allows the client and other involved parties to go through "reentry" without major risk. In other words, the client can try out a return-to-work without fear of automatically surrendering full workers' compensation benefits. It

Table 3.1
Rehabilitation Return-to-Work Goals

---

1. Return to work—Same job and same employer

2. Return to work—Same job and same employer, but modified duties or work schedule

3. Return to work—Same employer but different job

4. Return to work—Different job and different employer

5. Return to work—Different job (retraining) and same or different employer

---

also permits the employer to maintain some control in the situation. Because this technique places the responsibility on the client, it challenges the client in a medically and psychologically safe way. Usually, the client reenters the work environment, renews bonds with the job and coworkers, and once again has a stake in maintaining employment. With a return to compatible work, vocational rehabilitation has been achieved once appropriate follow-up is completed (Lynch et al., 1992).

Programmatic Approaches to Direct Service Delivery

Work hardening, work tolerance screening, and head injury rehabilitation services are examples of treatment approaches in private sector rehabilitation.

Work Hardening

Work hardening and similar programs, sometimes referred to as work conditioning, work readiness, work capabilities, and workout/workup (Lett, McCabe, Tramposh, & Tate-Henderson, 1988), have been used to facilitate return to work. Work hardening programs use real or simulated work activities in a relevant work environment, in conjunction with physical conditioning tasks, to improve the biomechanical, neuromuscular, cardiovascular and metabolic, behavioral, attitudinal, and vocational functioning of the persons served (Commission on Accreditation of Rehabilitation Facilities, 1994). The structure and format of work hardening programs vary with regard to space, equipment, staff, and methods. In whatever manner a program is designed, however, the common goal is to attain a physical level of competence that will allow a client to return to work. Such programs have been proven effective.

As industrial injuries require attention to the interaction among a person's physical, social, and psychological functioning, increasing emphasis has been given to interdisciplinary approaches in work hardening programs. Various rehabilitation professionals focus on development of strength and endurance, education to teach safe job performance to prevent reinjury, identification of transferable skills, worksite evaluation and job analysis, evaluation of productivity and safety in the workplace, and development of worker behaviors. The rehabilitation counselor has become an integral player in such interdisciplinary work hardening programs. Because return to the preinjury position is the outcome of choice, the rehabilitation counselor frequently functions as a case manager (Williams, 1989), keeping the clients, "their families, treating professionals, insurance adjusters, and employers focused on those activities which make the greatest contribution to the return to work" (p. 40).

Work Tolerance Screening/Functional Capacity Evaluation

The return-to-work process is aided by information obtained from work tolerance screening or functional capacity evaluations. A typical functional capacity evaluation includes tests of manual materials handling capabilities, aerobic capacity, posture, and mobility tolerance (Wickstrom, 1990). In short, it translates physical tolerances into vocationally relevant terms. Such evaluations contribute useful case management information for the rehabilitation team by providing (a) a baseline functional analysis to determine the client's individual physical capacity, (b) a benchmark for determining the client's progress during a conditioning or work hardening program, and (c) assistance in establishing basic physical tolerance guidelines for return to work. Data from an objective functional capacities evaluation (e.g., recommendations for pacing, work posturing, exertion, reasonable workplace accommodations, or reassignment) provide physical guidelines for a return-to-work plan and also bridges medical and physical treatment and vocational rehabilitation efforts.

Head Injury Rehabilitation

Head injury rehabilitation programs have developed as a cost-effective rehabilitation approach that is attuned to the functional changes present during the various stages of recovery from head injury. Coma stimulation, acute rehabilitation, extended rehabilitation (based in hospitals or skilled nursing facilities), behavioral rehabilitation, community reentry, comprehensive day treatment, day care, outpatient services, community or home care, and community living are examples of the different program approaches. Kay (1989) noted that such programs apply "specialized techniques that will 'remediate' the cognitive and behavioral deficits of this population with implicit or explicit promises of functional gain" (e.g., return to work) (p. 159).

The dramatic increase in head injury rehabilitation programs has resulted in significant career opportunities for rehabilitation counselors. In staffing such programs, graduate-degreed rehabilitation counselors are hired for positions as life skills counselors, behavior specialists, personal adjustment counselors, vocational specialists, case managers, and program managers and administrators. Those professionals with bachelor's degrees in rehabilitation services or entry-level graduate training are frequently hired as providers of generic community reentry services, with duties such as job coaching, implementation of behavioral plans, and instruction in daily living skills (McMahon & Fraser, 1988; McMahon, Shaw, & Mahaffey, 1988). Doctoral-trained rehabilitation psychologists are in particular demand if proficient in behavior management, neuropsychology, cognitive retraining, family therapy, or administration.

Models for Professional Consultation in the Private Sector

In addition to direct services, the private sector provider is often called upon to act as a consultant. Historically, the primary area for such consultative activity has been within the legal system because most legal definitions of disability reflect the importance of work in relation to normal functioning. For instance, in most workers' compensation cases, the percentage of disability is based on a consideration of both loss of bodily function and earning capacity. Consequently, in such cases, percentage of disability is determined by an examination of the injured worker's pre- and postinjury earning capacity, in addition to loss of physical functioning. Disability insurance, such as Social Security Disability Insurance (SSDI) and personal injury policies, also defines disability in occupational terms. Moreover, in personal injury cases, the impact of injury upon one's ability to earn an income often weighs considerably in the determination of an award. Divorce is another arena in which earning capacity affects maintenance and property settlements (Lynch, 1989). The provisions of the Americans with Disabilities Act of 1990 have increased employer demand for thorough job analysis and consultation regarding accommodations in the workplace (T. Field & Norton, 1992).

Given the importance of vocational and earning capacity in such matters, the legal system has looked toward individuals with training and experience in vocational rehabilitation to assess and render opinions concerning vocational and rehabilitation implications for specific cases (Andersen, 1979; Deutsch, Sawyer, Jenkins, & Kitchens, 1986; T. F. Field, 1993; T. Field, McCroskey, Sink, & Wattenbarger, 1978; Havranek, Grimes, Field, & Sink, 1994; Matkin, 1995; Sink & King, 1978; Williams & Maze, 1994). In legal terminology, such individuals serve as "vocational experts." Typical vocational expert duties are listed in Table 3.2.

Table 3.2
Vocational Expert Responsibilities

1. Critically reviewing supporting documentation (e.g., medical, psychiatric)

2. Performing a vocational diagnostic interview

3. Noting critical work behaviors

4. Translating residual functional capacity into vocationally relevant terminology

5. Selecting, administering, scoring, and interpreting the appropriate assessment tools (e.g., tests of intelligence, achievement, aptitude, vocational interests)

6. Locating, assessing, and integrating rehabilitation research relevant to the type of disability involved

7. Understanding vocational development theory, job requirements, and the world of work

8. Securing labor market and wage information

9. Presenting logical and substantiable conclusions based on objective findings

Vocational Expert Credentials

The credibility of vocational opinions is related directly to the competence of the individual who conducted the vocational evaluation. Training and experience are often the gauges used to measure the vocational expert's competence during legal proceedings.

Training

It is safe to say that no individual is intimately familiar with the physical demands and skill requirements of all the nearly 13,000 occupations described in the *Dictionary of Occupational Titles* (DOT) (U.S. Department of Labor, 1991a). With appropriate training, however, one can acquire the skills and knowledge necessary to accurately identify the critical components of occupations and also to evaluate the capacities of individuals with disabilities to perform them. To determine whether rehabilitation service providers possess the requisite knowledge and skills to serve as vocational experts, contractors of these services typically assess such factors as educational attainment and certifications or licenses held. Generally, a master's degree in vocational rehabilitation counseling (or a closely related area) is an acceptable educational criterion, especially when such coursework as medical and psychosocial aspects of disability, career development, occupational information, job placement, and vocational evaluation have been completed. Additionally, persons credentialed as certified rehabilitation counselors (CRCs) or licensed as vocational or rehabilitation psychologists tend to be recognized as meeting accepted professional standards. Furthermore, such factors as membership in and service to professional associations, subscriptions to professional journals, attendance at regional and national conferences, presentation of scholarly papers, publication of journal articles, awards or honors received, and so forth, help to establish the professional base from which the vocational expert's opinions are provided.

Experience

In addition to appropriate training, vocational expertise requires evidence of demonstrated practical experience in the assessment of vocational potential and the actual job placement of individuals with disabilities. The importance of placement experience with persons with disabilities, as opposed to the general population, cannot be overstated. The significance of having a working knowledge of disability and resultant limitations is characterized by such practical concerns as assessment difficulties (e.g., modification of standardization procedures and appropriateness of norm groups), attitudinal obstacles, architectural barriers, and job modification and restructuring techniques, as well as psychosocial adjustment considerations, legislative or legal issues, and a host of other variables unique to people with disabilities (Lynch et al., 1992).

Vocational Expert Functions

Vocational experts may perform a variety of functions, depending on the case and their particular role in the case. Some functions include vocational assessment, employability opinions, placeability opinions, preparation for testimony, and testimony including direct examination, cross-examination, and redirect examination.

Vocational Assessment

Vocational assessment is a formal process used to obtain and compare information about occupational requirements in order to describe and predict an individual's vocational functioning level. This relatively objective process attempts to identify, measure, and evaluate (both quantitatively and qualitatively) the worker traits of the individual with respect to occupational demands. To assist in this process, the U.S. Department of Labor has classified virtually all occupations nationwide according to worker trait characteristics and worker trait groups, which include (a) degree of worker interaction with data, people, and things; (b) physical demands; (c) working conditions; (d) general educational development; (e) specific vocational preparation; and (f) aptitudes, interests, and temperaments (J. E. Field & Field, 1992; T. Field & Field, 1992; Havranek et al., 1994; U.S. Department of Labor, 1991b).

The vocational expert must evaluate each client with respect to such occupational characteristics. Toward this end, it is helpful if the client's treating physician addresses the areas of physical capacity (e.g., standing tolerance, lifting tolerance) and working conditions (e.g., environmental restriction) in the final medical report on permanent physical impairment. It is suggested that counselors describe these physical tolerance categories in detail to the physician so that each variable can be rated relative to speed and tolerance. In this manner, permanent physical impairment can be translated into functionally relevant vocational terms. The form in Appendix 3.A presents an example of a physical capacity evaluation form that is helpful for quantifying an injured worker's residual functional capacity. Using a format such as this, the counselor can translate the client's permanent physical impairment into vocationally relevant terms, and then compare residual functional capacity to occupational demands.

A similar strategy can be employed in psychiatric cases. In cases where mental or emotional issues are operative, the rehabilitation counselor can request that the treating and/or examining psychiatrist or psychologist complete a mental residual functional capacity form (see example in Appendix 3.B).

In addition to the physical and/or mental–emotional issues, other worker traits can be assessed with a combination of interview and standardized testing techniques. The use of standardized testing techniques, in conjunction with the clinical interview, is preferable, because it allows comparative assessment with norm groups based on objectively derived data. Because literally thousands of standardized tests are on the market, the vocational expert should carefully evaluate the suitability and technical appropriateness (e.g., normative group, reliability, validity, reading level, standardization procedures) of instruments selected for a particular case. The review of instrument characteristics and applicability should also extend to computer software assessment programs because limitations of these tools and improper or inappropriate use of them can result in distortions or conclusions beyond what is reasonably defensible (Cutler, Cutler, & Ramm, 1995, p. 53). Unquestionably, vocational experts should be prepared to present evidence that they have been trained to administer, score, and interpret the instruments employed and that they thoroughly understand the comprehensive assessment process.

Employability Opinions

Once the client's vocational assets and limitations have been identified through a systematic evaluation process, the vocational expert must determine the jobs that are compatible with the client's residual capabilities and transferable skills. Typically, the vocational expert will employ the published resources of the U.S. Department of Labor. The most frequently cited references for defining and describing jobs in this country are the *Dictionary of Occupational Titles* (U.S. Department of Labor, 1991a), *The Revised Handbook for Analyzing Jobs* (U.S. Department of Labor, 1991b), and the *Guide to Occupational Exploration* (U.S. Department of Labor, 1993). Another helpful resource is the *Classification of Jobs* (J. E. Field & Field, 1992).

The *Classification of Jobs* (J. E. Field & Field, 1992) and *The Revised Handbook for Analyzing Jobs* (U.S. Department of Labor, 1991b) are particularly helpful in cross-referencing occupations that fall within specific skill and ability levels. These occupations then form the basis for determining the type, degree, and level of employment a particular individual is capable of performing. This relatively objective process is geared toward determining employability (i.e., capacity to perform in a particular occupation). Employability opinions tend to focus primarily on the client's skills and abilities as they relate to occupational requirements and, as such, do not consider external or tangential factors that may have an important effect on actual job placement.

Placeability Opinions

Placeability refers to the probability that the client will actually obtain and maintain work in a particular occupation (Gellman, Gendel, Glaser, Friedman, & Neff, 1957). Placeability opinions incorporate employability factors and are slightly more subjective. Essential aspects of placeability include, but are not limited to, the following factors: (a) availability and competition for jobs in a particular geographic area; (b) client's age, sex, race, social skills, interview behavior, and appearance; (c) employer attitudes; (d) architectural barriers; and (e) specific hiring requirements, including health, education, and work experience. Such factors have nothing to do with the client's capability to perform a particular job but are critical in determining whether the individual gets a job (Dunn, 1974). Vocational experts typically rely on placement-related research, their own placement experience, employer contacts, or published labor market information to assist with determining placeability.

When securing labor market data, geographic areas and information required vary according to the nature of the case. For Social Security purposes, the focus is on compatible occupations that exist in the national economy. In such cases, it is irrelevant whether specific jobs are available (i.e., actual job openings); rather, the question is whether these occupations exist in significant numbers in the national economy (i.e., several regions of the country). On the other hand, in workers' compensation and personal injury cases, the focus is on jobs that are reasonably attainable or available within a reasonable distance from a client's home.

When rendering opinions concerning existence or availability of specific occupations or jobs, vocational experts should use documentation drawn from large, representative samples of the particular labor market under consideration. Published occupational information concerning type, number, wages, and future outlook of various occupations is available from the Department of Labor's Bureau of Labor Statistics, and from many state and local sources (e.g., manufacturer association surveys, county business patterns). Vocational experts may also contact local employers regarding immediate and future job openings. Heavy reliance on the latter job survey technique, however, is unsound from a sampling theory perspective. In this regard, the possibility of nonrepresentativeness and limited sample size may lead to spurious conclusions. An appropriate mix of published labor market information and job surveys will yield a fairly accurate index of the existence, availability, and wages of occupations compatible with the client's residual capabilities (Lynch et al., 1992).

The threefold process of assessing vocational assets and limitations, determining occupations that are compatible for an individual with such assets and limitations, and establishing the existence, availability, and wages of appropriate occupations within a specific geographic area, provides a relatively accurate indication of a client's employability and placeability. From this information, it is a relatively routine process to calculate residual income earning capacity and, in conjunction with placeability considerations, to arrive at a percentage of work disability.

In the final report, the vocational expert should logically detail results of all assessment procedures and present conclusions in such a manner that the referral question is adequately addressed within the context of the applicable legal definition of disability. If the vocational expert has done a thorough job, as reflected in the report and conclusions, professional involvement with the case may end at this point.

If evaluation techniques are questionable, the report is poorly written, conclusions appear unwarranted by results, or a dispute remains between parties, vocational experts can be requested or subpoenaed to provide a discovery deposition and/or to present and defend their findings before a judge, jury, or hearing examiner.

Preparation for Testimony

Prior to testimony, the vocational expert should meet with the involved attorney to assist with organizing the presentation. The attorney, in turn, should explain how evidence is presented at the trial and what questions will be asked on direct examination. The vocational expert may request that the attorney outline direct examination questions that will be asked, including those related to qualifications. With the attorney, the vocational expert should examine carefully and confirm the relevance and accuracy of all assessment procedures, methods, and resources employed to arrive at the vocational expert's conclusions. The attorney should fully understand the purpose and usefulness of each component of the assessment. Additionally, notes, protocols, records, and files should be assembled in an orderly and easily accessible fashion so that they can be quickly referenced to refresh recollection of information. The attorney should have a clear understanding of their contents and, as legal proceedings are adversarial in nature, any weaknesses or vulnerabilities that might be revealed by the opposing legal counselor on cross-examination (Kornblum, 1974).

Direct Examination

Because vocational expert testimony represents an area generally unfamiliar to most individuals, the expert should request that the attorney organize questions to elicit testimony in a way that can be easily understood by laypersons. Typically, direct examinations cover a description of the vocational expert's current job duties, educational background, past work experience, and professional credentials, as well as the specifics of the evaluation, including tests administered, results obtained, conclusions drawn, and supporting rationale. The meaning and significance of procedures and technical terms should be explained in readily understandable language. The vocational expert should not hesitate to qualify an opinion, as the law does not require absolute certainty. However, for an opinion to be admissible, it has to be stated to a "reasonable degree of professional certainty" (i.e., more likely than not). The opinions expressed have to be formed in a manner consistent with professional rehabilitation practice, such that it would be accepted by others in the profession (McCormick, 1972).

Testimony should be characterized by simplicity. The most effective witnesses are those who can translate technical terms into simple, everyday language that can be understood by the general public (Kornblum, 1974). Effective, convincing witnesses (a) talk neither too much nor too little; (b) remain calm and poised; (c) answer neither too quickly nor too slowly; (d) use narrative, smoothly flowing statements; and (e) provide original analogies and personal descriptions (Brodsky, 1991). The counselor should recognize that his or her primary responsibility is to provide accurate and thoroughly developed information that will allow the judge and jury to reach intelligent decisions and conclusions (Vallario & Emener, 1991). Finally, the credibility of the expert requires objective testimony about the client, not for or against the client, regardless of the source of one's fee. Sommerness (1995) offered the following advice on credibility:

> Credibility means, in the simplest terms, believability. If, for instance, all you do is examinations for attorneys who represent injured employees, sooner or later people are going to question your credibility. Bias is to prejudice what credibility is to honesty. Prejudice is a conscious act of intent; bias is impropriety. If all you do is independent medical evaluations (IMEs) for insurance companies or their lawyers, you shouldn't be surprised if someone questions the motives as being protective of that financial relationship rather than concerned with ascertaining the true condition of the employee that has been examined. The key is to find a balance: do work for both the insurance industry and the attorneys who represent injured people. An astute lawyer has credible medical people targeted to work with the injured person before the other side can use those same people for an IME. Lawyers know whether the person/clinic is credible, so they want to have the person do the evaluation. If medical professionals choose to sell their testimony, they will be busy for awhile because, unfortunately, there are always people looking to buy that kind of assistance. But they will not last. Sooner or later it will catch up with them and they will be finished as experts. By selling out as "professional witnesses," clinicians will have a predictably short shelf life. They will become used goods rapidly. Credible medical professionals, on the other hand, are sought for their competence, honesty, and objectivity by both sides. (p. 558)

Brodsky (1981) suggested the following rules for an expert witness:

1. Prepare all basic exhibits and outlines of testimony carefully, arranging them in an orderly sequence, before taking the witness stand.
2. Speak loud enough for all to hear and do not talk too fast. Endeavor to obtain and hold the interest of the judge or jury.
3. Avoid unnecessary conversation with the judge or opposing legal counsel. Be courteous, fair, and frank. Keep calm and even-tempered, even in trying circumstances.
4. State qualifications fully, but without "puffing" or indulgence in the trivial. Do not be flattered by offers to concede qualifications, for this may be a ploy to prevent the judge or jury from learning important details.
5. After reviewing qualifications, state results and opinions. Follow with a clear and adequate explanation of methods employed in reaching conclusions.
6. Present testimony as you would wish to have it presented if you were the judge. Observe any doubts which may appear to arise in the judge or jury's mind; and try to assist in resolving them. This, after all, is a primary function of an expert witness.
7. Hold to the essentials of the testimony. Develop a sense of proportion. Avoid unimportant detail.
8. Avoid the appearance of being an incorrigible partisan. Face up to the strong points which may be presented by opposing witnesses. Endeavor to

demonstrate that, while those points should be given consideration, they must be viewed in the context of the total picture.

9. If not prepared to answer a question, be honest enough to say so. A bluffer is easily detected; and then a cloud is placed over the entire testimony.

10. Be concise. After a point is made, stop talking. (p. 7)

Cross-Examination

Following direct examination, the opposing attorney will have an opportunity to cross-examine. There are five possible objectives in cross-examination: (a) to question qualifications, (b) to show a basis for bias (e.g., an extraordinary fee or predisposition to testify for either plaintiffs or defendants), (c) to challenge an opinion because it was improperly obtained (e.g., by using questionable procedures), (d) to discredit the factual bases of the opinion, and (e) to establish favorable facts through admissions by the vocational expert (Kornblum, 1974). Attorneys attempt to assume control of cross-examination "by use of tone of voice, by questions that elicit yes or no answers, by facial expressions, by gestures, by eye-contact, by dramatic interpersonal posturing, and by taking the witness to a planned destination" (Brodsky, 1991, p. 139).

Cross-examination can be intimidating and anxiety provoking. However, it is important to understand what is happening, to not feel controlled, and to be comfortable with your level of performance (Brodsky, 1991). Sound preparation will lessen anxiety considerably. In other words, if evaluation procedures were comprehensive, results and conclusions substantive, and opinions based on sound evidence, the vocational expert should be well prepared to endure the rigors of cross-examination.

The intimidating aspects can be reduced by understanding the general rules and format an opposing attorney will follow. Kornblum (1974) suggested the following:

1. Expect all questions to be brief, to the point, and leading. Questions will be designed to elicit a yes or no response and not a narrative answer.

2. Expect to be required to give a precise response to the questions asked. If an evasive, nonresponsive answer is given, do not expect to be "let off the hook" easily.

3. Once the cross-examining attorney's desired point has been established, expect the examination on this topic to cease and turn to another area.

4. As a general rule, the opposing attorney will ask only a question for which he or she knows the expert's answer, usually because during deposition the expert committed himself or herself to a reply.

5. Do not expect a logical sequence of questioning on cross-examination. The opposing attorney recognizes that the chances of getting spontaneous testimony are greater if the expert does not have an opportunity to contemplate a line of questioning and anticipate answers. Expect cross-examination to

commence and end (as these are the most impressionable moments) on an important area.

6. Expect the opposing attorney to be well prepared. If an expert has been deposed, testimony is known, and therefore research and critical questions can be prepared by the cross-examining attorney beforehand.

7. Lastly, remain polite and courteous at all times.

Redirect Examination

Doubts, weaknesses, or gaps exposed in the vocational expert's testimony during cross-examination can be dealt with in redirect examination. Prior to trial, one should know the strengths and weaknesses of the evidence and carefully review with the attorney the best method of recovering from exposures or exaggeration of such weaknesses. Thus, it is essential to prepare for redirect as well as direct examination. Following redirect examination, the vocational expert's legal involvement in the case is ended.

Life Care Planning

Life care planning is an offshoot of the medical and catastrophic case management services that rehabilitation counselors have been asked to provide in the private sector. Life care plans are often utilized by the injured person, the family, the insurance carrier, and the legal system to estimate and plan for long-term needs and costs associated with a severe disabling condition. Counselors who are accustomed to working with catastrophic injuries (e.g., spinal cord injuries, multiple amputations, severe brain trauma, severe burns) often see their job not only as involving vocational rehabilitation but also as providing a broad range of counseling services that enhance the patient's quality of life and long-term care (Deutsch et al., 1986). Life care planning addresses the challenges and costs that persons who have experienced a catastrophic injury face following acute rehabilitation. Rehabilitation counselors who have experience with catastrophic injuries, combined with formal rehabilitation training in assessment, independent living, and medical, psychosocial, and occupational aspects of disability, have ideal preparation for developing life care plans.

The life care planning consultant must have knowledge of rehabilitation technology and independent living aids, and be willing to keep up-to-date as new resources become available. Because a written report is usually required, the rehabilitation counselor who prepares life care plans needs to be organized, factual, and able to provide supporting documentation. The cost of long-term living care for a person with a disability is relative to the following:

(a) the extent of injury and its sequelae, (b) the prognosis for further recovery of mental and/or physical function, (c) the extent and effect of future medical intervention, (d) the extent to which rehabilitation might help, (e) future personal need and desire, (f) future interest rates, and (g) future medical and consumer price inflation. (Bush, 1990, p. 47)

In developing a life care plan, the consultant should consider (a) projected future evaluations, (b) projected therapeutic modalities, (c) diagnostic testing/educational assessment, (d) wheelchair needs, (e) wheelchair accessories and maintenance, (f) orthopedic equipment needs, (g) orthotics/prosthetics, (h) aids for independent function, (i) home furnishings and accessories, (j) drug and supply needs, (k) home care and facility care, (l) future medical care—routine, (m) future medical care—surgical intervention or aggressive treatment plan, (n) transportation, (o) potential complications, (p) architectural renovations, and (q) leisure and/or recreational equipment and services (Deutsch et al., 1986, p. 13).

Disability Management

Disability management and health promotion practices are utilized by major U.S. employers to keep their workplaces healthy and to manage skyrocketing disability costs. Corporate America is becoming increasingly aware of the value of investing in its human as well as its capital resources to excel and maintain profitability. According to Tate, Habeck, and Galvin (1986), disability management combines the clinical and case management practices of vocational rehabilitation counseling, the multidisciplinary team approach of rehabilitation, and principles of organizational development and program administration into a comprehensive framework that is managed and coordinated within the firm (i.e., workplace). With the emergence of private sector rehabilitation services and with employers increasingly recognizing the value of taking the lead in rehabilitating injured workers, there are new opportunities for rehabilitation counselors to provide valuable services directly within the workplace.

Disability management provides a variety of opportunities for private sector rehabilitation counselors. Consultation, in the form of client assessment, psychosocial and/or vocational counseling, placement intervention, and employee educational programming (e.g., back protection or stress management), may be offered at the worksite (Backer, 1986). The private sector rehabilitation counselor may also provide assistance in creating or administering workplace disability management programs, review company rehabilitation procedures, develop and conduct in-house training programs on rehabilitation issues, provide a critical review of disability cases (Backer, 1986; Shrey, 1990), and set up information systems to monitor program effectiveness and cost–benefits (Gottlieb, Vandergoot, & Lutsky, 1991). While employers are believed to prefer internal sources (i.e., their own employees) for job identification–analysis and implementation of affirmative action, they are more willing to turn to a consulting rehabilitation agency or professional for modification and restructuring (e.g., return-to-work interventions for mid-career workers with disabilities), accessibility and job accommodation strategies or modifications, or disability awareness training (Greenwood, Schriner, & Johnson, 1991).

For disability management to be successful, Shrey (1990) emphasized the following basic principles: (a) Disability management is an active process; (b) the process enables the employer both to exert control and to assume responsibility as a proactive decision maker, planner, and coordinator of interventions and services; and (c) the process promotes disability prevention strategies, rehabilitation treatment concepts, and safe work-return programs designed to control the personal and economic costs of workplace injury and disability (p. 93). The common threads in successful corporate disability management programs are employer awareness and sensitivity to the economic costs of injury and disability, along with a corporate philosophy that the worker is the employer's most important asset.

Summary

The past 20 years have witnessed significant industry growth in the private rehabilitation sector. As a result, numerous career opportunities have developed for rehabilitation counselors. To function effectively in the private sector, rehabilitation counselors need to apply their valued competencies in new contexts while maintaining their professional standards and ethics. Under the scrutiny of the legal system, for example, private sector counselors functioning as vocational experts must be thoroughly trained, appropriately experienced, and totally accountable for their procedures and opinions. Because the ultimate value of expert opinions lies in the skill, ability, preparedness, and objectivity of the rehabilitation professional, ethical standards must be continually appraised and professional competencies constantly honed.

Rehabilitation counseling is a field that requires understanding of individual differences and individual adjustment within the context of work, leisure, and family environments. The emerging opportunities for rehabilitation counselors in the private sector reflect some of the changes in societal and personal environments during the past couple of decades. Medical technology has enhanced life-saving potential for thousands of individuals who sustain head injuries and require ongoing rehabilitation to resume independent lives. Consequently, skyrocketing medical costs and increased emphases on health promotion and independent living have resulted in a need to define and manage the high costs of disability. To address this need, public policy has shifted attention and encouraged responsibility for solving rehabilitation problems to local communities and the private sector. All these factors have had an impact on the development and expansion of private sector rehabilitation. In the future, the field of rehabilitation counseling must continue to keep abreast not only of the factors that positively affect the quality of life of clients but also of the continually evolving environmental and societal factors that shape career opportunities for professional rehabilitation counselors. Building on these successes of the past 20 years, private sector rehabilitation counselors will continue to discover opportunities to apply their unique skills, talents, and knowledge in the evolving marketplace.

Appendix 3.A
Sample Physical Capacities Evaluation Form

Physical Capacities Evaluation

Client/Patient Name _____ Date _____

DIRECTIONS: Circle or fill in the blank representing full capacity for each activity. Any item that you cannot answer should be marked N/A.

In an 8-hour workday, the patient can:

										Continuously	With rest
Sit	1	2	3	4	5	6	7	8	(hours)	_____	_____
Stand	1	2	3	4	5	6	7	8	(hours)	_____	_____
Walk	1	2	3	4	5	6	7	8	(hours)	_____	_____

	Never	Seldom (1% to 5%)	Occasionally (6% to 33%)	Frequently (34% to 66%)	Continuously (67% to 100%)
Lift (pounds):					
10	_____	_____	_____	_____	_____
11–20	_____	_____	_____	_____	_____
21–50	_____	_____	_____	_____	_____
51–100	_____	_____	_____	_____	_____
Carry (pounds):					
10	_____	_____	_____	_____	_____
11–20	_____	_____	_____	_____	_____
21–50	_____	_____	_____	_____	_____
51–100	_____	_____	_____	_____	_____

(Continues)

	Never	Seldom (1% to 5%)	Occasionally (6% to 33%)	Frequently (34% to 66%)	Continuously (67% to 100%)
Bend:	_____	_____	_____	_____	_____
Squat:	_____	_____	_____	_____	_____
Crawl:	_____	_____	_____	_____	_____
Reach above shoulder:	_____	_____	_____	_____	_____

Patient can use head and neck in:

Static Position   **Frequent Flexing**   **Frequent Rotating**

☐ Yes ☐ No   ☐ Yes ☐ No   ☐ Yes ☐ No

Patient can use hands for repetitive actions such as:

Simple Grasping   **Pushing and Pulling**   **Fine Manipulating**

	Simple Grasping	Pushing and Pulling	Fine Manipulating
Right	☐ Yes ☐ No	☐ Yes ☐ No	☐ Yes ☐ No
Left	☐ Yes ☐ No	☐ Yes ☐ No	☐ Yes ☐ No

Patient can use feet for repetitive movements as in operating foot controls:

Right   **Left**   **Both**

☐ Yes ☐ No   ☐ Yes ☐ No   ☐ Yes ☐ No

Restriction of activities involving:

	No Restriction	Mild	Moderate	Total
Unprotected heights	_____	_____	_____	_____
Being around moving machinery	_____	_____	_____	_____
Exposure to marked changes in temperature and humidity	_____	_____	_____	_____
Driving automotive equipment	_____	_____	_____	_____
Exposure to dust, fumes, and gases	_____	_____	_____	_____

(Continues)

Additional comments: _____

_____

_____

_____

_____

_____

_____

_____

_____

_____

_____

_____

_____

_____

_____

_____

_____

_____

_____

_____

_____

_____

_____

_____

_____
Printed Name and Title of Person Completing Form

_____
Signature

Appendix 3.B
Sample Mental Residual
Functional Capacity Assessment

Mental Residual
Functional Capacity Assessment

Client/Patient Name _____ Date _____

DIRECTIONS: Each mental activity is to be evaluated within the context of the individual's capacity to sustain that activity over a normal workday and workweek, on an ongoing basis.

	No Evidence of Limitation	Mildly Limited	Moderately Limited	Markedly Limited
A. Understanding and Memory				
1. Ability to remember locations and worklike procedures	_____	_____	_____	_____
2. Ability to understand and remember very short and simple instructions	_____	_____	_____	_____
3. Ability to understand and remember detailed instructions	_____	_____	_____	_____
B. Sustained Concentration and Persistence				
4. Ability to carry out very short and simple instructions	_____	_____	_____	_____
5. Ability to carry out detailed instructions	_____	_____	_____	_____
6. Ability to maintain attention and concentration for extended periods	_____	_____	_____	_____

(Continues)

	No Evidence of Limitation	Mildly Limited	Moderately Limited	Markedly Limited
7. Ability to perform activities within a schedule, maintain regular attendance, and be punctual within customary tolerances	___	___	___	___
8. Ability to sustain an ordinary routine without special supervision	___	___	___	___
9. Ability to work in coordination with or proximity to others without being distracted by them	___	___	___	___
10. Ability to make simple work-related decisions	___	___	___	___
11. Ability to complete a normal workday and workweek without interruptions from psychologically based symptoms and to perform at a consistent pace without an unreasonable number and length of rest periods	___	___	___	___

C. Social Interaction

12. Ability to interact appropriately with the general public	___	___	___	___
13. Ability to ask simple questions or request assistance	___	___	___	___
14. Ability to accept instructions and respond appropriately to criticism from supervisors	___	___	___	___

(Continues)

	No Evidence of Limitation	Mildly Limited	Moderately Limited	Markedly Limited
15. Ability to get along with coworkers or peers without distracting them or exhibiting behavioral extremes	_____	_____	_____	_____
16. Ability to maintain socially appropriate behavior and to adhere to basic standards of neatness and cleanliness	_____	_____	_____	_____

D. Adaptation

17. Ability to respond appropriately to changes in the work setting	_____	_____	_____	_____
18. Ability to be aware of normal hazards and take appropriate precautions	_____	_____	_____	_____
19. Ability to travel in unfamiliar places or use public transportation	_____	_____	_____	_____
20. Ability to set realistic goals or make plans independently of others	_____	_____	_____	_____

Comments: _____

_____

_____

_____

_____

_____

Printed Name and Title of Person Completing Form

_____

Signature

References

Alston, R. J. (1991). Counseling persons with industrial injury: Strategies for rehabilitation counselors. *Journal of Applied Rehabilitation Counseling, 22*(1), 3–6.

Americans with Disabilities Act of 1990, 42 U.S.C. § 12101 *et seq.*

Andersen, R. (1979). Vocational expert testimony: The new frontier for the rehabilitation professional. *Journal of Rehabilitation, 45*(3), 39–40.

Backer, T. (1986). Disability management: Implications for clinical practice and consultation in the workplace. *Journal of Applied Rehabilitation Counseling, 17*(3), 38–42.

Bell, C. G. (1993). The Americans with Disabilities Act and injured workers: Implications for rehabilitation professionals and the Workers' Compensation system. *Rehabilitation Psychology, 38,* 103–115.

Benshoff, J. J., & Souheaver, H. G. (1991). Private sector rehabilitation and the Americans with Disabilities Act. *Journal of Applied Rehabilitation Counseling, 22*(4), 27–31.

Berkowitz, M., & Berkowitz, E. D. (1991). Rehabilitation in the work injury program. *Rehabilitation Counseling Bulletin, 34,* 182–196.

Brodsky, S. (1981). Ten commandments for an expert witness. *Social Action and the Law, 7*(1), 7.

Brodsky, S. (1991). *Testifying in court: Guidelines and maxims for the expert witness.* Washington, DC: American Psychological Association.

Bruyere, S., & Shrey, D. E. (1991). Disability management in industry: A joint labor-management process. *Rehabilitation Counseling Bulletin, 34,* 227–242.

Bush, G. (1990). Calculating the cost of long-term living: A four-step process. *Journal of Head Trauma Rehabilitation, 5*(1), 47–56.

Carkhuff, R. (1971). *The development of human services.* New York: Holt, Rinehart and Winston.

Cheit, E. F. (1961). *Injury and recovery in the course of employment.* New York: Wiley.

Clifton, D. W. (1995). Managed care and workers' compensation. In S. J. Isernhagen (Ed.), *The comprehensive guide to work injury management* (pp. 698–738). Gaithersburg, MD: Aspen.

Commission on Accreditation of Rehabilitation Facilities. (1994). *1994 standards manual and interpretive guidelines for organizations serving people with disabilities.* Tucson, AZ: Author.

Council on Rehabilitation Education. (1991). *Accreditation manual for rehabilitation counselor education programs.* Champaign-Urbana, IL: Author.

Cutler, F., Cutler, G., & Ramm, A. (1995). Vulnerable points and unresolved issues of computer models for determining lost earning capacity. *Journal of Applied Rehabilitation Counseling, 26*(4), 53–55.

Deutsch, P., Sawyer, H., Jenkins, W., & Kitchens, J. (1986). Life care planning in catastrophic case management. *Journal of Private Sector Rehabilitation, 1*(1), 13–27.

Donovan, M. R. (1994). Introduction to outpatient case management. In M. R. Donovan & T. A. Mason (Eds.), *Outpatient case management: Strategies for a new reality* (pp. 19–36) Chicago: American Hospital Publishing.

Dunn, D. (1974). *Placement services in the vocational rehabilitation program.* Menominee: University of Wisconsin–Stout, Research and Training Center.

Eccleston, S. M. (1992). The relationship between the Americans with Disabilities Act and Workers' Compensation. In S. M. Eccleston (Ed.), *The Americans with Disabilities Act: Implications for Workers' Compensation* (pp. 3-6). Cambridge, MA: Workers' Compensation Research Institute.

Field, J. E., & Field, T. F. (1992). *Classification of jobs* (4th rev.). Athens, GA: Elliott & Fitzpatrick.

Field, T. F. (1993). *Strategies for the rehabilitation consultant: Transferability, loss of employment, lost earning capacity, and damages.* Athens, GA: Elliott & Fitzpatrick.

Field, T., & Field, J. (1992). *Work fields.* Athens, GA: Elliott & Fitzpatrick.

Field, T., McCroskey, B., Sink, J., & Wattenbarger, W. (1978). The role and functions of the vocational expert in judicial hearings. *Psychosocial Rehabilitation Journal, 2*(2), 17-27.

Field, T., & Norton, P. (1992). *ADA resource manual for rehabilitation consultants.* Athens, GA: Elliott & Fitzpatrick.

Gellman, W., Gendel, H., Glaser, N., Friedman, S., & Neff, W. (1957). *Adjusting people to work.* Chicago: Jewish Vocational Service.

Gottlieb, A., Vandergoot, D., & Lutsky, L. (1991). The role of the rehabilitation professional in corporate disability management. *Journal of Rehabilitation, 57*(2), 23-28.

Greenwood, R., Schriner, K. F., & Johnson, V. (1991). Employer concerns regarding workers with disabilities and the business–rehabilitation partnership: The PWI practitioners' perspective. *Journal of Rehabilitation, 57*(1), 21-25.

Hansen, C. E., & Perlman, L. G. (1993). Private sector rehabilitation: Insurance, trends and issues for the 21st century. *Journal of Rehabilitation, 59*(3), 12-16.

Havranek, J., Grimes, J. W., Field, T., & Sink, J. (1994). *Vocational assessment: Evaluating employment potential.* Athens, GA: Elliott & Fitzpatrick.

Hershenson, D. B. (1990). A theoretical model for rehabilitation counseling. *Rehabilitation Counseling Bulletin, 33,* 268-278.

Huneke, B. K., Gaiser, W. R., & Rowe, M. (1995). Union Pacific Railroad medical quality assurance process: Innovations in work injury management. *Journal of Applied Rehabilitation Counseling, 26*(4), 42-45.

Kaiser, J., & Brown, J. (1988). Ethical dilemmas in private rehabilitation. *Journal of Rehabilitation, 54*(4), 27-30.

Kay, T. (1989). Response to "Programming for occupational outcomes following traumatic brain injury." *Rehabilitation Psychology, 34,* 159-160.

Kornblum, G. (1974). The expert as witness and consultant. *The Practical Lawyer, 20*(3), 13-34.

Larson, B. A. (1995). Work rehabilitation: The importance of networking with the employer for achieving successful outcomes. In S. J. Isernhagen (Ed.), *The comprehensive guide to work injury management* (pp. 483-497). Gaithersburg, MD: Aspen.

Leahy, M., Shapson, P., & Wright, G. (1987). Rehabilitation practitioner competencies by role and setting. *Rehabilitation Counseling Bulletin, 31,* 119-130.

Leahy, M. J., Szymanski, E. M., & Linkowski, D. (1993). Knowledge importance in rehabilitation counseling. *Journal of Applied Rehabilitation Counseling, 24*(4), 36-45.

Lett, C., McCabe, N., Tramposh, A., & Tate-Henderson, S. (1988). Work hardening. In S. Isernhagen (Ed.), *Work injury: Management and prevention* (pp. 195-229). Rockville, MD: Aspen.

Lewis, S., Ramseur, J., & Sink, J. (1979). The role of private rehabilitation: Founder, catalyst, competitor. *Journal of Rehabilitation, 45*(3), 17-19.

Livneh, H. (1995). The tripartite model of rehabilitation intervention: Basics, goals, and reha-bilitation strategies. *Journal of Applied Rehabilitation Counseling, 26*(1), 25-29.

Lynch, R. K. (1984). The vocational expert. *Rehabilitation Counseling Bulletin, 27,* 18-25.

Lynch, R. K. (1989). Use of the vocational expert in spousal maintenance cases. *State Bar of Wisconsin: 1989 Annual Convention Proceedings* (pp. 239-245). Madison: State Bar of Wisconsin.

Lynch, R. K., Lynch, R. T., & Beck, R. (1992). Rehabilitation counseling in the private sector. In R. Parker & E. Szymanski (Eds.), *Rehabilitation counseling: Basics and beyond* (2nd ed., pp. 73-101). Austin, TX: PRO-ED.

Lynch, R. K., & Martin, T. (1982). Rehabilitation counseling in the private sector: A training needs survey. *Journal of Rehabilitation, 48*(3), 51-53.

Matheson, L. N. (1995). Getting a handle on motivation: Self-efficacy in rehabilitation. In S. J. Isernhagen (Ed.), *The comprehensive guide to work injury management* (pp. 514-542). Gaithersburg, MD: Aspen.

Matkin, R. (1982). Rehabilitation services offered in the private sector: A pilot investigation. *Journal of Rehabilitation, 48*(4), 31-33.

Matkin, R. (1995). Private sector rehabilitation. In S. E. Rubin & R. T. Roessler (Eds.), *Foundations of the vocational rehabilitation process* (pp. 375-398). Austin, TX: PRO-ED.

McCormick, C. (1972). *Handbook of the law of evidence.* St. Paul, MN: West.

McMahon, B., & Fraser, R. (1988). Basic issues and trends in head injury rehabilitation. In S. Rubin & N. Rubin (Eds.), *Contemporary challenges to the rehabilitation counseling profession* (pp. 197-216). Baltimore: Brookes.

McMahon, B., Shaw, L., & Mahaffey, D. (1988). Career opportunities and professional preparation in head injury rehabilitation. *Rehabilitation Counseling Bulletin, 31,* 344-354.

Mitchell, L. K., Brodwin, M. G., & Benoit, R. B. (1990). Strengthening the workers' compensation system by increasing client efficacy. *Journal of Applied Rehabilitation Counseling, 21*(4), 22-26.

Patterson, J. B. (1988). Considerations in the public image of rehabilitation counselors in private sector rehabilitation. *Journal of Private Sector Rehabilitation, 3*(2), 67-73.

Quinn, J. (1993). *Successful case management in long-term care.* New York: Springer.

Rasch, J. (1985). *Rehabilitation of worker's compensation and other insurance claimants.* Springfield, IL: Thomas.

Sampson, E. M. (1994). The emergence of case management models. In M. R. Donovan & T. A. Mason (Eds.), *Outpatient case management: Strategies for a new reality* (pp. 77-94). Chicago: American Hospital Publishing.

Shoemaker, R. J., Robin, S. S., & Robin, H. S. (1992). Reaction to disability through organization policy: Early return to work policy. *Journal of Rehabilitation, 58*(3), 18-24.

Shrey, D. (1990). Disability management: An employer-based rehabilitation concept. In S. Scheer (Ed.), *Multidisciplinary perspectives in vocational assessment of impaired workers* (pp. 89-106). Rockville, MD: Aspen.

Sink, J., & King, W. (1978). The vocational specialist's preparation for court testimony—Fact or fantasy? *Careers, 3*(2), 1-2, 6.

Sommerness, W. D. (1995). Testifying in court: You and your records. In S. J. Isernhagen (Ed.), *The comprehensive guide to work injury management* (pp. 557-564). Gaithersburg, MD: Aspen.

Szymanski, E. M., Linkowski, D. C., Leahy, M. J., Diamond, E. E., & Thoreson, R. W. (1993). Human resource development: An examination of perceived training needs of certified rehabilitation counselors. *Journal of Applied Rehabilitation Counseling, 24*(4), 58-70.

Tate, D. G. (1992). Factors influencing injured employees' return to work. *Journal of Applied Rehabilitation Counseling, 23*(2), 17-20.

Tate, D., Habeck, R., & Galvin, D. (1986). Disability management: Origins, concepts, and principles for practice. *Journal of Applied Rehabilitation Counseling, 17*(3), 5-12.

Trief, P. M., & Donelson, R. G. (1995). The potential impact of the workers' compensation system on quality of life outcomes: A clinical analysis. *Journal of Occupational Rehabilitation, 5,* 185-193.

U.S. Department of Labor, Employment and Training Administration. (1991a). *Dictionary of occupational titles* (4th ed.). Washington, DC: Author.

U.S. Department of Labor, Employment and Training Administration. (1991b). *The revised handbook for analyzing jobs.* Washington, DC: Author.

U.S. Department of Labor, Employment and Training Administration. (1993). *Guide to occupational exploration.* Washington, DC: Author.

Vallario, J. P., & Emener, W. G. (1991). Rehabilitation counseling and the law: Critical considerations of confidentiality and privilege, malpractice, and forensics. *Journal of Applied Rehabilitation Counseling, 22*(2), 7-14.

Wickstrom, R. (1990). Functional capacity testing. In S. Scheer (Ed.), *Multidisciplinary perspectives in vocational assessment of impaired workers* (pp. 73-88). Rockville, MD: Aspen.

Williams, J. (1989). The rehabilitation counselor: A critical member of the work hardening program staff. *Journal of Private Sector Rehabilitation, 4*(1), 39-44.

Williams, J. M., & Maze, M. E. (1994). *Role of the rehabilitation expert in administrative law and civil proceedings.* Hunt Valley, MD: American College Testing.

Workers' Compensation Research Institute. (1993). *1993 Annual report/Research review.* Cambridge, MS: Author.

Chapter 4

Independent Living

Margaret A. Nosek

Independent living is one of the greatest hopes of people with severe disabilities. Numerous factors, however, inhibit the ability of many people with disabilities in the United States to reach and maintain this goal; these factors include environmental inaccessibility, overprotective attitudes of relatives and providers, lack of economic resources, ignorance of the concepts and techniques of independent living, lack of necessary support services, and a bias toward institutionalization in service provision systems. Billions of public dollars are currently being spent on maintaining millions of Americans with disabilities in situations of unproductive dependency, situations that impose artificial limits on the individual's potential for enjoying quality of life and contributing to society. As the movement for independent living grows stronger, as the United States progresses toward becoming an accessible society, and as more people with severe disabilities become independent, contributing citizens, solutions on a national scale will be at hand.

Independent living is defined as control over one's life based on the choice of acceptable options that minimize reliance on others in making decisions and in performing everyday activities (Frieden, Richards, Cole, & Bailey, 1979). This includes managing one's day-to-day affairs, participating fully in community life, fulfilling a range of social roles, and making decisions that lead to self-determination and the minimization of nonproductive physical and psychological dependence upon others. Independence implies an optimally responsible and productive exercise of the power of choice. It further implies that each person with a disability, regardless of mental or physical ability, should be encouraged and assisted, with due respect for cultural or subcultural affiliation, to achieve a high quality of life, and to achieve independence and productivity in the least restrictive environment. Finally, independent living is intended to apply to people with all types of disabilities (National Council on Disability, 1983).

To live independently, people with disabilities may require a wide range of support services. People with severe physical disabilities frequently require assistance with personal care, domestic tasks, transportation, equipment maintenance, and architectural modifications of home and workplace. Those with sensory disabilities may additionally require assistance with communication (e.g., as provided by readers and interpreters). People with mental impairments who wish to live independently may require supervision and assistance with cognitive tasks as provided by personal advocates. Those who are unsuccessful in finding employment require income maintenance and financial assistance with daily living expenses. All can benefit from information and referral for these types of services and service providers, training in independent living skills, and self-advocacy.

Ultimately, all of the 49 million people with disabilities in the United States (Bureau of the Census, 1993) could benefit from an increased awareness of the philosophy and techniques of independent living. Those who would benefit most would be those 3% who have the most severe disabilities (McNeil, 1993). Regardless of the severity of their disability, almost all people residing in private and government-operated institutions can benefit in some way from independent living support services. For a large percentage, it could mean being able to live in the community following a lifestyle of their own choice and with the opportunity to realize their potential for making productive contributions to society. For those with the most severe disabilities, it could mean receiving life support and enrichment services in a dignified and humane manner, maximizing the quality of life. It can also be assumed that services for independent living could benefit those who have been rejected by the vocational rehabilitation system. Also included should be the uncounted thousands of people with disabilities who reside in rural areas and who have little access to service providers.

The rise of independent living as a national priority is primarily the result of the cooperative activities of individuals with severe disabilities whose collective efforts have become known as the independent living movement. Independent living carries many of the hallmarks of a social movement as it develops into a national network of service-providing programs. Its successes are beginning to have a dramatic effect on the entire disability-related service system, challenging many of the premises upon which that system has been built. The study of independent living, therefore, requires an understanding of (a) the origins of the independent living movement, (b) the philosophical foundation of the independent living movement, (c) the scientific study of independence, and (d) the provision of independent living services.

Origins

Historically, there were serious deficiencies in disability-related service delivery systems for individuals with severe disabilities due to the narrowness of traditional approaches. Prior to the independent living movement, traditional services for people with severe disabilities had emphasized medical recovery and employability as the major indicators of success. This narrow focus relegated a large population of people with disabilities to the limited life options of institutional placement or extensive dependence on family care because their potential for recovery or employment and their ability to live independently in the community either were not recognized or were grossly underestimated by the rehabilitation and social service systems.

According to DeJong (1979a), it is difficult to pinpoint the time when or where the movement for independent living began. The movement has sprung from two main sources. The first source grew out of the efforts of people with disabilities to seek a more fulfilling life in an "able-bodied" world. The second source was due to the efforts of rehabilitation professionals to reach people with disabilities for whom a vocational goal was, until recently, unfeasible. While the efforts of both groups often converge on specific legislation, their interests and origins are sufficiently different to warrant separate consideration.

Indigenous Origins

The program for students with disabilities at the University of Illinois at Champaign–Urbana was among the first to facilitate community living for people with severe physical disabilities. In 1962 four students with severe disabilities were transferred from a nursing home to a modified home near the campus. The students' program not only emerged as a significant self-help effort but also was instrumental in making the University of Illinois one of the most architecturally accessible institutions of its time.

Also in the early 1960s, an American named Justin Dart, Jr., who was serving as president of Japan Tupperware, initiated a program through that company to offer employment and independent living skills training to institutionalized Japanese with physical disabilities. Dart, who has served as chairman of the President's Committee on Employment of People with Disabilities, has since become an eminent leader in the international independent living movement and has been a major author of independent living policies adopted by the U.S. government, including being one of the primary advocates for passage of the Americans with Disabilities Act (ADA) in 1990.

It was not until the early 1970s that the movement gained greater visibility and momentum with the creation of the Center for Independent Living (CIL) in Berkeley, California. The CIL was formed by several students with severe disabilities at the University of California at Berkeley as a way to obtain the services they needed to move from a wing of the university health center into apartments in the community. The Berkeley CIL was incorporated in 1972 as a community-based, self-help group to be managed primarily by people with disabilities. The purpose of the CIL was to broaden the approaches and services available to people with disabilities so that they might acquire the necessary knowledge, skills, confidence, and assistance to participate more fully in society. The Berkeley CIL provides a wide range of related services, including peer counseling, advocacy services, training in independent living skills, attendant referral, health maintenance counseling, housing referral, and wheelchair repair (B. M. Brown, 1978; Pflueger, 1977; Zukas, 1975). Unlike some other centers that followed, the Berkeley CIL has no residential program. This program has served as a model for a network of over 200 independent living centers that have since developed with the assistance of federal and state funding.

The provision of independent living support services took different forms in different parts of the country as the movement was gaining momentum. On the east coast, the Boston Center for Independent Living (BCIL) began its activities in 1974. BCIL emphasizes transitional housing and attendant services (Fay, 1977). Centers and organizations with a similar philosophy developed soon thereafter in Houston, Denver, Columbus, Ann Arbor, and other locations. The common element in most of these early residential programs was shared attendant services. Independent Life Styles in Houston, for example, is a set of units in a condominium complex that is available for people who wish to have 24-hour access to a pool of attendants located at the complex. The corporation is led by an elected resident in the program. Examples of some other early approaches to the concept of independent living include Cooperative Living (Stock & Cole, 1977), New Options (Cole, Sperry, Board, & Frieden, 1979), and programs in Illinois (Jeffers, 1978), New England (Driscoll, Marquis, Corcoran, & Fay, 1978), Massachusetts (Bartels, 1978), California (B. M. Brown, 1978), and Houston (Frieden, 1978). The various program models that were originally used are described by Frieden (1978), Frieden and Frieden (1981), and Frieden et al. (1979).

Professional Origins

Developing concurrently with the organizational initiatives of people with disabilities were the efforts of rehabilitation professionals in the formulation of national legislation. In 1959 House Report 361 was introduced, containing language that would extend independent living services to individuals for whom employment was not an obtainable objective (Urban Institute, 1975). That attempt failed, and in 1961 a new bill, written largely by the National Rehabilitation Association, was introduced. The new bill contained a separate title on independent living services. That bill also failed.

If adopted, the 1961 bill would have authorized $15 million in the first year and $25 million in the second year for independent living rehabilitation services. The new title was to be administered by state vocational rehabilitation (VR) agencies that were to enter into cooperative arrangements with other state agencies providing income assistance and health-related services. Opposition to the bill by the administrative branch of the federal government contributed to its demise.

A weak, backdoor version of an independent living rehabilitation services program was introduced in the 1956 amendments to the Vocational Rehabilitation Act of 1918. The amendments provided for an "extended evaluation" of applicants with severe disabilities whose suitability for VR services could not be immediately determined. While awaiting final eligibility determination, these individuals could receive support services that would enhance their chances for vocational rehabilitation.

Full-fledged recognition of independent living as a service option came with the 1978 amendments to the Rehabilitation Act of 1973. Title VII of these amendments authorized funding for independent living services provided by state VR agencies (Part A); for community-based, consumer-operated independent living centers, funded either directly or through state VR agencies (Part B); and for services to older individuals with blindness (Part C).

Divergent Views of Independent Living

The concept of independent living rehabilitation has changed since it was originally introduced to Congress. Since then, medical and rehabilitation technology has advanced significantly. Individuals needing independent living rehabilitation services are now routinely prepared for gainful employment by state VR agencies.

DeJong (1979b) identified differences in the concept of independent living services as advocated by those in the independent living movement versus VR professionals. One difference is that many rehabilitation professionals view independent living as an alternative to a vocational goal; the term *independent living rehabilitation* is treated as distinct from *vocational rehabilitation.* Independent living rehabilitation, according to this view, refers to those medical and social services that enable people with disabilities to live in the community short of being gainfully employed. From this perspective, independent living and vocational rehabilitation are seen as unrelated goals.

Throughout the history of the legislative debate on independent living, fear has been expressed that independent living would dilute the specificity of the vocational outcome. Some professionals feared that independent living services would result in the same charges of nonaccountability often levied against more ill-defined social services, such as those administered under Title XX of the Social Security Act.

Those whose involvement in the movement for independent living does not originate in the VR tradition reject the notion that independent living and VR are unrelated goals. Such a conception is viewed as potentially deleterious because it implicitly places an arbitrary upper limit on the goals a person with a disability might set for himself or herself where no upper limit should be set. Because limits tend to be self-fulfilling, vocational objectives should be seen as an integral part of the independent living goal, not as an unrelated goal (DeJong, 1979b).

Philosophical Foundation of the Independent Living Movement

Both philosophically and strategically, the independent living movement is the product of at least five social movements active in the 1970s: civil rights, consumerism, self-help, demedicalization, and deinstitutionalization (DeJong, 1979b). From the civil rights movement, independent living has absorbed an awareness of the injustice of exclusion based solely on personal characteristics that are beyond the individual's control. Similarly gained was an insistence on the inherent right of the individual to take his or her rightful place in the mainstream of society and the right to certain income and medical assistance benefits, educational benefits, and other entitlements without which many people with disabilities would be confined involuntarily to long-term care institutions.

From consumerism, independent living developed a focus on the individual's responsibility to evaluate and control the services he or she receives and to assess his or her own needs. In the spirit of self-help groups that developed to address problems and needs not dealt with by other institutions in society, independent living has incorporated as one of its key services, peer counseling—people with disabilities sharing experiences and techniques for living independently with other people with disabilities.

Demedicalization is a trend that is challenging the dominance of medical professionals in selected spheres of human life. As has occurred in the movement for natural childbirth and the hospice movement for people with terminal illnesses, there is an acceptance in the independent living movement of disability as one part of life and an encouragement of greater responsibility of individuals for their own care. The moral and economic justification for deinstitutionalization was established first with ex-offenders and then with people labeled as having mental retardation who were confined to government-operated residential facilities. The goal of the independent living movement to assist people with severe disabilities, especially those with significant functional limitations, in moving into settings of their own choice in the community has met with numerous environmental and attitudinal barriers not encountered by others.

DeJong (1979b) set out three major propositions that cut across all these movements and underlie the philosophical context of the community-based independent living movement:

1. *Consumer sovereignty*—People with disabilities, the actual consumers of the services, and not professionals, are the best judges of their own inter-

ests. They should ultimately determine how services should be organized on their behalf.

2. *Self-reliance*—People with disabilities must rely primarily on their own resources and ingenuity to acquire the rights and benefits to which they are entitled.

3. *Political and economic rights*—People with disabilities are entitled to participate fully and freely in the political and economic life of the community.

Primary moving forces in the evolution of the philosophy and practice of the movement have been recommendations and action plans generated through national conferences on independent living (DeJong, 1979a, 1979b, 1979c; DeJong & Hughes, 1982; Institute for Educational Leadership, 1984; Institute on Rehabilitation Issues, 1980).

The philosophy of the independent living movement is based on firmly held convictions about the behavioral expectations placed on people with disabilities. Fundamentally, the movement advocates that people with disabilities should play, to the maximum of their potential, the same social roles as people without disabilities. It rejects the traditional expectations that people with disabilities are childlike and helpless. Furthermore, it rejects the medical–rehabilitation model that underlies traditional services.

In receiving rehabilitation services, the individual with a disability is expected to follow the medical model. As defined by DeJong (1979b), this model identifies the physician or medical professional as the technically competent expert and the primary decision maker in the person's care. The patient is expected to assume the sick role, to cooperate with those caring for him or her, and to focus on the remediation of the illness through medical intervention. The sick role exempts the person from normal social activities and responsibilities, including any responsibility for his or her illness. The sick person is expected to view being sick as undesirable and to do everything possible to facilitate his or her recovery with the assistance of a medical professional. The role is intended to be temporary; however, in the context of permanent physical disability, it is often inappropriately extended over a lifetime. Because their disabilities are frequently an irrevocable part of their existence, people with disabilities, as a result of the sick role, begin to view not only the condition but also their own personhood as undesirable. As a consequence, they begin to accept the dependency prescribed under the sick role as normative for the duration of the disability. Thus, the sick role removes from people with disabilities the obligation to take charge of their own affairs.

Elements of the medical model may also be seen in vocational rehabilitation programs. Here, problems are usually defined in terms of physical functioning, that is, inadequacy in the performance of activities of daily living and in skills necessary for gainful employment. The problem is viewed as existing within the individual and as best treated through appropriate cooperation with programs run by trained professionals. Successful outcomes in VR are measured not only in levels of physical functioning and employment, but also in terms of degrees of cooperation with prescribed programs. Unlike individuals in the sick role, however, the individual is not viewed as exempt from normal social activities and responsibilities in a VR setting.

The situation of people with the most severe disabilities poses an enigma for vocational rehabilitation. Typically, people who are perceived as having severe functional limitations and limited potential for developing marketable job skills are either rejected for services or placed in programs where the intended outcome is sheltered employment or return to institutional living. Yet, in the population, some people with severe disabilities fulfill major social responsibilities and make productive contributions to their families and communities, many times without benefit of rehabilitation services. These people, referred to in the movement as "survivors" or those with "do-it-yourself" independence (Jones & Summerville, 1983), often achieve higher levels of independence and productivity than people with less severe disabilities who are easily accepted for rehabilitation services and complete vocational training programs. In reality, it is the latter who could also benefit from independent living training and support services. This enigma casts serious doubt on the validity of heavily weighting functional abilities or severity of disability as a criterion for service eligibility.

DeJong (1979b) further stated that the independent living paradigm has emerged in part as a response to the anomaly of people with the most severe physical disabilities. According to the independent living paradigm, the problem does not reside in the individual; it often resides in the solution offered by the rehabilitation paradigm, which contains the dependency-inducing potential of the physician–patient or professional–client relationship. The locus of the problem is not the individual, but the environment that tends to limit the choices available to people with disabilities. Of particular importance are the works by DeJong (1981) and DeJong and Lifchez (1983), which extensively document these barriers. To cope with environmental barriers, the person with a disability must shed the patient or client role for the consumer role. Advocacy, peer counseling, self-help, consumer control, and barrier removal are the trademarks of the independent living paradigm.

The new and revolutionary model of the person with a severe disability as self-sufficient and productive in a mainstreamed social environment has posed serious challenges to public policy, which continues to place disability-related services under a medical categorization. Application of the medical model and the sick role to healthy people with disabilities is unnecessary and counterproductive, contributing to the dependence and isolation that the independent living movement seeks to eliminate. DeJong (1979b, p. 62) compared the rehabilitation and independent living paradigms, as depicted in Table 4.1.

In recent years, as the philosophical foundation for the independent living movement has continued to develop, there have been modifications in the concepts of the locus of the problem and the locus of the solution. Attributions of causation are not easily delineated as being internal or external to the individual.

Table 4.1
A Comparison of the Rehabilitation and Independent Living Paradigms

	Paradigm	
Item	**Vocational Rehabilitation**	**Independent Living**
Definition of the problem	Physical impairment and lack of vocational skill	Dependence on professionals, relatives, etc.
Locus of the problem	In the individual	In the environment, in the rehabilitation process
Solution to the problem	Professional intervention by a physician, physical therapist, occupational therapist, rehabilitation counselor, etc.	Peer counseling, advocacy, self-help, consumer control, removal of barriers
Social role	Patient/client	Consumer
Who controls	Professional	Consumer
Desired outcomes	Maximum activities of daily living, gainful employment	Independent living

Note. From *The Movement for Independent Living: Origins, Ideology, and Implications for Disability Research* (Occasional Paper No. 2), by G. DeJong, 1979b, East Lansing: University Center for International Rehabilitation, Michigan State University.

Current thought in the independent living movement analyzes problems and solutions in terms of the characteristics of both the individual and the environment and the complex interrelationship between the two.

Nosek, Narita, Dart, and Dart (1982), after analyzing the roots of prejudice and discrimination against people with disabilities and the resulting environmental and policy barriers, addressed independent living in terms of quality of life, productivity, and responsibility to the self and society. They warned of setting independent living goals according to hypothetical ideals without regard for the person's realistic chances for success, resulting in unnecessary feelings of failure. They also warned of uncritically accepting society's concept of the "good life," suggesting that laws of reason and concern for quality of life be applied instead in developing independent living goals. They cited the example of life in a 10 × 10 foot room on an institutional or poverty-level budget; it could be viewed as a prison, or it could "be perceived as an opportunity to create a mini-universe of exceptional beauty, a personally satisfying and socially valuable productivity, an eloquent advocacy for self-reliant responsibility for life" (p. 27). Development of the ability to exercise efficient control over the variables in one's environment is taken as the keystone of the independent living process. *The immediate goal of independent living, then, is to assist individuals in their efforts to become as physically, psychologically, intellectually, socially, and economically responsible as possible.*

Scientific Study of Independence

As a scientific study, independent living is virtually unbroken, but fertile, ground. The preponderance of rehabilitation literature focuses on the restoration or creation of normal functioning in clients and, while mentioning independence as a goal, devotes little effort to defining and operationalizing it as a construct. Discussions of independence in the psychological, sociological, and anthropological literature tend to assume the potential for normal levels of physical and mental functioning, implying necessarily reduced independence by people with functional impairments. This narrow treatment of both disability and independence forms the basis of many of the problems faced by people with disabilities.

A survey of the literature in the areas of independent living, psychology, sociology, and public policy reveals five different constructs, all labeled independence:

1. Independence in the context of infant and child development

2. Independence as a psychological characteristic

3. Independence as a measure of an individual's social status

4. Independence in connection with an individual's functional abilities

5. Independence in a behavioral sense

The following sections contain brief characterizations of these five constructs.

Developmental Aspects of Independence

The socialization process in the United States emphasizes the learning of independence in childhood in terms of being as physically and emotionally self-reliant as possible; however, it also emphasizes the development of acceptable forms of dependence. Children are taught to obey their parents; to turn to them for guidance and help in meeting their needs; and to seek recognition, approval, affection, and support in socially acceptable ways. Successful socialization, then, involves the acquisition of a culturally approved balance between dependence and independence (Stendler, 1954).

Discussions of independence and dependence can be distinguished according to instrumentality and emotionality. In the instrumental sense, independence refers to the process of accomplishing physical tasks and the individual's ability and desire to do so without assistance. In the emotional sense, it refers to the lack of need for affection, approval, and acceptance in social interactions (Heathers,

1955). This emotional element of the development of independence in children is given much less attention in the examination of independence of adults, as discussed later.

Infants move from their relatively helpless, passively dependent state to an actively dependent state when they first learn to associate others with the satisfaction of their needs. In developing instrumental dependence, they learn various techniques for stimulating and motivating others to help them reach their goals. The earliest and most imprecise technique is crying, followed as the child develops by gesturing and finally linguistic verbalization in an ascending scale of effective communication. Parents, the socializing agents, teach which techniques are acceptable and/or effective by responding or not responding (Heathers, 1955).

For children with disabilities, the crucial step of developing instrumental dependence is complicated by many disability-related factors. Delayed or impaired abilities to gesture or use oral language prolong the period in which response is generated by the very imprecise stimulus of crying. Children who are cognitively ready but physically unable to effectively communicate which needs must be met and how they can best be met experience increased anxiety and frustration and fail to develop an understanding of the relationship between their actions and the response of the environment, factors that can lead to learned helplessness. This step is integrally linked to sensorimotor development in that, through exploring the environment, children increase the number of occasions in which they need to seek help. Delays or impairments in the exploration process (as imposed by the disability, barriers in the environment, or protective attitudes of the parents and teachers) reduce opportunities to discover new, more effective and socially acceptable techniques for eliciting needed help.

The development of emotional dependence is another step toward maturity. Among its components are the seeking of physical contact, proximity, attention, and recognition (Beller, 1957). Parent–child interactions help mold the child's need for reassurance (trust), affection (expressed both physically and symbolically), and approval. The latter is highly influenced by the parents' expectations of the child as expressed by whether they reward, ignore, or punish certain behaviors. When children learn to seek approval by conforming to others' requirements, they take the second step toward maturity, that is, becoming ready for mutual relations in which they seek to satisfy the needs of others in return for having their own needs met (Heathers, 1955).

Positive, productive forms of instrumental and emotional reinforcement from parents, teachers, and other professionals can encourage autonomy and emotional self-reliance. The cumulative effect of negative environmental conditions can be seen in the overdependence, predominance of external locus of control, and learned helplessness sometimes found among people with disabilities (Hiroto, 1974; Hung, 1978; Maier & Seligman, 1976; Weisz, 1979). Special devices and techniques should be used to minimize or circumvent the effects of the disability, and a close scrutiny of child-rearing practices and general education should be conducted to ensure that children with disabilities are given equal access to the experiences and opportunities for development that are generally available to others.

Emotional self-reliance has also been described as the ability to face threats of injury or rejection without requiring emotional support (Heathers, 1955). Beller (1955) expanded this concept by considering initiative, the desire to overcome obstacles in the environment, carrying activities to completion, and getting satisfaction from work or activity. Independence is thus seen as autonomous achievement striving, dependent upon spontaneous exploration of the environment. Such exploration requires initiative and the ability to cope with and overcome obstacles. The extent to which persons are able to successfully complete these activities determines the amount of satisfaction they get from work and the intensity of their desire to do things for themselves (Beller, 1957; Turner & Szymanski, 1990).

Autonomy, a central construct in Erikson's (1965) developmental theory of the life cycle, is closely related to the concept of independence. Autonomy, the second of Erikson's eight stages of the life cycle (autonomy vs. shame and doubt), is attendant upon muscular maturation and associated with freedom of choice. If the experience of autonomy is not gradual or well guided, or if it is weakened by an initial loss of trust, children turn against themselves all their urges to discriminate and to manipulate, gaining power by stubborn and minute control and overmanipulating themselves (Erikson, 1965). If children are to develop a meaningful sense of autonomy, it is necessary that they be permitted to make choices and discover the boundaries of self-determination (Kofta, 1980; Mussen, Conger, & Kagan, 1969).

In a study of children with disabilities, the Carnegie Council on Children (Gliedman & Roth, 1980) offered a thorough treatment of the psychological and social development of people with disabilities from the earliest ages. Several sections focused on the effect of the social pathology, the stigma attached to disability, and the application of the norms of the nondisabled population on the self-concept and behaviors of the people with disabilities. The authors proposed that the special social situations of children with disabilities might radically alter the nature and order of the stages through which they progress.

Gliedman and Roth (1980) analyzed Erikson's developmental theory as applied to children with disabilities. Regarding the second stage, they posed the question of what is the right balance of autonomy and protection when the child "explores the social and physical world in ways that are profoundly different from the ways of the able-bodied child, or when the child is more vulnerable to injury or illness. . . . When does protection become overprotection?" (p. 100). When children with disabilities acquire the ability to feel shame, their limitations may cause an exaggerated sense of powerlessness. Although Gliedman and Roth credited Erikson's (1965) theory with explaining many problem behaviors common among people with disabilities, they criticized the theory for forcing one to describe the development of the person with a disability as a deviation from the norm. The sequential relationship of the stages does not allow for circumstances that limit social situations and experiences. For example, many people with disabilities can never achieve full control of their bodily functions yet must participate in social situations and develop a positive, adult identity as if they had full control. Erikson's theory appears unable to accommodate the special situations and experiences that influence the development of many people with disabilities, such as pain and threat of death, lack of acknowledgment of the ability to love and achieve intimacy, and excessive contact with professionals and institutional settings.

Psychological Aspects of Independence

In the psychological literature, independence is most frequently discussed as a personality trait as opposed to a developmental stage. In fact, Cattell (1965) identified independence as the most substantially inherited of source personality traits. He described the independent person as unconventional, assertive, active, alert, and cheerful (Lobel, 1982). This type of inherently independent-minded person was studied by Jones and Summerville (1983). In conducting a needs assessment survey of independent living program clients, they identified a group that they labeled "do-it-yourself independent" persons, those who achieved independent living status without the benefit of an independent living program. On four of five indicators of independence (having modified one's home, preferring self-management of finances, using more independent transportation, and ability to perform activities of daily living), this group showed a greater degree of independence than those who achieved independence through an independent living program. Do-it-yourself independent persons tended to have fewer multiple physical impairments. They were more likely to have received educational counseling and formal education after the onset of disability, and 47% of them were employed. They tended to have a network of social support, they were more aware of resources available to assist them, and they were more interested in playing the role of advocate for other people with disabilities. Barriers to education were lack of money, transportation problems, lack of awareness of educational options, and inaccessible facilities. In employment, they faced inadequate job opportunities, discrimination, transportation problems, and loss of benefits, especially medical benefits. Jones and Summerville recommended that independent living programs focus as much on the removal of barriers to social independence as on physical rehabilitation so that more people with disabilities might pursue independence on their own.

In her study of minority adolescent college students' usage of special services, Troutt (1980) set forth a succinct and practical definition of independence. She defined independence as behaviors that reflect the ability of adolescents to make separate and responsible decisions and choices and to assume responsibility for these decisions and choices without immediate parental supervision. This includes the ability to manage life in the areas of one's competence and the capacity to seek and make use of help when the realization of one's goals requires assistance. Although developed from a different discipline, this definition, with its focus on decisions and choices, harkens back to Frieden et al.'s (1979) definition of independent living presented earlier.

Social Status, Functional Abilities, and Behaviors

Independence as a life status indicator has been operationally defined by the independent living movement (Budde, Petty, & Nelson, 1983; Clark & Rice, 1980; Frieden et al., 1979; Massachusetts Rehabilitation Commission, n.d.; Muzzio, 1980, 1981; Rice, Roessler, Greenwood, & Frieden, 1983; University of Washington, 1982; Wilkerson, Weinhouse, & Jamero, 1982) and includes such variables as the following:

- Mobility, at home and within the community, including use of public transportation
- Activities of daily living
- Use of personal assistants (attendants)
- Use of assistive equipment
- Communication abilities
- Source and amount of income
- Living arrangement, including housing and housemates
- Employment status
- Education level
- Use of leisure time
- Health status, including fulfilling health maintenance requirements
- Marital status
- Social life
- Self-concept

Many of these variables have functional and cognitive components and may be broken down into discrete abilities or levels by various assessment instruments used for determining independent living outcomes in rehabilitation and independent living program settings. Some programs choose four or five variables as key indicators, usually including mobility, employment and/or income, activities of daily living, and living arrangement. It is noteworthy that these components are among the most functionally oriented on the list. This approach tends to focus on observable behaviors and environmental circumstances with virtually no examination of the psychological characteristics that underlie such behaviors.

A curious anomaly exists in that, although most independent living programs in the country assess independence primarily in terms of functional capacities or environmental circumstances, almost all subscribe to a definition of independence focusing on psychological and social factors developed by Frieden et al. (1979) and adopted into the *National Policy for People with Disabilities* (National Council on Disability, 1983), which was mentioned earlier. Undoubtedly, this discrepancy exists because there is currently no practical technique for assessing control in a service provision setting. Rather, it is dealt with somewhat unsystematically under the label of "peer counseling." Nevertheless, this conflict between ideology and practice points out the need for a comprehensive operational definition of the construct.

Wilkerson, in an unpublished manuscript (1982), stated, "Living independently for a . . . person [with a severe disability], as for anyone, entails much more than an approximation of 'normal' physical functioning. Indeed, physical functioning may play little or no role in the definition of independence for a person who has other priorities" (p. 27). She cited Clowers, Haley, Unti, and Feiss (1979), DeJong (1979a), DeJong and Wenker (1979), Frieden et al. (1979), Heumann (1977), Muzzio et al. (1979), Pflueger (1977), and Roberts (1977) as observing that the independent living movement does not suggest the absence of assistance, even in the necessities of day-to-day living. Independence is defined by control or self-direction, not by style or content, and must be determined by each individual in terms that are meaningful to him or her.

In describing the components of independence, Wilkerson (1982) mentioned two lines of change in one's life: (a) psychosocial characteristics, such as self-esteem, self-direction, and locus of control, and (b) behavior, such as living arrangement, daily activities, and participation in family and community life. Although many instruments exist for measuring psychosocial characteristics, she claimed that the independent living program environment has neither the time nor the research orientation to administer them. Even though behaviors are easier to assess, the length of time required for change to occur may be considerable. Behaviors do, however, automatically reflect limitations placed on the individual's independent living status by the environment, even though these limitations may not be obvious. According to Wilkerson, "the absence of an independent behavior does not incriminate the environment as the deterrent to independence. On the other hand, while psychosocial or internal orientation to independent living may have been achieved, environmental constraints can still squelch independent living" (p. 31). The greatest disadvantage of traditional assessments of skill acquisition is that the possession of a skill does not necessarily mean it will be used.

The Four Major Components of Independence

Diverse notions of independence can be distilled into four components:

1. Perceived control of one's life

2. Physical and cognitive autonomy

3. Psychological self-reliance

4. Environmental resources

Perceived control is the expectation of being able to make decisions and engage in actions that will attain desirable consequences and avoid unfavorable ones (Baron & Rodin, 1978). It includes both self-control and control of the environment. Self-control is the ability to direct one's physical and mental abilities, emotions, and behavior, as embraced in Haworth's (1986) notion of competence. Perceived control also includes the belief that one can execute courses of actions required to deal with prospective situations, as in Bandura's concept of self-efficacy (1982, 1989). Environmental control is the perception that one is able to exert power over human and material elements in the environment that particularly affect one's life. This is similar to the notion of internal locus of control presented by Rotter (1954) and others (e.g., Lefcourt, 1976; Phares, 1976). Control is enabled by predictability, which in turn is provided by education and informing people of what will happen to them in advance so that they can prepare for an event (Kiernat, 1987; Schulz, 1976). Adler (1930) described the need to control one's personal environment as inherent to life itself. A plethora of studies support his view with evidence associating lack of control with helplessness, declining health, and death (Seligman, 1975).

Physical and cognitive functioning refers to the most basic survival abilities, such as moving about, dressing, eating, and processing sensory input. These are the activities of daily living that have been the subject of considerable analysis in the rehabilitation literature (Alexander & Fuhrer, 1984; M. Brown, Gordon, & Diller, 1983; Salkind, Beckwith, Nelson, & McGregor, 1982). To accomplish basic life tasks, individuals may elect to use equipment or assistance from another person, examples being automobiles, eyeglasses, or someone to cook, clean, or maintain a checkbook. People with high autonomy in this area are capable of doing these things for themselves when necessary.

Psychological self-reliance is generally associated with the emotional autonomy, ego integrity, self-confidence, assertiveness, sense of purpose, cleverness, and decision-making skills necessary to judge effectively which actions must be taken to meet the demands of a variety of situations and to initiate those actions. It includes coping, the capacity to handle stressful situations, and mastery, the ability to meet new challenges (Lowry, 1989). Whereas physical functioning has an instrumental, task-oriented character, psychological self-reliance includes managerial or executive functions. The person with high psychological self-reliance is emotionally stable, capable of functioning with little group support, and able to fulfill a range of social roles.

Environmental resources include all physical and social elements external to the individual that can either facilitate or obstruct the achievement of personal goals (Rice et al., 1983). Factors such as family support, geographic location, terrain, economic situation, political climate, educational opportunities, architectural accessibility, support services, and cultural values are among the environmental elements relevant to developing independence. The perceived availability of resources in the environment is particularly crucial in considering independence. A resource is just as useless whether it is perceived to be unavailable or truly unavailable.

The four components have a complex interrelationship that is frequently reciprocal in nature. The most obvious of these is between physical autonomy and environmental resources. The less one is able to do for oneself, the more one must rely on other people or things in the environment. Very few of us grow our own food or walk to work. If, because of a disability, a person cannot dress himself or herself, some other person or device must be secured to compensate for this lack of ability so that the desired outcome, being dressed, can be accomplished. As the availability of environmental resources increases, demands on physical abilities decrease. Witness so-called modern conveniences: It is important to distinguish between reliance on conveniences, where the physical ability remains intact but is not used, and reliance on necessities, where environmental resources are used to substitute for an ability that does not exist. For example, both a person with tetraplegia and a person without a disability may be able to drive a car out of the garage; however, if the electric garage door opener malfunctions, the person without a disability may be able to accomplish the task adequately by opening the door manually, but the person with tetraplegia may be unable to accomplish the task at all. Thus, the compensatory relationship between ability and environment is largely a matter of convenience for the general population, but is more a matter of necessity for people with disabilities.

Psychological self-reliance is strongly influenced by physical abilities and environmental factors, especially during early development (Stendler, 1954; Troutt, 1980). The more one is able to understand and physically manage the environment, the greater the confidence and self-esteem one develops. Being able to physically explore the environment and learn from it enables gaining an experience base upon which to develop the executive abilities necessary to succeed in society. The degree to which environmental resources are available to facilitate development strongly influences the manner in which genetic traits are expressed. For the child with spina bifida, an environment that provides opportunities and necessary support (e.g., personal assistance, mobility aides) for engaging in activities such as integrated play, music lessons, trips to museums, and the like, can enable that child to express natural talents and interests. Psychological self-reliance is thus a product of genetics and environmental influences. Conversely, psychological elements are the catalysts for engaging environmental resources to compensate for physical inabilities. Resources may abound, but if the person is unable to recognize, access, or manage them, they are of little use. Once children with spina bifida grow up, they must be able to manage their own support systems, including people and material resources, in order to carry on effectively as independent persons.

The interrelationship of perceived control with physical, environmental, and psychological components is the most complex of all. It has already been said that the presence of physical abilities, environmental resources, and a sense of worth and competence enhances feelings of control over one's life (Perlmuter, Monty, & Chan, 1986). This feeling of control, however, does not have a direct effect on these three components; rather, it is a by-product of them. People feel in control when they believe they have value and the ability to deal effectively with their environment, that is, when they have a high sense of self-efficacy (Bandura, 1982, 1989).

The strongest effect of perceived control is observed on the interaction of the three components. The more people sense that they have control, the more effective they can be in using resources to enhance their abilities. Studies done as early as 1967 have demonstrated that, after long periods of institutional care, people with physical or mental disabilities can successfully manage their own lives in the community, where they have more control (Edgerton, 1967; Rock, 1988). This can be seen even more clearly in reverse. When circumstances are such that people feel they have little control, as under oppressive regimes or confinement, the incentive is reduced to enhance abilities or better one's situation by more effective management of resources (White & Janson, 1986). In institutions, functioning may even deteriorate (Avorn & Langer, 1982), and dependency tends to increase. In a 3-year survey of 3,400 residents of 176 nursing homes, Booth (1986) found that even in homes with the highest standards of care, the less residents had control over their own lives, the more they lost control over the use of their faculties. Conversely, nursing home residents demonstrated enhanced alertness, active participation, and sense of well-being when allowed control over participation in social and leisure activities (Langer & Rodin, 1976). Several studies of elderly, chronically ill, and physically disabled populations have demonstrated the benefits of increasing perceived control over personal health and the environment (Avorn & Langer, 1982; Langer & Rodin, 1976; Schulz, 1976). Thus, "the fundamental issue is [no longer] whether patients should have options to exercise control, but under which conditions and in what form these options will prove decisive in relation to individual well-being" (Schulz, 1976, p. 563). Of all the four components, control appears to be the least related to functioning, but the most strongly related to independence overall.

Evaluating Outcomes of Independent Living

Within recent years, there has been a sharp rise in interest in methods for evaluating independent living status. This is partly due to increased government spending to seed and support independent living programs and the requirements for accountability, and partly due to the realization by leaders of the independent living movement that to serve people with disabilities better, there must be a more refined concept of goals and a practical method for determining progress toward meeting them. (See the 1987 review by Nosek of outcomes assessment in independent living.)

Assessment of environmental and life-status indicators plays an important part in the research of Gerben DeJong, who conducted the first empirically based studies to operationalize the construct of independent living. In a study of 111 people with spinal cord injuries, DeJong, Branch, and Corcoran (1984) assessed independent living in terms of living arrangement and productivity. Their analysis of these elements showed that severity of disability and unmet in-home needs were significant in their absence as predictors.

The Arkansas Rehabilitation Research and Training Center at the University of Arkansas has made many significant contributions toward refining the evaluation process for independent living. It treats personal change as one of four critical areas for assessment in evaluating the effectiveness of independent living programs. Roessler and Rubin (1980) stated that program services should contribute to client gains in physical functioning, vocational potential, educational skills, avocational interests, psychosocial functioning, and economic independence. Clark and Rice (1980) noted several assessment instruments that could be used in each of these areas. Drawing on Stoddard, Katsuranis, Toms, and Finnegan (1980) and Sigelman, Vengroff, and Spanhel (1979), another member of the Arkansas team, Roessler (1981), listed the following areas of independent living service needs for personal change:

1. Health functions
    a. Increase the overall physical health of the individual
    b. Decrease impairments in bodily systems
    c. Decrease the amount of pain experienced
    d. Increase the individual's participation in life activities

2. Social–attitudinal functions
    a. Improve the level of acceptance of self and abilities
    b. Improve the individual's social skills
    c. Increase the individual's motivation to improve self

3. Mobility functions
    a. Increase the individual's manual skills for manipulating objects and devices
    b. Increase the individual's capability to move at home, in the workplace, and from place to place in the community
    c. Decrease the individual's difficulty in participating in other physical activities

4. Cognitive–intellectual functioning
    a. Increase the individual's intellectual capacity to manipulate symbols and objects
    b. Increase the individual's capability to acquire or store in memory new cognitions and behavior patterns and/or to transfer learning to new situations

5. Communication functioning
    a. Decrease the individual's difficulties in sending and receiving messages
    b. Decrease the individual's difficulty in exchanging information and ideas with other people (p. 11)

For each of the above areas, Roessler (1981) analyzed available assessment instruments. Roessler gave similar treatment to environmental change, particularly concerning independent living services to influence physical, social, economic, and human service environment change.

Salkind et al. (1982) indexed over 130 instruments used to measure independence. The diversity in content and level of detail of the instruments is notable, although the majority are geared toward people with mental retardation. Only 7 instruments had been tested for reliability and validity; 13 instruments contained some type of measure of control or decision making.

A study by Nosek (1984) examined the relative roles of personality, social status, and functional abilities in assessing independent living status. She asked a sample of 67 people with severe orthopedic impairments, referred by colleges and independent living programs, to complete the *Sixteen Personality Factors Questionnaire* (16PF) by Cattell, Eber, and Tatsuoka (1970); the *Barthel Index of Functional Abilities* modified by Granger, Albrecht, and Hamilton (1979); and a demographic questionnaire. Based on the Independence Scale of the 16PF as a measure of psychological independence and the *Independent Living Scale* by DeJong and Hughes (1982) as a measure of social independence, subjects were grouped as being high and low on levels of independence. Subjects who scored high on psychological independence tended to live in less restrictive settings, have fewer communication problems, and spend shorter time in comprehensive rehabilitation facilities. Those with high social independence tended to have assertive, self-assured, and self-sufficient personalities; higher levels of education; more earned income; and spouses. Both groups of highly independent persons tended to have hired attendants, good health, and more transportation options; be outgoing and female; and perceive themselves as being independent. Functional abilities did not have any statistically significant relationship to levels of psychological and social independence.

Nosek's findings (Nosek, 1984; Nosek, Parker, & Larsen, 1987) illustrate the importance of psychological factors in the ability to control one's living environment in relation to levels of productivity, social participation, and independence. The implications for service delivery and policy in education, rehabilitation, and independent living programs lie chiefly in assessment, eligibility criteria, individualized program planning, and evaluation methodologies. Bringing these issues forward reveals the need for more research on developmental influences and service delivery techniques that encourage independence for people with disabilities.

After an extensive search of the literature and consultation with experts, Nosek and Fuhrer (1991) constructed the *Personal Independence Profile* (PIP) to operationalize the construct of independence. The PIP consists of items measuring perceived control over one's life, selected from Flanagan's (1978) quality of life domains; Fordyce's *Independence Scale* (1953), which deals with psychological factors such as competitiveness, self-esteem, and group autonomy; and Meenan, Gertman, and Mason's (1980) *Arthritis Impact Measurement Scale* (AIMS), which is a Guttman-type ordering of general functional ability items.

Cluster analysis of the three PIP scales from 185 subjects yielded three dominant profiles of independence: Profile A, independently minded and relatively nondisabled; Profile B, independently minded and relatively disabled; and Profile C, nonindependently minded. Individuals having the first profile demonstrated average levels of psychological independence, tended to feel in control of things important to them, and had relatively good physical status. Individuals with the second profile exhibited relatively high levels of psychological independence and control, but a high degree of physical impairment. This group was similar to the first group except for having severe physical impairments. Those with the third profile had relatively low levels of control over their lives and were unable or unwilling to take the initiative to make changes, but exhibited no common factors for physical independence. Further analysis regarding health and productivity revealed that Profile A had the highest indicators of both, whereas Profile C had the lowest indicators of both. Profile B, interestingly, had a low number of trips to the doctor or emergency room, but the highest number of days in the hospital. Also, despite their low rate of physical functioning, those with Profile B had a high rate of productivity.

In attempting to break ground for a better understanding of independence, these studies have demonstrated the complexity of this construct and the multiplicity of factors, both individual and environmental, that affect its expression. This information provides a greater appreciation for the difficulty of developing services to support and enhance individuals' independence amid a diversity of need.

Provision of Independent Living Services

The centers for independent living in Berkeley and Boston established the model upon which a national network of independent living programs has been developed and independent living funding legislation has been enacted. This model was described by Frieden et al. (1979) as a community-based, nonprofit, nonresidential program that is controlled by the consumers with disabilities it serves. It provides directly, or coordinates indirectly through referral, those services that assist individuals with severe disabilities to increase personal self-determination and to minimize unnecessary dependence upon others. The 1992 Rehabilitation Act Amendments specify that, in order to receive federal funding, independent living centers must provide four core services: (a) information and referral, (b) peer counseling, (c) independent living skills training, and (d) community advocacy; 51% of the members of their board of directors must be people with disabilities; and they must serve a variety of disability types. Other services often provided by independent living centers are housing assistance; attendant referral, readers, and interpreters; financial and legal advocacy; community awareness and barrier removal programs, transportation provision or registry, equipment maintenance and repair, and social–recreational services.

The most comprehensive analysis to date of the full range of independent living programs has been done by the Independent Living Research Utilization (ILRU) project at The Institute for Rehabilitation and Research in Houston, Texas. This project has developed a directory of over 400 programs that deliver independent living support services (ILRU, 1990). Surveys of these programs have been conducted by ILRU in 1979 and biennially from 1984 through 1994. Analysis of data collected in these surveys revealed an extensive set of information about the evolution of independent living programming. For example, the establishment of new independent living programs increased slowly throughout the 1970s; rose steeply between 1980 and 1981 after federal funding (through Title VII, Part B, of the Rehabilitation Act of 1973 as amended in 1978) became available; plateaued for a year; then rose steadily through 1990. In 1988 a typical program was about 9 years old, was located in a moderately sized urban setting, and operated on a total median budget of $255,059. Most programs drew the majority of their funds from federal and state grants. The typical program had a staff of nine, five of whom had disabilities. Most had a board of directors of whom more than half had disabilities. The most common services offered included information and referral, housing and attendant referral, consumer advocacy, community advocacy, peer counseling, and independent living skills training. Direct services were delivered to 53 people per month and 636 per year; an additional 123 per month and 1,476 per year required only information or referral.

The profile of a typical program in 1988 had changed little from 2 years earlier. There were only slight increases in mean budget ($2,839) and staff (one person). However, a clear trend was noted for increased volume of service delivery; the mean number of requests for information and referral rose from 89 to 123, and 10 more people per month obtained direct services. Considerably more boards were composed of at least 51% members with disabilities, rising significantly from 59% to 82%. The typical consumer remained between the ages of 18 and 65, was white, had an orthopedic disability, and resided in the same community as the program (Nosek, Zhu, & Howland, 1992).

Funding trends for independent living centers (ILCs) are proving to be dynamic, influenced by federal and state policy changes and the availability of public moneys. ILRU's 1994 survey showed that fewer ILCs received federal funding and fewer federal dollars were allotted (Chanpong, 1996). Even though a greater number of ILCs received state funding, fewer dollars were allocated. The 1994 for-profit ventures and other business activity increased by a small margin, but not enough to compensate for the decline in federal and state funding. Successful fund-raising and business activity now must make up a larger portion of program operating budgets. Many ILCs may have a difficult financial battle in the future.

In 1994 the average number of consumers served per center was 690, with 1,925 information and referral contacts annually, a slight increase over Nosek et al.'s (1992) findings. Consumer contacts ranged from 20 per year at a small rural center to more than 6,200 at one large urban center. The type of consumers served is becoming more heterogeneous. As Heumann (1994) pointed out, "centers are expanding to be more representative of the community across disabilities, to be representative of older people, people with AIDS, people with psychiatric problems, cognitive and learning difficulties, to focus on women's issues, issues of African-Americans, Latin Americans, Native Americans, Asian Americans, and peoples having alternative lifestyles" (p. 2). The ethnic diversity of consumers varied widely nationally, but was either equal to or slightly greater than the percentage in the general population (Richards, 1995). However, as reported by the National Council on Disability (NCD; formerly the National Council on the Handicapped) (1993), data on the impact of the disability in different population segments, such as minority individuals, are lacking, and it is not clear that the needs of different groups are being addressed adequately. The NCD (1993) report called for development of "culturally specific" service models.

In addition to the four core services, most had ongoing community education and outreach programs, as well as individual advocacy and legal services. More than half (55%) of the centers offered referral and training of personal assistance, and most created publications for consumers and performed accessibility evaluations. Seventy percent offered assistive devices, equipment services, and other aids for people with hearing or visual impairments. Only 16 ILCs (7%) offered employment services and career counseling. The average number of CIL staff was 13 paid people (ranging from 2 to 49 persons), a substantial increase over the 1988 figures.

A national network of independent living centers, programs, and advocacy groups has developed since 1975. Sixty-five percent of the centers are members of the National Council on Independent Living (NCIL), 77% reported being associated with a state network of ILCs, and 35% were part of regional and local networks. More than half (57%) of the ILCs send representatives to serve on the Statewide Independent Living Council (SILC). The 1994 CIL survey asked about national information infrastructure (Internet) linkages, because it has been mandated that all ILCs obtain connectivity. About 65% of the ILCs reported dial-in connectivity with DimeNet, the Disabled Individual Movement for Equality Network electronic bulletin board service. DimeNet was established by the National Council on Independent Living. In addition to DimeNet, 20% of ILCs reported Internet connections.

Although SILCs were given significant planning authority and responsibility through passage of the 1992 Rehabilitation Act Amendments, SILCs, in many cases, comprised individuals who had minimum understanding of the intended role of the SILCs and little or no preparation for their roles as SILC members (Smith, Frieden, & Richards, 1995). As Michaels (1994) pointed out, with changes in the Rehabilitation Act, "the SILCs finally have real authority to carry out their responsibilities" (p. 9).

The focus on transitional services and independent living sharpened as the time for reauthorization of the Individuals with Disabilities Education Act of 1990 (IDEA) approached. Heumann (1994) specifically cited the importance of the

IDEA legislation, along with the Rehabilitation Act and the ADA, as "important pieces of legislation" for producing change. The importance of the IDEA legislation as it relates to transitional series and independent living cannot be overstated. Efforts toward effective transition from school to work and independent living will be effective only if the quality of education provided students with disabilities is comparable to that provided to other students in public and private school systems. This point was highlighted in a 1993 NCD report developed around four "critical questions," one of which was "How can special education and general education systems work together across federal, state, and local levels to ensure that students with disabilities will achieve desired outcomes?" (p. 2).

Assuming that independent living is a "desired outcome," it appears obvious that one part of the answer to this question will involve research on effective linkages between schools and service agencies, such as ILCs, to determine how best to reduce the likelihood that young people with disabilities are not lost in the transition from school support systems to community support systems. Giordano and D'Alonzo (1994) cited model approaches to independent living that complement transition to employment.

That the relationship between the long-established state and federal vocational rehabilitation service system and the more recently established ILC service system has not always been a cordial one is widely acknowledged. In the years since the first ILCs were established in 1972, differences in philosophy and approach to service delivery have strained working relationships between the ILCs and vocational rehabilitation agencies. The differences between the traditional rehabilitation approach and the independent living philosophy came to surface with the 1992 Amendments to the Rehabilitation Act. Shreve (1994) cited resistance from representatives of state vocational rehabilitation agencies to change mandated by the 1992 amendments. Michaels (1994), likewise, cited problems in some states related to cooperation between some states' vocational rehabilitation agencies and SILCs in formulating statewide independent living plans mandated as one condition for allocation of Federal Title VII funds to each state.

Notwithstanding differences in philosophy and approach between these two components of the disability service system—independent living and vocational rehabilitation—the important role that employment plays in attainment of independence by most people with disabilities is clear. This was emphasized by the results of the 1986 national survey of disabled Americans conducted by Louis Harris and Associates, which had as one of its conclusions, "Not working is perhaps the truest definition of what it means to be disabled: two thirds of all disabled Americans between the ages of 16 and 64 are not working" (p. 4). Unfortunately, the 1994 national poll yielded similar results, indicating that two thirds of Americans with disabilities are unemployed (Louis Harris and Associates, 1994). Furthermore, the proportion of Americans with disabilities who were unemployed but who would prefer to work increased from 66% in 1986 to 79% in 1994 (Louis Harris and Associates, 1994). The impact that not working has on the lives of people with disabilities is perhaps best reflected in the finding that 6 in 10 adults with disabilities live in households with earnings of $25,000 or less, compared with less than 4 in 10 non-disabled adults; this gap widened to 22% in 1994 from 16% in 1986 (Louis Harris and Associates, 1994). Clearly, opportunities for work have significant impact on the quality of lives of people with disabilities, and efforts to enhance vocational options—including those involving more effective collaboration between ILCs and vocational rehabilitation agencies in addressing the vocational and related support needs of people with disabilities—should be given the highest priority.

Independent Living Program Evaluation

Independent living programs were developed in response to community needs, and therefore are highly variable in their characteristics. Although sharing a common purpose, they vary greatly in structure, staffing, budget, and service delivery style. This variability has made program evaluation extremely challenging.

Early efforts to develop independent living program evaluation protocols focused primarily on evaluation of program operations and the amount of benefits clients received from the programs' services (Clowers et al., 1979; DeJong & Hughes, 1982: Muzzio, 1980; Muzzio et al., 1979; Schmidt, Collignon, Stoddard, & Barrett, 1978) before the construct of independence had even been discussed. Since 1983 this focus has expanded to include assessment of individual client gain in a more comprehensive sense, independent of specific services offered by a program.

Documentation of efforts to assess the success of independent living programs began in California (Counts, 1978; Hiehle & Robins, 1982; Muzzio, 1980; Muzzio et al., 1979; Schmidt et al., 1978) and continued in Washington (Taylor, 1979; Wilkerson, 1982). The Arkansas Research and Training Center also contributed to the refinement of evaluation methodology in independent living (Roessler, 1981), as mentioned earlier. Consumer satisfaction has been examined by Budde et al. (1983). Frieden and Nosek (1985) gave a comprehensive review of evaluation literature in independent living.

In 1985 the NCD developed a set of 11 standards for independent living centers based on national hearings and extensive input from the independent living field. Using these standards, Berkeley Planning Associates (1986) conducted a comprehensive assessment of program operations and client gain in 156 independent living programs nationally. Their findings clearly showed significant client benefit and satisfaction from participating in independent living program activities, but also reaffirmed the extensive variability in program characteristics, making analysis difficult.

In an effort to study this variability more closely, Nosek, Jones, and Zhu (1989) applied the original program criteria from Title VII of the 1978 Rehabilitation Act Amendments to their 1986 survey of 163 programs nationally. They found that only 51% of programs receiving funds met requirements for consumer involvement in direction, management, and service delivery. There was no relationship between compliance and amount of Title VII funds received. It was also shown that complying programs offered significantly more services and served significantly more people than noncomplying programs.

The NCD's standards have been the foundation for recent efforts to develop a set of indicators for independent living center status to determine eligibility for receipt of Title VII funds. Building on work of Lachat and Williams (1984), work of Budde et al. (1983), and input from an advisory committee, the Rehabilitation Services Administration is developing such indicators in hopes of building an operational standard to guide the expenditure of federal funds. Solidification of the independent living center concept is most noticeable in the requirement that 51% of the principal governing body must consist of people with disabilities, and programs must serve people with a variety of disability types.

Even though independent living center indicators have yet to be entered into federal regulation, research shows a marked tendency for programs to shift their structure even more toward consumer control (Nosek et al., 1989). Although some may see standardization as a step toward bureaucratization, it is clearly evident that the basic independent living philosophy of fostering consumer sovereignty, self-reliance, and political and economic rights continues to characterize this movement.

Recommendations

Research

By identifying psychological factors as key components of independent living, questions arise regarding influences that precipitate the development and expression of those factors. There is a need for further field research to obtain more information on the characteristics of survivors—the resilient ones, those who are independent, productive, and happy despite severe physical limitations and barriers in their environment. This might be followed by a study of the effect of the same limitations on persons of less personal resilience to determine the economic and life-quality consequences of societal barriers to independent living. Such studies should be conducted using representative samples of people with disabilities of varying types and degrees of severity, as well as nondisabled people in the general public as a basis for comparison.

Research should also be conducted to identify those conditions that encourage the development of the traits common to resilient persons. What is the effect of segregated educational programs, prolonged hospitalization, extensive contact with medical professionals, and limited peer interaction on the development of assertiveness, self-confidence, and self-sufficiency, three critical personality traits found to be common among highly independent people with disabilities? What role does the family play in this developmental process? What are the long-term effects of an overprotective childhood environment? What techniques used by family, teachers, and medical professionals are effective in offering children with severe disabilities the opportunity to be in situations that foster the development of resilient personality traits? To what extent can psychological independence be trained in an educational setting? Information regarding these questions would likely generate productive changes in early childhood and public school programs.

Health status and health maintenance practices are critical factors in the individual's ability to live independently. Although it has been observed that better health tends to correlate with high independence levels, much more information is needed to search for causal relationships. It could be hypothesized that good health and health maintenance practices are prerequisites for independence. A major study is called for regarding the amount and nature of health maintenance education for people with disabilities, with background information gathered on the cost of preventable disability-related medical problems to individuals and society.

The scientific study of independence and independent living should be encouraged on the national level, with substantial funding available and with special incentives for investigators with disabilities. There should be ongoing scientific efforts to gather and analyze data on the independent living needs of people with disabilities, to evaluate methods for meeting those needs, to provide technical assistance to providers of independent living support services and those who wish to initiate such services, and to explore and demonstrate innovative methods, including the use of technology, for delivering independent living services and living independently for people with all types of disabilities. A special fund should be established to support research and development of technology to assist people with disabilities where market conditions otherwise make such research and development economically unfeasible to the developer or unduly expensive to the consumer with a disability. In addition, this fund should be used to establish a clearinghouse where information about such technology can be readily obtained by people with disabilities.

Instruction in independent living should be an integral part of all public education. Programs should be developed to train and certify specialists in independent living in postsecondary educational programs. These specialists should play a significant role in the development of educational policies and curricula, especially those designed to promote the independence of people with disabilities. Public schools and all postsecondary programs with a disability focus should be required to offer relevant instruction in independent living.

Services

In its 1986 report to Congress, titled *Toward Independence,* the NCD made the following recommendations:

1. Congress should require the agency in each state designated to administer Title VII, Part A of the Rehabilitation Act to allocate no less than 50% of available funds to purchase services from independent living centers that

meet the standards approved by the National Council on Disability. No more than 10% of available funds should be used for administrative purposes. The remaining funds should be used at the discretion of the administering agency in any way that assists people with severe disabilities to achieve independence and productivity in their communities.

2. Congress should provide core funding under Title VII, Part B of the Rehabilitation Act, for independent living centers that meet the standards approved by the National Council on Disability. Such centers should be allowed to apply and compete for this funding on an equal basis with state vocational rehabilitation agencies.

3. Congress should require the Health Care Financing Administration to study the institutional bias within its programs for people with disabilities and to develop appropriate measures for eliminating such biases. The criteria should be developed in consultation with the [NCD] and be reported in hearings before Congress within one year from date of enactment of this requirement. The evaluation criteria should include a focus on the following topics:

    A. Comprehensive personal assistant services, including long-term, short-term (respite), and emergency attendants, readers, interpreters, and advocates for . . . [people with mental retardation].

    B. Case management assistance for independent living, including transition to services from the hospital to the home, institution to community, and from parents' home to independence in the community; and assistance in equipment selection and maintenance, and in locating sources for other independent living support services.

    C. Family support and consumer education services, including financial and personal counseling and training in self-directed and family-provided home care, including the use of equipment and medication, and independent living skills training.

    D. Habilitative and rehabilitative training, including prevocational services.

    E. Comprehensive medical insurance for people with disabilities who are unable to obtain adequate insurance through their employers or who are ineligible for other federal medical benefits.

4. Congress should amend the Internal Revenue Code to establish a tax credit for taxpayers with disabilities who incur unreimbursed expenses directly related to independent living, employment, and efforts to secure employment, including personal assistant services, special transportation, assistive devices, and other support services. (pp. G-42–G-48)

Conclusion

Over a decade ago, Justin Dart, Jr. (personal communication, 1985), decreed a manifesto for the movement for independent living that provides guidance for today and the future:

Persons with disabilities must create a tidal wave of irresistibly rational and positive advocacy that will inflame the moral passion of the world. They must firmly establish in the consciousness of the culture the proposition that all human beings . . . [regardless of disability] acting individually in their daily lives, and collectively through the families, communities, public and private organizations, and nations which they constitute, are absolutely responsible to prevent disability, and to create a social and physical environment in which the independence, prosperity, and equality of every person will be a natural result of the process of culture.

References

Adler, A. (1930). Individual psychology. In C. Murchison (Ed.), *Psychologies of 1930*. Worcester, MA: Clark University Press.

Alexander, J. L., & Fuhrer, M. J. (1984). Functional assessment of individuals with physical impairments. In A. S. Halpern & M. J. Fuhrer (Eds.), *Functional assessment in rehabilitation* (pp. 45-59). Baltimore: Brookes.

Americans with Disabilities Act of 1990, 42 U.S.C. § 12101 *et seq.*

Avorn, J., & Langer, E. J. (1982). Induced disability in nursing home patients: A controlled trial. *Journal of the American Geriatric Society, 30,* 397-400.

Bandura, A. (1982). Self-efficacy mechanism in human agency. *American Psychologist, 37,* 122-147.

Bandura, A. (1989). Human agency in social cognitive theory. *American Psychologist, 44*(9),1175-1184.

Baron, R., & Rodin, J. (1978). The urban environment. In A. Baum, J. E. Singer, & S. Valins (Eds.), *The urban environment: Vol. 1. Advances in experimental psychology.* (pp. 145-192). Hillsdale, NJ: Erlbaum.

Bartels, E. C. (1978). IL in Massachusetts. *American Rehabilitation, 3*(6), 32-33.

Beller, E. K. (1955). Dependence and independence in young children. *Journal of Genetic Psychology, 87,* 25-35.

Beller, E. K. (1957). Dependence and autonomous achievement striving related to orality and anality in early childhood. *Child Development, 55,* 287-315.

Berkeley Planning Associates. (1986). *Comprehensive evaluation of the Title VII, Part B Centers for Independent Living Program.* Berkeley, CA: Author.

Booth, T. (1986). Institutional regimes and induced dependency in homes for the aged. *The Gerontologist, 26,* 418-423.

Brown, B. M. (1978). Second generation: West coast. *American Rehabilitation, 3*(6), 23-30.

Brown, M., Gordon, W. A., & Diller, M. (1983). Functional assessment and outcome measurement: An integrative review. In E. L. Pan, T. Backer, & C. L. Vash (Eds.), *Annual review of rehabilitation* (Vol. 3, pp. 93-120). New York: Springer.

Budde, J. F., Petty, C. R., & Nelson, C. F. (1983). *Independent living center program evaluation* (draft). Lawrence: University of Kansas, Research and Training Center on Independent Living.

Bureau of the Census. (1993). *Census '90: 1990 census of population: Social and economic characteristics: Texas.* Washington, DC: U.S. Department of Commerce.

Cattell, R. B. (1965). *The scientific analysis of personality.* Chicago: Aldine.

Cattell, R. B., Eber, H. W., & Tatsuoka, M. M. (1970). *Handbook for the Sixteen Personality Factor Questionnaire (16PF).* Champaign, IL: Institute for Personality and Ability Testing.

Chanpong, G. (1996). *Centers for independent living: 1994 national survey summary.* Houston: ILRU.

Clark, W., & Rice, D. (1980). *Implementation of independent living programs in rehabilitation.* Fayetteville: Arkansas Rehabilitation Research and Training Center, University of Arkansas.

Clowers, M., Haley, D., Unti, W., & Feiss, C. (1979). *Independent living project: Final report.* Seattle: Division of Vocational Rehabilitation and University of Washington.

Cole, J., Sperry, J., Board, M., & Frieden, L. (1979). *New options training manual.* Houston: Institute for Rehabilitation and Research.

Counts, R. (Ed.). (1978). *Independent living rehabilitation for severely handicapped people: A preliminary appraisal.* Washington, DC: Urban Institute.

DeJong, G. (1979a). Independent living: From social movement to analytic paradigm. *Archives of Physical Medicine and Rehabilitation, 60,* 435–446.

DeJong, G. (1979b). *The movement for independent living: Origins, ideology, and implications for disability research* (Occasional Paper No. 2). East Lansing: University Center for International Rehabilitation, Michigan State University.

DeJong, G. (1979c). *Report of the national conference on independent living service regulations per P.S. 95–602.* Boston: Tufts University, Medical Rehabilitation Research and Training Center.

DeJong, G. (1981). *Environmental accessibility and independent living outcomes: Directions for disability policy and research.* East Lansing: University Center for International Rehabilitation, Michigan State University.

DeJong, G., Branch, L. G., & Corcoran, P. J. (1984). Independent living outcomes in spinal cord injury: Multi-variate analyses. *Archives of Physical Medicine and Rehabilitation, 65,* 66–73.

DeJong, G., & Hughes, J. (1982). Independent living: Methodology for measuring long-term outcomes. *Archives of Physical Medicine and Rehabilitation, 63,* 68–73.

DeJong, G., & Lifchez, R. (1983). Physical disability and public policy. *Scientific American, 548*(6), 40–49.

DeJong, G., & Wenker, T. (1979). Attendant care as a prototype independent living service. *Archives of Physical Medicine and Rehabilitation, 60,* 477–482.

Driscoll, J. V., Marquis, B., Corcoran, P. J., & Fay, F. A. (1978). Second generation: New England. *American Rehabilitation, 3*(6), 17–21.

Edgerton, R. B. (1967). *The cloak of competence: Stigma in the lives of the mentally retarded.* Berkeley: University of California Press.

Erikson, E. (1965). *Childhood and society.* New York: Columbia University Press.

Fay, F. (1977). *The BCIL report.* Boston: Tufts University, Regional Medical Rehabilitation Research and Training Center.

Flanagan, J. C. (1978). A research approach to improving our quality of life. *American Psychologist, 33,* 138–147.

Fordyce, W. E. (1953). *Application of a scale of dependency to concepts of self, ideal self, mother, and father.* Unpublished doctoral dissertation, University of Washington, Seattle.

Frieden, L. (1978). IL: Movement and programs. *American Rehabilitation, 3*(6), 6–9.

Frieden, L., & Frieden, J. (1981). Independent living in Sweden and the Netherlands. *Mainstream, 7*(1), 6–9.

Frieden, L., & Nosek, M. (1985). *The efficacy of the independent living program model based on descriptive and evaluative studies.* Washington, DC: National Rehabilitation Information Center.

Frieden, L., Richards, L., Cole, J., & Bailey, D. (1979). *ILRU sourcebook: A technical assistance manual on independent living.* Houston: Institute for Rehabilitation and Research.

Giordano, G., & D'Alonzo, B. J. (1994). The link between transition and independent living. *American Rehabilitation, 20*(1), 2–6.

Gliedman, J., & Roth, W. (1980). *The unexpected minority: Handicapped children in America.* New York: Harcourt Brace Jovanovich.

Granger, C. V., Albrecht, G. L., & Hamilton, B. B. (1979). Outcome of comprehensive medical rehabilitation measurement by PULSES profile and Barthel index. *Archives of Physical Medicine and Rehabilitation, 60,* 145–154.

Haworth, L. (1986). *Autonomy: An essay in philosophical psychology and ethics.* New Haven, CT: Yale University Press.

Heathers, G. (1955). Acquiring dependence and independence in nursery-school play. *Journal of Genetic Psychology, 87,* 177–191.

Heumann, J. (1977). Independent living programs. In S. Stoddard Pflueger (Ed.), *Independent living: Emerging issues in rehabilitation* (pp. 60–62). Washington, DC: Institute for Research Utilization.

Heumann, J. E. (1994). A message from the assistant secretary. *Independent Living, 6*(2), 2.

Hiehle, G., & Robins, B. (1982). *The California independent living center: Programs for people.* Sacramento, CA: Department of Rehabilitation.

Hiroto, D. S. (1974). Locus of control and learned helplessness. *Journal of Experimental Psychology, 102,* 187–193.

Hung, Y. (1978). Internal–external locus of control in physically handicapped students. *Bulletin of Educational Psychology, 11,* 113–122.

Independent Living Research Utilization. (1990). *ILRU directory of independent living programs.* Houston: Author.

Individuals with Disabilities Education Act of 1990, 20 U.S.C. § 1400 *et seq.*

Institute for Educational Leadership. (1984). *Challenges of emerging leadership* (Report to the Charles Stewart Mott Foundation). Washington, DC: Author.

Institute on Rehabilitation Issues. (1980). *Implementation of independent living programs in rehabilitation: Report from the study group.* Seventh Institute on Rehabilitation Issues. Hot Springs: Arkansas Rehabilitation Research and Training Center.

Jeffers, J. S. (1978). The Illinois approach. *American Rehabilitation, 3*(6), 16–33.

Jones, B., & Summerville, J. (1983). Avenues and steps to do-it-yourself independence for the physically disabled. *Journal of Rehabilitation, 49*(4), 30–35.

Kiernat, J. M. (1987). Promoting independence and autonomy through environmental approaches. *Topics in Geriatric Rehabilitation, 3*(1),1–6.

Lachat, M. A., & Williams, M. (1984). *The evaluation system for independent living.* East Kingston, NH: Center for Resource Management.

Langer, E. J., & Rodin, J. (1976). The effects of choice and enhanced personal responsibility for the aged: A field experiment in an institutional setting. *Journal of Personality and Social Psychology, 34,* 191–198.

Lefcourt, H. M. (1976). *Locus of control: Current trends in theory and research.* New York: Wiley.

Lobel, T. E. (1982). Personality variables and cognitive inconsistency. *Personality and Individual Differences, 2,* 333–334.

Louis Harris and Associates, Inc. (1986). *The ICD Survey of Disabled Americans: Bringing disabled Americans into the mainstream.* New York: Author.

Louis Harris and Associates, Inc. (1994). *N.O.D./Harris Survey of Americans with Disabilities.* Washington, DC: National Organization on Disability.

Lowry, L. (1989). Independence and dependence in aging: A new balance. *Journal of Gerontological Social Work, 13,* 133–146.

Maier, S. F., & Seligman, M. P. (1976). Learned helplessness: Theory and evidence. *Journal of Experimental Psychology, 105,* 3–46.

Massachusetts Rehabilitation Commission. (n.d.). *Independent living client report and functional gain inventory.* Boston: Author.

McNeil, J. M. (1993). *Americans with disabilities: 1991–92, current population reports, P70-33.* Washington, DC: Bureau of the Census.

Meenan, R. F., Gertman, P. M., & Mason, J. H. (1980). Measuring health status in arthritis: The arthritis impact measurement scales. *Arthritis and Rheumatism, 23,* 146–153.

Michaels, R. E. (1994). Title VII: A major step forward. *Independent Living, 6*(2), 8–10.

Mussen, P. H., Conger, J. J., & Kagan, J. (1969). *Child development and personality.* New York: Harper and Row.

Muzzio, T. (1980). *Independent living programs and evaluation, basic principles for developing a useful system: Issues in independent living.* Houston: Independent Living Research Utilization.

Muzzio, T. (1981). Program evaluation for independent living programs. In T. Mulligan (Ed.), *Implementing independent living center. Conference proceedings.* Hot Springs, AR: Region VI Rehabilitation Continuing Education Program.

Muzzio, T., LaRocca, J., Koshel, J., Durman, E., Chapman, B., & Gutowski, M. (1979). *Final report: Planning for independent living rehabilitation: Lessons from the Section 130 demonstrations.* Washington, DC: Urban Institute.

National Council on Disability. (1983). *National policy for persons with disabilities.* Washington, DC: Author.

National Council on Disability. (1986). *Toward independence: 1986 report to Congress.* Washington, DC: Author.

National Council on Disability. (1993). *Meeting the unique needs of minorities with disabilities: A report to the President and the Congress.* Washington, DC: Author.

Nosek, M. A. (1984). *Relationships among measures of social independence, psychological independence, and functional abilities in adults with severe orthopedic impairments.* Unpublished doctoral dissertation, University of Texas at Austin.

Nosek, M. A. (1987). Outcome analysis in independent living. In M. J. Fuhrer (Ed.), *Rehabilitation outcomes: Analysis and measurement* (pp. 71-83). Baltimore: Brookes.

Nosek, M. A., & Fuhrer, M. (1991). The measure of independence: A study of three profiles. *Archives of Physical Medicine and Rehabilitation, 71*(10), 797.

Nosek, M. A., Jones, S. D., & Zhu, Y. (1989). Levels of compliance with federal requirements in independent living centers. *Journal of Rehabilitation, 55,* 31-37.

Nosek, M. A., Narita, Y., Dart, Y., & Dart, J. (1982). *A philosophical foundation for the independent living and disability rights movement* (Occasional Paper No. 1). Houston: Institute for Rehabilitation and Research.

Nosek, M., Parker, R., & Larsen, S. (1987). Psychosocial independence and functional abilities: Their relationship in adults with severe musculoskeletal impairments. *Archives of Physical Medicine and Rehabilitation, 68,* 840-845.

Nosek, M. A., Zhu, Y., & Howland, C. A. (1992). The evolution of independent living programs. *Rehabilitation Counseling Bulletin, 35,* 174-189.

Perlmuter, L. C., Monty, R. A., & Chan, F. (1986). Choice, control, and cognitive functioning. In M. M. Baltes & P. B. Baltes (Eds.), *The psychology of control and aging* (pp. 99-118). Hillsdale, NJ: Erlbaum.

Pfleuger, S. S. (1977). *Independent living: Emerging issues in rehabilitation.* Washington, DC: Institute for Research Utilization.

Phares, E. J. (1976). *Locus of control in personality.* Morristown, NJ: General Learning Press.

Rehabilitation Act of 1973, 29 U.S.C. § 791 *et seq.*

Rehabilitation Act Amendments of 1978, P.L. 95-602, 92 Stat. 2955 (codified as amended in scattered sections of 29 U.S.C.).

Rehabilitation Act Amendments of 1992, P.L. 102-569, 106 Stat. 4344 (codified as amended at 29 U.S.C. 791 *et seq.*).

Rehabilitation Services Administration. (1988). *Transmittal of report: Caseload statistics, state vocational rehabilitation agencies, fiscal year 1987* (RSA-IM-88-22). Washington, DC: U.S. Department of Education, Office of Special Education and Rehabilitative Services.

Rice, B. D., Roessler, R. T., Greenwood, R., & Frieden, L. (1983). *Independent living rehabilitation program development, management and evaluation.* Fayetteville: Arkansas Rehabilitation Research and Training Center, University of Arkansas, Arkansas Rehabilitation Services, Institute for Rehabilitation and Research.

Richards, L. (1995). Key findings from the 704 reports of 1995. *ILRU Insights, 13*(4), 4.

Roberts, E. V. (1977). Foreword. In S. Stoddard Pfleuger (Ed.), *Independent living: Emerging issues in rehabilitation* (pp. u–tv). Washington, DC: Institute for Research Utilization.

Rock, P. J. (1988). Independence: What it means to six disabled people living in the community. *Disability, Handicap & Society, 3*(1), 27-35.

Roessler, R. T. (1981). *Strategies for evaluating independent living programs.* Fayetteville: Arkansas Rehabilitation Research and Training Center, University of Arkansas, Arkansas Rehabilitation Services, Institute for Rehabilitation and Research.

Roessler, R. T., & Rubin, S. (1980). *Goal setting: Guidelines for diagnosis and rehabilitation program development.* Fayetteville: Arkansas Rehabilitation Research and Training Center, University of Arkansas.

Rotter, J. B. (1954). *Social learning and clinical psychology.* Englewood Cliffs, NJ: Prentice-Hall.

Salkind, N. J., Beckwith, R. M., Nelson, C. F., & McGregor, P. A. (1982). *A summary of instruments that assess independence* (Report No. 1). Lawrence: Research and Training Center on Independent Living, University of Kansas.

Schmidt, B., Collignon, F., Stoddard, S., & Barrett, L. (1978). *In search of standards for independent living.* Berkeley, CA: Berkeley Planning Associates.

Schulz, R. (1976). Effects of control and predictability on the physical and psychological well-being of the institutionalized aged. *Journal of Personality and Social Psychology, 33,* 563–573.

Seligman, M. P. (1975). *Helplessness.* San Francisco: Freeman.

Shreve, M. (1994). The greater vision: An advocate's reflections on the Rehabilitation Act Amendments of 1992. *American Rehabilitation, 20*(1), 8–13.

Sigelman, C. K., Vengroff, L. P., & Spanhel, C. L. (1979). Disability and the concept of life functions. *Rehabilitation Counseling Bulletin, 23*(2), 103–113.

Smith, Q. W., Frieden, L., & Richards, L. (1995). Independent living. In *Encyclopedia of Disability and Rehabilitation.* New York: MacMillan Reference.

Stendler, C. B. (1954). Possible causes of overdependency in young children. *Child Development, 25*(2), 125–146.

Stock, D. D., & Cole, J. (1977). *Cooperative living.* Houston: Institute for Rehabilitation and Research.

Stoddard, S., Katsuranis, F., Toms, L., & Finnegan, D. (1980). *Evaluation report on the state's independent living centers funded by AB 204: Final report.* Berkeley, CA: Berkeley Planning Associates.

Taylor, C. (Ed.). (1979). *Independent living rehabilitation project: Services, assessment, research, program planning. Final report.* Seattle: University of Washington Department of Rehabilitation Medicine.

Troutt, B. (1980). Independence and ego identity reflected in minority students' utilization of the support services in the academic special program. *Dissertation Abstracts International, 41*(5–A), 2029.

Turner, K. D., & Szymanski, E. M. (1990). Work adjustment of people with congenital disabilities: A longitudinal perspective from birth to adulthood. *Journal of Rehabilitation, 56*(3), 19–24.

University of Washington. (1982). *Independent living program evaluation data package.* Seattle: Author.

Urban Institute. (1975). *Report of the comprehensive needs study.* Washington, DC: U.S. Department of Health, Education, and Welfare, Rehabilitation Services Administration.

Vocational Rehabilitation Act of 1918, 29 U.S.C. § 31 *et seq.*

Vocational Rehabilitation Act Amendments of 1956, P.L. 84-937, 70 Stat. 956, ch. 903 (codified as amended at 29 U.S.C. § 31 *et seq.*).

Weisz, J. R. (1979). Perceived control and learned helplessness among mentally retarded and non-retarded children: A developmental analysis. *Developmental Psychology, 15,* 311-319.

White, C. B., & Janson, P. (1986). Helplessness in institutional settings: Adaptation or iatrogenic disease? In M. M. Baltes & P. B. Baltes (Eds.), *The psychology of control and aging* (pp. 297-313). Hillsdale, NJ: Erlbaum.

Wilkerson, D. (1982). *A measure of independence: Perspectives on evaluation in independent living.* Unpublished manuscript, University of Washington, Seattle.

Wilkerson, D. L., Weinhouse, S., & Jamero, P. M. (1982). *Independent living center evaluation: Washington state data system and data from the first year of Title VII.* Seattle: Independent Living Evaluation Project, University of Washington.

Zukas, H. (1975). *CIL history: Report of the state of the art conference Center for Independent Living* (PSA Grant 45-p 45484/9-01). Berkeley, CA: Center for Independent Living.

Chapter 5

School-to-Adult Life Transition and Supported Employment

Cheryl Hanley-Maxwell, Edna Mora Szymanski,
and Laura Owens-Johnson

ransition and supported employment are separate but interrelated topics that are important to rehabilitation counseling practice. Rehabilitation counselors who serve children, adolescents, and young adults must understand the process of transition from school to adult life (Daniels, 1987; Hanley-Maxwell & Collet-Klingenberg, 1995; Szymanski, Hanley-Maxwell, & Asselin, 1992; Turner & Szymanski, 1990). Rehabilitation counselors who work with persons with severe disabilities of any age must understand supported employment and related approaches to rehabilitative service delivery (Hanley-Maxwell & Bordieri, 1989; Szymanski & Parker, 1989; Szymanski, Shafer, Danek, & Schiro-Geist, 1990).

Although they are separate but related topics, supported employment and school-to-adult life transition have been intertwined in documents including federal initiatives from the Office of Special Education and Rehabilitation Services (Will, 1984a, 1984b) and the Institute on Rehabilitation Issues documents (Eleventh Institute on Rehabilitation Issues, 1984; Twelfth Institute on Rehabilitation Issues, 1985), and from federal priorities for preservice training in rehabilitation counseling (*Federal Register*, 1988). The interrelationship of topics has caused confusion, which necessitates clarification in terms. Therefore, the major sections of this chapter are (a) terminology, (b) transition, and (c) supported employment.

Terminology

School-to-adult life transition, frequently referred to simply as transition, is a confusing *life stage* for all students, especially students with disabilities (Daniels, 1987; Pallas, 1993). Supported employment is a rehabilitation *service option* that has been accompanied by rapidly changing and sometimes confusing terminology (Szymanski, Buckley, Parent, Parker, & Westbrook, 1988; Wehman, 1995).

Various definitions of school-to-adult life transition have been proposed over the years. The definition introduced in the Transition Initiative of the Office of Special Education and Rehabilitative Services (OSERS) described transition as "an outcome-oriented process encompassing a broad array of services and experiences that lead to employment" (Will, 1984a, p. 2). Since that time, the concept of transition has become a national priority for all students through the enactment of America 2000 (U.S. Department of Education, 1991) and has expanded in the focus from work to whole life (Halpern, 1993).

Supported employment has been defined as:

> competitive work in integrated work settings—(a) for individuals with severe handicaps for whom competitive employment has not traditionally occurred, or (b) for individuals for whom competitive employment has been interrupted or intermittent as a result of a severe disability, and who, because of their handicap, need on-going support services to perform such work. [This] term includes transitional employment for individuals with chronic mental illness. (Rehabilitation Act Amendments, 1986)

The 1992 amendments to the Rehabilitation Act (Public Law [P.L.] 102-569) revise the parameters of supported employment and place more focus on consumer choice and self-determination (Wehman & Kregel, 1994).

The inclusion of the term "transitional employment" in the 1986 definition of supported employment caused terminology confusion. First, already existing confusion between supported employment and school-to-adult life transition was compounded. Second, a time-limited, job site–centered intervention strategy for clients with varying disabilities had to be renamed to avoid confusion (Szymanski & Parker, 1988).

Supported employment is a rehabilitation service and employment option for persons with severe disabilities who require ongoing support to obtain and maintain employment (Rusch & Hughes, 1989). School-to-adult life transition is a process or life stage experienced by students with and without disabilities as they complete their education. For students with disabilities, school-to-adult life transition frequently is aided by special education and/or rehabilitation services (Daniels, 1987; Szymanski & Danek, 1985; Szymanski & King, 1989), which may or may not include supported employment. In addition to supported employment, school-to-adult life transition encompasses a broad array of possible services and outcomes, including college training, independent living, and on-the-job training (Hanley-Maxwell & Collet-Klingenberg, 1995; Szymanski, Hershenson, & Power, 1988), and is thus not synonymous with supported employment. Although supported employment can be a transition service or outcome option (Will, 1984a), it can also be used for persons with severe disabilities who are not involved in school-to-adult life transition but who, nonetheless, require time-enduring support services in order to obtain and maintain community employment (Rusch, 1990).

Transition

Transition is a multifaceted topic. On the one hand, transition is part of the lifelong process of career development (Szymanski, 1994, in press), and thus is informed by related literature (see Szymanski & Hershenson, Chapter 10, this text). On the other hand, transition is a political event, linking education to the economy (Apple & Zenk, 1996) and legislated in special education and rehabilitation statutes (see Jenkins, Patterson, & Szymanski, Chapter 1, this text). To prepare rehabilitation counselors to serve consumers in transition, we address the following topics: (a) the history of transition services, (b) recent transition legislation, (c) the career development context of transition, (d) transition outcomes, (e) phases of transition, and (f) rehabilitation counselor roles in transition.

History of Transition Services

Although the term *transition* was not widely applied to the movement from school into work until the 1980s, the concept is not new. In fact, interest in transition seems to be cyclical (Szymanski, 1994). Halpern (1992) termed this tendency to recycle transition interest, often with new terminology, as "new wine in old bottles" (p. 202). The historical context of transition services can inform current policy decisions. For this reason, we present a brief history of the evolution and context of transition in special education and rehabilitation through discussion of (a) general history, (b) transition in rehabilitation and special education, (c) the work–study era, (d) career education, and (e) the OSERS transition initiative.

General History

Transition has remained the focus of legislation throughout much of this century (Smith & Rojewski, 1993). From the 1917 Smith–Hughes Act, which created the Federal Board of Vocational Education, to the School-to-Work Opportunities Act of 1994, politicians and educators have wrestled with the problems of preparing young people for employment. The field of vocational education has had a strong influence on this movement (Szymanski, Hanley-Maxwell, & Asselin, 1992). In fact, the

> conceptual linking of school and work was perhaps the most important legacy of the vocational movement. . . . By linking school and work, vocational education helped to institutionalize the idea that education could eliminate poverty, dead-end jobs, and worker alienation. But such conditions are not susceptible to purely educational correction; they exist because jobs requiring skills, offering high wages, and providing satisfying work are (and always have been) in short supply. (Kantor, 1994, p. xiv)

Further, "the assumption that we will find long-term answers to the dropout dilemma and to the realities of poverty and unemployment by keeping our attention within the schools is dangerously naive" (Apple & Zenk, 1996, p. 70). Nonetheless, despite periodic questions, the assumed linkage of school and work remains strong today and forms the basis for school reform efforts (Carnevale, 1995; Osterman, 1995) and transition.

Transition in Rehabilitation and Special Education

Rehabilitation counselors have long been involved in transition programs. State vocational rehabilitation (VR) programs and rehabilitation counselors have worked in cooperative vocational training programs with special education since the 1940s (DiMichael, 1950). In deafness rehabilitation, cooperative relationships between VR agencies and school programs have been traced back as far as the 1930s (Danek & McCrone, 1989). However, this history appears to have been lost in present practice for a variety of reasons related to policies and procedures.

Historically, transition policy and service delivery have been complicated by involvement of two different federal service delivery systems: vocational rehabilitation and special education. These systems differ in statutory definitions for disability eligibility standards, evaluative criteria, and staff qualifications. Thus, although there is much rhetoric about linkages between the systems, there are differences that make finding common ground difficult. For example, some students with physical disabilities may not receive special education services, although they may be eligible for vocational rehabilitation services from the state VR agency. Similarly, some students who receive special education services because of a mild disability (e.g., a mild learning disability, a mild speech impairment) may not qualify to receive VR services because their disability is not a handicap to employment (Szymanski, King, Parker, & Jenkins, 1989). Differences between special education and VR legislation, policy, and programs are summarized in Table 5.1.

The Work–Study Era

Early cooperative relationships between state VR agencies and school districts were facilitated by the VR funding formula. To receive their federal allocation, state VR agencies were required to secure a percentage of matching state dollars

Table 5.1

Differences Between Vocational Rehabilitation and Special Education

Category of Difference	Special Education	Vocational Rehabilitation
Eligibility and service provision	Disability and need for special education	Physical or mental impairment that results in a substantial impediment to employment
	Feasibility of employability as a result of services	
	Severe disability (if priority of services is in effect)	
	Free, appropriate public education	Financial need required for few services
Funding	Federal, state, and local; largest share local and state	78.7% federal; 21.3% state; nolocal funding
Evaluation	Compliance with law	Compliance with law
	Identification and service of all eligible children	Numbers rehabilitated; percentage classified severely disabled
	Service in the least restrictive environment	Cost-benefit in relation to dollars spent and client wages
Personnel	Usually certified or licensed in their discipline (e.g., certified teachers)	Often lacking in related preservice education or certification

Note. Adapted from "The State–Federal Rehabilitation Program: Overview and Interface with Special Education," by E. M. Szymanski, J. King, R. M. Parker, and W. M. Jenkins, 1989; *Exceptional Children, 56,* p. 76.

for VR services. Cooperative work–study programs, which flourished in public schools during the 1960s and early 1970s, provided a convenient source for these matching funds. VR agencies assigned rehabilitation counselors and provided funds for community work–study programs for students with disabilities, and schools designated teachers to provide associated instruction and related services. This arrangement enabled many state VR agencies to claim the salary of the assigned teacher as "in-kind" state matching funds. Thus, the cooperative work–study programs often were financially beneficial to the participating VR agencies (Szymanski & Danek, 1985; Szymanski, King, et al., 1989).

The number of cooperative work–study programs decreased dramatically between 1977 and 1980 (Bullis & Foss, 1983), apparently due to a combination of legislation and administrative action. The 1975 Education for All Handicapped Children Act (now referred to as the Individuals with Disabilities Education Act) made schools responsible for education, including vocational education, for students with disabilities through age 21 or graduation (Podemski, Price, Smith, & Marsh, 1984). The 1973 Rehabilitation Act required VR agencies to seek other service dollars (e.g., Medicaid) prior to funding rehabilitation services (Szymanski, King, et al., 1989). The combination of these two laws placed work–study programs in a precarious position, which was further complicated by two memos from the Rehabilitation Services Administration (RSA). The first memo, in 1978, ordered states to cease in-kind fund matching practices, such as those used in work–study programs. Although the order was rescinded by a second memo in 1979, there is little doubt that it had a negative impact on the number of work–study programs (Szymanski & Danek, 1985; Szymanski, King, et al., 1989).

Interestingly, during the same years that the number of work–study programs declined, the federal agencies charged with administering rehabilitation programs (i.e., RSA) and special education (i.e., Bureau of Education for the Handicapped [BEH]) issued two formal, joint memos calling for RSA and BEH to collaborate in transition planning. Finally, the creation of the U.S. Department of Education led to the housing together of RSA and BEH (the latter is now called Office of Special Education Programs [OSEP]) in the Office of Special Education and Rehabilitative Services (OSERS) (Szymanski, King, et al., 1989).

Career Education

At about the same time that the work–study movement began to decline, the career education movement came into being. Specifically, career education began in the 1970s and ended in 1982. Whereas the work–study movement was directly linked to employment, career education "was diffuse in its goals, oriented to both elementary and secondary education, available to students with and without disabilities, implemented in both regular and special education environments, and broadly structured as a general education movement" (Halpern, 1992, p. 205). Both work–study and career education can be seen as precursors of the next stage, the transition initiative.

The OSERS Transition Initiative

The 1984 OSERS transition initiative (Will, 1984a) occurred 2 years after the end of the career education legislation (Halpern, 1992). Unlike the career education movement, however, the transition initiative was concerned only with students with disabilities and their movement into employment.

The OSERS initiative operationalized transition in three paths, which were termed bridges. The first bridge, *transition without special services,* described the course of action taken by those individuals who did not need disability-specific services. The second bridge, *transition with time-limited services,* illustrated the path taken by those students who, with limited services from vocational rehabilitation or other disability-related agencies, could make the transition to work. The third bridge, *transition with ongoing services,* addressed the needs of those students with severe disabilities who needed ongoing services, such as supported employment (Will, 1984b), in order to remain employed (Will, 1984a).

Recent Transition Legislation

Although transition had been mentioned in earlier special education legislation, it was the 1990 Individuals with Disabilities Education Act (IDEA) that really brought it into focus for students with disabilities. Specifically, this legislation defined transition as

> a coordinated set of activities for a student, designed within an outcome-oriented process, which promotes movement from school to post-school activities, including post-secondary education, vocational training, integrated employment (including supported employment), continuing and adult education, adult services, independent living, or community participation. The coordinated set of activities shall be based on the individual student's needs, taking into account the student's preferences and interests. [IDEA, § 602(a)]

In addition, the 1990 amendments firmly placed transition planning in the Individualized Education Program (IEP), the planning document that guides a student's program. Specifically, the IEP is to include a statement of the needed transition services for a student with disabilities beginning no later than age 16 and annually thereafter (and when determined appropriate for the individual, beginning at age 14 or younger), including, when appropriate, a statement of the interagency responsibilities or linkages (or both) before the student leaves the school setting.

The amendments also provided for a safety net in the event that problems occurred in coordinating with other agencies. In the case where a participating agency, other than the educational agency, fails to provide agreed-upon services, the educational agency shall reconvene the IEP team to identify alternative strategies to meet the transition objectives [IDEA, § 602(a)(20)].

At the same time that the IDEA amendments were being implemented, interest in the linkage of school and work resulted in a major initiative—the School-to-Work Opportunities Act of 1994—to address the transition challenges faced by the general population. This act provides states with federal assistance to develop and implement a statewide school-to-work transition system. The goal for this system is to ensure students a seamless transition from secondary education into meaningful, high-quality employment and/or further education. Under this legislation, significant partnerships must be developed at the state, regional, and local levels to bring together educators, business–industry–labor, and community-based organizations to integrate academic and vocational technical education and to more closely align secondary and postsecondary curricula (Brustein & Mahler, 1994, p. 3). At the time of this revision, special education and rehabilitation leaders are working to assure that students with disabilities are included in the partnerships and programs established through this act (S. Hall, personal communication, November 1995).

The Career Development Context of Transition

As we noted earlier, transition is one aspect of career development, which is a life-long process that begins at birth and continues long after completion of school (Szymanski, 1994). The career development context of transition has been addressed in some depth by Szymanski, Turner, and Hershenson (1992), Rojewski (1994), and Szymanski (1994). In addition, career development is the topic of Chapter 10 by Szymanski and Hershenson in this text.

Briefly, career development involves the interaction of individual, contextual, mediating, environmental, and outcome factors throughout the life span (Szymanski, Hershenson, Enright, & Ettinger, 1996). It is a developmental and cognitive process (Lent & Hackett, 1994). Although there has been much discussion about the relative applicability of career development theories to people with disabilities (see, e.g., Conte, 1983; Curnow, 1989), the heterogeneous nature of the population of people with disabilities means that such theories are neither applicable nor nonapplicable (Szymanski, Hershenson, et al., 1996). Rather, disability poses a risk factor (Rojewski, 1994). Although the impact of disability is quite imprecise, there are a few points that can be made to guide rehabilitation counselors in transition planning:

1. Disability presents a risk factor for career development. The potency of this risk increases with severity of disability (Rojewski, 1994). Many other factors, including socioeconomic status, parental attitudes, and opportunity structures, also mediate the impact of disability on career development (Szymanski & Hanley-Maxwell, 1996).

2. Frequency of chores has been shown to be positively related to employment of people with congenital disabilities (Victor, McCarthy, & Palmer, 1986). Therefore, counselors and teachers should encourage chores at home and in school.

3. Interests are learned (Mitchell & Krumboltz, 1990). Limited experiences can accompany disabilities and thus limit the interpretability of interest inventories (Szymanski, 1994). Similarly, the presence or absence of similar role models (e.g., those of same race and gender, similar disability) can influence career development (Betz & Fitzgerald, 1995). Thus, it is important to examine previous experiences and consider providing enrichment opportunities to assist students in career planning.

4. Premature foreclosure on career goals is a major problem. In fact, counselors need to assist clients in exploring and evaluating a wide range of alternatives before they begin to solidify their career paths (Blustein, 1992). Thus, it is important to remember that "the transition component of the Individualized Educational Program (IEP) addresses a point in time on the career development con-

tinuum and should expand rather than restrict the range of occupational choices available to a student" (Szymanski, 1994, p. 404).

5. Culture is an important determinant of the appropriateness of career development, and therefore transition goals (Betz & Fitzgerald, 1995). Although independence is a common goal in majority U.S. cultures, interdependence, community membership, and family contributions are often goals in many other cultures.

Transition Outcomes

Past educational practices have not produced desirable outcomes for students with disabilities. Data from follow-up studies include disturbing results related to dropout rates, employment statistics, and community adjustment for former special education students.

Whereas dropout rates for students without disabilities were estimated to be between 12% (Benz & Halpern, 1987) and 16% (Edgar, 1988), dropout rates for students with disabilities were significantly greater. The highest dropout rates were reported for students with behavioral or emotional disturbances. Data from the National Longitudinal Transition Study (Wagner, Blackorby, Cameto, & Newman, 1993) revealed that as many as 48% of students with emotional disturbance dropped out of high school. This same database showed that nearly 30% of students with mild mental retardation and over 28% of students with learning disabilities also exited school by dropping out. Although other follow-up studies varied in the exact percentages of dropouts, all studies indicated that students with disabilities are at least twice as likely as their nondisabled counterparts to exit school through dropping out (Benz & Halpern, 1987; Edgar, 1987). Students who dropped out of school had dismal postschool outcomes. When considering dropouts with learning or behavioral disabilities, data indicated that only 39% were working or receiving any type of educational program (Edgar, 1987). Furthermore, students who drop out of high school special education programs participate less in postsecondary academic programs, independent living, and community life (Wagner et al., 1993).

Graduation from high school improves outcomes for special education students, but not significantly. Employment statistics reported by follow-up studies vary in their exact percentage of graduates who begin working immediately after graduation. However, postschool employment data of all studies consistently reflect poor outcomes for a large portion of former students with disabilities (Bruininks, Lewis, & Thurlow, 1989; Edgar, 1987; Hasazi, Gordon, & Rose, 1985; Kortering & Edgar, 1988; Mithaug, Horiuchi, & Fanning, 1985; Neel, Meadows, Levine, & Edgar, 1988; Scuccimarra & Speece, 1990; Sitlington & Frank, 1990; Wagner et al., 1993). Unemployment rates range from a low of 16% (Edgar, 1987) to a more typically higher percentage of 37% (Wagner et al., 1993) for graduates with learning disabilities. Graduates with mental retardation and emotional disturbance do not fare as well. Unemployment rates for these graduates are approximately 50% or greater (Edgar, 1987; Wagner et al., 1993). Graduates who did obtain employment do not earn enough money to sustain themselves. Only 18% of graduates with learning disabilities and 5% of graduates with mental retardation earn at least minimum wage (Edgar, 1987). Average annual wages range from a low of $8,274 for graduates with mild mental retardation to a high of $11,671 for graduates with learning disabilities (Wagner et al., 1993).

Postschool outcomes also indicate difficulties in other areas of life. Establishing social relationships and independent living appear to be difficult for many former students (Benz & Halpern, 1987; Chadsey-Rusch, DeStefano, O'Reilly, Gonzalez, & Collet-Klingenberg, 1992; Chesler, 1982; Fafard & Haubrich, 1981; Sitlington, Frank, & Carson, 1992; Wagner et al., 1993; Zigmond & Thornton, 1985). Wagner et al. (1993) found that independent living outcomes varied according to disability category: 34% for graduates with learning disabilities, 21% for graduates with emotional disturbance, and 15% for graduates with mild mental retardation. Furthermore, Wagner et al. (1993) found that while independent living rates increased for all groups the longer they were out of school, arrest rates and parenting rates also increased.

A variety of factors appear to contribute to these outcomes. These factors include method of school leaving, graduation versus dropping out (Fourqurean & LaCourt, 1990; Wagner et al., 1993); special education placement, type of disability, and percentage of time spent in regular classroom (Benz & Halpern, 1987; Edgar, 1987; Fourqurean & LaCourt, 1990; Wagner et al., 1993); and vocational experiences, training, and employment during high school (Hasazi et al., 1985; Mithaug et al., 1985; Wagner et al., 1993). Although recent research by Heal and Rusch (1995) and Sitlington and Frank (1990) cast doubts on the effect of vocational training on improved employment outcomes, all research has consistently supported the critical connection between high school *employment* and postschool employment (Fourqurean & LaCourt, 1990; Fourqurean, Meisgeier, Swank, & Williams, 1991; Hasazi et al., 1985; Scuccimarra & Speece, 1990; Sitlington & Frank, 1990).

Transition, as it has been implemented in the past, is clearly not effective. Effective transition requires renewed emphasis on interagency and interdisciplinary collaboration and cooperation (Szymanski, Hanley-Maxwell, & Parker, 1990) and a commitment to educational programs based on the demands of adult life in the areas of community, leisure–recreational, residential, and vocational skills. Although many professionals view the transition process as having definite, predetermined beginning and end points, transition preparation actually encompasses all of primary and secondary education (Turner & Szymanski, 1990). If students with disabilities are going to be successful in the transition process, and in remaining employed and living as independently as possible after graduation, the transition process must start prior to the beginning of formal education and extend beyond the first job placement.

To enable successful transition, all education and rehabilitation interventions must adhere to the criterion of ultimate functioning, which stipulates that interventions must be designed to prepare an individual "to function as productively and independently as possible in socially, vocationally, and domestically integrated adult community environments" (Brown et al., 1980, p. 6). To be effective in facilitating transition, rehabilitation counselors must understand the phases of transition and the role of the rehabilitation counselor in the transition process.

Phases of Transition

Transition involves three distinct phases requiring transdisciplinary cooperation: (a) school services, (b) transition planning, and (c) postsecondary services. The phases may vary in content and target according to the needs of the individual being served, but remain rather constant in their application.

School Services

Quality school services should be examined for the presence of many factors, which are related to the content and application of curricula (Hanley-Maxwell, 1986; Wehman, 1986). Curricula must be based on the skill demands of a maximally independent adult life. Content should reflect academic, social, vocational, and independent living areas, and should focus on the acquisition of core skills (i.e., survival skills), higher order skills (i.e., skills that enable adaptability and independence), and goal-specific skills (Hanley-Maxwell & Collet-Klingenberg, 1995). Curriculum development is a highly individualized task that is particular to both the student and the community. School personnel must continually assess and reassess available community options and analyze specific skill requirements critical to the student's success in those options.

Whether the immediate goal is employment or postsecondary education (e.g., college), curricula must be functional; that is, they must be based on those skills required for survival in a variety of target settings once the student leaves secondary school. Curricula also must be designed to promote generalization across different adult situations rather than to foster highly specific skill acquisition. Skills selected for inclusion in any curriculum must be examined for their value in multiple life settings and must be taught in a manner that will enhance the learner's ability to use these skills when and where they are needed (Hanley-Maxwell, 1986). Quality curricula can be recognized by instruction that is (a) developed as the result of ecological assessment, (b) integrated, (c) community based, and (d) based on sound teaching procedures.

Ecological Assessment. Current and potential future education, employment, residential, and community setting demands form the context for the assessment of skill assets and needs (Browder & King, 1987; Brown-Glover, 1992). Areas assessed include the individual's strengths and limitations in specific tasks, the individual's existing and potential support systems (Pancsofar, 1986), and the individual's and family's personal interests and goals.

Content for the assessment of individual strengths and limitations must be grounded in the identification of potential skill needs and includes task-specific analysis, analysis of social skills needed for survival in targeted settings (Rusch, Schutz, & Agran, 1982; Snell & Grigg, 1987), and process skills or "integrative" skills needed in various target situations (i.e., known and potential future work and living environments). Potential skill needs are identified through observations at the targeted sites; interviews with knowledgeable individuals, such as coworkers and supervisors (Rusch, Rusch, Menchetti, & Schutz, 1980); reviews of existing curricular materials in the targeted skill area; and selections from some of the commercially available products designed to measure life skills, such as the *Life Centered Career Education Competency Rating Scale* (Brolin, 1991), *Test for Everyday Living* (Halpern, Irvin, & Landman, 1979), the *Street Survival Skills Questionnaire* (Linkenhoker & McCarron, 1980), and the *National Independent Living Skills Screening Instrument* (Sands, Woolsey, & Dunlap, 1985). The selected skills form the foundation for assessment, instruction (Hanley-Maxwell, 1986), and consideration of possible adaptation and accommodation needs (Parker, Szymanski, & Hanley-Maxwell, 1989).

The actual assessment of the individual's strengths and limitations is used to determine programmatic needs (Parker et al., 1989). The core of the assessment process is the systematic examination of the individual's performance of essential skills; information about the person's learning history, future goals and aspirations, and likes and dislikes (Hanley-Maxwell & Bordieri, 1989) or interests; and the identification of adaptation needs (e.g., partial participation, materials adaptation, setting adaptation, task resequencing).

The assessment process also identifies potential facilitating and inhibiting relationships that may affect the success of adult outcomes. This portion of the assessment focuses on support systems (e.g., friends, family, and potential relationships in future jobs or residences) (Hanley-Maxwell & Bordieri, 1989) and self-efficacy of the individual. Available supports and potential support sources are matched to the individual's current and projected support needs and wishes, and needed self-efficacy skills are targeted for acquisition.

Integrated Instruction. Students with disabilities should receive their education in integrated school settings (Gartner & Lipsky, 1989; Wehman, 1986), that is, with students who do not have disabilities. Debates continue about how regular education teachers may accommodate students with the most severe disabilities in their classrooms, to what degree students with severe disabilities can be integrated into regular education settings, and how to best enhance the social integration of students with disabilities. Nonetheless, it is clear that students with disabilities must receive exposure to nonspecial, nonsheltered environments and that students without disabilities need regular, positive exposure to people with disabilities (Stainback, Stainback, & Bunch, 1989).

Community-Based Instruction. A second critical characteristic of effective instruction is the integration of school into the larger context of home, employment, and community. This integration takes the form of providing instruction in realistic settings and focusing on community survival skills, that is, skills necessary for effective functioning in a variety of community settings (e.g., restaurants, stores). Academics take on a different perspective when they are placed in the context of community use. For example, arithmetic is more meaningful when purchasing lunch in a popular fast food restaurant than when completing worksheets in the classroom. In community-based instruction, skill sequences (i.e., curricula) are altered, methods used for instruction and management are different, and the impact of skill competency on community survival is reevaluated.

People with severe disabilities often have difficulties applying skills learned in one situation to a new situation; that is, they often have problems generalizing learned behaviors across situations. Community-based instruction helps to eliminate many of these generalization problems (Stainback, Stainback, Nietupski, & Hamre-Nietupski, 1986). The natural variation and reality of community-based school experiences will enhance the probability that skills learned during the school years will provide a sound foundation for later successful functioning in community settings. Thus, it is not surprising that Hasazi et al. (1985) found that the best predictor of postschool employment was employment while in high school.

Teaching Procedures. Teaching methodologies also affect the long-term success of transition. Student independence can be enhanced by teaching that utilizes the naturally occurring cues and consequences characteristic of the community settings in which students will eventually be expected to function (Berg, Wacker, & Flynn, 1990; Renzaglia & Hutchins, 1988). Students who are taught with single-skill, single-situation methodologies and artificial cues and consequences may not be able to function on their own in community settings. Single-skill, single-situation (e.g., classroom vs. different community settings) methodologies can work against generalization. In addition, consistent use of artificial cues and consequences (e.g., verbal prompts from the teacher and gold stars) can make students dependent. Such dependencies can pose formidable obstacles in employment, because jobs rarely stay the same, and supervisors neither consistently use verbal prompts to stimulate work performance nor give gold stars to reinforce completion. Quality instruction, which is focused on increasing student independence, helps students to (a) identify potential consequences for their behavior, (b) identify and respond to natural reinforcers, and (c) use feedback (e.g., from coworkers or supervisors) to guide future behavior.

Using feedback to guide future behavior is part of the problem-solving process inherent in teaching social skills (Chadsey-Rusch, 1986). Problem solving is effectively taught in community-based sites by guiding students through the process and then gradually withdrawing that guidance. Problem solving includes teaching students to identify the problem, generate potential solutions, list potential resources needed, predict potential outcomes, select the "best" solution, and assess the success of that solution in obtaining the desired outcome (Chadsey-Rusch, 1986). It also includes teaching and reinforcing appropriate initiation, self- assertion, and self-correction. The success of these teaching procedures is enhanced when they are used in the context of a systematically planned transition process.

Transition Planning

Formal planning for transition should begin at least 3 to 5 years prior to graduation. Parents, guardians, and students with disabilities should be encouraged and provided with the skills to participate as equal members of the decision-making team (Wehman, 1986; Wehman, Moon, Everson, Wood, & Barcus, 1988). Other team members include representatives of multiple disciplines and service delivery systems, including special education teachers, vocational education teachers, rehabilitation counselors, adult service agency representatives (vocational and residential), mental health counselors or case managers, child welfare or court-appointed social workers, advocates or attorneys, and possibly employers or business community representatives (Everson & Moon, 1986; Hanley-Maxwell & Chadsey-Rusch, 1986).

The transition team is charged with developing specific, formalized plans necessary for the transition of the student from school to community living. Formalized plans are designed to increase the coordination of services and to delineate staff and agency responsibilities (Wehman, 1986; Wehman, Moon, et al., 1988). Transition plans should include (a) student goals and objectives (reflecting job, home, community skills); (b) specific services needed to accomplish those goals; and (c) referral to appropriate agencies, specific placements, and specific follow-up procedures and/or services.

As mandated by IDEA, students and parents are active and important members of the multidisciplinary team, not passive participants present merely to okay a plan of action decided in advance by school staff (Ford et al., 1989; Schnorr, Ford, Savern, Park-Lee, & Meyer, 1989). Home–school collaboration and active parent involvement have been discussed for many years in the special education literature. Strategies to enhance collaboration are provided in a number of sources (e.g., Ford et al., 1989; Wehman, Moon, et al., 1988). More recent trends in collaboration and particularly in the involvement and direction of the transition planning process by students and their families have included the use of quality-of-life planning strategies, such as McGill Action Planning System (Forest & Lusthaus, 1987), Lifestyles Planning Process (O'Brien & Lyle, 1987), Personal Futures Planning (O'Brien, 1987), the family-centered approach to early intervention (Dunst, Trivette, & Deal, 1988), and Choosing Options and Accommodations for Children or COACH (Giangreco, Cloninger, & Iverson, 1993). These processes are designed to ensure that planning takes a lifelong perspective and students and their families are provided with the vehicle to take charge of their own lives through a visioning foundation to the planning process.

Participation in planning requires the individual student to have the skills to identify needed resources, acquire identified resources, set goals, organize time and tasks, and prioritize tasks, or to receive assistance in accomplishing these tasks. Because the IEP plays a pivotal role in transition planning, students should be taught to take increasingly greater control over their lives (Michaels, 1994).

Participation in IEP development is an excellent forum for the practice of such skills as planning, self-advocacy, and responsibility. However, recent research questions the ability of 17- and 18-year-old students to make career choices that will continue after exiting school (Shapiro & Lentz, 1991). The results of this research suggest that any plans that students and their families make must be flexible enough to accommodate the real changes that will occur in the postschool environment and that students must learn to make choices, follow through with choices, and revise plans accordingly.

Postsecondary Services

The third phase of the transition process addresses the question: Transition to what? Answers to this question pervade all other transition issues. Although postsecondary services are discussed last in this chapter, in reality, the identification of potential postsecondary goals must be the first step in planning for transition from early education forward. The ultimate goal is to move students into meaningful, remunerative employment and maximally independent living arrangements. As such, school-to-adult life transition may include a broad array of possible services and outcomes, such as college training, independent living, on-the-job training, and supported employment (Szymanski, Hershenson, & Power, 1988).

Rehabilitation Counselor Roles in Transition

Because rehabilitation counselors are specialists in the vocational behavior of persons with disabilities (Hershenson, 1988), they are well suited as transition professionals (Wright, Emener, & Ashley, 1988). However, rehabilitation counseling was excluded from the list of related services in the Education for All Handicapped Children Act, passed in 1975. This omission resulted in difficulty for some school districts that wished to employ rehabilitation counselors (Szymanski & Danek, 1985).

Fortunately, this situation was partially resolved in 1986 when the House of Representatives Report 99-860, accompanying passage of the Individuals with Disabilities Education Act of 1990, specifically indicated that rehabilitation counseling could be considered a related service in the special education of students with disabilities. Subsequently, the Individuals with Disabilities Education Act of 1990 (P.L. 101-476) (also known as the Education of the Handicapped Act Amendments of 1990) specified rehabilitation counseling, in statute, as a related service. House Report 101-544 (1990), which was cited in House Report 101-787 at the final passage of the act, described the importance of rehabilitation counseling in special education:

> Rehabilitation counseling is a counseling profession with a specific focus on disability, including career development and employment preparation of people with disabilities. As a result, rehabilitation counseling is an important related service in special education as well as an important transition service in preparing students

with disabilities for employment or postsecondary education. It is the intent of the committee that rehabilitation counseling be considered a related service and be provided to all students with disabilities for whom this service is necessary for the achievement of the individualized education program. It is also the intent of the Committee to have rehabilitation counseling considered as an allowable transition service. School rehabilitation counseling is an important component of transition services because none of the other professionals involved in special education have clear responsibility for transition planning and preparation. Furthermore the rehabilitation counseling discipline embodies the wide range of knowledge needed for successful school to work transition, i.e., vocational implications of disability, career development, career counseling for individuals with disabilities, job placement, and job modification. Therefore, rehabilitation counselors are professionally prepared to provide the appropriate counseling services as well as to coordinate the services of the special education disciplines, adult service providers, and postsecondary education agencies to ensure effective planned transition services for students with disabilities. (pp. 7–8)

This legislation allows schools to hire rehabilitation counselors to assist students in transition; however, rehabilitation counselors must provide considerable public education to overcome the general lack of knowledge about the importance of rehabilitation counseling in school-to-work transition (Szymanski, Hanley-Maxwell, & Asselin, 1990). Conversely, rehabilitation counselors need to become more knowledgeable about special education and other school services (Hanley-Maxwell & Chadsey-Rusch, 1986).

The rehabilitation counselor's roles in the transition process depend on (a) the setting in which the rehabilitation counselor is employed; (b) the disabilities, ages, and specific needs of the students; and (c) the resources of the setting, the family, and the community. Szymanski and King (1989) listed the following potential rehabilitation counseling functions for transition:

(a) career and psychosocial counseling; (b) consultation with special and vocational education teachers, school counselors, and other education professionals regarding the vocational implications of disability and potential educational adaptations; (c) coordination of school, family, and community efforts in career planning and preparation; (d) job placement, job analysis, job modification and restructuring, and placement follow-up; (e) work adjustment counseling; (f) coordination of job support services (e.g., job coaches, transportation, personal care attendants) during transition; (g) referral to and coordination with adult service agencies [e.g, state VR agencies); (h) specialized planning and linkage with postsecondary programs and support services for students with disabilities; and (i) development of individual transition plans. (pp. 4–5)

The functions described by Szymanski and King (1989) are appropriate mainly for school-employed rehabilitation counselors; however, many of these services may also be provided by rehabilitation counselors employed in other settings (e.g., state VR agencies, medical settings, private sector rehabilitation companies). Also, many additional services related to special education and transition can be provided by rehabilitation counselors, depending on their employment setting. For example, rehabilitation counselors may provide consultation to parents of infants, toddlers, and young children with disabilities about career development and adult independence possibilities. Rehabilitation counselors in medical settings may assist students with disabilities during their time of transition into school after a period of hospitalization. Rehabilitation counselors employed in student services offices of colleges and universities may provide services to facilitate the students' opportunities to benefit from postsecondary education. Private sector rehabilitation counselors may provide education and transition planning for adolescents with traumatic injuries, expert testimony relating to the impact of acquired disability on children and adolescents and their resultant service needs, vocational assessment, and life care planning (Lynch & Lynch, Chapter 3, this text).

Regardless of the setting, the rehabilitation counselor's role varies with the age of the students served. Ideally, rehabilitation counselors should begin serving students with disabilities at a very young age (i.e., during the elementary and early childhood years). Involvement with children this young would take the form of consulting with parents regarding career development and informing teachers of the need for developing work-related skills and attitudes and the need to expose children to occupational information throughout their school years (Turner & Szymanski, 1990).

During the junior high and high school years, community training provided by the school and other agencies is particularly important. With students in Grades 7 through 12, the rehabilitation counselor must assume a more active role in the transition process. Assisting students in obtaining information through vocational assessment, counseling students and their families regarding career options, providing expert input into curriculum development, and assisting in the establishment of community-based training sites are some of the more salient services that rehabilitation counselors may render (Szymanski & King, 1989).

For students nearing graduation, rehabilitation counselors need to participate in identifying specific job and residential sites, as well as securing needed funding and support services for such placements. By the time the student leaves high school, the rehabilitation counselor should have established a firm counseling relationship with the student. Through such a relationship, the counselor should have acquired information concerning the student's past behavior and future needs. Such knowledge will assure that the rehabilitation counselor can facilitate a smooth move for the student who is in the transition process (Hanley-Maxwell & Chadsey-Rusch, 1986).

Supported Employment

Supported employment is a potential transition outcome for students with severe disabilities. It is also a possible rehabilitation service and/or outcome for persons of any age who have severe disabilities and require ongoing support to obtain or maintain employment (Szymanski & Parker, 1988). Rehabilitation counselor roles in supported employment vary according to the setting in which the rehabilitation counselor is employed and the services needed by the client (Szymanski & Parker, 1989). Regardless of setting and role, it is important for rehabilitation counselors to understand supported employment features, models, and services. To this end, the following topics are discussed: (a) core features of supported employment, (b) supported employment service delivery, and (c) rehabilitation counseling in supported employment.

Core Features of Supported Employment

The core features of supported employment have been described in the August 14, 1987, *Federal Register.* These core features are competitive employment, integrated settings, workers with severe disabilities, and ongoing support. The definition specifies that supported employment is a service for persons with severe disabilities who would otherwise be unable to obtain or maintain competitive employment. Although early supported employment demonstration projects often targeted people with mental retardation, supported employment is a potent service for individuals with a wide range of other severe disabilities (Buckley, Mank, & Cioffi, 1988), including deafness and hearing impairments (Danek, Seay, & Collier, 1989), blindness and visual impairment (Hanley-Maxwell, Griffin, Szymanski, & Godley, 1990), chronic mental illness (McDonald-Wilson, Mancuso, Danley, & Anthony, 1989), traumatic brain injury (Kruetzer & Morton, 1988; Wehman, 1990), and cerebral palsy (Wehman, Revell, et al., 1990).

Competitive employment in integrated settings allows individuals with severe disabilities to earn wages and other benefits while working alongside other workers without disabilities. In addition to wages, working conditions and job security are important outcomes (Wehman & Kregel, 1992), and integration of individuals with disabilities is a critical outcome. Social integration, contact, and relationships with nondisabled individuals who are not paid to be with the supported employee are emphasized (Wehman & Kregel, 1992; Wehman & Moon, 1987). For a supported employment site to be acceptable, it must include the physical and social integration of individuals with disabilities (Rusch, Chadsey-Rusch, & Johnson, 1991).

The ongoing support feature is what makes supported employment different from other rehabilitation services (Wehman, 1988). Support is provided to enable the individual to maintain effective functioning in the work environment. Because the individual and the environment are interrelated, support is provided to both (Szymanski, Hanley-Maxwell, & Parker, 1990). This ongoing support focuses on increased job retention. In time-limited services the provision of rehabilitation services enables the individual to function independently within his or her environment, whereas in supported employment the severity of the disability is such that support is needed for the individual and the environment to enable continued, stable, effective functioning of that person as a worker (Szymanski, Hanley-Maxwell, & Parker, 1987; Szymanski & Parker, 1988).

Models of Supported Employment Service Delivery

One of the distinguishing characteristics of supported employment, compared with traditional time-limited services, is the stipulation that long-term support must be provided once community employment has been secured. Although some time-limited vocational options offer some follow-along, supported employment, by definition, provides ongoing on-the-job interventions as needed by the individual.

For those individuals who do require supported employment services, support may come in many forms. Currently, the most frequently used form of support is job coaching. Commonly used job coaching formats can be classified as group or individual models (Moon & Griffin, 1988; Rhodes & Valenta, 1985).

It is important to note that, as individualized service is a major feature of supported employment, individualized models of supported employment services can also be expected. Many variations that match the particular individual being served, the employment site constraints, the community, and the community's economic base, are appropriate as long as the essential core features of supported employment are retained (Bellamy, Rhodes, Mank, & Albin, 1988). Some of these variations include the use of coworkers as mentors or trainers. Job coaches serve as support consultants to employers and train one set of naturally available cue and consequence providers (i.e., coworkers) to be more effective in their interactions with the coworker who has a disability. Additionally, coworkers are taught to interact more effectively with each other. Also, as the support consultant, the job coach is able to engineer the social and physical environment so that the worker with a disability is not always the target of change (Hagner, Rogan, & Murphy, 1992; Nisbet & Hagner, 1988).

Supported employment is not restricted to the models identified above. Imagination and the four core features—individuals with severe disabilities, competitive work, integrated settings, and ongoing support—are the only limits placed on new variations. A final ideological qualifier should be used in the creation of new models. That qualifier is that any model developed should be maximally under the control of and should enhance the independence of the supported employee.

Group Models

Current group models include the enclave and mobile crew. Although these approaches are under severe criticism for the inherent limits on integration and the potential highlighting of deviance caused by grouping, they are models that are commonly found within currently identified supported employment programs. Federal standards specify that each group must not exceed eight individuals with disabilities (*Federal Register,* August 14, 1987). Group models vary in the type of work, the place where the work is performed, the availability and type of integration with nondisabled individuals, and the wages earned (Wolfe, 1992).

Enclave. The term *enclave* refers to a group of individuals who collectively accomplish a set of work tasks at a specific place of employment. The number of employee vacancies filled by members in the enclave vary, depending on the amount of work completed by the total enclave. In one variation, each member of the enclave fills one employee vacancy, completing all the work tasks related to this position. Another variation is a job sharing arrangement in which as many as four persons may complete the tasks associated with one job. Any other combination that falls within these two extremes is an acceptable variation. Enclaves may be congregated, in which all employees with disabilities are located within the same working area (Rhodes & Valenta, 1985); or they may be dispersed, in which the employees with disabilities are all located within the same building or employment site, but are dispersed throughout the available work areas (Udvari-Solner, 1990). An enclave is thought to be an appropriate supported employment model for individuals with more severe disabilities or behavior challenges due to the often repetitive and stable nature of the work tasks (Mank, Rhodes, & Bellamy, 1986; Moon & Griffin, 1988; Rhodes & Valenta, 1985).

Frequently, people employed in the enclave are paid directly from the business. In these cases the work is not contracted from the company; instead the number of "employee slots" (or vacancies) to be filled is negotiated. The related work is then distributed among the workers with disabilities (Mank et al., 1986; The President's Committee on Employment of the Handicapped [now called the President's Committee on Employment of People with Disabilities], 1987; Szymanski, Hanley-Maxwell, & Parker, 1987). In cases where work is contracted from the business, all pay is funneled through the service provider. Enclave employees then receive pay and benefits provided by the agency, not the business. Regardless of the contractual arrangement, the enclave performs all work on one business' premises.

Studies conducted in 1990 indicated that enclave models served less than 25% of the total number of individuals in supported employment. Hourly wages for individuals working in enclaves during 1990 ranged from $2.69 to $3.52, with the average hours worked per week ranging from 17.11 to 28.7 (Wolfe, 1992). Thirty-two percent of individuals who worked in this model received no fringe benefits (i.e., insurance, vacation, and sick pay) (Wolfe, 1992).

Because integration is one of the main outcomes of supported employment, it is important to note the lack of integration that occurs in this model. Approximately 83% of the individuals surrounding workers in an enclave have disabilities, which contrasts with 42% found in individual placement models (Wolfe, 1992).

Mobile Crew. A mobile crew forms contractual relationships with businesses to perform a service. The crew generally moves from business to business performing this service (e.g., janitorial service, lawn care). As with the enclave model, the mobile work crew is provided with ongoing supervision by a job coach. Hourly wages for mobile work crews during 1990 varied from $2.85 to $3.03, and the average hours worked per week ranged from 12.23 to 27.6 (Wolfe, 1992). Twenty-eight percent of individuals who worked in this model received no fringe benefits. Of all the models assessed by Kregel, Wehman, and Banks (as cited in Wolfe, 1992), the mobile work crew offered the fewest chances for integration with nondisabled individuals.

Generally, group model providers indicate that these models are used for people for whom an individual placement has been deemed not appropriate. Group models offer more intense, daily support as opposed to the occasional (and fading) support of individual placements. Thus, they are held to be more restrictive. In additional, the integration limitations previously mentioned add to the restrictiveness of these options. Providers of group models must ensure that, at the very least, supported employees are integrated with people who do not have disabilities during coffee and lunch breaks and, more important, during working hours at the various job sites (Bellamy, Rhodes, & Albin, 1986; President's Committee, 1987; Szymanski, Hanley-Maxwell, & Parker, 1987). Employment of coworkers who do not have disabilities is one method suggested to achieve increased integration. These model workers do not supervise; they work alongside employees with disabilities. Additional integration-enhancing methods include scheduling mobile work crew hours during typical work hours (8:00 to 5:00) and physically integrating enclave members throughout the employer's work spaces.

Group models are not considered to be the optimal choice for individuals in supported employment. Generally, individuals participating in group models work fewer hours per week and receive much lower pay than those in individual models. With the combination of limited hours worked and low pay, it is clear that many supported employees in the group models will never earn a living wage, which would enable more integration beyond employment. Expectations for individuals in group models often are lower in terms of abilities and potential for moving into an individual service model. Decrease of support or fading has been found to be extremely limited in these models (Johnson & Rusch, 1990). Given these issues, group models should be looked at with some reservation.

Individual Model

The concept behind supported employment is that individuals with severe disabilities should be given opportunities to work in valued, integrated jobs and be provided with the support necessary to complete the job to employer expectations. Because of its potential for normalization, the individual placement model is considered by many professionals to be the least restrictive of all the job coaching variations of supported employment, and is the most prevalently used approach to supported employment. Over 50% of all supported employees are served in an individual support model (Wolfe, 1992). In this type of model, relevant services include (a) one-to-one instruction at the targeted job site, (b) systematic fading of the job coach, and (c) regular follow-along through on-site visits for the employ-ment duration of the supported employee (Moon & Griffin, 1988). The service delivery format ensures that integration will occur on the physical level. However, it is up to the job coach to ensure that social integration also occurs. Other varia-tions of the individual model, such as those suggested by Nisbet and Hagner (1988), seek to enhance integration potential by utilizing "(a) the informal support that is available within work environments . . . [and] (b) the formal support that is part of the natural business world such as employee training or employee assis-tance" (p. 263).

Service Delivery Phases

The supported employment models previously mentioned have several com-monalities. They all must basically adhere to a five-component process structure: (a) job development, (b) job placement, (c) job-site training and adaptation, and (d) ongoing assessment and follow-along, and (e) ecological assessment. The fifth component, ecological assessment, is woven throughout the other four compo-nents (Parker et al., 1989). These processes are also found in the Choose–Get–Keep model of supported employment for people with mental illness (McDonald-Wilson et al., 1989). The specific activities within each phase of the process vary according to the disability of the person being served, but the essential structure remains the same. These five components are described below.

Ecological Assessment

Assessment in supported employment is ecological assessment. The fundamental elements of this assessment are the same as those described in the discussion of assessment for transition planning and preparation. However, ecological assess-ment in supported employment is more specific in the scope of its content in that the supported employee is assessed within the context of potential job sites. The individual's strength and limitations in specific jobs are assessed along with existing and potential support systems for that individual in the targeted com-munity and/or job site (Pancsofar, 1986).

Job Development

Job development is a continuous process that occurs throughout all phases of service delivery. Each phase provides further essential feedback needed for the refinement of available job options, as well as identification of future placement possibilities (Szymanski, Buckley, et al., 1988). Continuing job development has potentially positive implications for supported employees. Expansion of the num-ber and types of jobs developed can enhance the mobility of workers as they build experiential histories that allow them to access better jobs (Patterson & Curl, 1990). Job development activities may differ according to the type of sup-port model employed (e.g., mobile work crew, enclave, individual placement).

For example, job developers, when developing sites for group placements, may need to identify sites that can physically accommodate small groups of employees, or accept the structural and ideological changes that often accompany enclaves such as in job sharing (Szymanski, Hanley-Maxwell, & Parker, 1987). The job development process should be individualized based on findings from the assessment of the supported employee, with special attention given to individual interests and goals. Individualization enhances the potential for a good job match. Once a job is found, it is important to emphasize to the individual and the family that the job is a stepping stone in a career, and not the individual's last job.

Job Placement

Job placement in supported employment is slightly different from job placement for competitive employment. The enduring presence of the service provider is both a hindrance and an asset in the placement process. As an asset, this presence will encourage some employers to take a chance with a person traditionally not considered employable. As a hindrance, the continued (yet often intermittent) presence of the service provider may subtly influence the employer's (a) perception of the competency of the potential employee or (b) degree of commitment to that employee. Furthermore, the presence of the coach may pose a physical accommodation problem at the worksite (Nisbet & Hagner, 1988). Due to these issues, it is essential that job coaches take on more of a consultative role with employers and coworkers rather than the traditional specialist role used in the past. The role of the job coach has changed toward being a facilitator of employment, working with the supported employee, supervisors, and coworkers. A coach no longer assumes that he or she is the only one who can provide support to the supported employee. Job coaches develop natural supports, identify accommodations or modifications, and continually strategize how to decrease coach-provided support.

The placement process in supported employment approaches includes the examination of data from many sources to ensure the optimal job–consumer match. Ecological assessment data are used to enhance the match between all aspects of the job and worker abilities, interests, and potential support systems (Parker et al., 1989; Schalock & Kiernan, 1990). Assessment data are also used to plan interventions, circumvent difficulties, and accommodate individual idiosyncrasies through planning the use of job restructuring or the inclusion of assistive devices and technology (Hanley-Maxwell & Bordieri, 1989). Such careful, detailed matching appears to be highly correlated with successful placements (Martin, 1986).

Training

The primary concern of job-site training for supported employment is not merely skill acquisition, but also the maintenance and generalization of those skills (Berg et al., 1990). Short- and long-term skill needs of supported employees must be reflected in both skill content and training methodology used. Content is usually covered by the use of thorough, individualized service plans that are developed through the synthesis of information obtained from assessments (Hanley-Maxwell, 1986). Behaviorally based training methods are used to teach specific skills. These preplanned, systematic methods include, but are not limited to, the use of behavioral objectives, individualized reinforcement, varying levels of assistance, error correction, and maintenance and generalization–enhancing procedures (Hanley-Maxwell, Szymanski, Seay, & Parker, 1990; McLoughlin, Garner, & Callahan, 1987).

Job analysis is a vital part of training. Although job analysis has been done in rehabilitation services, the application to supported employment extends the content examined and methodology for obtaining job data. Content extension is accomplished by including social survival skills and job-related skills along with critical vocational skills (Rusch et al., 1982). To obtain this information, coworkers performing the job or a highly similar job are systematically observed. These observations are then validated through interviews with prospective employers or supervisors (Rusch et al., 1980). The individuality of each job and its setting is highlighted by this approach to job analysis. The identified skills then form the basic content of the assessment and training components (Hanley-Maxwell, 1986).

Individual assessments are completed from the foundation developed by the job analysis. Individual assessment is used not to determine readiness or eligibility but to determine programmatic needs (Parker et al., 1989). This determination is accomplished through a systematic examination of the individual's performance of essential work and work-related skills. Potentially problematic areas of the job analyses are further explicated in the process of task analysis, in which each job element is broken into its component steps. These steps are then logically ordered in the sequence in which they are performed. Task analyses are the primary tools of this assessment (Parker et al., 1989).

Individual assessment is an ongoing process. The art of assessment is the process of providing someone with a compass from which to chart his or her own course of action rather than laying out a detailed map from which the person dares not deviate (Pancsofar, Steere, & Wood, 1993, p. 1). An assessment should be person centered, considering the person first. It should uncover an individual's abilities, skills, talents, gifts, uniqueness, individuality, and interests rather than focusing on deficiencies. Limitations should be acknowledged in context. It is important to spend time with the individual to determine an appropriate job match as well as the type and degree of supports needed. For example, an assessment can determine the feasibility of Social Security Work Incentives, such as a Plan for Achieving Self-Support (PASS). Other forms of data gathered include information about the person's past learning history, future goals and aspirations, and likes and dislikes (Hanley-Maxwell & Bordieri, 1989). Results of individual assessment form the content for on-the-job training.

Adaptation is also a primary concern during training for several reasons. First, skill deficits cannot always be remediated through training. Second, training may be more efficient when adaptation is considered first. Last, the use of adaptation or assistance may enhance the independence of the individual supported employee.

Adaptation in supported employment is no different from adaptation in any other service delivery model. It includes the development and implementation of assistive devices and technology, from the simplest to the most complex (Stack, 1988; Wehman, Wood, Everson, Goodwyn, & Conley, 1988).

Ongoing Support and Follow-Along

The *Federal Register* (May 12, 1988) refers to follow-up as ongoing support. Ongoing support is further defined in the Rehabilitation Act Amendments of 1992 (P.L. 102-569) as services needed to support and maintain an individual with severe handicaps in supported employment. Clearly follow-up is concerned with the long-term maintenance of critical skills and the enhancement of the flexibility of supported employees in accommodating environmental changes. A formal follow-up program is designed to assist in early identification of problems, establish follow-up schedules, provide on-the-job intervention, obtain validation of significant others, plan interventions by others, plan and implement systematic withdrawal follow-up, and evaluate adjustment (Rusch, 1986). Follow-up in supported employment must include

> continuous or periodic job skill training services provided at least twice monthly at the worksite throughout the term of employment. . . . The term also includes other support services provided at or away from the work site . . . if skill training services are also needed by, and provided to, that individual at the work site. (*Federal Register,* August 14, 1987)

Service providers for employees with mental illness do not have to provide follow-up services on the same schedule, but must provide services based on the needs of each individual supported employee (*Federal Register,* August 14, 1987). Although the 1987 and 1992 regulations refer to the minimal number of times that follow-up training services must be provided at the worksite, they do not specify all the targets of those services. Service targets must not be only supported employees; they must also include those other persons in the related environments of the supported employee (e.g., caretakers, employers, coworkers).

Whereas ongoing support is a specific target of supported employment services, funding for supported employment is time limited. Supported employment training/job stabilization under vocational rehabilitation must not exceed 18 months. Ongoing funding for long-term support must be in place once vocational rehabilitation funding has ended. Generally long-term support funds are provided by another agency (e.g., mental health). The responsible agency varies from state to state. With funds becoming increasingly limited, many individuals are ending up on waiting lists. Thus, other long-term funding options must be considered.

One option for long-term funding is the Social Security work incentive program, PASS. The PASS plan allows individuals to set aside income or resources to pay for their own support through their SSI (Supplemental Security Income) payments. Each plan must be individualized, be in writing, have a specified work goal, and a specific time frame. A PASS is usually written for 18 months, but can be extended up to 4 years. This type of long-term funding allows the individual to be in control of the types of supports he or she receives and who provides them (Social Security Administration, 1992).

Rehabilitation Counseling Interventions

The delivery of rehabilitation counseling services in supported employment is complicated by the severity of client disabilities and the complexity of the involved service delivery systems (Patterson, Buckley, & Smull, 1989; Szymanski & Parker, 1989). As with transition, specific rehabilitation counseling roles and interventions will depend on the setting in which the rehabilitation counselor is employed, the needs of the consumer, and the resources of the community.

Interventions can be provided directly, arranged and coordinated, or supported through consultation. They can generally be classified according to the four dimensions of the ecological model of rehabilitation counseling: person, environment, perceptions, and interactions (Szymanski & Parker, 1989). Examples of person-based interventions include rehabilitation counseling and skill training (e.g., job coaching) (Szymanski & Parker, 1989). Environment-based interventions include job modification and restructuring (Hanley-Maxwell, Rusch, & Rappaport, 1989) and identification and mobilization of natural supports (Hagner et al., 1992). An important perception-based intervention is clarification of the goal-related perceptions and expectations of consumers, families, and involved professionals (Szymanski, Hershenson, & Power, 1988). Interactions-based interventions are exemplified by problem resolution based on (a) analyses of antecedents, behaviors, contexts, and consequences (Snell & Grigg, 1987) or (b) analysis of the communicative message value of the problem behavior (Negri-Shoultz, Shoultz, & Majure, 1990).

Supported employment poses numerous ethical challenges to rehabilitation counselors (Patterson et al., 1989; Patterson & Curl, 1990). Supported employment programs often compromise consumer choice (Martin & Mithaug, 1990), and the presence of job coaches can inhibit the natural supports available in the workplace and isolate the consumer from coworkers (Hagner et al., 1992).

The programmatic complexities of supported employment are further complicated by indications that consumers with mild disabilities and those who do not need ongoing support are being served in supported employment programs (Kregel & Wehman, 1989; Lagomarcino & Rusch, 1988). Many consumers, including those who do not require ongoing support, can benefit from some services associated with supported employment, including the identification and use of natural supports in the workplace (Nisbet, Rogan, & Hagner, 1989) and short-term job coaching (Szymanski & Parker, 1989). These services can and should be regular components of time-limited rehabilitation services. However, the use of supported employment, with characteristic ongoing support, for persons with less severe disabilities who do not require ongoing support "(a) constitutes an overly intrusive intervention, (b) creates unnecessary and unwarranted dependence, and (c) decreases services available to individuals with more severe disabilities" (Patterson & Curl, 1990).

Whether rehabilitation counseling interventions are provided directly, coordinated, or supported by consultation, it is important for rehabilitation counselors to be aware of and to ensure that the services conform to quality standards (Hanley-Maxwell & Bordieri, 1989; Nisbet & Callahan, 1988; Sandow, Rhodes, Mank, Ramsing, & Lynch, 1989). The complexity of supported employment and the potential for compromising consumer rights require ethical vigilance (Patterson et al., 1989). For this reason, the following principles of intervention, which are generally applicable to rehabilitation counseling, are imperative to evaluating supported employment interventions.

1. Interventions should be designed to be maximally under the control of the individual, rather than others.
2. Interventions should be designed to facilitate individual independence and autonomy.
3. The least intrusive means that are still effective should be used.
4. The most natural interventions for the particular work environment should be used. (Szymanski & Parker, 1989, p. 68)

Summary

Transition is a process that spans both the secondary and postsecondary years. It is a process that leads to a variety of postsecondary outcomes for former special education students. For some students, if the transition process is to be successful, the primary outcome needs to be supported employment.

The goal of transition is to provide opportunities for meaningful employment and independent living for young adults leaving school. Implied goals are to avoid service interruptions, prevent service duplication, and decrease training stagnation. However, if past history continues to be repeated, the goal of transition will not be met.

Currently, for the majority of young adults with disabilities, employment is not a reality and in many cases it is not even an expectation. Special education is not preparing the vast majority of young adults with disabilities for productive work or independent living outcomes once they leave the shelters of home and school. Rehabilitation services are in many cases merely extending the training provided by the school under the assumption that individuals must pass through a continuum of "prevocational" or "work adjustment" training toward an eventual goal of community employment—if they receive services at all.

Quality transition services must be cooperatively planned to eliminate these damaging outcomes. Quality issues in transition and supported employment will continue to take precedence in the future.

Transition as a concept has been well thought out as it relates to students who are not college bound. However, little attention has been given to students with learning, physical, or emotional disabilities who are moving into higher education before entering the world of work. Future quality issues related to transition will revolve around the refinement of practices already established for students moving immediately into employment, the creation of practices to empower students who are college bound, and the enhancement of student participation in the various phases and processes.

Supported employment will turn to similar issues of quality. Supported employment has evolved from a combination of a variety of factors. Knowledge in the area continues to develop rapidly. Future areas of interest include (a) the refinement of training and support strategies designed to ensure maximal consumer control and independence; (b) program models for supported employees who are not mentally retarded; and (c) the development of variations for people who need sporadic rather than intense, ongoing support.

Each of these services (i.e., transition and supported employment) will continue to challenge rehabilitation counseling and the related disciplines involved in their provision. The challenges will stretch professionals' current abilities to interact across disciplinary lines and basic beliefs about the rights and abilities of those people who have been labeled disabled.

References

Apple, M. W., & Zenk, C. (1996). American realities: Poverty, economy, and education. In M. Apple (Ed.), *Cultural politics and education* (pp. 68–90). New York: Teachers College Press.

Bellamy, G. T., Rhodes, L. E., & Albin, J. M. (1986). Supported employment. In W. E. Kiernan & J. A. Stark (Eds.), *Pathways to employment for adults with developmental disabilities* (pp. 129–138). Baltimore: Brookes.

Bellamy, G. T., Rhodes, L. E., Mank, D. M., & Albin, J. M. (1988). *Supported employment: A community integration guide.* Baltimore: Brookes.

Benz, M. R., & Halpern, A. S. (1987). Transition services for secondary students with mild disabilities: A statewide perspective. *Exceptional Children, 53,* 507–514.

Berg, W. K., Wacker, D. P., & Flynn, T. H. (1990). Teaching generalization and maintenance of work behavior. In F. R. Rusch (Ed.), *Supported employment: Models, methods, and issues* (pp. 145–160). Sycamore, IL: Sycamore.

Betz, N. E., & Fitzgerald, L. F. (1995). Career assessment and intervention with racial and ethnic minorities. In F. T. L. Leong (Ed.), *Career development and vocational behavior of racial and ethnic minorities* (pp. 263–279). Mahwah, NJ: Erlbaum.

Blustein, D. L. (1992). Applying current theory and research in career exploration to practice. The *Career Development Quarterly, 41,* 174–184.

Brolin, D. E. (1991). *Life Centered Career Education: A competency based approach* (3rd ed.). Reston, VA: The Council for Exceptional Children.

Browder, D. M., & King, D. (1987). Comprehensive assessment for longitudinal curriculum development. In D. M. Browder (Ed.), *Assessment of individuals with severe handicaps* (pp. 25–53). Baltimore: Brookes.

Brown, L., Falvey, M., Pumpian, I., Baumgart, D., Nisbet, J., Ford, A., Schroeder, J., & Loomis, R. (1980). *Curricular strategies teaching severely handicapped students functional skills in school and nonschool environments.* Madison: University of Wisconsin–Madison and Madison Metropolitan School District.

Brown-Glover, P. (1992). Applications for youth with mild mental retardation. In P. Wehman (Ed.), *Life beyond the classroom: Transition strategies for young people with disabilities* (pp. 237–260). Baltimore: Brookes.

Bruininks, R., Lewis, D., & Thurlow, M. (1989). *Assessing outcomes, costs and benefits of special education programs.* Minneapolis: University of Minnesota.

Brustein, M., & Mahler, M. (1994). *School-to-Work Opportunities Act: Overview.* Alexandria, VA: American Vocational Association.

Buckley, J., Mank, D. M., & Cioffi, A. R. (1988). Supported employment for individuals with "other" disabilities. In C. Hanley-Maxwell & D. Harley (Eds.), *Special report: An examination of the impact of supported employment on our nation's citizens with severe disabilities* (pp. 25–33). Washington, DC: President's Committee for Employment of People with Disabilities.

Bullis, M., & Foss, G. (1983). Guidelines for assessing job-related social skills of mildly handicapped students. *Career Development for Exceptional Individuals, 9,* 89–97.

Carnevale, A. P. (1995). Enhancing skills in the new economy. In A. Howard (Ed.), *The changing nature of work* (pp. 238–251). San Francisco: Jossey-Bass.

Chadsey-Rusch, J. (1986). Identifying and teaching valued social behavior. In F. R. Rusch (Ed.), *Competitive employment: Issues and strategies* (pp. 273–288). Baltimore: Brookes.

Chadsey-Rusch, J., DeStefano, L., O'Reilly, M., Gonzalez, P., & Collet-Klingenberg, L. (1992). Assessing the loneliness of workers with mental retardation. *Mental Retardation, 30*(2), 85–92.

Chesler, B. (1982, July–August). ACLD committee survey on LD adults. *ACLD Newsbrief, 145,* 1, 5.

Conte, L. (1983). Vocational development theories and the disabled person: Oversight or deliberate omission. *Rehabilitation Counseling Bulletin, 26,* 316–328.

Curnow, T. C. (1989). Vocational development of persons with disability. *Vocational Guidance Quarterly, 37,* 269–278.

Danek, M. M., & McCrone, W. P. (1989). The mandate for transition services: Myth or reality? In T. E. Allen, B. W. Rawlings, & A. Schildroth (Eds.), *Deaf students and the school-to-work transition* (pp. 1–29). Baltimore: Brookes.

Danek, M. M., Seay, P. C., & Collier, M. (1989). Supported employment and deaf people: Current practices and emerging issues. *Journal of Applied Rehabilitation Counseling, 20*(3), 34–43.

Daniels, J. L. (1987). Transition from school to work. In R. M. Parker (Ed.), *Rehabilitation counseling: Basics and beyond* (pp. 283–317). Austin, TX: PRO-ED.

DiMichael, S. (1950). *Vocational rehabilitation of the mentally retarded* (Rehabilitation Services series No. 123). Washington, DC: U.S. Department of Health, Education and Welfare.

Dunst, C., Trivette, C., & Deal, A. (1988). *Enabling and empowering families: Principles and guidelines for practice.* Cambridge, MA: Brookline Books.

Edgar, E. (1987). Secondary programs in special education: Are many of them justifiable? *Exceptional Children, 53,* 555-561.

Edgar, E. (1988). Employment as an outcome for mildly handicapped students: Current status and future directions. *Focus on Exceptional Children, 21,* 1-8.

Education for All Handicapped Children Act of 1975, 20 U.S.C. § 1400 *et seq.*

Eleventh Institute on Rehabilitation Issues. (1984). *Continuum of services: School to work.* Menomonie: Research and Training Center, University of Wisconsin–Stout.

Everson, J. M., & Moon, M. S. (1986). Transition services for young adults with severe disabilities: Professional roles and implications for inservice training. In C. Hanley-Maxwell & J. Chadsey-Rusch (Eds.), *Enhancing transition from school to the workplace for handicapped youth: The role of vocational rehabilitation* (pp. 18-35). Champaign: University of Illinois.

Fafard, M. B., & Haubrich, P. A. (1981). Vocational and social adjustment of learning disabled young adults: A follow-up study. *Rehabilitation Counseling Bulletin, 4,* 122-130.

Federal Register. (1987, August 14). Rehabilitation Act Amendments of 1986: The State Supported Employment Services Program; Final Regulations (34 C.F.R. Part 363) *52*(157), 30546-30552.

Federal Register. (1988, May 12). Rehabilitation Act Amendments of 1986: The State Vocational Rehabilitation Services Program; Final Regulations (34 C.F.R. Part 361) 53(92), 16982-16983.

Ford, A., Schnorr, R., Meyer, L., Davern, L., Black, J., & Dempsey, P. (1989). *The Syracuse community-referenced curriculum guide for students with moderate and severe disabilities.* Baltimore: Brookes.

Forest, M., & Lusthaus, E. (1987). The kaleidoscope: Challenge to the cascade. In M. Forest (Ed.), *More education/integration* (pp. 1-16). Downsville, Ontario: Allam Roeher Institute.

Fourqurean, J. M., & LaCourt, T. (1990). A follow-up of former special education students: A model for program evaluation. *Remedial and Special Education, 12*(1), 16-23.

Fourqurean, J. M., Meisgeier, C., Swank, P. R., & Williams, R. E. (1991). Correlates of postsecondary employment outcomes for young adults with learning disabilities. *Journal of Learning Disabilities, 24,* 400-405.

Gartner, A., & Lipsky, D. K. (Eds.). (1989). *Beyond separate education: Quality education for all.* Baltimore: Brookes.

Giangreco, M., Cloninger, C., & Iverson, V. (1993). *Choosing options and accommodations for children (COACH): A guide for planning inclusive education.* Baltimore: Brookes.

Hagner, D., Rogan, P., & Murphy, S. T. (1992). Facilitating natural supports in the work place: Strategies for support consultants. *Journal of Rehabilitation, 23*(1), 29-42.

Halpern, A. (1992). Transition: Old wine in new bottles. *Exceptional Children, 58,* 202-211.

Halpern, A. (1993). Quality of life as a conceptual framework for evaluating transition outcomes. *Exceptional Children, 59*(6), 486-498.

Halpern, A., Irvin, L., & Landman, J. (1979). *Test for Everyday Living.* Monterey, CA: CTB/McGraw-Hill.

Hanley-Maxwell, C. (1986). Curriculum development. In F. R. Rusch (Ed.), *Competitive employment: Issues and strategies* (pp. 187–198). Baltimore: Brookes.

Hanley-Maxwell, C., & Bordieri, J. E. (1989). Purchasing supported employment: Evaluating the service. *Journal of Applied Rehabilitation Counseling, 20*(3), 4–11.

Hanley-Maxwell, C., & Chadsey-Rusch, J. (1986). *Enhancing transition from school to the workplace for handicapped youth: The role of vocational rehabilitation.* Champaign: University of Illinois.

Hanley-Maxwell, C., & Collet-Klingenberg, L. (1995). *Design of effective curricular practices in transition from school to the community: Research synthesis.* Eugene: National Center to Improve the Tools of Educators, University of Oregon.

Hanley-Maxwell, C., Griffin, S. L., Szymanski, E. M., & Godley, S. H. (1990). Supported and time-limited transitional employment services. *Journal of Visual Impairment and Blindness, 84,* 160–166.

Hanley-Maxwell, C., Rusch, F. R., & Rappaport, J. (1989). A multi-level perspective on community employment problems for adults with mental retardation. *Rehabilitation Counseling Bulletin, 32,* 266–280.

Hanley-Maxwell, C., Szymanski, E. M., Seay, P., & Parker, R. M. (1990). Application for learning principles in the clinical practice of supported employment. *Vocational Evaluation and Work Adjustment Bulletin, 23,* 125–131.

Hasazi, S., Gordon, L. R., & Rose, C. A. (1985). Factors associated with the employment status of handicapped youth exiting high school from 1979–1983. *Exceptional Children, 51,* 455–469.

Heal, L. W., & Rusch, F. R. (1995). Predicting employment for students who leave special education high school programs. *Exceptional Children, 61,* 472–487.

Hershenson, D. B. (1988). Along for the ride: The evolution of rehabilitation education. *Rehabilitation Counseling Bulletin, 31,* 204–217.

House of Representatives Report 99–860. (1986). *Report to Accompany HR 5520, the Individuals with Disabilities Education Act Amendments of 1986.*

House of Representatives Report 101–544. (1990). *Report to Accompany HR 1013, the Individuals with Disabilities Education Act Amendments of 1990.*

House of Representatives Report 101–787. (1990). *Conference report to Accompany S. 1824, the Individuals with Disabilities Education Act Amendments of 1990.*

Individuals with Disabilities Education Act of 1990, 20 U.S.C. § 1400 *et seq.*

Johnson, J. R., & Rusch, F. R. (1990). Analysis of hours of direct training provided by employment specialists to supported employees. *American Journal of Mental Retardation, 94,* 674–682.

Kantor, H. A. (1994). Managing the transition from school to work: The false promise of youth apprenticeship. *Teachers College Record, 95,* 442–461.

Kortering, L., & Edgar, E. (1988). Special education and rehabilitation: A need for cooperation. *Rehabilitation Counseling Bulletin, 31,* 178–184.

Kregel, J., & Wehman, P. (1989). Supported employment: Promises deferred for persons with severe disabilities. *Journal of The Association for Persons with Severe Handicaps, 14,* 293–303.

Kreutzer, J. S., & Morton, M. V. (1988). Traumatic brain injury: Supported employment and compensatory strategies for enhancing vocational outcomes. In P. Wehman & M. S. Moon (Eds.), *Vocational rehabilitation and supported employment* (pp. 291–312). Baltimore: Brookes.

Lagomarcino, T. R., & Rusch, F. R. (1988). A descriptive analysis of reasons why supported employees separate from their jobs. In C. Hanley-Maxwell & D. Harley (Eds.), *Special report: An examination of the impact of supported employment on our nation's citizens with severe disabilities* (pp. 45–49). Washington, DC: President's Committee on Employment of People with Disabilities.

Lent, R. W., & Hackett, G. (1994). Sociocognitive mechanisms of personal agency in career development: Pan theoretical prospects. In M. L. Savickas & R. W. Lent (Eds.), *Convergence in career development: Implications for science and practice* (pp. 77–101). Palo Alto, CA: CPP.

Linkenhoker, D., & McCarron, L. (1980). *Street Survival Skills Questionnaire*. Dallas: McCarron–Dial Systems.

Mank, D. M., Rhodes, L. E., & Bellamy, G. T. (1986). Four supported employment alternatives. In W. E. Kiernan & J. A. Stark (Eds.), *Pathways to employment for adults with developmental disabilities* (pp. 139–154). Baltimore: Brookes.

Martin, J. E. (1986). Identifying potential jobs. In F. R. Rusch (Ed.), *Competitive employment: issues and strategies* (pp. 165–186). Baltimore: Brookes.

Martin, J. E., & Mithaug, D. E. (1990). Consumer directed placement. In F. R. Rusch (Ed.), *Supported employment: Models, methods, and issues* (pp. 87–110). Sycamore, IL: Sycamore.

McDonald-Wilson, K., Mancuso, L. L., Danley, K. S., & Anthony, W. A. (1989). Supported employment for people with psychiatric disability. *Journal of Applied Rehabilitation Counseling, 20*(3), 50–57.

McLoughlin, C. S., Garner, J. B., & Callahan, M. (1987). *Getting employed, staying employed.* Baltimore: Brookes.

Michaels, C. A. (1994). *Transition strategies for persons with learning disabilities.* San Diego: Singular.

Mitchell, L. K., & Krumboltz, J. D. (1990). Social learning approach to career decision making: Krumboltz's theory. In D. Brown, L. Brooks, & Associates, *Career choice and development: Applying contemporary theories to practice* (2nd ed., pp. 145–196). San Francisco: Jossey-Bass.

Mithaug, D. E., Horiuchi, C., & Fanning, P. (1985). A report on the Colorado statewide follow-up survey of special education students. *Exceptional Children, 51,* 397–404.

Moon, S., & Griffin, S. (1988). Supported employment service delivery models. In P. Wehman & S. Moon (Eds.), *Vocational rehabilitation and supported employment* (pp. 17–30). Baltimore: Brookes.

Neel, R., Meadows, N., Levine, P., & Edgar, E. (1988). What happens after special education: A statewide follow-up study. *Behavior Disorders, 13,* 209–216.

Negri-Shoultz, N. A., Shoultz, M. D., & Majure, A. (1990). The analysis of challenging behavior: What are these behaviors communicating? What do supported employment personnel need to know? *Rehabilitation Education, 4,* 333–346.

Nisbet, J., & Callahan, M. (1988). *Assessing the quality of supported employment services.* Durham: The Institute on Disability, University of New Hampshire.

Nisbet, J., & Hagner, D. (1988). Natural supports in the workplace: A reexamination of supported employment. *Journal of The Association for Persons with Severe Handicaps, 13*, 260–267.

Nisbet, J., Rogan, P., & Hagner, D. (1989). Squeezing long-term supports out of short-term programs: Independence issues and supported employment. *Journal of Applied Rehabilitation Counseling, 20*(3), 21–25.

O'Brien, J. (1987). A guide to lifestyle planning. In T. Bellamy & B. Wilcox (Eds.), *The activity catalogue: A programming guide for youth and adults with severe disability* (pp. 75–189). Baltimore: Brookes.

O'Brien, J., & Lyle, C. (1987). *Framework for accomplishment.* Decatur, GA: Responsive Systems Associates.

Osterman, P. (1995). The youth labor market: Skill deficiencies and public policy. In A. Howard (Ed.), *The changing nature of work* (pp. 211–237). San Francisco: Jossey-Bass.

Pallas, A. M. (1993). Schooling in the course of human lives: The social context of education and the transition to adulthood in industrial society. *Review of Educational Research, 63*, 409–447.

Pancsofar, E. L. (1986). Assessing work behavior. In F. R. Rusch (Ed.), *Competitive employment: Issues and strategies* (pp. 93–102). Baltimore: Brookes.

Pancsofar, E. L., Steere, D., & Wood, R. (1993). Consumer assessment: Ten important considerations. *The Advance, 4*(3), 1–3.

Parker, R., Szymanski, E. M., & Hanley-Maxwell, C. (1989). Ecological assessment in supported employment. *Journal of Applied Rehabilitation Counseling, 20*(3), 26–33.

Patterson, J. B., Buckley, J., & Smull, M. (1989). Ethics in supported employment. *Journal of Applied Rehabilitation Counseling, 20*(3), 12–20.

Patterson, J. B., & Curl, R. M. (1990). Ethics education in supported employment preparation. *Rehabilitation Education, 4*, 247–260.

Podemski, R. S., Price, B. J., Smith, E. C., & Marsh, G. E. (1984). *Comprehensive administration of special education.* Rockville, MD: Aspen.

President's Committee on Employment of the Handicapped. (1987). *Fact sheet on supported employment.* Washington, DC: Author.

Rehabilitation Act Amendments of 1986, 29 U.S.C. § 701 *et seq.*

Rehabilitation Act Amendments of 1992, 29 U.S.C. §§ 706(8), 794, 794a, 794b.

Renzaglia, A., & Hutchins, M. (1988). A community-referenced approach to preparing persons with disabilities for employment. In P. Wehman & M. S. Moon (Eds.), *Vocational rehabilitation and supported employment* (pp. 91–110). Baltimore: Brookes.

Rhodes, L. E., & Valenta, L. (1985). Industry-based supported employment: An enclave approach. *Journal of the Association for Persons with Severe Handicaps, 10*, 12–20.

Rojewski, J. W. (1994). Applying theories of career behavior to special populations: Implications for secondary vocational transition programming. *Issues in Special Education and Rehabilitation, 9*(1), 7–26.

Rusch, F. R. (1986). On integrated work: An interview with Lou Brown. In F. R. Rusch (Ed.), *Competitive employment issues and strategies* (pp. 334–346). Baltimore: Brookes.

Rusch, F. R. (1990). *Supported employment: Models, methods, and issues.* Sycamore, IL: Sycamore.

Rusch, F. R., Chadsey-Rusch, J., & Johnson, R. R. (1991). Supported employment: Emerging opportunities for employment integration. In L. H. Meyer, C. A. Peck, & L. Brown (Eds.), *Critical issues in the lives of people with severe disabilities* (pp. 145–169). Baltimore: Brookes.

Rusch, F. R., & Hughes, C. (1989). Overview of supported employment. *Journal of Applied Behavior Analysis, 22,* 351–363.

Rusch, F. R., Rusch, J. C., Menchetti, B. M., & Schutz, R. P. (1980). *Survey-train-place: Developing a school-aged vocational curriculum for the severely handicapped student.* Unpublished manuscript, Department of Special Education, University of Illinois, Urbana.

Rusch, F. R., Schutz, R. P., & Agran, M. (1982). Validating entry-level survival skills for service occupations: Implications for curriculum development. *Journal of The Association for the Severely Handicapped, 7,* 32–41.

Sandow, D., Rhodes, L., Mank, D. M., Ramsing, K. D., & Lynch, W. F. (1989). *Assuring quality in supported employment.* Eugene: Specialized Training Program, College of Education, University of Oregon.

Sands, D. J., Woolsey, T., & Dunlap, W. R. (1985). *National Independent Living Skills Screening Instrument.* Tuscaloosa: The University of Alabama.

Schalock, R. L., & Kiernan, W. E. (1990). Interagency service delivery coordination. In F. R. Rusch (Ed.), *Supported employment: Models, methods, and issues* (pp. 215–228). Sycamore, IL: Sycamore.

Schnorr, R., Ford, A., Savern, L., Park-Lee, S., & Meyer, L. (1989). *The Syracuse curriculum revision manual: A group process for developing a community referenced curriculum guide.* Baltimore: Brookes.

School-to-Work Opportunities Act of 1994, 20 U.S.C. § 6101 *et seq.*

Scuccimarra, D., & Speece, D. (1990). Employment outcomes and social integration of students with mild disabilities: The quality of life two years after high school. *The Journal of Learning Disabilities, 23,* 213–219.

Shapiro, E. S., & Lentz, F. E. (1991). Vocational–technical programs: Follow-up of students with learning disabilities. *Exceptional Children, 58,* 47–59.

Sitlington, P. L., & Frank, A. R. (1990). Are adolescents with learning disabilities successfully crossing the bridge into adult life? *Learning Disabilities Quarterly, 13*(2), 97–111.

Sitlington, P. L., Frank, A. R., & Carson, R. (1992). Adult adjustment among high school graduates with mild disabilities. *Exceptional Children, 59*(3), 221–233.

Smith, C. L., & Rojewski, J. W. (1993). School-to-work transition: Alternatives for educational reform. *Youth and Society, 25,* 222–250.

Smith–Hughes Act of 1917, 20 U.S.C. § 11 *et seq.*

Snell, M. E., & Grigg, N. C. (1987). Instructional assessment and curriculum development. In M. E. Snell (Ed.), *Systematic instruction for persons with severe handicaps* (pp. 64–109). Columbus, OH: Merrill.

Social Security Administration. (1992). *Red book on work incentives—A summary guide to Social Security and Supplemental Security Income work incentives for people with disabilities* (SSA Report No. 64–030). Washington, DC: Author.

Stack, R. P. (1988). The rehabilitation engineer and technological services. In P. Wehman, W. Wood, J. M. Everson, R. Goodwyn, & S. Conley (Eds.), *Vocational education for multi-handicapped youth* (pp. 173–196). Baltimore: Brookes.

Stainback, W., Stainback, S., & Bunch, G. (1989). Introduction and historical background. In S. Stainback, W. Stainback, & M. Forest (Eds.), *Educating all students in the mainstream of regular education* (pp. 3–14). Baltimore: Brookes.

Stainback, W., Stainback, S., Nietupski, J., & Hamre-Nietupski, S. (1986). Establishing effective community-based training stations. In F. R. Rusch (Ed.), *Competitive employment: Issues and strategies* (pp. 103–114). Baltimore: Brookes.

Szymanski, E. M. (1994). Transition: Life-span, life-space considerations for empowerment. *Exceptional Children, 60,* 402–410.

Szymanski, E. M. (in press). School to work transition: Ecological considerations for career development. In W. E. Martin & J. L. Swartz (Eds.), *Applied ecological psychology for schools within communities: Assessment and intervention.* Mahwah, NJ: Erlbaum.

Szymanski, E. M., Buckley, J., Parent, W. S., Parker, R. M., & Westbrook, J. D. (1988). Rehabilitation counseling in supported employment: A conceptual model for service delivery and personnel preparation. In S. E. Rubin & N. M. Rubin (Eds.), *Contemporary challenges to the rehabilitation counseling profession* (pp. 111–133). Baltimore: Brookes.

Szymanski, E. M., & Danek, M. M. (1985). School to work transition for students with disabilities: Historical, current and conceptual issues. *Rehabilitation Counseling Bulletin, 29,* 81–89.

Szymanski, E. M., & Hanley-Maxwell, C. (1996). Career development of people with developmental disabilities: An ecological model. *Journal of Rehabilitation, 62*(1), 48–55.

Szymanski, E. M., Hanley-Maxwell, C., & Asselin, S. (1990). Rehabilitation counseling, special education, and vocational special needs education: Three transition disciplines. *Career Development for Exceptional Individuals, 13,* 29–38.

Szymanski, E. M., Hanley-Maxwell, C., & Asselin, S. (1992). The vocational rehabilitation, special education, vocational education interface. In F. R. Rusch, L. DeStefano, J. Chadsey-Rusch, L. A. Phelps, & E. M. Szymanski (Eds.), *Transition from school to adult life: Models, linkages, and policy* (pp. 153–171). Sycamore, IL: Sycamore.

Szymanski, E. M., Hanley-Maxwell, C., & Parker, R. M. (1987). *Supported employment and time-limited transitional employment service delivery: An introductory guide for rehabilitation professionals.* Austin: The University of Texas at Austin, Special Education Department.

Szymanski, E. M., Hanley-Maxwell, C., & Parker, R. M. (1990). Transdisciplinary planning for supported employment. In F. R. Rusch (Ed.), *Supported employment: Models, methods, and issues* (pp. 199–214). Sycamore, IL: Sycamore.

Szymanski, E. M., Hershenson, D. B., Enright, M. S., & Ettinger, J. (1996). Career development theories, constructs, and research: Implications for people with disabilities. In E. M. Szymanski & R. M. Parker (Eds.), *Work and disability: Issues and strategies in career development and job placement* (pp. 79–126). Austin, TX: PRO-ED.

Szymanski, E. M., Hershenson, D. B., & Power, P. W. (1988). Enabling the family in supporting transition from school to work. In P. W. Power, A. Dell Orto, & M. B. Gibbons (Eds.), *Family interventions throughout chronic illness and disability* (pp. 216–233). New York: Springer.

Szymanski, E. M., & King, J. (1989). Rehabilitation counseling in transition planning and preparation. *Career Development for Exceptional Individuals, 12,* 3–10.

Szymanski, E. M., King, J., Parker, R. M., & Jenkins, W. M. (1989). The State–Federal Rehabilitation Program: Overview and interface with special education. *Exceptional Children, 56,* 70–77.

Szymanski, E. M., & Parker, R. M. (1988). Supported employment and time-limited transitional employment training: Options for rehabilitation counselors. *Journal of Applied Rehabilitation Counseling, 19*(2), 11-15.

Szymanski, E. M., & Parker, R. M. (1989). Rehabilitation counseling in supported employment. *Journal of Applied Rehabilitation Counseling, 20*(3), 65-72.

Szymanski, E. M., Shafer, M. S., Danek, M. M., & Schiro-Geist, C. (1990). Supported employment in rehabilitation education. *Rehabilitation Education, 4*, 233-246.

Szymanski, E. M., Turner, K. D., & Hershenson, D. (1992). Career development of people with disabilities: Theoretical perspectives. In F. R. Rusch, L. DeStefano, J. Chadsey-Rusch, L. A. Phelps, & E. M. Szymanski (Eds.), *Transition from school to adult life: Models, linkages, and policy* (pp. 391-406). Sycamore, IL: Sycamore.

Turner, K. D., & Szymanski, E. M. (1990). Work adjustment of people with congenital disabilities: A longitudinal perspective from birth to adulthood. *Journal of Rehabilitation, 56*(3), 19-24.

Twelfth Institute on Rehabilitation Issues. (1985). *Supported employment: Implications for rehabilitation services.* Hot Springs: University of Arkansas, Arkansas Rehabilitation Research and Training Center.

Udvari-Solner, A. (1990). *Variables associated with the integration of individuals with intellectual disabilities in supported employment settings.* Unpublished doctoral dissertation, University of Wisconsin–Madison.

U.S. Department of Education. (1991). *America 2000: The President's Educational Strategy.*

Victor, J., McCarthy, H., & Palmer, J. T. (1986). Career development of physically disabled youth, *Annual Review of Rehabilitation, 5*, 97-150.

Vocational Rehabilitation Act Amendments of 1986, P.L. 99-506, 29 U.S.C. § 31 *et seq.*

Wagner, M., Blackorby, J., Cameto, R., & Newman, L. (1993). *What makes a difference? Influences on postschool outcomes of youth with disabilities.* Menlo Park, CA: SRI International.

Wehman, P. (1986). Transition for handicapped youth from school to work. In J. Chadsey-Rusch (Ed.), *Enhancing transition from school to the workplace for handicapped youth* (pp. 22-39). Champaign-Urbana: University of Illinois.

Wehman, P. (1988). Supported employment: Toward zero exclusion of persons with severe disabilities. In P. Wehman & S. Moon (Eds.), *Vocational rehabilitation and supported employment* (pp. 3-16). Baltimore: Brookes.

Wehman, P. (1990). Supported employment: Model implementation and evaluation. In J. S. Kreutzer & P. Wehman (Eds.), *Community integration following traumatic brain injury* (pp. 185-204). Baltimore: Brookes.

Wehman, P. (1995). Editorial. *Journal of Vocational Rehabilitation, 5*, 169-171.

Wehman, P., & Kregel, J. (1992). Supported employment: Growth and impact. In P. Wehman, P. Sale, & W. Parent (Eds.), *Supported employment: Strategies for integration of workers with disabilities* (pp. 3-28). Stoneham, MA: Butterworth-Heinemann.

Wehman, P., & Kregel, J. (1994). Toward a national agenda for supported employment. *Journal of Vocational Rehabilitation, 4*, 231-242.

Wehman, P., & Moon, M. S. (1987). Critical values in employment programs for persons with developmental disabilities: A position paper. *Journal of Applied Rehabilitation Counseling, 18*(1), 12-16.

Wehman, P., Moon, M. S., Everson, J. M., Wood, W., & Barcus, J. M. (1988). *Transition from school to work: New challenges for youth with severe disabilities.* Baltimore: Brookes.

Wehman, P., Revell, W. G., Kregel, J., Kreutzer, J., Callahan, M., & Banks, P. D. (1990). Supported employment: An alternative model for vocational rehabilitation of persons with severe neurologic, psychiatric, or physical disabilities. In J. Kregel, P. Wehman, & M. S. Shafer (Eds.), *Supported employment for persons with severe disabilities: From research to practice* (Vol. 3, pp. 101–114). Richmond: Rehabilitation Research and Training Center on Supported Employment, Virginia Commonwealth University.

Wehman, P., Wood, W., Everson, J. M., Goodwyn, R., & Conley, S. (1988). *Vocational education for multihandicapped youth.* Baltimore: Brookes.

Will, M. (1984a). *OSERS programming for the transition of youth with severe disabilities: Bridges from school to working life.* Washington, DC: Office of Special Education and Rehabilitative Services, U.S. Department of Education.

Will, M. (1984b). *Supported employment for adults with severe disabilities: An OSERS program initiative.* Washington, DC: Office of Special Education and Rehabilitative Services, U.S. Department of Education.

Wolfe, P. S. (1992). Supported employment: A review of group models. In P. Wehman, P. Sale, & W. Parent (Eds.), *Supported employment: Strategies for integration of workers with disabilities* (pp. 3–28). Stoneham, MA: Butterworth-Heinemann.

Wright, T. J., Emener, W. G., & Ashley, J. M. (1988). Rehabilitation counseling and client transition from school to work. In S. E. Rubin & N. Rubin (Eds.), *Contemporary challenges to the rehabilitation counseling profession* (pp. 135–151). Baltimore: Brookes.

Zigmond, N., & Thornton, H. (1985). Follow-up of postsecondary age learning disabled graduates and drop-outs. *Learning Disabilities Research, 1*(1), 50–55.

Chapter 6

Ethics and Ethical Decision Making in Rehabilitation Counseling

Jeanne Boland Patterson

thical behavior is one of the requirements of being an effective and competent rehabilitation counselor. In addition to the wide range of knowledge and skills needed by rehabilitation counselors, they must (a) use the knowledge and skills in an ethical manner, (b) recognize ethical dilemmas that are inherent in their profession, and (c) possess ethical decision-making skills to resolve ethical dilemmas. Ethics and ethical behavior are complex issues. They require far more than common sense or the desire to work with clients. Knowledge of ethics for professional rehabilitation counselors is as important as knowledge of medical, psychological, or vocational information related to individuals with disabilities. As Pharis and Hill (1983) stated, "ethical and professional behaviors are every bit as much a relevant index of a professional's competence as are levels of knowledge, skill, and experience" (p. 183).

Ethics

Webster's Ninth New Collegiate Dictionary (1985) defined ethics as "a set of moral principles or values" and "the principles of conduct governing an individual or group" (p. 426). The complexity of ethics is evident in Van Hoose and Kottler's (1985) description of ethics: "Ethics is concerned with questions that have no ultimate answers, yet are important to planning one's life, justifying one's activities, and deciding what one ought to do" (p. 3). For rehabilitation counselors, ethics encompasses legal, value, and moral issues. Consider the following example:

> *Kelly Smith, a rehabilitation counselor, is assisting a client, Lynn, in securing employment. An employer calls Kelly about a temporary vacancy with the company. Kelly is sure Lynn will want the position, if Lynn learns of its availability. Kelly believes the vacancy will meet Lynn's immediate need for employment, but is aware that Lynn has more skills than required to do the job. Furthermore, Kelly does not believe that 6 months from now Lynn will be satisfied with the job. However, Kelly also believes that the temporary job may become a permanent position. What should Kelly do?*

The numerous factors that influence the many decisions rehabilitation counselors face each day, as well as Kelly's decision, are addressed in the remainder of this chapter.

Code of Ethics

In 1972 the National Rehabilitation Counseling Association (NRCA) adopted a code of ethics for rehabilitation counselors, which was used by rehabilitation counselors until 1987. In 1987 a committee representing the NRCA, the American Rehabilitation Counseling Association (ARCA), and the Commission on Rehabilitation Counseling Certification (CRCC) completed 2 years of work on a revised code, the Code of Professional Ethics for Rehabilitation Counselors (Code, 1988; see Appendix 6.A). The Code is one source of assistance for rehabilitation counselors when they encounter ethical dilemmas. A code of ethics provides rehabilitation counselors with the profession's position on various behaviors and responsibilities of its members. It also provides protection to clients, counselors, the profession, and society at large. The purpose of any code of ethics is to

1. Provide a position on standards of practice to assist counselors in deciding what to do when situations of conduct arise in his work.

2. Clarify the counselor's responsibility to the client and protecting the client from the counselor's violation of, or failure to fulfill, these responsibilities.

3. Give the profession some assurance that the practices of its members will not be detrimental to the general functions and purposes of the profession.

4. Give society some guarantee that the services of the counselor will demonstrate a sensible regard for the social codes and moral expectations of the community in which he works.

5. Provide the counselor with some grounds for safe guarding his own privacy and integrity. (Shertzer & Stone, 1980, pp. 391–392)

Although the CRCC was concerned primarily about enforceability of the 1972 code, the three professional associations were critically evaluating the code because of many other limitations: narrow application (state agencies vs. other settings employing rehabilitation counselors), contradictions with other codes used by rehabilitation counselors (e.g., the American Counseling Association Code of Ethics), and the fact that the code was not widely used as a guide by rehabilitation counselors (Brubaker, 1977; Cottone, 1982; Matkin & May, 1981).

The revised code, the Code of Professional Ethics for Rehabilitation Counselors, consists of 10 canons and 72 rules. As stated in the preamble to the Code, the canons are general standards of an aspirational nature, whereas the rules provide more exacting standards that suggest appropriate actions in specific circumstances. For example, Canon 3 states that "Rehabilitation counselors shall serve as advocates for people with disabilities," whereas Rule 3.2 [R3.2] states that "Rehabilitation Counselors will assure, prior to referring clients to programs, facilities, or employment settings, that they are appropriately accessible."

Any code of ethics, however, provides only broad guidelines. When using a code to assist in ethical decision making, a counselor may find that there are two applicable (and contradictory) rules (Stude & McKelvey, 1979; Van Hoose & Kottler, 1985). Therefore, counselors must be thoroughly familiar with their profession's code of ethics, but at the same time recognize that using the code is only one part of the ethical decision-making process. As Tarvydas (1987) stated, ethical behavior is much more than "simplistic, mechanical adherence to a code of ethics" (p. 52).

Counselors are also guided by laws. Some ethical dilemmas have legal components, and legal and ethical issues frequently overlap. Although some unethical acts may be legal, any illegal act is unethical, because R1.1 requires rehabilitation counselors to "obey the laws and statutes in the legal jurisdiction in which they practice." In distinguishing between legal and ethical issues, rehabilitation counselors must consider that

> ethical codes do not supersede the law. In general, a code of ethics may add to or clarify existing laws and policy, but does not condone behavior that is contrary to the established laws of a society. Conversely, laws are finite and cannot cover every situation between people in general and counselors and clients in specific. Ethical standards are necessary to assist the counselor in professional conduct that is in the client's and society's best interest. (Stude & McKelvey, 1979, p. 456)

Thus, rehabilitation counselors must know their code of ethics and applicable laws.

Ethical Decision Making

Various models have been developed to explain and/or assist in ethical decision making. Emener, Wright, Klein, Lavender, and Smith (1987) identified three modes of response to ethical dilemmas: (a) nonconscious awareness, where the individual responds without awareness of the ethic involved; (b) conscious self-awareness, where the counselor thinks about the ethic involved; or (c) consultation, where the counselor refers to a code of ethics, or consults with a colleague, supervisor, or professional group. They found that almost half of the rehabilitation counselors responded to ethical dilemmas with "unconscious awareness," and only about 25% of the counselors sought some form of consultation regarding an ethical decision. Counselors were most likely to seek consultation from their supervisors when the issues involved (a) confidentiality and a client's legal proceedings, (b) conflicts between the client's interests and the welfare of the community, (c) illegal behavior of a client that might harm the client and/or the community, and (d) termination of the rehabilitation counseling relationship with a client.

Nonconscious awareness and conscious self-awareness fall into what Kitchener (1986) calls "intuitive" decisions. These decisions, which are based on morals, beliefs, and prior experience, are the most common ways of responding to ethical dilemmas. Because intuition may not lead to the best ethical decisions, particularly when the situation is unexpected or unique, Kitchener (1984) recommended a "critical–evaluative" approach to ethical dilemmas, which can help individuals deal with unexpected or unique situations and provide a method of evaluating one's intuitive responses. The critical–evaluative approach consists of three hierarchically arranged levels of moral reasoning. In seeking to resolve an ethical dilemma, the rehabilitation counselor begins with the first tier, consisting of laws and ethical rules. In the absence of laws or when the code does not provide clear direction or contains contradictory rules, then the counselor moves to the second and higher level of norms, called ethical principles.

Using Kelly's situation, from the beginning of the chapter, as an example, Kelly might consider the federal regulation that states that clients must work for 60 days before they can be considered successfully rehabilitated, and their cases closed ("26" closures). Kelly can also consult the Code, which states that (a) the client should not be placed in a situation that is damaging to the interest and welfare of the client or the employer and (b) clients should be placed only in positions that are consistent with their overall abilities, interests, and aptitudes [R2.9]. If Kelly does not believe that these considerations specifically address the problem, Kelly may move to Kitchener's second tier, ethical principles.

Ethical Principles

The most critical principles for evaluating ethical concerns are those set forth by Beauchamp and Childress (1989): autonomy, beneficence, nonmaleficence, justice, and fidelity. These are discussed in the following sections.

Autonomy

The principle of autonomy encompasses both self-autonomy and the autonomy of others, and states that individuals have the right to make their own decisions.

According to Kitchener (1984), "autonomy is based on the assumption that an individual has the ability to make competent and rational decisions" (p. 46). Rehabilitation counselors must remain cognizant that with most of their clients, competence is not an all-or-nothing proposition. Powell (1984) stated, "competence has practical utility as a concept only when we give it a context. A person may be competent to do one thing but not another. . . . We need always to be clear about the context in which we are assessing competence" (p. 58). Therefore, Beauchamp and Childress (1989) suggested that any restrictions on autonomy should be limited to areas of true incompetence.

Balancing issues of competence and autonomy is most difficult for rehabilitation counselors working with individuals with severe mental illness or profound mental retardation. Regardless of their disability, however, all individuals should have the right to make choices, defined as "the opportunity to make an uncoerced selection from two or more alternative events, consequences, or responses. By uncoerced, we mean that there are no programmed implicit or explicit consequences for selecting one alternative over the others except for the characteristics of the alternatives themselves" (Brigham, 1979, p. 132).

Although promoting autonomy is consistent with facilitating independence in people with disabilities, rehabilitation counselors may compromise this principle when clients have an emotional or mental illness. Armed with their professional knowledge, rehabilitation counselors may presume they know what is best for these clients. Furthermore, they may be concerned that clients will make bad choices (Guess, Benson, & Siegel-Causey, 1985) or that autonomy for these individuals may hamper the acquisition of independent living skills (Knowlton, Turnbull, Backus, & Turnbull, 1988). However, Bannerman, Sheldon, Sherman, and Harchik (1990) reminded counselors that legislation guarantees the right of choice for people with developmental disabilities. Moreover, they said, "People should be allowed to exercise as much choice as their abilities allow whether it involves expressing a simple preference or weighing the advantages and disadvantages of several options during complex decision making" (p. 82).

Nonmaleficence and Beneficence

Nonmaleficence—not causing physical or emotional harm to others—prohibits the professional from both (a) purposefully harming an individual and (b) acting in ways that might cause harm to others. Although harm is not specifically addressed in the Code, other than in Canon 2, which requires rehabilitation counselors to "protect the welfare of people and groups with whom they work," the potential for harm exists in all phases of the rehabilitation process, from assessment to placement. The potential for harm exists when (a) inappropriate services are provided, (b) assessment results are misused, or (c) rehabilitation plans are not carefully monitored. Harm is also possible when counselors recommend the placement of clients in jobs that could exacerbate their disability. Beneficence— contributing to the welfare of or helping individuals—undergirds rehabilitation counseling. In resolving ethical dilemmas and weighing ethical principles, however, the principle of nonmaleficence generally presents a stronger ethical obligation than beneficence.

One issue frequently faced by rehabilitation counselors is being helpful without becoming parental or authoritarian. This occurs when "an authority has knowledge of what is good for an individual and undertakes to regulate that person's behavior according to what the authority believes to be good" (Kitchener, 1984, p. 49). Although it is critical for rehabilitation counselors to balance beneficence and autonomy, achieving this balance is difficult. The counselor may feel "pulled in two directions: the benevolent authoritarian versus the absolute respecter of a client's autonomy" (Fitting, 1984, p. 70). One way to balance beneficence and autonomy is to ask the question, "How serious are the potential consequences of a client's making his or her own decision?"

Justice

The principle of justice relates to fairness and encompasses beliefs related to equal access and equal treatment. Justice is frequently both a legal and an ethical issue (e.g., discrimination [R1.9]). Rehabilitation counselors in state agencies frequently weigh, consciously or unconsciously, the principle of justice when they determine who will be accepted for services. Believing in the dignity and worth of all individuals with disabilities, rehabilitation counselors must guard against discriminating on the basis of a client's disability, ethnicity, gender, or personality. Limited resources also influence justice in rehabilitation, when counselors must decide (a) who is most needy or (b) whether to expend more on one client and less on other clients.

Fidelity

The principle of fidelity embodies keeping promises, being honest, and being loyal. Honesty is a particularly critical principle in rehabilitation counseling, because it is central to the counseling relationship. Lying to a client is disrespectful, prevents the development of trust in the relationship, and impedes or inhibits the goals of rehabilitation. Although many rehabilitation counselors would never consider lying to a client in the counseling relationship, they may do so when the purpose is research. Yet the Code clearly states that "When methodological requirements of a study necessitate concealment or deception, Rehabilitation Counselors will ensure that participants understand the reasons for this action" [R8.5]. Furthermore, as Lindsey (1984) pointed out, "Misinformation or inadequate information makes it impossible for subjects to exercise, adequately and responsibly, their right to choose whether or not to participate in a given research endeavor" (p. 81). Honesty is also addressed in R1.2, which states that "Rehabilitation Counselors will be thoroughly familiar with, will observe, and will discuss with their clients the legal limitations of their services, or benefits offered to clients so as to facilitate honest and open communication and realistic expectations."

The principle of fidelity also includes confidentiality and informed consent, which are addressed in numerous rules within the Code. For example, rehabilitation counselors must (a) "make clear to clients, the purposes, goals, and limitations that may affect the counseling relationship" [R2.1]; (b) accurately represent their role to clients [R2.2]; (c) "inform clients or the clients' legal guardians of factors that may affect clients' decisions to participate in rehabilitation services, and . . . obtain written consent after clients or their legal guardians are fully informed of such factors" [R2.5]; (d) "inform clients at the onset of the counseling relationship of the limits of confidentiality" [R6.1]; (e) "not forward to another person, agency, or potential employer, any confidential information without written permission of clients or their legal guardians" [R6.3]; (f) "obtain written permission from clients or their legal guardians prior to taping or otherwise recording counseling sessions" [R6.7]; (g) "make known the purpose of testing and the explicit use of the results to clients prior to administration" [R7.5]; (h) protect confidentiality in research data [R8.1]; and (i) fully protect the identity of clients in "presenting case studies in classes, professional meetings, or publications" [R8.3].

Kitchener (1984) suggested that ethical principles are *prima facie* valid. She said, "moral principles are neither absolute nor relative, but they are always ethically relevant and can be overturned only when there are stronger ethical obligations" (p. 52). When principles are in conflict or do not appear to provide assistance in resolving an ethical dilemma (as in the example of Kelly), rehabilitation counselors should turn to ethical theory for guidance.

Ethical Theory

The last tier in Kitchener's (1984) model is ethical theory. Although there are three types of ethical theories, normative ethical theories, meta-ethical theories, and good reason theories (Gewirth, 1975), rehabilitation counselors are concerned primarily with normative ethical theories, which attempt to "systematically establish general principles for determining right or wrong or good or evil" (Nielsen, 1972, p. 121). In this case, *normative* means "what the behavior of professionals should be rather than what it is" (Bayles, 1981, p. 16). In facing an ethical dilemma, a rehabilitation counselor should ask, "Do I want my action to be a general or universal law?"

Ethical principles are both teleological and deontological. Teleological theories hold that "actions are right because of the goodness of their consequences," whereas deontological theories hold that "certain kinds of actions are inherently right or right as a matter of principle, because of their being the kinds of actions that they are or because of their conforming to some formal principle" (Gewirth, 1975, p. 977). Like psychologists, rehabilitation counselors "use the term [teleology] to describe purposive behavior rather than the consequences of behavior" (Eyde & Quaintance, 1988, p. 150). In adjudicating ethical complaints, the CRCC considers the seriousness of the behaviors involved by considering (a) potential harm (a teleological consideration) and (b) whether the behavior is deliberate, persistent, or both.

Because of the complexity of ethical theory, Kitchener (1984) recommended the good reasons approach to making ethical decisions when ethical principles conflict; the good reasons approach is based on the golden rule. In considering alternative courses of action using the good reasons approach, rehabilitation counselors should ask (a) what they "would want for themselves or for others they love who are in the same circumstances" or (b) which action would produce "the least amount of avoidable harm" (Kitchener, 1986, p. 309).

To make ethical decisions, counselors must consider their code of ethics, applicable laws, ethical principles, and ethical theory. Ethical decision making provides a systematic approach, using a sequence of steps, to help counselors reach a decision and choose a course of action.

The Ethical Decision-Making Process

Tymchuk (1982) identified the following process factors to assist counselors in "gathering information, weighing interests, and reaching decisions" (p. 167): balancing the rights of the client with the public interest; resolving ethical mandates that conflict with legal actions; protecting clients in areas where recognized standards do not exist; considering justice and equality, particularly in instances where the rights of the client must be balanced with the rights of a parent or guardian; assuring the participation and involvement in the decision-making process of all individuals who are affected by a decision; using guardians and/or advocates; and using levels of decisions, specifically those required in various types of research. According to Tymchuk (1982), these processes that "represent society's ground rules for reaching moral decisions" (p. 167) are generally used in conjunction with the following four decision criteria: (a) cost, (b) time and effort, (c) benefits and risks, and (d) other aspects, such as long term versus short term and chance of occurrence when risks are involved.

Before an individual can determine the decision process, however, the ethical dilemma must be recognized. Flowers and Parker (1984) stated that many everyday ethical conflicts faced by rehabilitation counselors go unnoticed or are purposely ignored, and "nearly every act of rehabilitation counselors during working hours (and to some extent during nonworking hours) offers potential ethical considerations and the concomitant possibility of damage to the client, the relatives and acquaintances of the client, the rehabilitation agency, the profession, the counselor involved, and even the community" (p. 56). Counselors, regardless of setting, must be alert for ethical conflicts throughout the rehabilitation process. To assist counselors in identifying potential ethical dilemmas, Table 6.1 presents the rehabilitation process (utilizing the state agency status system, described in greater detail by Brabham, Mandeville, & Koch, Chapter 2, this text) and questions related to the Code of Professional Ethics for Rehabilitation Counselors.

Table 6.1

Questions To Facilitate Ethical Behavior in the Rehabilitation Process[a]

Pre-Client Meeting

1. Do I have a copy of and working knowledge of the Code of Professional Ethics for Rehabilitation Counselors?

2. Do I have an understanding of my personal values?

3. Do I have copies or knowledge of applicable agency/company/facility rules, regulations, and policies?

4. Are there disparities between agency rules and the Code that I need to communicate to the agency or ethics committee?

5. Do I have any personal problems or conflicts that may interfere with my professional effectiveness?

Initial Meeting

6. Have I followed up on the referral in a timely manner?

7. Did I inform the client at the onset of the interview of the limits of confidentiality?

8. Have I discussed with clients the legal limitations of their services and benefits available?

9. Do clients have realistic expectations of the services and benefits that are available to them?

10. Have I discussed with clients the purposes, goals, and limitations that may affect our relationship?

11. Is this a dual relationship that could impair my judgment or risk exploitation of the client?

12. Have I obtained written consent of the client or the client's legal guardian?

13. Have I referred the client to other specialists as the needs of the client dictate?

14. Do my written reports contain only germane data, and have I made every effort to avoid undue invasion of privacy?

Plan Development

15. Have I promptly supplied the necessary information for evaluation services?

16. Are there defined policies and practices within any agency cooperatively serving rehabilitation clients?

17. Have I investigated ways in which the family might become involved in the client's rehabilitation and secured the client's permission to involve the family?

(Continues)

Table 6.1 *Continued.*

18. Did I inform the client of the purpose of any testing and the explicit use of the results prior to referring a client for testing?

19. Have I carefully reviewed any assessment results for a client who may not have been represented in the standardized norm group?

20. Do I understand the effects of socioeconomic, ethnic, disability, and cultural factors on test scores?

21. Did I explain any assessment results in terms the client could understand?

22. Have I secured from other specialists appropriate reports and evaluations that are essential for rehabilitation planning or service delivery?

Plan Completion

23. Does this plan reflect the joint efforts between the client and me?

24. Is this an integrated, individualized plan that offers reasonable promise of success?

25. Is this plan consistent with the abilities and circumstances of the client?

26. Is there a fair mutual understanding of the rehabilitation plan by all agencies cooperating in the rehabilitation of the client?

27. Was the plan developed with such mutual understanding?

Plan Implementation

28. Am I persistently monitoring the plan to ensure its continued viability and effectiveness?

29. Did I ensure that any program or facility was appropriately accessible prior to referring a client to that program or facility?

30. Am I remaining aware of the actions taken by cooperating agencies on behalf of my client?

31. Have I acted as an advocate for my client in ensuring effective service delivery?

Placement

32. Have the client and I worked together in considering employment in only jobs and circumstances that are consistent with the client's overall abilities, vocational limitations, physical restrictions, general temperament, interest and aptitude pattern, social skills, education, general qualifications, and other relevant characteristics and needs?

33. Would any positions we are considering result in damaging the interest and welfare of either the client or the employer?

(Continues)

Table 6.1 *Continued.*

34. Did I ensure that any employment setting was appropriately accessible prior to referring a client to that employer?

35. Did I provide the employer with only job-relevant information about the client?

Follow-up/Case Closure

36. Are both the client and the employer satisfied with this placement?

37. Have I provided for any postemployment services that may be indicated?

38. Does this closure suggest any areas in which I have not promoted the welfare of the client?

Closed/Not Rehabilitated

39. Does this decision actually reflect that the client is not eligible (or feasible)?

40. Have I responded to external pressures in reaching this decision?

41. Have I allowed assessment data to inappropriately screen out a client?

42. Have I discontinued the relationship because it is expected that the relationship can be of no benefit to the client?

43. Have I referred the client to another agency that may be able to assist the client?

---

[a]Wording of the questions is based on "The Code of Professional Ethics for Rehabilitation Counselors," 1988, *Rehabilitation Counseling Bulletin, 31,* pp. 255–268.

Identifying potential conflicts is the initial step in maintaining ethical standards. Ethical decision making is the next, and perhaps the most important, step. Tymchuk (1982) outlined the following process for making ethical decisions:

▶ **Step 1.** Describe the parameters of the situation.

Step 2. Describe the potential issues involved.

Step 3. Describe the guidelines already available that might affect each issue (e.g., values, law, codes, practice, research).

Step 4. Enumerate the alternative decisions for each issue.

Step 5. Enumerate the short-term, ongoing, and long-term consequences for each alternative.

Step 6. Present evidence (or the lack thereof) for those consequences as well as the probability of occurrence.

Step 7. Rank order and vote on the decisions. (p. 170)

In addition to the questions recommended by Kitchener (1986) (e.g., What would I want for a member of my family? What action will produce the least harm?), additional questions have been formulated to assist individuals in making ethical decisions. These include Would I want what I was doing published in the newspaper? Would I like my family to know? Will it make me proud? Is it legal? What effect will it have on the behavior of others? How will I feel? (Blanchard & Peale, 1988).

Rehabilitation counselors must be able to recognize ethical conflicts, identify competing interests among involved parties, develop alternative courses of action, describe short- and long-term consequences for each alternative, reach a decision, and describe a rationale for the decision. Kitchener (1986) identified four components of ethics education that can be translated into ethics skills for rehabilitation counselors:

1. *Interpreting the situation as a moral one.* Rehabilitation counselors must possess the ability to determine whether their actions affect the welfare of others and hypothesize what impact or consequences their actions may have on the individuals involved. Factors that complicate this process include individual differences in identifying and/or interpreting situations, sensitivity, emotional reactions, and moral empathy (ability to see oneself in a client's position).

2. *Formulating a moral course of action.* Factors that influence this process include age and education, as well as one's ability to integrate the various moral considerations into a course of action.

3. *Deciding what to do.* As Van Hoose and Kottler (1985) pointed out, there is a difference between "attitudinal morality" (what individuals believe) and "behavioral morality" (what individuals say and do on the basis of their beliefs). Kitchener (1986) described this as the preemption of moral ideals by less noble motives (e.g., friendship, loyalty, money, self-interest, ambition).

4. *Implementing a plan of action.* Ego strength and a sense of moral responsibility to act ethically are factors that influence actions. "There is not necessarily a perfect correlation between what one believes and how one acts" (Van Hoose & Kottler, 1985, p. 25). Some individuals will behave unethically, even when they know their actions are wrong.

Rehabilitation counselors who possess ethics skills recognize that acting ethically (a) may not *feel good;* (b) often requires balancing a lesser harm against a greater harm, or violating one ethical principle to uphold another; (c) requires that counselors consider the public trust in the profession; and (d) requires that counselors tolerate the ambiguity of ethical decision making. They recognize that few absolutes exist and that certainty is virtually impossible (Kitchener, 1986). The ambiguity of ethical decision making is also evident in Van Hoose and Kottler's (1985) statement:

If one has a specific, responsible rationale for a given behavior, can defend it as justifiable under the circumstances, and the results turn out favorably, one is in the clear. If, however, the result turns out poorly and somebody complains or files suit, the same action may be construed as irresponsible, unethical, incompetent, or illegal. (p. 42)

Importance of Ethical Decision Making

In a survey of 267 ARCA and NRCA members, of whom 49% were rehabilitation counselors, Pape and Klein (1986) found that (a) only 30% of the respondents referred to a code of ethics to resolve an ethical dilemma, and (b) 45% of the respondents were aware of unethical behavior by a rehabilitation colleague, agency, or company. These findings support Van Hoose and Kottler's (1985) contention that "the majority of ethical violations result not from willful disregard of professional codes, but, rather, from ignorance and poor judgment" (p. 10). Nonetheless, "persons are ultimately responsible for their ethical decisions and behaviors" (p. 170).

It should be evident that ethical behavior can be neither equated with common sense nor viewed as an inherent trait. Flowers and Parker (1984) pointed out, "Ethical conduct goes beyond common sense, sound judgment, and work experience" (p. 62). Nonetheless, ethical decision making is a skill that can be learned by practitioners (Handelsman, 1986). Why, then, do some rehabilitation counselors behave unethically?

Unethical Behavior

The following situations, cited by Flowers and Parker (1984, p. 55), are examples of unethical behavior:

1. The sale of a 60-year-old boat by a division counselor to a client for $1,000. It was paid for by division funds as a "rehabilitation expense" but was still drydocked and unusable.

2. The purchase of some yarn for an 85-year-old grandmother who "liked to knit but had no yarn," and who was then listed as rehabilitated.

3. The use of state money to outfit a staff softball team with silk-screened shirts and caps.

4. The purchase for $1,789 of a small tractor for an area motel owner although he neither requested nor received it. When he told local division officials he had bought one already, the machine was given to the Douglas County Hospital.

Other examples of unethical behavior by rehabilitation counselors include (a) hiring a client to clean a counselor's house and paying for the service from on-the-job training funds; (b) going into a business partnership with a rehabilitation client; (c) having a sexual relationship with a client; and (d) changing a report on a client to reflect the desires of the insurance company rather than the counselor's judgment.

Each of these situations reflects (a) a lack of sound judgment, (b) desire for financial gain, and/or (c) external pressures. This is consistent with the definition of an unethical individual:

> One who lacks sufficient integrity, moral commitment, and sound judgment to maintain standards of right and wrong actions in . . . professional practice. . . . [The individual] may be unaware of or unconcerned about the ethical standards of . . . [the] profession and ignorant of the possible negative effects of . . . [the] behavior. (Van Hoose & Kottler, 1985, p. 109)

Unethical rehabilitation counselors, whether acting out of ignorance or purposefulness, are dangerous not only to their clients' welfare, but to "the effectiveness of their institutions, the integrity and reputation of their colleagues, and the stability of their profession" (Van Hoose & Kottler, 1985, p. 108).

It is important to note the difference between unethical behavior and incompetent behavior, and the conditions that contribute to each. Incompetent behavior reflects training and skill deficits, poor judgment, or inability to recognize one's limitations, whereas unethical behavior generally results from external pressures, the pursuit of personal gain or professional enhancement, ignorance, lack of a philosophical base, and conflict between ethical principles and agency regulations (Van Hoose & Kottler, 1985). Typical examples of unethical behavior include "violation of confidentiality, negligent practice, sexual activity with a client, certain conflicts of interest, and questionable financial arrangements" (Levenson, 1986, p. 315).

Van Hoose and Kottler (1985) identified a number of common "slightly" unethical behaviors: (a) telling clients little white lies, (b) focusing on oneself in the interview, (c) becoming personally involved with clients beyond acceptable limits, (d) promoting dependencies in clients, (e) deceiving clients for "therapeutic" purposes, (f) exceeding personal competence levels, (g) imposing personal values on clients, (h) denying responsibility for errors, and (i) practicing with personal and professional rigidity.

Responding to Unethical Practices

With 45% of the respondents in Pape and Klein's (1986) survey reporting that they were aware of unethical behavior on the part of a colleague, agency, or company, one might ask whether the unethical behaviors were addressed at all, formally or informally. Unfortunately, the answer is probably not. However, Rules 4.9 and 4.10 in the Code of Professional Ethics for Rehabilitation Counselors states,

> Rehabilitation Counselors who know of an ethical violation by another Rehabilitation Counselor will informally attempt to resolve the issue with the counselor, when the misconduct is of a minor nature and/or appears to be due to lack of sensitivity, knowledge, or experience. If the violation does not seem amenable to an informal solution, or is of a more serious nature, Rehabilitation Counselors will bring it to the attention of the appropriate committee on professional ethics.
>
> Rehabilitation Counselors possessing information concerning an alleged violation of this Code, will, upon request, reveal such information to the Commission on Rehabilitation Counselor Certification or other authority empowered to investigate or act upon the alleged violation, unless the information is protected by law. (Code, 1988, pp. 261–262)

Levenson (1986) outlined a number of reasons unethical behavior is frequently ignored:

1. Professional bonding that takes the form of an implicit expectation that colleagues do not report or testify against one another

2. Fear of ostracism by colleagues that could result in professional isolation

3. Fear of being sued for libel

4. Belief that nothing positive will happen

5. Belief that one's own behavior is not always perfect

6. Belief that the source of information (client or colleague) may not be truthful

7. Misunderstanding one's professional responsibility by believing that one must be detective, judge, and jury

Rehabilitation counselors may also face an ethical dilemma when a client reports unethical behavior, but "does not want to get involved." In this case, the counselor may be faced with two competing ethical principles: a responsibility to protect the public and upholding the rights of the individual client. Although the path of least resistance may be to ignore or go along with unethical behavior, Flowers and Parker (1984) stated, "in the long run failure to correct a pattern of ethical violations results in irreparable damage. Furthermore, patterns of ethical violation, if ignored by peers, may lead to more serious violations and ultimately implicate the entire profession" (p. 56).

The implications of not reporting are clear in the area of sexual misconduct. Although only a small number of professionals engage in sexual acts with their clients (Levenson, 1986), Bouhoutsos, Holroyd, and Lerman (1983) reported that, of those who did, 75% to 80% engaged in sexual acts with more than one client.

Levenson (1986) cautioned counselors against discounting allegations from clients and encouraged the discussion of rumors, when the information was obtained from colleagues. Because the procedures for initiating complaints of unethical behavior differ among professions, states, and work settings, Levenson (1986) suggested the following options for counselors when they learn of a colleague's unethical practice from a client: (a) obtain written consent from the client; (b) carefully help the client explore feelings and resolve conflicts over reporting; (c) inform the client that sexual activity between a counselor and client is unethical; (d) consider whether the client has resolved self-blame or guilt issues; (e) in selected instances, such as "clients with more serious underlying psychopathology who may become psychotic, suicidal, or homicidal after having been sexually abused" (p. 316), refer the client to an appropriate professional; (f) discuss the allegations directly with the accused; (g) formally report the case, if the allegation is credible, to the counselor's supervisor and state licensing board or certification commission; and (h) notify third-party payers, when the counselor construes sexual acts as treatment.

Factors Influencing Ethical or Unethical Behavior

Ferrell and Gresham (1985) identified two major classifications of variables that influence ethical behavior: (a) individual variables (knowledge, values, attitudes, and intentions derived from one's personal background, as well as socialization characteristics, such as education and experience) and (b) organizational variables (external factors, such as other organizations, and internal factors, such as peers and supervisors). Social psychologists have debated whether behavior results from the interaction of situational and individual behaviors or solely from situational variables (e.g., contingencies of reinforcement, learning history, and the influence of significant others) (Stead, Worrell, Spalding, & Stead, 1987).

Other studies (see Ferrell & Gresham, 1985) found that organizational factors, such as philosophy, expectations, policies, and supervision, often exert greater influence over ethical versus unethical decisions than do individual factors (values, past experiences, knowledge, and attitudes). Stead et al. (1987) found that unethical decisions resulted from an individual's decision history (a social-learning variable), which overshadowed individual variables, such as sex, age, nationality, type of religion, frequency of church attendance, years of full-time work experience, and race. Unethical decisions may also be a function of one's stage of moral development and ethical reasoning.

Stages of Ethical Reasoning

Building on the work of Piaget (1965) and Kohlberg (1984), Van Hoose and Paradise (1979) outlined five developmental stages of ethical reasoning:

1. *Punishment orientation*—rigidly adhering to social standards regarding punishment.

2. *Institutional orientation*—attending to the expectations of an institution or other higher authorities.

3. *Societal orientation*—maintaining societal standards, procuring the approval of others, and avoiding difficulties.

4. *Individual orientation*—promoting individual welfare, without discounting laws and the welfare of society.

5. *Principle or conscience orientation*—demonstrating concern for the client, with the individual following internal standards without regard for legal and social consequences.

The following example illustrates the type of ethical decision an individual might make in different stages:

> *A client who is receiving workers' compensation payments while receiving reha-bilitation for a work-related injury tells the counselor that she is going to another state to visit her sister who has recently had a baby. The client indicates that she will return in about 2 weeks. The counselor calls the insurance adjuster to inform him that the client is "unavailable" for rehabilitation and compensa-tion payments should be suspended until the client returns to town. When the client returns, she finds the letter that her payments have been suspended and she is unable to pay her rent. The client angrily calls the counselor, who finds that the working relationship with the client has been severely damaged.*
>
> *Two weeks later the counselor faces the same situation with a different client. The counselor informs the client about the "availability to work" requirement linked to part of the rehabilitation compensation benefit. In this case, they negotiate the length of time the client will be gone and outline activities upon the client's return.*

It is obvious with the first client that the rehabilitation counselor is operating from the level of Stage 1 (punishment orientation) or Stage 2 (institutional orien-tation), whereas with the second client the counselor is operating at the level of Stage 4 (individual orientation) or even Stage 5 (principle or conscience orienta-tion). According to Pelsma and Borgers (1986), the change in the counselor can be explained by an experiential learning model (Kolb, 1984). According to this model, learning occurs through the resolution of conflicts between one's (a) concrete experience (affective/feeling), (b) reflective observation (perceptual/observing), (c) abstract conceptualization (symbolic/thinking), and (d) active experimentation (behavioral/doing). Therefore, the change in the counselor in the preceding exam-ple comes from the resolution of conflict between the counselor's experience with the first client and the reflective observation, as well as abstract conceptualization that occurred following the incident. The counselor's active experimentation led to different behavior with the second client.

In describing their model, Pelsma and Borgers (1986) set forth the following assumptions: (a) the stage at which a counselor functions varies according to the specific situation, the particular individuals involved, and the counselor's previous training and experience; (b) some ethical decisions are more correct than others; (c) the counselor's ethical orientation is the foundation for the decision; (d) "overlapping and continuous," the ethical orientations are on a "developmental continuum" that spirals up "the ethical reasoning scale" (p. 313) toward higher levels of ethical reasoning; and (e) the reasoning process may be at a higher level than the behavior that one exhibits.

Personal and Professional Values

In entering a profession, rehabilitation counselors must acquire the values of the profession and reconcile those with the personal values that they bring with them. To do so, they must understand their personal values. One way to accomplish this is through various values-clarification exercises.

The basic philosophical tenets that reflect the values of the profession of rehabilitation counseling encompass beliefs about individuals, the impact of disability, and the strategies that achieve the goals of rehabilitation (Maki & Riggar, 1985). These tenets include (a) recognition that, regardless of the severity of a disability, all individuals need respect and encouragement; (b) consideration of disability issues within an environmental context, because the environment can increase or diminish the severity of a disability; (c) client participation in the development and execution of rehabilitation plans, which reflect the assets and unique characteristics of individual clients; (d) involvement of the multiple disciplines and agencies, as well as the significant others, in providing rehabilitation services; (e) comprehension of the dangers in applying predictor variables (particularly those based on group outcomes) to individual clients; and (f) full integration and participation of individuals with disabilities in the general life of their communities through appropriate resource allocation, societal commitment, and review by rehabilitation professionals of the principles guiding this full participation (Wright, 1983). The beliefs of rehabilitation counselors encompass the human dignity of all individuals, the value of individual abilities, and freedom of choice (Szymanski, 1987), as well as "basic beliefs in human rights, the value of work, and a partnership with persons with disabilities" (Szymanski, 1985, p. 2). In acting on these beliefs, rehabilitation counselors advocate for individual, societal, and environmental adaptations that promote full participation of individuals with disabilities in society (Greenwood, 1987).

Other values inherent in the profession of rehabilitation counseling include the dignity and worth of all individuals; the ability of people with disabilities to become self-sufficient and contributing members of society; the right of individuals with disabilities to equal opportunity; and the psychological benefits of independence and self-sufficiency to individuals with disabilities (Bozarth, 1981). Most rehabilitation counselors embrace the preceding values, although some do not. The following two statements reflect two different value systems: "I work for whomever pays my bill" versus "I have to fight with my supervisor over every service I need to provide to my clients."

In considering the stages of moral development and the values inherent in rehabilitation counseling, one can see why "ethical decisions at any given time represent a blend of feelings, beliefs, prejudices, and experiences" (Van Hoose & Kottler, 1985, p. 170). It is also evident that ethical behavior is related to one's personal values, identity as a professional, ability to recognize ethical situations, and knowledge of ethical decision-making models.

Another aspect of values that counselors must consider is the degree to which they impose their values on their clients. Rule 2.3 minimally addresses this area by stating that "Rehabilitation counselors will be continually cognizant of their own needs, values, and of their potentially influential position, vis-à-vis clients." Consciously or unconsciously, a counselor's values may influence whether an individual is viewed as eligible or feasible for rehabilitation or what types of services are offered. Value issues, which counselors may bring with them to the counseling relationship (and which could result in potential harm to clients) include abortion, lifestyle (homosexuality), and ethnicity.

To aid counselors in developing a style of ethics, Van Hoose and Kottler (1985) developed a series of questions, including the following:

1. What would you be willing to do for money?

2. In what circumstances would you lie to a client?

3. When would you divulge confidential information?

4. To what extent would you practice something that you are not qualified to practice or in which you lack competence?

5. How tolerant are you of colleagues' unethical practices?

6. How would you remedy a situation if you found out that you had made a mistake or a wrong diagnosis?

7. To what extent would you accept responsibility for negligence or errors?

8. To what extent do you impose your own morality on clients?

9. How much of yourself do you commit to your work?

10. To what extent do you evaluate your effectiveness? (pp. 41–42)

As counselors grow and acquire new experiences, their answers to these questions may change. Therefore, it is important for counselors to periodically address these questions throughout their counseling careers.

Ethical Issues in Rehabilitation Counseling

By virtue of the profession, each rehabilitation counselor faces similar ethical issues. However, each setting and service provided, and occasionally clients with specific types of disabilities (e.g., AIDS), also present unique ethical dilemmas. The following discussion highlights both common ethical issues, as well as those related to specific settings or services. In reviewing these issues, it is important to keep in mind Taylor's (1985) belief that "rehabilitation is rehabilitation" and that "the rehabilitation practitioner can practice ethically in any setting" (p. 223).

Conflicting Loyalties

Regardless of setting, rehabilitation counselors at some point in their careers come face to face with conflicting loyalties between clients and agencies or companies or between clients and colleagues. For example, a counselor may be told by his or her supervisor to place a client or close the case within 30 days. The counselor may feel that the client needs additional services prior to placement, but is afraid of jeopardizing his or her own employment with the agency. In this example, agency policy or needs are conflicting with client needs (Geist, Curin, Prestridge, & Schelb, 1973). Sometimes, the emphasis on "26" closures may determine which clients a counselor can or is willing to accept for services. Counselors who pride themselves on having the highest successful closure rate in a state may be outstanding counselors or they may be counselors who take few or no risks. They may be accepting "marginally" eligible or ineligible clients, providing minimal services, or providing inappropriate services (e.g., providing supported employment services to a client for whom such services were not intended).

In proprietary rehabilitation, the rehabilitation counselor may work for a private rehabilitation company that receives referrals from insurance companies. The companies may have interests that conflict with the client's welfare. Frequently, the rehabilitation counselor is also involved with two attorneys, one representing the client and one representing the insurance company. The insurance company is generally concerned with limiting the quantity of service to reduce costs, and the profit motive of the rehabilitation company can result in policies more favorable to the insurance company than to the client, in an effort to generate future referrals (Matkin & May, 1981).

There may also be conflicting loyalties or competing interests in the provision of supported employment services among (a) clients, (b) the families and advocates of clients, (c) employers, (d) other social service professionals, and (e) rehabilitation supervisors and management (Patterson & Curl, 1990). For example, a client may want to work, but the client's family may have concerns about (a) the loss of the client's monthly disability benefit or (b) the client's safety.

Canon 2 of the Code of Professional Ethics for Rehabilitation Counselors states, "The primary obligation of rehabilitation counselors is to their clients, defined as people with disabilities who are receiving services from rehabilitation counselors." Although this canon clearly indicates that the rehabilitation counselor's loyalty must be to the client, this does not diminish the anguish experienced by rehabilitation counselors when they realize that competing interests are at work. Furthermore, rehabilitation counselors have an obligation to "respect the rights and reputation of any institution, organization, or firm with which they are associated when making oral or written statements. In those instances where they are critical of policies, they attempt to effect change by constructive action within the organization" [R1.8].

When a rehabilitation counselor is told to change a report to conform with the wishes of an insurance company or when a rehabilitation counselor is told that all clients with psychiatric disabilities will receive only supported employment services, the counselor has to decide on a course of action. Sometimes these counselors feel that their only recourse is to resign their job, an option that may not be viable when job opportunities are limited or income and employment benefits (e.g., health insurance) are required for a family's survival.

Confidentiality

Confidentiality is frequently misunderstood by rehabilitation counselors. Canon 6 states, "Rehabilitation Counselors shall respect the confidentiality of information obtained from clients in the course of their work," but there are numerous limitations on confidentiality in rehabilitation counseling. Although state–federal vocational rehabilitation (VR) programs require clients to sign release forms to obtain medical records, the same is not true in the Workers' Compensation (WC) system. As Taylor (1985) noted, "the client is presumed to have given up a large measure of his right to privacy by accepting the benefits offered" (p. 225). In numerous states' WC systems, client records are exchanged routinely between physicians, insurance adjusters, attorneys, and rehabilitation counselors. For example, in Georgia, copies of most correspondence are sent to the insurance company and any attorneys that may be involved. To minimize any potential misunderstandings, rehabilitation counselors should closely adhere to R6.1 of the Code and notify clients "at the onset of the counseling relationship of the limits of confidentiality." In any service setting, counselors must guard against gossip, such as discussing clients over coffee breaks or in public areas where they may be overheard. Not only may clients be jeopardized, discussions of clients in public, even though names or other identifying information are not revealed, convey an unprofessional image.

Confidentiality is also an issue with certain disabilities, such as AIDS. Although counselors may confront this issue in any setting, it is especially problematic for counselors working in residential settings. In *Tarasoff v. Regents of University of*

California (1976), the court ruled that a therapist who knows that a client is a threat to another individual has a responsibility or "duty to warn" the other person. Duty to warn, therefore, is a limitation of confidentiality. Nonetheless, there is not general agreement in terms of the behavior of professionals and their duty to warn a partner of a client with AIDS (Stanard & Hazler, 1995), nor are the laws consistent across states (Hopkins & Anderson, 1990). Various guidelines (e.g., Cohen, 1990; Costa & Altekruse, 1994) have been set forth that can provide assistance to counselors. For example, Woods, Marks, and Dilley (1990) indicated that a counselor should have the following facts before one has a duty to warn or a "duty to protect" the other individual: (a) the client is HIV infected, (b) the client engages in unsafe behavior on a regular basis, (c) the behavior is actually unsafe, (d) the client intends to continue the behavior, and (e) HIV transmission is likely to occur. Even with guidelines such as these, however, rehabilitation counselors still face a number of issues related to AIDS and confidentiality. Harding, Gray, and Neal (1992) identified 14 dilemmas, including the following:

1. What evidence of infection is sufficient to determine if a client is infected with HIV? Is client self-identification sufficient evidence of infection, or should written test results be provided?

2. What level of imminent danger is required to trigger the counselors' obligation to warn? In view of the as yet unquantifiable difference in risk between occasional and steady partners, should the situations be treated differently?

3. If the client "promises" to notify the partner(s), has the therapist completed her or his ethical or legal responsibility, or is subsequent confirmation necessary?

4. Is there an obligation to inform professional health authorities in addition to the individual at risk? If so, what is the appropriate process in the therapist's particular jurisdiction?

5. What records should be maintained to reflect the factors the counselor took into consideration in making a determination to maintain confidentiality or to protect third parties? (p. 302)

Because of the legal and ethical issues surrounding AIDS and confidentiality, it is critical for counselors to be very familiar with their state laws, as well as policies that have been set forth by their agencies or institutions.

The term privileged communication is frequently mistaken for confidentiality. Confidentiality refers to "an ethical decision not to reveal what is learned in the professional relationship," whereas privileged communication is a "legal right granted to certain professionals not to testify in a court of law regarding confidential information obtained in their professional relationship" (Hummell, Talbutt, & Alexander, 1985, pp. 53-54). It is important to note that privileged communication exists for clients, and clients, of course, can waive this right.

There are two types of privileged communication: absolute and conditional. It is generally held that counselors possess conditional privileged communication (Denkowski & Denkowski, 1982; Marsh & Kinnick, 1970); however, "the courts have generally held that unless professionals have been granted privileged communication by statute, none exists" (Hummell et al., 1985, p. 59). Even with statutes that specify privileged communication, the court may waive the right. With or without a state statute granting privileged communication, counselors have an ethical responsibility to maintain confidential information, except when clients may present a danger to themselves or to others [R6.2].

Dual Relationships

Dual relationships refer to "overlapping roles" in which the counselor interacts with a client on different levels. According to Kitchener (1988),

> Conflicts of interest arise when the obligations of one role category (e.g., being a professional and attending to the welfare of the client or consumer) conflict with one's own personal, political, or business obligations or interests. In such situations what comes into question is the willingness and the ability of . . . [professionals] to place the interests of those who are served above . . . [their] own. (p. 218)

Three examples of dual relationships include (a) providing rehabilitation services to friends, (b) becoming friends and engaging in social activities with clients, and (c) having sexual relationships with clients. The last example is obviously unethical. There are instances, however, where the first two examples may occur. For example, in small communities counselors may know their clients, may live next door to them, and may meet them at social events. The Code states, "Rehabilitation counselors make every effort to avoid dual relationships that could impair their professional judgments or increase the risk of exploitation" [R2.3]. Although Haas and Malouf (1989, p. 57) suggested that "dual relationships cannot be avoided completely and are not inherently unethical," reasons for avoiding dual relationships whenever possible are clearly identified within the Code. There can be a real or a potential risk to one's professional judgment and an increase in the risk of exploitation of a client.

To assist counselors in determining which dual relationships are most likely to lead to difficulties, Kitchener (1988) recommended examining role expectations, role obligations, and power and prestige factors. She noted that (a) different roles (e.g., friend, counselor, supervisor) promote different expectations from people; (b) different roles encompass different obligations (e.g., confidentiality is generally an obligation of the counselor's role); and (c) power and prestige vary between people. The more divergence that exists in expectations, obligations, or power and prestige, the greater the potential for misunderstanding, harm, divided loyalties, exploitation, and loss of objectivity. If one considers the different expectations, obligations, and power one has as a counselor compared with what one has as a friend, it is evident that one must carefully consider these factors.

Ethnicity and Gender

The increased attention on cultural diversity and gender issues in rehabilitation has highlighted a number of ethical dilemmas for counselors. A counselor's competence and bias are important considerations in considering ethical issues associated with ethnicity and gender. This means that rehabilitation counselors need to be sensitive to and have knowledge of issues related to ethnicity and gender, recognize biases that they may have, and consider possible damage that may result to clients. Failure to address these issues can result in an underutilization of rehabilitation services, premature termination of services, or failure to receive the full benefit of services (Asbury, Walker, Belgrave, Maholmes, & Green, 1994; James, DeVivo, & Richards, 1993; Sue & Zane, 1987).

Examples of ethnicity and gender issues include (a) stereotyping women and recommending only "traditional" employment opportunities, (b) failing to consider the importance of cultural autonomy as well as individual autonomy (Burn, 1992), and (c) failing to appreciate the client's own belief system (Cayleff, 1986). Any of these actions can result in a violation of one or more of the five ethical principles previously described. The client's welfare is strongly linked to "the cross-cultural literacy, attunement, and responsiveness of the counselor" (Burn, 1992, p. 580). Or, as Cayleff stated, "the sex, race, class, and sexual orientation of the client must be considered, understood, and honored to prevent doing harm, serve the client's welfare, respect autonomous principles, and, ultimately, to provide effective counseling" (p. 346).

Setting and Service Issues

Each setting in which a rehabilitation counselor may work and each service that a rehabilitation counselor may provide can also present ethical dilemmas for the counselor.

State–Federal VR Issues

Pape and Klein (1986) identified the following ethical issues of rehabilitation counselors working in the state–federal VR system: (a) providing "quasi" rehabilitation or minimal services instead of focusing on the needs of individual clients; (b) serving clients with less severe disabilities and not serving more "difficult" clients; (c) focusing on "26" closures; (d) approving services to ineligible clients to meet agency quotas; and (e) providing assessment, counseling, and training to clients without providing placement services. Economic restraints and service priorities are two additional areas that may result in conflict for counselors.

Proprietary Rehabilitation

Ethical dilemmas may result in the private sector when (a) the rehabilitation counselor is asked to testify against a client in a workers' compensation hearing or assess a client's motivation (Cottone, 1982); (b) the quantity of services is limited by the insurance company (Matkin & May, 1981); (c) rehabilitation counselors are asked to act as insurance adjusters; (d) rehabilitation counselors change companies and must decide whether to take their cases to the new company (Taylor, 1985); and (e) clients need services, but are not eligible for those services under system rules and regulations (Taylor, 1985). Conflicts of interest are especially problematic because the counselor is "spending one party's money to further the welfare of somebody else" (Bolling, 1991, p. 81).

Supported Employment Services

In addition to conflicting interests, which have already been addressed, Patterson, Buckley, and Smull (1989) identified the following overlapping areas that may present ethical issues for rehabilitation counselors in providing supported employment services:

1. *Client–job match.* In an effort to meet quotas, counselors may be tempted to minimally match clients and jobs. It is easier to place clients in available jobs than to find new jobs. Also, the client–job match includes interests that may be discounted or ignored when clients have severe mental retardation.

2. *Appropriate wages and integrated work settings.* Although these are legally mandated as part of supported employment services, rehabilitation counselors may not advocate for the most appropriate wage for their clients or seek "truly" integrated work settings. Even integrated work settings do not assure that clients are part of the social environment of the workplace.

3. *Limited competence and diminished capacity.* As noted in earlier sections, rehabilitation counselors must promote independence and allow clients to make as many decisions as possible. The severity of a client's disability should never diminish the importance of quality of life and dignity, or the client's right to self-determination, respect, and truthfulness.

Other areas of ethical concern include (a) maintaining contact with referral sources; (b) adopting the value of "zero exclusion," which means that no individual, regardless of severity of disability, is excluded from services (Wehman, 1988); (c) acquiring the knowledge and skills in functional assessment, job development, job analysis, training, and the procedures for selecting and implementing support strategies that specific individuals in specific jobs need to succeed (Buckley, Mank, & Sandow, 1990); (d) balancing the wishes of the guardian or parent with the advocacy role of the counselor; and (e) evaluating one's own expectations and assumptions regarding individuals with disabilities and one's abilities to succeed in supported employment and guarding against underestimating the capacities of individuals with disabilities (Nosek, 1988; Rubenfeld, 1988).

Case Management

Some counselors provide case management services, particularly in rehabilitation hospitals where they are part of the interdisciplinary treatment team. In providing case management services, rehabilitation counselors frequently face a number of ethical issues related to managed care. Although many of these issues are similar to those described in proprietary rehabilitation, there are additional issues. Advocacy is particularly challenging, given the array of stakeholders (e.g., hospital administrators, insurance personnel, family members, and health care team members). The rehabilitation counselor must serve as a patient advocate, despite competing interests that demand cost containment, profit and growth, effective and appropriate care, timely patient discharge to the most independent lifestyle possible, and long-term return on investments (McClinton, 1995).

The emphasis on outcomes in case management has also contributed to ethical issues. For example, payors value outcomes that reflect the minimization of costs, whereas facility or hospital administrators favor outcomes whose related treatment costs are maximally recoverable. The conflict for the counselor arises when the desired outcome is not cost-effective. Prevention programs are a prime example. Many insurance programs do not cover mammograms, because their research suggests that it costs more to pay for the mammogram than to provide treatment for the relatively small number of women who develop breast cancer (Banja, 1994).

For counselors working as case managers, issues of competence may arise when they find themselves discussing a treatment plan with an individual who has sustained a brain injury or stroke or with family members who may be overwhelmed with depression, confusion, or anxiety over the care of their loved one. How can counselors assure themselves that the individual or family member is competent to sign the plan? The counselor should consider the individual's ability to (a) express a preference or evidence a choice, (b) comprehend the information that is being conveyed, (c) use the information, and (d) have insight or reasoning as to the consequences of the decision (Banja, 1993). When counselors have serious reservations related to competency, they need to address these with the attending physician or other qualified health professionals who can perform more sophisticated assessments of the patient's judgmental capacity (Banja, 1993).

Summary

According to Geiger (1986), "Professionalism rests on two bases: knowledge and ethics" (p. 1). Rehabilitation counselors have a responsibility to their clients and their profession to acquire and maintain the knowledge and skills to provide the highest quality of services they can to individuals with disabilities. To be competent professionals, they must use their knowledge and skills in an ethical manner.

Ethical behavior requires that rehabilitation counselors have the skills to (a) recognize ethical situations; (b) thoroughly understand their code of ethics and the laws under which they practice; (c) apply the principles of autonomy, beneficence, nonmaleficence, justice, and fidelity, and integrate them into a moral course of action; (d) exercise a good reasons approach when faced with conflicting ethical principles; (e) identify competing interests (including their own) which are involved in an ethical dilemma; (f) critically evaluate ethical decisions they make; (g) establish collaborative relationships based on mutual respect and informed consent with clients; and (h) continually monitor their own behavior and upgrade their knowledge and skills.

Appendix 6A
Code Of Professional Ethics For Rehabilitation Counselors[1]

Preamble

Rehabilitation Counselors are committed to facilitating personal, social, and economic independence of individuals with disabilities. In fulfilling this commitment, Rehabilitation Counselors work with people, programs, institutions, and service delivery systems. Rehabilitation Counselors recognize that both action and inaction can be facilitating or debilitating. Rehabilitation Counselors may be called upon to provide counseling; vocational exploration; psychological and vocational assessment; evaluation of social, medical, vocational, and psychiatric information; job placement and job development services; and other rehabilitation services, and do so in a manner that is consistent with their education and experience. Moreover, Rehabilitation Counselors also must demonstrate adherence to ethical standards and must ensure that the standards are enforced vigorously. The Code of Professional Ethics, henceforth referred to as the Code, is designed to facilitate the accomplishment of these goals.

The primary obligation of Rehabilitation Counselors is to their clients, defined in this Code as people with disabilities who are receiving services from Rehabilitation Counselors. The basic objective of the Code is to promote the public welfare by specifying and enforcing ethical behavior expected of Rehabilitation Counselors. Accordingly, the Code consists of two kinds of standards, Canons and Rules of Professional Conduct.

The Canons are general standards of an aspirational and inspirational nature reflecting the fundamental spirit of caring and respect which professionals share. They are maxims which serve as models of exemplary professional conduct. The Canons also express general concepts and principles from which more specific Rules are derived. Unlike the Canons, the Rules are more exacting standards that provide guidance in specific circumstances.

Rehabilitation Counselors who violate the Code are subject to disciplinary action. A Rule violation is interpreted as a violation of the applicable Canon and the general principles embodied thereof. Since the use of the Certified Rehabilitation Counselor (CRC) designation is a privilege granted by the Commission on Rehabilitation Counselor Certification (CRCC), the CRCC reserves unto itself the

---

[1]From "Code of Professional Ethics for Rehabilitation Counselors," 1988, *Rehabilitation Counseling Bulletin, 31,* pp. 255–268. Reproduced with the permission of the American Counseling Association. The Commission on Rehabilitation Counselor Certification has adopted this code, as have the following professional organizations: American Rehabilitation Counseling Association, National Rehabilitation Counseling Association, and National Council on Rehabilitation Education.

power to suspend or to revoke the privilege or to approve other penalties for a Rule violation. Disciplinary penalties are imposed as warranted by the severity of the offense and its attendant circumstances. All disciplinary actions are undertaken in accordance with published procedures and penalties designed to assure the proper enforcement of the Code within the framework of due process and equal protection of the laws.

When there is reason to question the ethical propriety of specific behaviors, persons are encouraged to refrain from engaging in such behaviors until the matter has been clarified. Certified Rehabilitation Counselors who need assistance in interpreting the Code should request in writing an advisory opinion from the Commission on Rehabilitation Counselor Certification. Rehabilitation Counselors who are not certified and require assistance in interpreting the Code should request in writing an advisory opinion from their appropriate professional organization.

Canon 1–Moral and Legal Standards

Rehabilitation Counselors shall behave in a legal, ethical, and moral manner in the conduct of their profession, maintaining the integrity of the Code and avoiding any behavior which would cause harm to others.

Rules of Professional Conduct

R1.1 Rehabilitation Counselors will obey the laws and statutes in the legal jurisdiction in which they practice and are subject to disciplinary action for any violation, to the extent that such violation suggests the likelihood of professional misconduct.

R1.2 Rehabilitation Counselors will be thoroughly familiar with, will observe, and will discuss with their clients the legal limitations of their services, or benefits offered to clients so as to facilitate honest and open communication and realistic expectations.

R1.3 Rehabilitation Counselors will be alert to legal parameters relevant to their practices and to disparities between legally mandated ethical and professional standards and the Code. Where such disparities exist, Rehabilitation Counselors will follow the legal mandates and will formally communicate any disparities to the appropriate committee on professional ethics. In the absence of legal guidelines, the Code is ethically binding.

R1.4 Rehabilitation Counselors will not engage in any act or omission of a dishonest, deceitful, or fraudulent nature in the conduct of their professional activities. They will not allow the pursuit of financial gain or other personal benefit to interfere with the exercise of sound professional judgment and skills, nor will Rehabilitation Counselors abuse their relationships with clients to promote personal or financial gain or the financial gain of their employing agencies.

R1.5 Rehabilitation Counselors will understand and abide by the Canons and Rules of Professional Conduct which are prescribed in the Code.

R1.6 Rehabilitation Counselors will not advocate, sanction, participate in, cause to be accomplished, otherwise carry out through another, or condone any act which Rehabilitation Counselors are prohibited from performing by the Code.

R1.7 Rehabilitation Counselors' moral and ethical standards of behavior are a personal matter to the same degree as they are for any other citizen, except as these may compromise the fulfillment of their professional responsibilities or reduce the public trust in Rehabilitation Counselors. To protect public confidence, Rehabilitation Counselors will avoid public behavior that clearly is in violation of accepted moral and ethical standards.

R1.8 Rehabilitation Counselors will respect the rights and reputation of any institution, organization, or firm with which they are associated when making oral or written statements. In those instances where they are critical of policies, they attempt to effect change by constructive action within organizations.

R1.9 Rehabilitation Counselors will refuse to participate in employment practices which are inconsistent with the moral or legal standards regarding the treatment of employees or the public. Rehabilitation Counselors will not condone practices which result in illegal or otherwise unjustifiable discrimination on any basis in hiring, promotion, or training.

Canon 2–Counselor–Client Relationship

Rehabilitation Counselors shall respect the integrity and protect the welfare of people and groups with whom they work. The primary obligation of Rehabilitation Counselors is to their clients, defined as people with disabilities who are receiving services from Rehabilitation Counselors. Rehabilitation Counselors shall endeavor at all times to place their clients' interests above their own.

Rules of Professional Conduct

R2.1 Rehabilitation Counselors will make clear to clients, the purposes, goals, and limitations that may affect the counseling relationship.

R2.2 Rehabilitation Counselors will not misrepresent their role or competence to clients. Rehabilitation Counselors will provide information about their credentials, if requested, and will refer clients to other specialists as the needs of clients dictate.

R2.3 Rehabilitation Counselors will be continually cognizant of their own needs, values, and of their potentially influential position, vis-à-vis clients, students, and subordinates. They avoid exploiting the trust and dependency of such persons. Rehabilitation Counselors make every effort to avoid dual relationships that could impair their professional judgments or increase the risk of exploitation. Examples of dual relationships include, but are not limited to, research with and treatment of employees, students, supervisors, close friends, or relatives. Sexual intimacies with clients are unethical.

R2.4 Rehabilitation Counselors who provide services at the request of a third party will clarify the nature of their relationships to all involved parties. They will inform all parties of their ethical responsibilities and take appropriate action. Rehabilitation Counselors employed by third parties as case consultants or expert witnesses, where there is no pretense or intent to provide rehabilitation counseling services directly to clients, beyond file review, initial interview and/or assessment, will clearly define, through written or oral means, the limits of their relationship, particularly in the area of informed consent and legally privileged communications, to involved individuals. As case consultants or expert witnesses, Rehabilitation Counselors have an obligation to provide unbiased, objective opinions.

R2.5 Rehabilitation Counselors will honor the right of clients to consent to participate in rehabilitation services. Rehabilitation Counselors will inform clients or the clients' legal guardians of factors that may affect clients' decisions to participate in rehabilitation services, and they will obtain written consent after clients or their legal guardians are fully informed of such factors. Rehabilitation Counselors who work with minors or other persons who are unable to give voluntary, informed consent, will take special care to protect the best interests of clients.

R2.6 Rehabilitation Counselors will avoid initiating or continuing consulting or counseling relationships if it is expected that the relationships can be of no benefit to clients, in which case Rehabilitation Counselors will suggest to clients appropriate alternatives.

R2.7 Rehabilitation Counselors will recognize that families are usually an important factor in clients' rehabilitation and will strive to enlist family understanding and involvement as a positive resource in promoting rehabilitation. The permission of clients will be secured prior to family involvement.

R2.8 Rehabilitation Counselors and their clients will work jointly in devising an integrated, individualized rehabilitation plan which offers reasonable promise of success and is consistent with the abilities and circumstances of clients. Rehabilitation Counselors will persistently monitor rehabilitation plans to ensure their continued viability and effectiveness, remembering that clients have the right to make choices.

R2.9 Rehabilitation Counselors will work with their clients in considering employment for clients in only jobs and circumstances that are consistent with the clients' overall abilities, vocational limitations, physical restrictions, general temperament, interest and aptitude patterns, social skills, education, general qualifications and other relevant characteristics and needs. Rehabilitation Counselors will neither place nor participate in placing clients in positions that will result in damaging the interest and welfare of either clients or employers.

Canon 3–Client Advocacy

Rehabilitation counselors shall serve as advocates for people with disabilities.

Rules of Professional Conduct

R3.1 Rehabilitation Counselors will be obligated at all times to promote access for people with disabilities in programs, facilities, transportation, and communication, so that clients will not be excluded from opportunities to participate fully in rehabilitation, education, and society.

R3.2 Rehabilitation Counselors will assure, prior to referring clients to programs, facilities, or employment settings, that they are appropriately accessible.

R3.3 Rehabilitation Counselors will strive to understand accessibility problems of people with cognitive, hearing, mobility, visual, and/or other disabilities and demonstrate such understanding in the practice of their profession.

R3.4 Rehabilitation Counselors will strive to eliminate attitudinal barriers, including stereotyping and discrimination, toward people with disabilities and will enhance their own sensitivity and awareness toward persons with disabilities.

R3.5 Rehabilitation Counselors will remain aware of the actions taken by cooperating agencies on behalf of their clients and will act as advocates of clients to ensure effective service delivery.

Canon 4–Professional Relationships

Rehabilitation Counselors shall act with integrity in their relationships with colleagues, other organizations, agencies, institutions, referral sources,

and other professions so as to facilitate the contribution of all specialists toward achieving optimum benefit for clients.

Rules of Professional Conduct

R4.1 Rehabilitation Counselors will ensure that there is fair mutual understanding of the rehabilitation plan by all agencies cooperating in the rehabilitation of clients and that any rehabilitation plan is developed with such mutual understanding.

R4.2 Rehabilitation Counselors will abide by and help to implement "team" decisions in formulating rehabilitation plans and procedures, even when not personally agreeing with such decisions, unless these decisions breach the ethical Rules.

R4.3 Rehabilitation Counselors will not commit receiving counselors to any prescribed courses of action in relation to clients, when transferring clients to other colleagues or agencies.

R4.4 Rehabilitation Counselors, as referring counselors, will promptly supply all information necessary for a cooperating agency or counselor to begin serving clients.

R4.5 Rehabilitation Counselors will not offer ongoing professional counseling/ case management services to clients receiving such services from other Rehabilitation Counselors without first notifying the other counselor. File review and second opinion services are not included in the concept of professional counseling/case management services.

R4.6 Rehabilitation Counselors will secure from other specialists appropriate reports and evaluations, when such reports are essential for rehabilitation planning and/or service delivery.

R4.7 Rehabilitation Counselors will not discuss in a disparaging way with clients the competency of other counselors or agencies, or the judgments made, the methods used, or the quality of rehabilitation plans.

R4.8 Rehabilitation Counselors will not exploit their professional relationships with supervisors, colleagues, students, or employees sexually or otherwise. Rehabilitation Counselors will not condone or engage in sexual harassment, defined as deliberate or repeated comments, gestures, or physical contacts of a sexual nature unwanted by recipients.

R4.9 Rehabilitation Counselors who know of an ethical violation by another Rehabilitation Counselor will informally attempt to resolve the issue with the counselor, when the misconduct is of a minor nature and/or appears to be due to lack of sensitivity, knowledge, or experience. If the violation does not seem amenable to an informal solution, or is of a more serious nature, Rehabilitation Counselors will bring it to the attention of the appropriate committee on professional ethics.

R4.10 Rehabilitation Counselors possessing information concerning an alleged violation of this Code, will, upon request, reveal such information to the Commission on Rehabilitation Counselor Certification or other authority empowered to investigate or act upon the alleged violation, unless the information is protected by law.

R4.11 Rehabilitation Counselors who employ or supervise other professionals or students will facilitate the professional development of such individuals. They provide appropriate working conditions, timely evaluations, constrictive consultation, and experience opportunities.

Canon 5–Public Statements/Fees

Rehabilitation Counselors shall adhere to professional standards in establishing fees and promoting their services.

Rules of Professional Conduct

R5.1 Rehabilitation Counselors will consider carefully the value of their services and the ability of clients to meet the financial burden in establishing reasonable fees for professional services.

R5.2 Rehabilitation Counselors will not accept for professional work a fee or any other form of remuneration from clients who are entitled to their services through an institution or agency or other benefits structure, unless clients have been fully informed of the availability of services from other such sources.

R5.3 Rehabilitation Counselors will neither give nor receive a commission or rebate or any other form of remuneration for referral of clients for professional services.

R5.4 Rehabilitation Counselors who describe rehabilitation counseling or the services of Rehabilitation Counselors to the general public will fairly and accurately present the material, avoiding misrepresentation through sensationalism, exaggeration, or superficiality. Rehabilitation Counselors are guided by the primary obligation to aid the public in developing informed judgments, opinions, and choices.

Canon 6–Confidentiality

Rehabilitation Counselors shall respect the confidentiality of information obtained from clients in the course of their work.

Rules of Professional Conduct

R6.1 Rehabilitation Counselors will inform clients at the onset of the counseling relationship of the limits of confidentiality.

R6.2 Rehabilitation Counselors will take reasonable personal action, or inform responsible authorities, or inform those persons at risk, when the conditions or actions of clients indicate that there is clear and imminent danger to clients or others after advising clients that this must be done. Consultation with other professionals may be used where appropriate. The assumption of responsibility for clients must be taken only after careful deliberation, and clients must be involved in the resumption of responsibility as quickly as possible.

R6.3 Rehabilitation Counselors will not forward to another person, agency, or potential employer, any confidential information without the written permission of clients or their legal guardians.

R6.4 Rehabilitation Counselors will ensure that there are defined policies and practices in other agencies cooperatively serving rehabilitation clients which effectively protect information confidentiality.

R6.5 Rehabilitation Counselors will safeguard the maintenance, storage, and disposal of the records of clients so that unauthorized persons shall not have access to these records. All nonprofessional persons who must have access to these records will be thoroughly briefed concerning the confidential standards to be observed.

R6.6 Rehabilitation Counselors, in the preparation of written and oral reports, will present only germane data and will make every effort to avoid undue invasion of privacy.

R6.7 Rehabilitation Counselors will obtain written permission from clients or their legal guardians prior to taping or otherwise recording counseling sessions. Even with guardians' written consent, Rehabilitation Counselors will not record sessions against the expressed wishes of clients.

R6.8 Rehabilitation Counselors will persist in claiming the privileged status of confidential information obtained from clients, where communications are privileged by statute for Rehabilitation Counselors.

R6.9 Rehabilitation Counselors will provide prospective employers with only job-relevant information about clients and will secure the permission of clients or their legal guardians for the release of any information which might be considered confidential.

Canon 7–Assessment

Rehabilitation Counselors shall promote the welfare of clients in the selection, utilization, and interpretation of assessment measures.

Rules of Professional Conduct

R7.1 Rehabilitation Counselors will recognize that different tests demand different levels of competence for administration, scoring, and interpretation, and will recognize the limits of their competence and perform only those functions for which they are trained.

R7.2 Rehabilitation Counselors will consider carefully the specific validity, reliability, and appropriateness of tests, when selecting them for use in a given situation or with particular clients. Rehabilitation Counselors will proceed with caution when attempting to evaluate and interpret the performance of persons with disabilities, minority group members, or other people who are not represented in the standardized norm groups. Rehabilitation Counselors will recognize the effects of socioeconomic, ethnic, disability, and cultural factors on test scores.

R7.3 Rehabilitation Counselors will administer tests under the same conditions that were established in their standardization. When tests are not administered under standard conditions, as may be necessary to accommodate modifications for clients with disabilities or when unusual behavior or irregularities occur during the testing session, those conditions will be noted and taken into account at the time of interpretation.

R7.4 Rehabilitation Counselors will ensure that instrument limitations are not exceeded and that periodic reassessments are made to prevent stereotyping of clients.

R7.5 Rehabilitation Counselors will make known the purpose of testing and the explicit use of the results to clients prior to administration. Recognizing the right of clients to have test results, Rehabilitation Counselors will give explanations of results in language clients can understand.

R7.6 Rehabilitation Counselors will ensure that specific interpretation accompanies any release of individual data. The welfare and explicit prior permission of clients will be the criteria for determining the recipients of the test results. The interpretation of assessment data will be related to the particular goals of evaluation.

R7.7 Rehabilitation Counselors will attempt to ensure, when utilizing computerized assessment services, that such services are based on appropriate research to establish the validity of the computer programs and procedures used in arriving at interpretations. Public offering of an automated test interpretation service will be considered as a professional-to-professional consultation. In this instance, the formal responsibility of the consultant is to the consultee, but the ultimate and overriding responsibility is to clients.

R7.8 Rehabilitation Counselors will recognize that assessment results may become obsolete. They will make every effort to avoid and prevent the misuse of obsolete measures.

Canon 8–Research Activities

Rehabilitation Counselors shall assist in efforts to expand the knowledge needed to more effectively serve people with disabilities.

Rules of Professional Conduct

R8.1 Rehabilitation Counselors will ensure that data for research meets rigid standards of validity, honesty, and protection of confidentiality.

R8.2 Rehabilitation Counselors will be aware of and responsive to all pertinent guidelines on research with human subjects. When planning any research activity dealing with human subjects, Rehabilitation Counselors will ensure that research problems, design, and execution are in full compliance with such guidelines.

R8.3 Rehabilitation Counselors presenting case studies in classes, professional meetings, or publications will confine the content to that which can be disguised to ensure full protection of the identity of clients.

R8.4 Rehabilitation Counselors will assign credit to those who have contributed to publications in proportion to their contribution.

R8.5 Rehabilitation Counselors recognize that honesty and openness are essential characteristics of the relationship between Rehabilitation Counselors and research participants. When methodological requirements of a study necessitate concealment or deception, Rehabilitation Counselors will ensure that participants understand the reasons for this action.

Canon 9–Competence

Rehabilitation Counselors shall establish and maintain their professional competencies at such a level that their clients receive the benefit of the highest quality of services the profession is capable of offering.

Rules of Professional Conduct

R9.1 Rehabilitation Counselors will function within the limits of their defined role, training, and technical competency and will accept only those positions for which they are professionally qualified.

R9.2 Rehabilitation Counselors will continuously strive through reading, attending professional meetings, and taking courses of instruction to keep abreast of new developments, concepts, and practices that are essential to providing the highest quality of services to their clients.

R9.3 Rehabilitation Counselors, recognizing that personal problems and conflicts may interfere with their professional effectiveness, will refrain from undertaking any activity in which their personal problems are likely to lead to inadequate performance. If they are already engaged in such activity when they become aware of their personal problems, they will seek competent professional assistance to determine whether they should suspend, terminate, or limit the scope of their professional activities.

R9.4 Rehabilitation Counselors who are educators will perform their duties based on careful preparation so that their instruction is accurate, up-to-date, and scholarly.

R9.5 Rehabilitation Counselors who are educators will ensure that statements in catalogs and course outlines are accurate, particularly in terms of subject matter covered, bases for grading, and nature of classroom experiences.

R9.6 Rehabilitation Counselors who are educators will maintain high standards of knowledge and skill by presenting rehabilitation counseling information fully and accurately, and by giving appropriate recognition to alternative viewpoints.

Canon 10–CRC Credential

Rehabilitation Counselors holding the Certified Rehabilitation Counselor (CRC) designation shall honor the integrity and respect the limitations placed upon its use.

Rules of Professional Conduct

R10.1 Certified Rehabilitation Counselors will use the Certified Rehabilitation Counselor (CRC) designation only in accordance with the relevant Guidelines promulgated by the Commission on Rehabilitation Counselor Certification.

R10.2 Certified Rehabilitation Counselors will not attribute to the mere possession of the designation depth or scope of knowledge, skill, and professional capabilities greater than those demonstrated by achievement of the CRC designation.

R10.3 Certified Rehabilitation Counselors will not make unfair comparisons between a person who holds the Certified Rehabilitation Counselor (CRC) designation and one who does not.

R10.4 Certified Rehabilitation Counselors will not write, speak, or act in ways that lead others to believe Certified Rehabilitation Counselors are officially representing the Commission on Rehabilitation Counselor Certification, unless such written permission has been granted by the said Commission.

R10.5 Certified Rehabilitation Counselors will make no claim to unique skills or devices not available to others in the profession unless the special efficacy of such unique skills or device has been demonstrated by scientifically accepted evidence.

R10.6 Certified Rehabilitation Counselors will not initiate or support the candidacy of an individual for certification by the Commission on Rehabilitation Counselor Certification if the individual is known to engage in professional practices which violate the ethical Rules prescribed by this Code.

References

Asbury, C., Walker, S., Belgrave, F., Maholmes, V., & Green, L. (1994). Psychosocial cultural and accessibility factors associated with participation of African-Americans in rehabilitation. *Rehabilitation Psychology, 39,* 113–122.

Banja, J. (1993). The incompetent client. *The Case Manager, 4*(1), 28–29.

Banja, J. (1994). The outcomes movement: Ethical implications for case managers. *The Case Manager, 5*(4), 40–42.

Bannerman, D. J., Sheldon, J. B., Sherman, J. A., & Harchik, A. E. (1990). Balancing the right to rehabilitation with the right to personal liberties: The rights of people with developmental disabilities to eat too many doughnuts and take a nap. *Journal of Applied Behavior Analysis, 23,* 79–89.

Bayles, M. D. (1981). *Professional ethics.* Belmont, CA: Wadsworth.

Beauchamp, T. L., & Childress, J. F. (1989). *Principles of biomedical ethics* (3rd ed.). New York: Oxford University Press.

Blanchard, K., & Peale, N. V. (1988). *The power of ethical management.* New York: Fawcett Crest.

Bolling, J. (1991). Profile John Banja: The case manager as an "ethics traffic controller." *The Case Manager, 2*(3), 76–81.

Bouhoutsos, J., Holroyd, J., & Lerman, H. (1983). Sexual intimacy between psychotherapist and patient. *Professional Psychology: Research and Practice, 14,* 185.

Bozarth, J. D. (1981). Philosophy and ethics in rehabilitation counseling. In R. M. Parker & C. E. Hansen (Eds.), *Rehabilitation counseling* (pp. 59–81). Boston: Allyn & Bacon.

Brigham, T. A. (1979). Some effect of choice on academic performance. In L. C. Perlmuter & R. A. Monty (Eds.), *Choice and perceived control* (pp. 131–142). Hillsdale, NJ: Erlbaum.

Brubaker, D. R. (1977). Professionalization and rehabilitation counseling. *Journal of Applied Rehabilitation Counseling, 8,* 208–217.

Buckley, J., Mank, D. M., & Sandow, D. (1990). Developing and implementing support strategies for individuals with developmental disabilities in the integrated employment setting. In F. R. Rusch (Ed.), *Handbook of supported employment: Models, methods, and issues* (pp. 131–144). Chicago: Sycamore.

Burn, D. (1992). Ethical implications in cross-cultural counseling and training. *Journal of Counseling and Development, 70,* 578–583.

Cayleff, S. (1986). Ethical issues in counseling gender, race, and culturally distinct groups. *Journal of Counseling and Development, 64,* 345–347.

Code of professional ethics for rehabilitation counselors. (1988). *Rehabilitation Counseling Bulletin, 31,* 255–268.

Cohen, E. (1990). Confidentiality, counseling, and clients who have AIDS: Ethical foundations of a model rule. *Journal of Counseling and Development, 68,* 282–286.

Costa, L., & Altekruse, M. (1994). Duty-to-warn guidelines for mental health counselors. *Journal of Counseling and Development, 72,* 346–355.

Cottone, R. R. (1982). Ethical issues in private-for-profit rehabilitation. *Journal of Applied Rehabilitation Counseling, 13*(3), 14–17, 24.

Denkowski, K., & Denkowski, G. (1982). Client–counselor confidentiality: An update of ratio-nale, legal status and implication. *Personnel and Guidance Journal, 60,* 371–375.

Emener, W. G., Wright, T. J., Klein, L. F., Lavender, L. A., & Smith, D. W. (1987). Rules of ethical conduct and rehabilitation counseling: Results of a national survey. *Journal of Applied Rehabilitation Counseling, 18*(3), 3–15.

Eyde, L. D., & Quaintance, M. K. (1988). Ethical issues and cases in the practice of personnel psychology. *Professional Psychology: Research and Practice, 19,* 148–154.

Ferrell, O. C., & Gresham, L. G. (1985). A contingency framework for understanding ethical decision making in marketing. *Journal of Marketing, 49,* 87–96.

Fitting, M. D. (1984). Professional and ethical responsibilities for psychologists working with the elderly. *Counseling Psychologist, 12*(3), 69–78.

Flowers, J. G., & Parker, R. M. (1984). Personal philosophy and vocational rehabilitation job per-formance. In W. G. Emener, A. Patrick, & D. K. Hollingsworth (Eds.), *Critical issues in reha-bilitation counseling* (pp. 45–64). Springfield, IL: Thomas.

Geiger, J. (1986). Editorial. *Journal of Teacher Education, 37*(3), 1.

Geist, G. O., Curin, S., Prestridge, R., & Schelb, G. (1973). Ethics and the counselor agency rela-tionship. *Rehabilitation Counseling Bulletin, 17,* 15–21.

Gewirth, A. (1975). Ethics. In the *Encyclopedia Britannica* (Vol. 6, pp. 976–998). Chicago: Encyclopedia Britannica.

Greenwood, R. (1987). Expanding community participation by people with disabilities: Impli-cations for counselors. *Journal of Counseling and Development, 16*(3), 2.

Guess, D., Benson, H. A., & Siegel-Causey, E. (1985). Concepts and issues related to choice-making and autonomy among persons with severe disabilities. *Journal of the Association for Persons with Severe Handicaps, 10,* 79–86.

Haas, L. J., & Malouf, J. L. (1989). *Keeping up the good work: A practitioner's guide to mental health ethics.* Sarasota, FL: Professional Resource Exchange.

Handelsman, M. M. (1986). Problems with ethics training by "osmosis." *Professional Psychol-ogy: Research and Practice, 17,* 371–372.

Harding, A., Gray, L., & Neal, M. (1992). Confidentiality limits with clients who have HIV: A review of ethical and legal guidelines and professional policies. *Journal of Counseling and Development, 71,* 297–305.

Hopkins, B., & Anderson, B. (1990). *The counselor and the law.* Alexandria, VA: American Asso-ciation for Counseling and Development.

Hummell, D. L., Talbutt, L. C., & Alexander, M. D. (1985). *Law and ethics in counseling.* New York: Van Nostrand Reinhold.

James, M., DeVivo, M., & Richards, J. (1993). Post injury employment outcomes among African-American and white persons with spinal cord injuries. *Rehabilitation Psychology, 38,* 151–164.

Kitchener, K. S. (1984). Intuition, critical evaluation and ethical principles: The foundation for ethical decisions in counseling psychology. *Counseling Psychologist, 12*(3), 43–55.

Kitchener, K. S. (1986). Teaching applied ethics in counselor education: An integration of psy-chological processes and philosophical analysis. *Journal of Counseling and Develop-ment, 64,* 306–310.

Kitchener, K. S. (1988). Dual role relationships: What makes them so problematic? *Journal of Counseling and Development, 67,* 217-221.

Knowlton, H. E., Turnbull, A. P., Backus, L., & Turnbull, H. R., III. (1988). Letting go: Consent and the "yes but . . . " problem in transition. In B. L. Ludlow, A. P. Turnbull, & R. Luckasson (Eds.), *Transition to adult life for people with mental retardation* (pp. 45-66). Baltimore: Brookes.

Kohlberg, L. (1984). *The psychology of moral development.* San Francisco: Harper & Row.

Kolb, D. (1984). *Experiential learning: Experience as the source of learning and development.* Englewood Cliffs, NJ: Prentice-Hall.

Levenson, J. L. (1986). When a colleague practices unethically: Guidelines for intervention. *Journal of Counseling and Development, 67,* 315-317.

Lindsey, R. T. (1984). Informed consent and deception in psychotherapy research: An ethical analysis. *Counseling Psychologist, 12*(3), 79-86.

Maki, D., & Riggar, T. (1985). Rehabilitation counseling: Orientations to practice. *Journal of Applied Rehabilitation Counseling, 16*(3), 2.

Marsh, J. J., & Kinnick, B. C. (1970). Let's close the confidentiality gap. *Personnel and Guidance Journal, 48,* 362-365.

Matkin, R. E., & May, R. (1981). Potential conflicts of interest in private rehabilitation: Identification and resolution. *Journal of Applied Rehabilitation Counseling, 12,* 15-18.

McClinton, D. (1995). Balancing the issue of ethics in case management. *Continuing Care, 14*(5), 13-14, 16.

Nielsen, K. (1972). Problems of ethics. In P. Edwards (Ed.), *The encyclopedia of philosophy* (Reprint ed., Vol. 3, pp. 117-134). New York: Macmillan.

Nosek, M. A. (1988). Independent living and rehabilitation counseling. In S. E. Rubin & N. M. Rubin (Eds.), *Contemporary challenges to the profession of rehabilitation counseling* (pp. 45-60). Baltimore: Brookes.

Pape, D. A., & Klein, M. A. (1986). Ethical issues in rehabilitation counseling: A survey of rehabilitation practitioners. *Journal of Applied Rehabilitation Counseling, 17*(4), 8-13.

Patterson, J. B., Buckley, J., & Smull, M. (1989). Ethics in supported employment. *Journal of Applied Rehabilitation Counseling, 20*(3), 12-20.

Patterson, J. B., & Curl, R. M. (1990). Ethics education in supported employment preparation. *Rehabilitation Education, 4,* 247-260.

Pelsma, D. M., & Borgers, S. B. (1986). Experience-based ethics: A developmental model of learning ethical reasoning. *Journal of Counseling and Development, 64,* 311-314.

Pharis, M., & Hill, K. (1983). Training for responsible professional behavior in psychology and social work. *Clinical Social Work Journal, 11,* 178-183.

Piaget, J. (1965). *The moral judgment of the child.* New York: Free Press.

Powell, C. J. (1984). Ethical principles and issues of competence in counseling adolescents. *The Counseling Psychologist, 12,* 57-68.

Rubenfeld, P. (1988). The rehabilitation counselor and the disabled client: Is a partnership of equals possible? In S. E. Rubin & N. M. Rubin (Eds.), *Contemporary challenges to the rehabilitation counseling profession* (pp. 31-44). Baltimore: Brookes.

Shertzer, B., & Stone, S. (1980). *Fundamentals of counseling.* Boston: Houghton Mifflin.

Stanard, R., & Hazler, R. (1995). Legal and ethical implications of HIV and duty to warn for counselors: Does Tarasoff apply? *Journal of Counseling and Development, 73,* 397–400.

Stead, W. E., Worrell, D. L., Spalding, J. B., & Stead, J. G. (1987). Unethical decisions: Socially learned behaviors. *Journal of Social Behavior and Personality, 2,* 105–115.

Stude, E. W., & McKelvey, J. (1979). Ethics and the law: Friend or foe? *Personnel and Guidance Journal, 57,* 453–456.

Sue, S., & Zane, N. (1987). The role of culture and cultural techniques in psychotherapy. *American Psychologist, 42,* 37–45.

Szymanski, E. M. (1985). Rehabilitation counseling: A profession with a vision, an identity, and a future. *Rehabilitation Counseling Bulletin, 59,* 2–5.

Szymanski, E. M. (1987, Fall). Rehabilitation counseling: A profession based on values. *Interaction,* p. 1.

Tarasoff v. Regents of University of California, 551 P.2d 334 (Cal. 1976).

Tarvydas, V. M. (1987). Decision-making models in ethics: Models for increased clarity and wisdom. *Journal of Applied Rehabilitation Counseling, 18*(4), 50–52.

Taylor, L. J. (1985). Being an ethical professional in private sector rehabilitation. In L. J. Taylor, M. Golter, C. Golter, & T. E. Backer (Eds.), *Handbook of private sector rehabilitation* (pp. 212–235). New York: Springer.

Tymchuk, A. J. (1982). Strategies for resolving value dilemmas. *American Behavior Scientist, 26,* 159–175.

Van Hoose, W. H., & Kottler, J. A. (1985). *Ethical and legal issues in counseling and psychotherapy* (2nd ed.). San Francisco: Jossey-Bass.

Van Hoose, W. J., & Paradise, L. V. (1979). *Ethics in counseling and psychotherapy.* Cranston, RI: Carroll Press.

Webster's ninth new collegiate dictionary. (1985). Springfield, MA: Merriam-Webster.

Wehman, P. (1988). Toward zero exclusion. In P. Wehman & M. S. Moon (Eds.), *Vocational rehabilitation and supported employment services* (pp. 3–14). Baltimore: Brookes.

Woods, G., Marks, R., & Dilley, J. (1990). *AIDS law for mental health professionals: A handbook for judicious practice.* San Francisco: The AIDS Health Project.

Wright, B. (1983). *Physical disability: A psychosocial approach.* New York: Harper & Row.

Chapter 7

Theoretical Foundations of the Counseling Function

Kenneth R. Thomas, Richard W. Thoreson, Randall M. Parker, and Alfred J. Butler

ithout adequate counseling, the core ingredient of rehabilitation counseling (Thomas & Parker, 1986), many rehabilitation clients would be unable to achieve the goals of the rehabilitation process. The ultimate goal of rehabilitation—the independent, effective, and full functioning of clients—is predicated upon, and intimately linked to, intensive counseling by a skilled, professional rehabilitation counselor.

The importance of a professional counseling relationship to rehabilitation is in the amelioration of handicaps created from the cumulative effects of psychosocial and physical barriers on persons with disabilities. The internalization of such barriers by persons with disabilities may lead directly to negative self-appraisal and severe psychosocial difficulties. Consequently, the primary task of rehabilitation counseling is the removal of such barriers, whether inflicted by oneself or by society.

Counseling, viewed in this manner, is directed toward establishing an interpersonal climate that facilitates behavioral change. It should not be, but frequently is, confused with "do-goodism." This confusion is a result of the failure to recognize that a critical blend of theoretical knowledge, positive attitudes, and valuing of the client is necessary for the formation of an effective rehabilitation counseling relationship. This triadic blend forms the essence of the factors needed to facilitate positive behavioral change.

In brief, the counselor seeks to create an atmosphere in which rehabilitation clients feel free to deal sensitively and constructively with such feelings as shame, anger, frustration, and disappointment that may have resulted from the barriers faced by persons with severe disabilities in our society. This focus on the psychosocial ramifications of disability and the emphasis on the removal of barriers to

225

promote a full personal, social, and work life are integral to a successful outcome in rehabilitation counseling.

This chapter presents a succinct review of relevant counseling research, summaries of major counseling theories, and conclusions and recommendations regarding the eclectic (or integrative) approach to counseling. The chapter concludes with eight statements representing the authors' viewpoint of rehabilitation counseling.

Review of Relevant Research

In the space of a few pages, we cannot comprehensively review the relevant research literature on counseling and psychotherapy as it relates to rehabilitation counseling. Our intent is to present a reasonable picture of the extent of the literature, recommend representative readings, summarize major themes, and provide specific examples of the literature of particular relevance to rehabilitation counseling.

Few professionals in the field can retain command of the extensive literature in counseling and psychotherapy, which includes hundreds of books, including general overview texts, research reviews, and presentations of specific viewpoints. As a barometer of the extent of the research literature in this area, Bergin and Garfield's (1994) *Handbook of Psychotherapy and Behavior Change*, which is the most ambitious review available, cited over 3,000 authors.

To keep reasonably up to date, one must read at least a score of the several dozen relevant journals available. Two specifically directed to rehabilitation counselors are *Rehabilitation Counseling Bulletin* and *Journal of Applied Rehabilitation Counseling*. Of more general interest are *Rehabilitation Psychology, Journal of Rehabilitation*, and *Journal of Counseling and Development*. Examples of other journals that contain research and theory of direct relevance to counselors include *Journal of Counseling Psychology, The Counseling Psychologist, Journal of Consulting and Clinical Psychology, Journal of Clinical Psychology, Psychiatry, Journal of Clinical Psychiatry, American Journal of Psychiatry, American Journal of Orthopsychiatry*, and *Psychotherapy: Theory, Research and Practice*.

The interested reader may wish to consult, in addition to this chapter, one or more of the following texts, which summarize major theories or approaches: Baruth and Huber (1985), Brammer, Abrego, and Shostrom (1993), Corey (1996), Corsini and Wedding (1989, 1995), Cottone (1992), Gilliland, James, and Bowman (1994), Patterson (1986), Prochaska (1984), and Riggar, Maki, and Wolf (1986). Many of the expositions of specific viewpoints cited in this chapter are referred to in these texts. Also, for a comprehensive overview of research and trends in counseling and psychotherapy, see Bergin and Garfield (1994). There are also periodic reviews of counseling, psychotherapy, and behavior therapy in *Annual Review of Psychology*. From the research literature, the following themes have been selected for brief attention: (a) the general effectiveness of counseling; (b) the relationship of client, counselor, and process characteristics to counseling outcome; and (c) special issues in rehabilitation counseling research.

Counseling and Psychotherapy Outcome Research

There has been considerable interest in counseling and psychotherapy research for at least the past 50 years (Bergin & Garfield, 1994). Those interested in such research traditionally have included counseling and psychotherapy researchers, educators, supervisors, and practitioners. However, consumers and policy makers have also shown considerable interest in counseling research (e.g., see Vanden-Bos, 1986, 1996). These "new consumers" have become increasingly interested in the outcomes of counseling and psychotherapy research as a basis for influencing policies regarding (a) eligibility for counseling, (b) the amount of reimbursement for counseling, (c) the training of professional counselors, and (d) the licensing and certifying of qualified counselors. The influence of this trend is equally prominent in rehabilitation. Debate is presently under way among policy makers, administrators, consumer groups, and practitioners regarding the proper role and functions, professional preparation, entrance requirements, and compensation for rehabilitation counseling services.

Researchers in counseling and psychotherapy, however, have been concerned primarily with process and outcomes. The reason for this dual focus is to better understand both the mechanism of change and the actual outcome. The resultant focus on comparative outcome research, the current norm in the field, provides a test of the relative advantages and disadvantages of alternative treatment strategies for clients who present different psychological, behavioral, and physical problems.

The many difficulties in demonstrating the relationship between treatment strategy and outcome follow directly from the complexity of the counseling relationship, which involves multiple external factors interacting with client and counselor characteristics to influence and create the consequent outcome. Demonstrating that outcomes of counseling can be shown to be a direct function of the interventions of professionally trained rehabilitation counselors has become a matter of considerable importance to all major constituent groups in the rehabilitation field.

The identification of measurable criteria of successful outcome is a hotly debated issue. General categories of outcome measures for counseling include affective, cognitive, and behavioral change criteria. Additional criteria for successful outcome, however, must be considered within the context of the broader goals of the rehabilitation process. In addition to the psychological indices noted, a number of others that reflect the client's economic and/or vocational status have been developed, including income, occupational status, occupational adjustment, vocational adequacy, and the closed-rehabilitated or "26" closure criterion. Others reflect client satisfaction with rehabilitation services, adjustment to disability, and physical functioning skills. For comprehensive reviews and critiques of rehabilitation outcome criteria, see Bolton (1974a, 1979b), Bolton and Parker (Chapter 13, this text), Walls and Tseng (1976, 1987), and Wright (1987). It may be concluded that a consensus exists at the present time that counseling produces an outcome that is demonstrably more effective than no treatment (Banta & Saxe, 1983; Lambert & Bergin, 1994; Luborsky, 1976; M. L. Smith & Glass, 1977; M. L. Smith, Glass, & Miller, 1980; VandenBos, 1996; VandenBos & Pino, 1980; Yates & Newman, 1980).

The most statistically sophisticated effort to assess the outcome of counseling and psychotherapy was accomplished by M. L. Smith and Glass (1977) and M. L. Smith et al. (1980), by employing a methodology referred to as meta-analysis. Matt (1989), summarizing results of meta-analysis research, underscored the wide use and promising outcomes of meta-analysis as a research tool in the social and health sciences. By using meta-analysis, M. L. Smith et al. were able to aggregate statistically the overall effects reported in 475 controlled outcome studies. Statistically, the average effect of psychotherapy, based on the 475 controlled studies containing 1,766 measured effects on tens of thousands of persons, is .85 standard deviation units. M. L. Smith and her colleagues (1980) summarized their findings by stating that "an applicant for therapy who is no better off than average (i.e., is at the 50th percentile) in psychological well-being, compared to all those who have not received psychotherapy, rises to the 80th percentile as a result of psychotherapy" (p. 124). That is, at the end of therapy, the individual is better off than 80% of those who are untreated but need therapy.

The Penn Psychotherapy Project (Luborsky, Crits-Christoph, Mintz, & Auerbach, 1988), which spanned 20 years, found psychotherapy had even larger effects than those reported by M. L. Smith et al. (1980). Luborsky et al. found that the average effect size for psychotherapeutic outcome was 1.05 standard deviation units. In percentages, ratings of clients' benefits by therapists were 22% large improvement, 43% moderate improvement, 27% some improvement, 7% no change, and 1% worse. Ratings of clients' benefits by observers and the clients themselves generally paralleled the therapists' ratings. Interestingly, the 65% moderate to large improvement (22% plus 43%) agrees with previous research by Mintz (1977) and Bergin and Lambert (1978). Luborsky et al. (1988) referred to the figure as the "magically recurrent 65%" (p. 266).

Seligman (1995) reported the results of a survey of *Consumer Reports* readers regarding the effects of therapy from mental health service providers (also reported in "Mental Health," 1995). Of 180,000 readers mailed the 1994 annual *Consumer Reports* survey with questions about various products (e.g., appliances and automobiles) and about mental health treatment, approximately 22,000 of the total sample responded (12% response rate). Respondents tended to be well educated, middle class, and middle aged (median age = 46 years); females and males were equally represented. Seven thousand (32% of respondents) reported they sought help for stress or emotional problems from individuals ranging from friends to mental health professionals in the previous 3 years. About 3,000 (14% of respondents) talked solely to friends, relatives, or clergy, and approximately 4,100 (19% of respondents) consulted a mental health professional, support group, or family physician (Seligman, 1995).

The results of treatment by mental health professionals were substantially positive, as enumerated below (Seligman, 1995):

1. Eighty-seven percent of those who said they felt "very poor" at the beginning of therapy were feeling "very good," "good," or "so-so" at the time of the survey. Of those feeling "fairly poor" at the onset of therapy, 92% were feeling "very good," "good," or "so-so" at the time of the survey.

2. Among respondents receiving therapy from 1 month to more than 2 years, those in longer term therapy showed more improvement than those getting shorter term treatment.

3. No differences in outcome were found between recipients of psychotherapy alone and recipients of psychotherapy plus medication.

4. Despite all mental health professionals' getting positive results, psychologists, psychiatrists, and social workers, who did equally well, were statistically significantly better in reported treatment outcomes than marriage counselors.

5. Family doctors did as well as mental health professionals with patients in treatment for 6 months or less, but had relatively inferior outcomes for longer term treatment.

6. No specific type of psychotherapy was better than any other across client problems.

7. Alcoholics Anonymous received the highest average outcome scores, statistically significantly higher than mental health professionals.

Whereas Seligman (1995) discussed eight potential limitations of the *Consumer Reports'* outcome survey, he emphasized the study's "main methodological virtue . . . [which is] its realism. It assessed the effectiveness of psychotherapy as it is actually performed in the field with the population that actually seeks it, and it is the most extensive, carefully done study to do this" (p. 971). Seligman's research has been roundly criticized for methodological errors, nonresponses, regression effects, and a variety of other concerns (Brock, Green, Reich, & Evans, 1996; Hunt, 1996; Mintz, Drake, & Crits-Christoph, 1996).

In summary, M. L. Smith et al. (1980), Luborsky et al. (1988), and Seligman (1995) presented persuasive evidence for the positive effects of counseling and psychotherapy. However, many issues in this realm remain (see Cooper, 1984; Dawes, 1994; Glass, McGaw, & Smith, 1981; Hedges & Olkin, 1985; Hunter, Schmidt, & Jackson, 1982; Jacobson & Christensen, 1996; Lambert & Bergin, 1994; Lambert & Hill, 1994; Light, 1983; Light & Pillemer, 1984; Rosenthal, 1980; Strupp, 1996; VandenBos, 1996; Yeaton & Wortman, 1984). For issues specific to rehabilitation counseling, see Emener (1980), Phillips, Butler, and Thomas (1988),

Szymanski and Parker (1989a, 1989b), Szymanski, Parker, and Butler (1990), Walls and Tseng (1987), and Wright, Leahy, and Riedesel (1987).

Client, Counselor, and Process Variables Related to Outcome

This section addresses the major themes in recent research and recommends selected readings. The complexity and extent of this literature, however, may overwhelm newcomers, as well as many seasoned practitioners.

For overviews of the relationship of client characteristics to outcome, see Bergin and Garfield (1994), Garfield (1994), Garfield and Bergin (1986), Kazdin (1986), Lambert, Shapiro, and Bergin (1986), Luborsky et al. (1988), Meltzoff and Kornreich (1970), and VandenBos (1986). Although a number of client variables (e.g., age, sex, marital status, cultural identity, socioeconomic status, problem type and severity, maturation, and attitudes) have shown some promise as predictors of outcome in isolated studies, no generalizations can be made at this time.

Greater attention has been paid to the importance of counselor characteristics, particularly those of professional qualifications and personal attributes (see Barrett & Wright, 1984; Berman & Norton, 1985; Beutler, Machado, & Neufeldt, 1994; Luborsky, Chandler, Auerbach, & Cohen, 1971; Meltzoff & Kornreich, 1970; Truax & Mitchell, 1971). Intense controversy has been generated from the fact that trained therapists have not been shown to be consistently superior to untrained or paraprofessional therapists. Although this research has been severely criticized on methodological grounds and on the narrowness of criteria used in assessing the impact of professional training, the type and extent of professional training (e.g., psychiatry, social work, or psychology) also have not been shown to be related to outcome in any systematic manner.

Substantial research has focused on what occurs within the counseling process (see Hill, 1982; K. I. Howard & Orlinsky, 1972; Kiesler, 1973; Marsden, 1971; Orlinsky, Grawe, & Parks, 1994; Truax & Mitchell, 1971). The studies that have attempted to relate approaches and techniques to client outcome, however, generally have been inconclusive. For the student or practitioner searching for definitive answers and surefire techniques, the literature on the relationship of client, counselor, and process variables to positive outcomes will be a disappointment. Although to date, it mainly has served to destroy myths and preconceptions, for careful and persistent readers, it can also suggest guidelines for training and practice.

Special Issues in Rehabilitation Counseling Research

The research on rehabilitation counseling process and outcome conceptually parallels that of generic counseling, with a few promising exceptions. Overviews, such as those of Bolton and Jacques (1978), Livneh and Sherman (1991), Riggar et al. (1986), and Wright (1980), tap many of the relevant issues, including the application of counseling to specific rehabilitation populations, special rehabilitation counseling orientations and adaptations, and measurement of client outcomes.

The *client* as a variable was reviewed from the perspective of the counselor by Thoreson, Smits, Butler, and Wright (1968) in their study of counselors' professional concerns. Client motivation and counselor responsibilities in coping with the "unmotivated client" emerged as primary concerns. The importance of these findings was punctuated in a later study (Tichenor, Thomas, & Kravetz, 1975), where it was found that discrepancies in problem perception between counselors and clients were associated with the counselor's viewing the client as "unmotivated." Most studies, however, have focused on requirements and procedures with specific disability groups, for example, individuals with chronic disabilities (Beyrakal, 1975; Fohs, 1991), clients with chronic pain (Reagles, 1984; J. K. Smith & Crisler, 1985), adolescents and young adults with severe head injury (Bergland & Thomas, 1991; Garske & Thomas, 1992), sexual adjustment of people with physical disabilities (Boyle, 1976; Robbins, 1985), computer-assisted instruction of students with physical disabilities (Alston & Burkhead, 1989), individual versus group counseling of people with physical disabilities (Bryan, 1974), prospective studies of persons with spinal cord injury (Krause & Crewe, 1987), group therapy with people with spinal cord injuries (Cimperman & Dunn, 1974), counseling with the renal dialysis patient (Ebra, 1975; Fisher, 1976), and working with loss and grief of people with traumatic disabilities (Krieger, 1976). These examples, representative of the rehabilitation-oriented literature on counseling of people with physical disabilities, are paralleled in studies focusing on people who are mentally retarded, emotionally disturbed, or abusing drugs or alcohol.

The *counselor* as a variable has received attention primarily in terms of his or her professional orientation, counseling style, and type of training. Work by Sather, Wright, and Butler (1968), for example, provided instrumentation for measuring counselor orientation along two dimensions, relationship versus situation orientation. In addition, research by Bolton (1974b) distinguished three verbal interaction styles of rehabilitation counselors, namely, therapeutic, information-giving, and information-exchanging styles.

Following a different line of inquiry, Szymanski and her colleagues (Szymanski, 1988; Szymanski & Parker, 1989a, 1989b; Szymanski, Parker, & Borich, 1990) took the lead in developing a more methodologically sophisticated design that controls for some of the extraneous, confounding variables in rehabilitation outcome research. Szymanski and Parker (1989a, 1989b) studied counselors' level of education and work experience as related to their competitive closure rate (annual number of clients closed in competitive employment divided by the number of clients in all closure statuses) for clients identified as having severe disabilities. By utilizing a sophisticated, aptitude–treatment interaction design, Szymanski and Parker were able to demonstrate that counselors with master's degrees in rehabilitation counseling obtained significantly more successful rehabilitation outcomes than counselors with bachelor's or unrelated master's degrees.

Studies on the correlates of educational training level within the counseling process, with the exception of the work by Szymanski and her colleagues, generally have been inconclusive, as have studies in the generic field of counseling and psychotherapy. Thomas (1990) criticized such studies in rehabilitation counseling for (a) failing to differentiate adequately between the terms *education* and *training;* (b) failing to control for the myriad of process, counselor, client, contextual, and other contaminating variables; and (c) having a preestablished and often self-serving agenda (e.g., showing that those with master's degrees in rehabilitation counseling are superior to those with other degrees). This agenda, Thomas asserted, is incongruent with the broader and more important research goal of identifying the most effective interventions for specific types of clients working with specific types of counselors under specific sets of circumstances. Dunn (1990), however, pointed out that "a validation study of the job-relatedness of the rehabilitation counseling master's degree is the essential first step toward the goal of ensuring that all persons with disabilities receive rehabilitation counseling services only from those qualified to provide them" (p. 170). Finally, for a presentation of methodological issues in the assessment of rehabilitation counselor performance, see Bolton (1979a, 1987), Wright et al. (1987), Phillips et al. (1988), and Szymanski, Parker, and Butler (1990).

Theories of Counseling and Psychotherapy: Diverging Points of View

In the search for a personal vantage point in counseling with the rehabilitation client, the student and the practitioner have the option of selecting from more than a dozen major approaches. For purposes of presentation, these approaches are categorized as psychoanalytic, humanistic, rational, behavioral, cognitive, and eclectic (or integrative).

Texts presenting comparative overviews of the approaches differ considerably in scope and depth. The texts of Baruth and Huber (1985), Brammer et al. (1993), Corey (1996), Corsini and Wedding (1989, 1995), Cottone (1992), Gilliland et al. (1994), Patterson (1986), Prochaska (1984), and Riggar et al. (1986) are representative of recent texts written at an introductory graduate level. The average "shopper" for a suitable counseling approach in rehabilitation practice may wish to consider the following points:

1. *What is the importance of theory in rehabilitation counseling?* A theory is more than a collection of principles, methods, or techniques; it is an attempt to organize and integrate knowledge and to answer questions in such a way as to make possible a systematic client description from which prediction and explanation concerning the client can be derived (Patterson, 1986). A theory provides a set of "blinders." It helps counselors determine where to focus their attention

(Hall & Lindzey, 1987). A theory is primarily useful in terms of how effectively it can generate verifiable predictions about a client. It also enables the counselor to develop hypotheses regarding client behavior that the counselor has not yet observed. In this way, theory provides a map or a model that prevents the counselor from becoming dazzled and confused by the complexity of conditions that characterizes rehabilitation.

2. *What are the underlying philosophical notions of the theory?* How does the theory view human nature? Is this view congruent with the counselor's own beliefs? In a related vein, how well developed and empirically verified are the theoretical bases of the approach? How fully does the theory describe and explain the development of normal and abnormal behavior and the dynamics of behavior change? All these factors must be congruent with the views and expectations of the counselor, or the approach will not be seriously accepted, except by the casual dilettante.

3. *What range and type of clients can feasibly be served by the approach?* What limits are imposed by such factors as the client's presenting problems, intellectual functioning, verbal expressivity, or therapeutic expectations? In most rehabilitation settings, the counselor is expected to work with clients possessing a wide range of characteristics, and the counselor's approach must be flexible enough to deal with client variability.

4. *What demands does a selected approach place on the counselor with respect to training, experience, personality attributes, verbal ability, and values?* Although most systems have few expectations concerning the counselor's background and traits, the demands made by some systems make them impractical for use by many practitioners. For example, to be trained in psychoanalysis, one must successfully go through analysis and meet a number of other stringent requirements.

5. *What are the explicit or implicit goals of counseling?* In many employment contexts, counselors are expected to limit their function to a narrower role than is prescribed by a given approach. What is the impact of this restriction? When an agency's goals for its clients are defined, for example, as job development and placement, counseling approaches that stress goals of personality integration become difficult to justify. Of equal importance is the question of who assumes the primary responsibility for setting the goals. Approaches vary considerably in flexibility regarding the relative roles of the counselor, client, and external agency in goal formulation.

6. *What specific techniques are used to achieve the goals of the theoretical approach?* Counseling techniques must also be considered as to the demands placed on the counselor and the client, the appropriateness for the agency context, the costs relative to the benefits obtained, and other practical constraints. For example, a behavioral approach that requires cooperation of outsiders to implement reinforcement schedules may not be appropriate for the client who is a "loner" or for the counselor who is practicing independently. Some techniques may place heavy demands on the counselor for specialized training, and others may have unrealistic requirements for client cooperation.

7. *What are the criteria for measuring change?* This issue is a major concern for the many counselors who require more than blind faith that their approach is effective. How can this be accomplished? Not all approaches make these criteria explicit or are geared to reliable, empirical measurement of change. In fact, in some cases, the criteria for change are not even theoretically congruent with the approach.

8. *How does one determine the relevance and appropriateness of a counseling approach for rehabilitation settings?* The selected approach ideally should (a) be congruent with the counselor's basic philosophy and theoretical orientation; (b) be consistent with his or her training and personality; (c) be applicable to the clients of the agency; (d) be accountable in terms of the benefits accrued; and (e) in general, mesh well with the specific rehabilitation context. No single approach has yet been blessed with a consensus of endorsements. The onus is upon the student and practitioner to apply their training, experience, and professional judgment to select an approach that best suits their unique responsibilities. The proliferation of counseling approaches has led to the development of integrative-eclectic models to cope with the plethora of theories and the welter of studies on the counseling and psychotherapy process. Currently, fewer individuals report strict theoretical allegiance than was the case a decade ago, with a preponderance of counselors identifying with some form of eclecticism (Bergin & Garfield, 1994; Garfield & Bergin, 1986; Garfield & Kurtz, 1976; G. S. Howard, Nance, & Myers, 1986; Norcross, 1986; D. S. Smith, 1982).

In the summaries that follow, the major theoretical contributions are highlighted. References are made to additional readings that will help the reader make comprehensive evaluations of these divergent points of view. The approaches reviewed here were chosen for their prominence in the general field of counseling and psychotherapy and their potential relevance to rehabilitation practice. The grouping, although somewhat arbitrary, is based on the similarity of major theoretical viewpoints, as well as present emphases in theory, research, and practice.

Psychoanalytic Approaches

Psychoanalytic approaches to counseling and psychotherapy originated with the early works of Jerome Breuer and Sigmund Freud, who used hypnosis to help patients remember and abreact early conflicts to treat their hysterical symptoms. Because Freud found hypnosis of limited value, he developed free association, which became the fundamental technique of psychoanalysis. Although at least some of Freud's theories and related concepts are still accepted by a majority of analysts, classical analysis is only one of several variants of psychoanalysis (Pine, 1990).

In its original form, psychoanalysis stressed the roles of the unconscious, infantile sexuality, and anxiety on psychic functioning. However, such later theorists as Alfred Adler (1963), Erich Fromm (1947), Karen Horney (1945), Carl Jung (1959), Otto Rank (1957), and Harry Stack Sullivan (1947) (i.e., the so-called neo-Freudians), considerably modified and elaborated Freud's original concepts, especially in deem-phasizing the role of infantile sexuality and stressing the role of social variables in anxiety and personality development. Other theorists, particularly Franz Alexander (1963) and Edward Bordin (1968), incorporated psychoanalytically derived concepts and techniques into shorter term counseling and therapy systems.

Basic to the use of classical psychoanalysis as a treatment method is an understanding of the role of the unconscious in psychic functioning. Briefly, Freud believed that the motivational forces in human behavior are both conscious and unconscious. In addition, he recognized that conscience (superego) may operate at both conscious and unconscious levels and that the very mechanisms by which the mind (ego) protects itself from anxiety may be unconscious. The three-part or tripartite structural model of the mind consists of (a) the ego with its executive functions that orient the individual to the external world and mediate between it and the individual's internal world; (b) the id, which represents those primary sexual/aggressive instincts that make demands on the mind; and (c) the superego, which is a structural modification of the ego responsible for unconscious guilt which arises from the internalization of parental prohibitions and proscriptions in the resolution of the Oedipus complex (Arlow, 1995).

Freud further believed that the individual retains in the unconscious primitive biological and sexual impulses, which, if expressed, would cause retribution from the individual's own superego and society at large. To prevent this punishment, the individual relies primarily on the defense mechanism of repression; that is, the individual represses these unacceptable impulses from conscious awareness. When repressed material in the unconscious threatens to escape into consciousness, the individual experiences what is called "signal anxiety." To alleviate this anxiety (i.e., threat to the ego), the individual uses a variety of defense mechanisms, including repression, compensation, sublimation, reaction formation, rationalization, displacement, and projection. Although both adjusted and distressed individuals use these defense mechanisms, their excessive use is considered indicative of a neurosis.

The therapist's role in helping neurotic individuals is to facilitate the bringing of the repressed material into consciousness, where it can be dealt with in a rational and socially acceptable manner. To accomplish this goal, the therapist relies primarily on the techniques of free association, interpretation, dream analysis, and analysis of transference and resistance.

Freud revised his theory of psychoanalysis several times, but he retained some key elements in each revision. These key elements include the existence of drives (instincts); the economic theory (hydraulic theory); the dynamic theory (the interplay between the systems preconscious and unconscious); the dual-instinct theory (sex, also called libido or Eros, and aggression, also called the death instinct or Thanatos); and the structure theory (id, ego, and superego). The ideas of psychosexual stages (oral, anal, phallic, latent, and genital) and the Oedipus complex (including associated concepts such as castration anxiety and penis envy) are additional key elements.

Freud believed psychopathology was the result of intrapsychic conflict arising primarily from sexual and aggressive issues during the Oedipal period (i.e., ages 3 through 6). Recent analytic theorists, on the other hand, including Otto Kernberg (1984), Heinz Kohut (1984), Margaret Mahler (1979), and D. W. Winnicott (1975), have placed primary emphasis on early (i.e., pre-Oedipal) object relations and development. The question at issue is whether emotional disturbance results from conflicts between the individual's instinctual drives and societal values or whether pathology results from developmental deficits. Also at issue is the relative importance of early-life caregiving versus the importance of how one resolves the Oedipus complex.

Unquestionably, the clinician's view of the origin of pathology determines, in part, the interventions selected. Classical theorists emphasize the interpretation of transference and resistance, dream analysis, and free association, whereas object relations theorists, for example, emphasize the real relationship, counter-transference interpretations, empathy, and the creation of what Winnicott (1965) called "a holding environment." Interestingly, modern psychoanalytic theorists are similar to person-centered therapists (discussed in the next section) in their emphasis on the development of the self, empathy, the real relationship, and the creation of a facilitative, therapeutic environment. Nonetheless, there are vast differences between the two groups in how they view the origin and nature of psychopathology, as well as how they view the treatment environment. However, in the case of both modern analysts and person-centered therapists, a major goal of therapy with people with disabilities would be to strengthen the cohesiveness of the self and improve self-esteem.

Many aspects of psychoanalytic theory have applications in rehabilitation counseling. Cook (Chapter 9, this text) suggests that psychoanalytic conceptualizations of the ego defenses (e.g., A. Freud, 1936; S. Freud, 1923/1961) are particularly useful in understanding the impact of disability on the individual. Cook lists four defense mechanisms, which are frequently mentioned in the literature on adjustment to physical disability: repression, projection, reaction formation, and regression. Cubbage and Thomas (1989) added to this list denial, compensation, displacement, sublimation, restriction of the ego, and rationalization. A discussion of the applications of defense mechanisms to psychological rehabilitation was also provided by Krueger (1984). By recognizing the role that defense mechanisms play in adjustment to disability, rehabilitation counselors are in a better position to understand the clients' behavior, and to recognize those defenses that are being used to promote coping. Other psychoanalytic concepts, which may have particular relevance to work with people with disabilities, are castration anxiety, fear of loss of love, narcissism, the concept of secondary gain, and the death instinct. A more detailed discussion of these issues was presented by Cubbage and Thomas (1989). Also, the reader may wish to consult Siller (1988) for a discussion of the intrapsychic aspects of attitudes toward people with disabilities.

As noted earlier, modern psychoanalytic theorists emphasize the importance of the integrity of the self and the role of empathy in the healing process (Kohut,

1984). Also, by creating a therapeutic "holding environment," patients or clients are helped to mend what have essentially been narcissistic injuries of the past (Winnicott, 1965). According to Thomas and McGinnis (1991), through the provision of empathy and creation of the holding environment advocated by Winnicott, rehabilitation counselors can facilitate a natural healing process in clients who are adjusting to the "impingement" of a physical disability.

Several psychoanalytic theorists (e.g., Bordin, Nachmann, & Segal, 1963; Erikson, 1950; Hendrick, 1943; Neff, 1985) have presented ideas that counselors could use to understand a client's vocational development, but little specific direction is offered in terms of how to facilitate development. Adler's (1963) conceptualization of striving for superiority as an innate drive and S. Freud's (1933/1964) concepts of introjection, identification, and sublimation are useful for understanding the motivational and directional aspects of vocational development. In addition, Adlerian concepts such as lifestyle and compensation for organic defect or organ inferiority may be viewed as potentially useful for understanding psychological adjustment to disability. A further contribution of psychoanalytic theory to rehabilitation practice is the recognition that early life experiences and child-rearing practices may have a considerable effect on later development and behavior, including development and behavior in the vocational realm.

Although psychoanalysis is inappropriate for use by rehabilitation counselors, due both to the length of time and the level of training required, a knowledge of psychoanalytic theory can contribute significantly to the counselor's understanding of human behavior and practice of counseling. In addition to those contributions already cited, psychoanalytic theory provides a framework for better understanding the structure of personality, the role of the unconscious, and the mechanisms of defense, especially as these concepts relate to the adjustment to disability process. It has also served as the basis for many of the more recently developed techniques and approaches to counseling. Readers interested in learning about recent developments in psychoanalysis may consult a variety of sources, including Eagle (1984), Greenberg (1991), Greenberg and Mitchell (1983), Hughes (1989), Kernberg (1984), Kohut (1984), Mahler (1979), Mitchell (1988), Reppen (1985), Stolorow, Brandchaft, and Atwood (1987), Summers (1994), and Winnicott (1965, 1975). Specific applications of psychoanalytic theory to a rehabilitation treatment context are provided by Rule (1984), Siller and Thomas (1995), and Thurer (1986).

Humanistic Approaches

The humanistic approaches reviewed, person-centered therapy and Gestalt therapy, represent only two of several that have a common fundamental belief that the client is the active agent of change in the counseling relationship. Emphasis is placed on the client's feelings and emotions rather than on overt behavior or rationality of beliefs. The counselor's role is deemphasized in favor of an optimistic view that, when given the freedom to explore themselves in warm and empathic counseling sessions, clients will successfully redirect their own lives.

Person-Centered Therapy

Person-centered therapy originated with Carl Rogers (1942, 1951, 1961, 1980) and was initially called client-centered counseling. It has been extended by the writings and research of a substantial number of associates, as documented by Bergin and Garfield (1971, 1994), Carkhuff and Berenson (1977), Kiesler (1973), and Raskin and Rogers (1995). Because person-centered counseling developed in part as a reaction against psychoanalytic therapy, its basic philosophical and theoretical foundations differ significantly from those set forth by Freud.

Human beings are viewed as innately good, basically realistic, and forward moving. Rogers recognized a number of innate components that include (a) the actualizing tendency as an inherent proclivity of the organism to develop all its capabilities in ways that serve to maintain the organism; (b) the tendency toward self-actualization that is symbolized in the self; (c) the capacity to perceive both situational events and internal stimuli, and to represent the perceptions in symbolic form; and (d) the organizing principle that integrates new experiences with past behavior and experience.

A fully functioning individual symbolizes his or her experiences accurately in awareness. Needs for positive regard from others and positive self-regard are met. Self-structure is consistent with perceived experience; experience will not be distorted or denied to awareness. Under conditions of suboptimal functioning, the individual senses a lack of congruence between self and experience; is defensive, anxious, and lacking in positive self-regard; and tends to deny, ignore, or distort the perception of discrepant responses.

The goal of person-centered counseling is for clients to become self-actualized through the development of all capacities that serve to maintain or enhance the self. Specific goals of counseling are determined primarily by clients who are assumed capable of developing a greater congruence between their behaviors and perceptions of self. Potential positive outcomes from the process of therapy include greater openness to experience, greater reduction of defensiveness, greater objectivity of perceptions, and greater self-acceptance. This latter outcome, especially in the case of persons who may have experienced substantial negative feedback from self or others due to the possession of a disability, is a significant structural goal. As a further result of successful person-centered counseling, clients become more effective in problem solving, acquire a more positive self-concept, and sense the real self as more congruent with the ideal self. Frequently, other people are perceived more favorably and accurately, and as more accepting. Finally, clients perceive their own behavior as being under their self-control (Meador & Rogers, 1984; Raskin & Rogers, 1995).

Although appropriate and effective techniques primarily involve reflection of feelings, the conditions of the therapeutic process are regarded as being of paramount importance. The necessary and sufficient conditions of therapeutic change identified by Rogers (1957) include the following:

1. Two persons are in contact.

2. One, the client, is in a state of incongruence, being vulnerable or anxious.

3. The other person, the counselor, is congruent in the relationship.

4. The counselor experiences unconditional positive regard toward the client.

5. The counselor experiences an accurate empathic understanding of the client's internal frame of reference.

6. The client perceives, to some extent, the positive regard and empathic understanding of the counselor.

The process of therapy, then, is described not in terms of specific rules, but as the logical outcome of the conditions just listed and the basic assumptions concerning personality change. During the process, the client becomes more open to experiencing feelings, more aware of incongruence between experience and self, and more aware of feelings that were previously denied to awareness or distorted. The counselor is expected to experience and communicate congruence (genuineness), unconditional positive regard (acceptance), and accurate empathy (understanding).

On the other hand, giving advice or directive suggestions of alternative solutions; interpretation, probing, role playing, or information giving; and admonishments or other impositions of the counselor's values are regarded as detrimental to client growth. Counselor introduction of psychometric test data, occupational information, or case history material is similarly eschewed.

Criteria for change are implied by the expected outcomes of this therapy. In operationalizing these criteria for purposes of research, client self-report techniques, such as measures of self-concept and indices of congruence between real and ideal self, are used.

Application of person-centered therapy to rehabilitation settings has received mixed reviews. Serious questions have been raised about its appropriateness for clients with limited intelligence or limited verbal expressivity, particularly those with severe mental retardation or severe psychoses. Notably, Rogers reversed his original dictum against using person-centered counseling with people with mental retardation and conducted extensive research to support therapy with people diagnosed as schizophrenic (Rogers, Gendlin, Kiesler, & Truax, 1967).

Because this approach emphasizes personal attributes (which may or may not be modified by training) rather than formal training in psychotherapy, the approach is within bounds for the majority of rehabilitation counselors. Goals of therapy may conflict with those set by some agencies. Perhaps most important is the potential role conflict for counselors, particularly those in state rehabilitation agencies, who are required to make substantive decisions, such as those concerning eligibility for rehabilitation services. Another commonly expressed criticism is that extensive counseling time is required. Other than cost, however, no serious objections have been raised to referral of clients to person-centered therapists for purchased services during the rehabilitation process. A thoughtful analysis of the merits and limitations of applying person-centered counseling in a state vocational rehabilitation agency context is provided by See (1986).

Gestalt Therapy

Gestalt therapy is usually attributed to Fritz Perls, with the books by Perls (1969) and Perls, Hefferline, and Goodman (1951) being landmark publications. The approach is based on psychoanalysis and existential philosophy. A major concept from Gestalt psychology is the perceptual field that represents the context and extent of what an individual perceives. The individual is viewed as striving to organize stimuli into wholes. This organization is accomplished within the context of figure–ground relationships. The figure constitutes the immediate need and the activities associated with meeting these needs; the ground refers to the physical and psychological surrounds. As shifts in stimuli occur, a gestalt, or unified understanding, is formed. Somewhat simplistically, people's abilities to shift, meet needs, and form complete gestalts are related to their complete and accurate awareness of both figure and ground. Anything that detracts from comprehensive and accurate awareness interferes with people's capacities to act effectively as fully functioning people.

According to Passons (1975, p. 14), Gestalt therapy is based on the following assumptions:

1. [A human being] . . . is a whole who is (rather than has) a body, emotions, thoughts, sensations, and perceptions, all of which function interrelatedly.
2. [Humans are] . . . a part of . . . [their] environment and cannot be understood outside of it.
3. [Humans are] . . . proactive rather than reactive. [They determine their] . . . own responses to external and proprioceptive stimuli.
4. [Humans are] . . . capable of being aware of their sensations, thoughts, emotions, and perceptions.
5. [A human being] . . . through self-awareness, is capable of choice and is thus responsible for covert and overt behavior.
6. [Humans possess] . . . the wherewithal and resources to live effectively and to restore . . . [themselves] through . . . [their] own assets.
7. [Humans] . . . can experience . . . [themselves] only in the present. The past and the future can be experienced only in the now through remembering and anticipating.
8. [A human being] . . . is neither intrinsically good nor bad.

An important concept in understanding personality development is what Perls referred to as ego boundary. Infants quickly learn to differentiate what is within themselves and what is outside. During development, the self and self-image are formed, the self being what the individual really is and the self-image reflecting the perceived expectations of others.

Growth is characterized by contact, sensing, excitement, and gestalt formations. Frustration facilitates growth in that it encourages people to mobilize resources and act on their own. Fully functioning people are comprehensively aware of their senses, can fully express themselves, have no major "incomplete" life experiences, are self-supporting, and are not maintaining self-images incongruent with the real self (Simkin & Yontef, 1984).

In Gestalt therapy, the major intermediate goal is increased awareness, for only with increased awareness can the "unfinished business" of life be recognized and confronted. The ultimate goal is the total integration of the individual by bringing together all elements of the self that have been disowned. Integration results in the client's becoming self-directive.

Perls (1969), Kempler (1973), Polster and Polster (1973), Polster (1995), and Zinker (1977, 1994) proposed a wide range of techniques, although there are significant differences of opinion as to the appropriateness of some. All techniques emphasize experiencing and awareness in the "here and now." Counselors are active, confrontational, probing, and authoritative. Role playing, the "hot seat," dream review, and client fantasizing are a number of acceptable techniques. All are designed to facilitate clients to fully experience concerns, feelings, attitudes, or disowned aspects of themselves. Nonverbal behavior is considered particularly significant. The bowed head or clenched fist is challenged to encourage clients to share the associated feeling. Frustration is employed to discourage dependency, mobilize resources, and encourage expression of feeling. For a comprehensive listing of "rules" and "games" of Gestalt therapy, see Levitsky and Perls (1970).

Criteria for change and evaluation of success are elusive in Gestalt therapy. Level of goal attainment is assessed primarily through clinical judgment, largely because appropriate objective measures of change have not been developed. Consequently, the approach has not been thoroughly verified by research. However, promising efforts have been made by Leslie Greenberg and colleagues, who have integrated into Gestalt theory several of the current theoretical and empirical developments in the mainstream of psychology. The resulting integration posits that Gestalt therapy involves the accessing of cognitive–affective schemata regarding tacit rules and beliefs, and, because all concerns of the individual are encoded in this manner, any therapy change must ultimately involve modification of these schemata through disconfirmation of the original schema (e.g., "All people are evil") through accessing previously unprocessed emotional experience and reintegrating emotion and cognition. Greenberg, Rice, and Elliott (1993) and Daldrop, Beutler, Greenberg, and Engle (1988) summarized these efforts at providing a coherent conceptual structure, operationalizing basic Gestalt therapy concepts and stipulating a set of task-guided interventions for various emotional problems presented by clients. These developments have led to reports of positive results in testing the efficacy of Gestalt therapy (see Beutler et al., 1991; Pavio & Greenberg, 1995).

Implications for rehabilitation do not differ significantly from those cited for person-centered therapy; however, techniques such as the "unfinished business game" and "I take responsibility" may be particularly relevant for some rehabilitation populations. Gestalt therapy has been used with children, adolescents, and adults, as well as with people diagnosed as having alcoholism, emotional disturbance, and mental retardation. Commonly treated presenting problems may include generalized anxiety, discomfort, psychosomatic disorders, and anomie. It is appropriate for clients who have difficulty in interpersonal relationships, as well as those with distorted or limiting self-images.

Counselor requirements are not as precisely specified as in the person-centered approach, but the counselor should be capable of a dynamic and active role in the counseling relationship. In view of the typical level of risk taking with clients, extensive training and personal therapy are required for recognition as a Gestalt therapist. The latter requirement makes the approach impractical for the majority of rehabilitation counselors. The techniques are sufficiently unconventional to rule out the approach in many agencies; however, counselors may wish to refer clients who require this form of confrontative and unconventional therapy to Gestalt therapists. For further information on the uses of Gestalt therapy in rehabilitation settings, see Allen (1986), Coven (1977, 1979), and H. Jung (1978).

Rational Approaches

In contrast to the humanistic approaches, which focus on client feelings, experiencing, and awareness, rational approaches emphasize a logical and intellectual solution to human problems. The approaches reviewed in this section are trait–factor counseling, rational–emotive behavior therapy, and reality therapy. Each has different historical precedents and has typically focused on a different clientele. They are grouped together somewhat arbitrarily on the basis of their "rational" emphasis. Cognitive and cognitive–behavioral approaches are discussed later under the heading "Cognitive Approaches."

Trait–Factor Counseling

The major spokesperson for trait–factor counseling was Edmund G. Williamson (1950, 1965), although he represented a point of view shared by a number of his colleagues at the University of Minnesota. Unlike Rogers and Perls, whose views stemmed from reactions against the clinical application of psychoanalysis, Williamson's viewpoint was developed from a long career in university testing and counseling services. It is the only approach cited in this chapter that emerged from vocational counseling and that emphasizes educational and vocational adjustment. It stresses the use of psychological assessment in the counseling process.

A basic assumption of the trait–factor approach is that each individual is born with the potential for both good and evil. The individual strives to develop his or her full potential, which may be viewed as excellence in all aspects of human development. However, according to this approach, the individual needs others in order to realize his or her fullest potential. Development is more likely to be fostered by rational processes than by affective or intuitive capacities. Assumptions directly related to counseling include the following:

1. Major traits of the individual are measurable and can be used to match an individual to a vocation or job.

2. Information derived from the individual in testing and diagnostic interviewing can be used in decision making concerning vocational and general life adjustment.

3. Information derived from the individual must be considered in light of demands made in the environment.

4. A major task in counseling is the systematic synthesis of information so that reasonable predictions can be made about the individual's "fit" with the job and other important dimensions of the environment.

The goal of counseling is to assist clients toward the optimal development in all aspects of their personalities. Considerable stress is placed on social enlightenment, self-understanding, and self-direction, rather than on autonomous individuation. The client is expected to be a responsible member of society and to conform to its mores and values.

Techniques of counseling are not fully explicated, but the steps in the counseling process have been delineated as follows:

1. *Analysis,* the initial step, involves the systematic collection of data and information about the client to acquire an understanding of the client's problem and the demands of current and future adjustment. Specific tools vary with the setting, but they include the initial interview, case history, medical history, and psychological tests. From these are derived the family history, health history, educational work history, and an overview of social, avocational, and vocational interests and objectives.

2. *Synthesis* is the summarizing and organizing of data to determine the client's assets, liabilities, adjustments, and maladjustments.

3. *Diagnosis* pertains to the summary of problems and their causes. Unlike medical diagnosis, which is almost solely the practitioner's responsibility, diagnosis involves the client's participation to the extent of his or her intellectual and emotional capabilities.

4. *Prognosis* refers to the counselor's specific predictions of probable outcomes, given a variety of possible courses of action and other contingencies.

5. *Counseling* is viewed as that phase in which the counselor assists the client in using internal and external resources to achieve optimal adjustment. It

involves a process of guided reeducation. Five categories of techniques have been identified: forcing conformity, changing the environment, selecting the appropriate environment, learning needed skills, and changing attitudes. These are general headings; specific techniques vary with the individual client and the presenting problem. Some common threads throughout include establishing rapport, cultivating self-understanding, and advising or planning a program of action. The counselor is active in the process, avoids being dogmatic, but may offer advice and information freely while encouraging the client to express ideas. Direct assistance in implementing the plan is proffered when necessary, and the counselor will involve others as deemed appropriate.

6. *Follow-up* involves the availability of the counselor to deal with recurring problems and to determine whether the counseling has been effective.

No systematic procedures have been developed to measure change under this approach. Because the approach has been used extensively in university settings, educational and vocational successes have been cited as appropriate indicators. Client job satisfaction and "job satisfactoriness" (the congruence between worker abilities and job demands) are constructs developed in the Minnesota Studies in Vocational Rehabilitation (Dawis, 1967). These constructs logically could be used in the trait–factor approach as indices of counseling effectiveness.

Of the approaches reviewed in this chapter, trait–factor counseling appears to parallel most closely the practice of a majority of rehabilitation counselors, particularly those in state agencies. A major counselor requirement is the ability to interpret psychological test results and to understand the merits and liabilities of psychological measurement. Goals of counseling are generally congruent with the broader goals of rehabilitation. Techniques are usually well within the repertoire of skills of most rehabilitation counselors and deemed appropriate in most settings. Some counselors, however, have difficulty in accepting the philosophical underpinnings of this approach. Moreover, the emphasis on the use of psychometric tests and other assessment techniques could be a significant disadvantage of the trait–factor approach, given the questionable validity of many of these techniques when applied to people with disabilities.

According to Chartrand (1991), the trait–factor approach has evolved recently into what would more accurately be called a "person × environment (P × E) approach" (Rounds & Tracey, 1990). Although there are many similarities between the trait–factor and person × environment approaches, some important differences include the emphasis in the person × environment approach on what is called "dynamic reciprocity" between the individual and the environment (Rounds & Tracey, 1990), client involvement in the assessment process, and an attempt by the counselor to attain congruence with client needs. A critical idea in this schema is that the person × environment fit is a reciprocal process in which the individual shapes the environment and the environment influences the individual (Chartrand, 1991). Moreover, it is assumed that individuals both seek out and create congruent environments. Collectively, these changes or additions appear to give the person × environment approach a more dynamic and less authoritarian flavor than the "old" trait–factor approach; however, the two approaches are rooted in similar theoretical and philosophical foundations and use many of the same assessment tools and cognitively based interventions. A recent application of the person × environment approach to rehabilitation counseling is provided by Kosciulek (1993).

Rational–Emotive Behavior Therapy

The theory and practice of rational–emotive behavior therapy (REBT) were initiated by Albert Ellis. His approach emerged from his clinical practice, which was primarily in sex and marital counseling. A key to understanding REBT is the so-called A-B-C paradigm: "When a highly charged emotional consequence (C) follows a significant Activating Event (A), A may be seen to, but does not actually, cause C. Instead, emotional consequences are largely created by B, the individual's Belief system" (Ellis, 1995b, p. 162). In other words, it is not what has happened that causes difficulty and stress, but the person's irrational beliefs about what has happened. If these beliefs can be rationally challenged and disputed, the undesirable emotional consequences will cease. Major assumptions underlying this approach to therapy include:

1. Humans have an innate potential for rational thinking.
2. Irrational thinking is acquired by learning, usually at an early age.
3. Perception, thinking, and emoting are interdependent and occur simultaneously.
4. Irrational beliefs, when they cause emotional disturbance, are primarily faulty and/or negative self-statements.
5. These irrational beliefs may be supplanted and thus overcome by inducing the individual to verbalize positive self-verbalizations.

One focal point in the theory is that illogical ideas form the basis of self-defeating attitudes and neuroses. In outline, these illogical beliefs are as follows:

1. I must do very well!
2. I am a bad or worthless person when I act weakly or stupidly.
3. I must be approved or accepted by people I find important!
4. I need to be loved by someone who matters to me a lot!
5. I am a bad, unlovable person if I get rejected.
6. People must treat me fairly and give me what I need!
7. People must live up to my expectations or it is terrible!
8. People who act immorally are undeserving, rotten people!
9. I can't stand really bad things or very difficult people!

10. My life must have few major hassles or troubles.
11. It's awful or horrible when major things don't go my way!
12. I can't stand it when life is really unfair!
13. I need a good deal of immediate gratification and have to feel miserable when I don't get it! (Ellis, 1989, pp. 227–228)

The main goal of REBT is to eliminate emotional disturbance by substituting rational beliefs and thinking for irrationality. As a result of successful REBT, clients become more independent of the evaluations of others and rely more on positive self-reinforcement for their behavior.

Conventional techniques used in psychoanalytic and person-centered therapy are avoided. Ellis views such techniques as free association, dream analysis, dynamically oriented interpretation, and reassurance as inefficient and irrelevant. Generally, the therapist uses an active, directive approach to identify the core of irrational ideas that are basic to the disturbed behavior, challenges the client to validate those ideas, and directively shows how they are illogical. Rational substitutes are introduced, and the client is taught to sequence them correctly. Homework assignments are often made. Clients, for example, may listen to cassette recordings of previous sessions or keep a journal documenting ways they have assailed irrational beliefs between sessions.

Criteria for success of the approach are couched in general terms, and include reduced anxiety and defensiveness, increased skills in attacking irrational beliefs and enhancing reality testing, greater levels of individuality and freedom of choice, and heightened self-confidence and self-acceptance (Ellis, 1995b). These criteria are garnered through therapists' reports. However, researchers have developed rational behavior scales, which show promise for assessing the effectiveness of REBT (e.g., *Jones Irrational Beliefs Test;* see Ellis, 1995b).

Applicability of REBT to rehabilitation settings is limited in several ways. REBT is probably not feasible for individuals who have low intelligence or severe thought disorders. It does not appear appropriate for educational and vocational decision making, but may be effective when low self-esteem, poor social skills, or lack of acceptance of disability interferes with rehabilitation. Counselors who wish to use REBT should receive specific training in the techniques beyond that usually incorporated in most formal counselor education programs. Certainly, referral of carefully selected clients to professional psychotherapists for REBT would be feasible and appropriate. See Ellis (1995a) and Ostby (1986) for discussions of rational–emotive behavior therapy as applied specifically to rehabilitation settings.

Reality Therapy

One other rational approach should be briefly noted. Reality therapy, a relative newcomer to the field of psychological treatment, was introduced by Glasser (1965, 1969). According to Glasser and Wubbolding (1995), reality therapy

Helps people examine their wants and needs, evaluate behaviors, and make future plans for fulfilling needs. It is mostly free of obscure psychological terminology, which leads to the misconception that it is easy to put into practice. Nevertheless, it is a practical method that can be used by therapists, counselors, teachers, parents, and others. (p. 293)

In the process of reality therapy, the counselor is verbally active, sets limits, is guided by a precise behavior contract with the client, and may engage in a wide variety of interactional techniques (e.g., confrontation and constructive arguing) that direct the client to the realities of the present and immediate future. The focus is on behaviors, not feelings, and particularly on how clients will act in a responsible manner on their own behalf.

The counselor's goal is to increase responsible client behavior. According to Glasser, a responsible behavior is one that satisfies one's needs without preventing others from satisfying theirs. The therapist may become didactic when clients need assistance in making effective choices; the counselor does not accept excuses or condone punishment.

Reality therapy has not been widely used in rehabilitation settings, but does appear to have potential value for several client groups (e.g., clients who are overly dependent, have alcohol or drug abuse problems, or are public offenders). Also, specific aspects of the approach, such as the personal involvement of the counselor, developing a contract with the client, and striving to help the client develop a success identity, are congruent with the goals and practices of rehabilitation. Although the basic tenets have been thoroughly documented, little research has been conducted to verify the utility of reality therapy. See Ososkie and Turpin (1986) for a discussion of the applications of reality therapy to rehabilitation counseling.

Behavioral Approaches

Behavioral approaches may be extended to include those counseling strategies that involve learning-theory principles and focus on change of behavior rather than feelings, attitudes, or beliefs. One approach, Krumboltz's behavioral counseling, has been selected for detailed review. Three others, Dollard and Miller's marriage of reinforcement and psychoanalytic theories, Wolpe's psychotherapy by reciprocal inhibition, and Rotter's social learning approach, are described briefly.

Expounded by John Krumboltz and a number of associates and students at Stanford University, behavioral counseling was developed initially for counseling services in the public school setting. Basic references include Krumboltz and Thoresen (1969, 1976) and Hosford and de Visser (1974). Highly eclectic in the use of techniques, its theoretical principles stem primarily from learning theory. Basic concepts include the following:

1. People have equal potentialities for good and evil.

2. People are capable of change.

3. Each person has unique problems that must be appreciated on an individual basis.

4. Behavior is guided by external conditions that are interpreted by the individual's cognitive processes.

There is little preoccupation with the causality and classification of maladaptive behavior. No assumptions are made about psychopathological processes. Current problems may stem from either learned maladaptive behavior or failure to have learned specific adaptive behaviors. The focus is on identifying the client's current problem, establishing specific behavioral goals to alleviate the problem, and selecting the most appropriate techniques to achieve the goal.

In their introduction, Krumboltz and Thoresen (1969) identified four general types of problems: (a) deficient decision-making skills, (b) ineffective academic (vocationally related) skills, (c) inappropriate social skills, and (d) self-defeating fears and anxieties. Essential features include four interrelated characteristics that enable behavioral counselors to respond flexibly and adapt new, continuously improving procedures to help their clients. The first concerns the process of formulating counseling goals. Of all the major approaches, behavioral counseling places the greatest emphasis on the process of goal formulation. A goal should meet three essential criteria (Krumboltz, 1966):

1. It must be desired by the client.

2. The counselor must be willing to help the client achieve the goal.

3. It must be possible to assess the extent to which the client achieves the goal.

A second feature is that the same set of techniques is not universally applicable. A procedure or combination of procedures is selected to help clients accomplish their unique goals. Third, there are no restrictions on the selection of techniques, except those imposed by ethical considerations. There is no recommended or approved list. Each counselor is encouraged to experiment and systematically explore new procedures, provided they are within the counselor's repertoire of skills. Finally, procedures should be modified on the basis of empirical evidence.

Three classifications of goals are recognized: (a) altering or diminishing maladaptive behavior, (b) learning the decision-making process, and (c) preventing problems. The latter classification includes the acquisition of new behaviors (e.g., job seeking skills) needed to prevent future difficulties.

With the wide range of continually evolving techniques permissible under this approach, no single listing is feasible. See Krumboltz and Thoresen (1969, 1976) for a comprehensive overview that includes reinforcement techniques, role playing, social modeling, counterconditioning, and cognitive techniques such as simulation and planning. Procedures that focus primarily on feeling, experiencing, and insight, while not expressly "forbidden," do not logically fit the system. One procedural element common to most behavioral techniques is the written contract, in which the commitments of the client and counselor toward achievement of specific goals are clearly identified.

Criteria for success using this approach tend to be unique to each client. Generally, these can be defined as the acquisition of adaptive behavior or extinction of problem behavior.

The behavioral approach appears to be applicable to a wide range of rehabilitation settings and clientele. No categories of clients are arbitrarily excluded. Presenting problems of substantial numbers of rehabilitation clients (e.g., absence of job seeking and maintaining skills, inappropriate social behaviors, and fears related to changing vocations) are amenable to behavioral counseling. Counselors would require special training in the application of techniques based on the learning theory model, as well as training in the skills of problem identification and goal formulation. Techniques that require cooperation of others, such as maintaining reinforcement contingencies, may set some limits on application.

Of the other behavior therapy approaches, three warrant brief mention. The theory of Dollard and Miller (1950) is of particular interest because it integrates learning theory and psychoanalysis. The techniques are reminiscent of psychoanalysis, but the explanation of behavior change is couched primarily in learning theory concepts. For a summary of this approach, see Patterson (1986).

Joseph Wolpe (1958, 1969, 1990) developed his therapeutic approach from studies of experimental neuroses in animals. In his investigations, he induced neurotic reactions in cats and found the reactions could be reduced by conditioned inhibition. The basic concept, reciprocal inhibition, refers to the elimination or weakening of such responses as anxiety or fear through the process of counterconditioning. Specific techniques include systematic desensitization, assertiveness training, aversion therapy, therapeutic sexual arousal, and operant conditioning methods.

Rotter's (1954) social learning theory, also summarized by Patterson (1986), is of interest more for its potential than for its direct impact on the field of counseling and psychotherapy. Its potential lies in the extension of learning theory to include concepts such as the locus of control. Locus of control refers to clients' perceptions of whether behavior is controlled by outside forces (external locus of control) or by themselves (internal locus of control). The potential of this approach appears to be not so much in the techniques proposed, but in the use of constructs for the explanation and measurement of social learning variables in the counseling process.

Cognitive Approaches

Mahoney and Lyddon (1988) declared that, in the previous decade, not only had cognitive theories come to dominate counseling research and practice, but "cognitivism" had become much more prominent throughout psychology. The explosion of cognitive theories, which Mahoney (1980) called the "cognitive revolution," refers to the shift in behavioral therapies from purely behavioral approaches to a cognitive mediation model. These changes came about in response to perceived shortcomings in traditional behavioral models.

Cognitive therapy (CT) continues to incorporate a behavioral emphasis. CT is based on the facts that one learns, that what one learns can be unlearned, that what one learns follows laws of learning, and that what is learned can be clearly specified. Furthermore, CT is based on the theory of personality that holds that how one thinks largely determines how one feels and behaves (Beck & Weishaar, 1989). It is based on the observation that dysfunctional, automatic thoughts that are exaggerated, distorted, mistaken, or unrealistic play a dominant role in psychopathology. If the cognitive therapist can help the client identify those automatic thoughts that he or she is experiencing, a simple and helpful explanation can be offered for what are often incomprehensible reactions (Freeman, Pretzer, Fleming, & Simon, 1990). The application to rehabilitation becomes apparent when the diverse impact of negative psychosocial attitudes internalized by rehabilitation clients is considered.

Cognitive therapy is both a theory and a set of strategies and techniques. The theory is based on information processing, which refers to the way clients synthesize, organize, and process data to develop plans of action. It may be useful to note that CT differs from rational–emotive behavior therapy in the manner in which a counselor or therapist deals with the cognitive distortions that interfere with realistic thinking. In REBT, a client's "irrational" beliefs are modified or eliminated through confrontation by the counselor. In CT, such distortions are translated into hypotheses to be tested by clients outside of therapy.

Another important difference between REBT and CT is in the assumption of CT that clients possess unique cognitive profiles corresponding to different psychological disorders. It is assumed, for example, that cognitive profiles for depression, panic disorder, and anxiety differ significantly and require different approaches. In REBT, on the other hand, it is assumed that all psychological disorders share a common core of underlying irrational beliefs.

Although the counselor using CT views problems as dysfunctional and the REBT counselor views problems as rationally unacceptable, both CT and REBT share a number of important characteristics with behavior therapy. They all are empirically based, present centered, and noninferential. The cognitive therapies, however, differ substantially from radical behaviorism and applied behavior analysis, which give no attention to internal events or cognitive, mediating processes. Yet all share a common basis in learning theory.

CT assumes that humans respond primarily to the cognitive representation of their environment rather than to the environment per se. These representations are considered to relate to the processes of learning. Most learning is cognitively mediated, and thoughts, feelings, and behaviors are all causally interactive. Therefore, clients with severe physical disabilities may erroneously internalize the thought that they are at fault when environmental barriers preclude their working in a job to which they aspire.

Cognitive therapy has been widely used in the treatment of depression. Hence, it may appeal to rehabilitation counselors who frequently deal with clients who become depressed in reaction to a disability. In this regard, Beck, Rush, Shaw, and Emery (1979) postulated three relevant concepts: the cognitive triad, schemas, and cognitive errors. The cognitive triad consists of a negative view of the self, a negative view of the world, and a negative view of the future. The triad, interestingly, dominates the content of the depressed individual's automatic thoughts. Schemas are relatively stable cognitive patterns that form the basis for an individual's interpretation of particular events or situations. The schemas of depressed persons may lead to distortions of reality and cognitive errors that involve faulty information processing. To compound matters, a depressed mood has a negative, reciprocal impact on cognitions. The cognitive triad, schemas, and cognitive errors of depressed individuals tend to elicit a heightened depressed mood, which reciprocally reinforces the triad, schemas, and errors. This reciprocal interaction of elements of depression accounts for the commonly noted downward spiral of depression.

To combat the downward spiral, the cognitive therapist attempts to break the pattern of negative, automatic thoughts that lead to a further depressed mood and biased recall and perceptions. The cycle may be broken (a) if clients can be induced to take more balanced views of themselves, their experiences, and their prospects; (b) if their mood can be elevated; or (c) if the biasing impact of their depressed mood on perception and recall can be counteracted.

This strategy requires the modification of dysfunctional beliefs. Thus, the basic approach of the cognitive therapist is to disrupt the cycle that perpetuates a client's depression. In cognitive therapy, a wide variety of techniques for modifying automatic, dysfunctional beliefs and assumptions are available. One technique is to develop alternative adaptive responses for dysfunctional thoughts. In this instance, the correction of exaggerations and distortions in automatic thoughts leads to an improvement in mood. Dysfunctional thought can also be handled through such techniques as "thought stopping," "scheduled worrying," replacement of these thoughts with more adaptive ones, and the development of plans for preventing or handling anticipated problems. Three additional techniques to elicit behavior change are

1. Decatastrophizing or the "what if" technique (Beck & Emery, 1979), which helps clients prepare for dreaded consequences

2. Reattribution techniques, which refer to the identification of ways for clients to test automatic thoughts and assumptions by considering alternative causes for events (e.g., "I cannot work because of a lack of adequate transportation")

3. Redefining in which the client is taught to move from an external to an internal focus, for example, by shifting from "I am lonely and unlovable" to "I need to reach out to other people and be caring" (Beck & Weishaar, 1989).

The therapeutic relationship is collaborative in that the counselor first identifies the sources of distress and dysfunction and then helps clients to clarify their goals. Clients, on the other hand, provide thoughts, images, and beliefs, and share the responsibility for setting an agenda for sessions and for doing homework between sessions. As in REBT, homework is commonly assigned in cognitive therapy. The homework enables therapy to proceed more quickly.

The process of cognitive therapy involves considerable information gathering in initial sessions. The cognitive therapist is active in the early stages and becomes less active in later stages of therapy. As CT proceeds, the emphasis shifts from the initial focus on client symptoms to client patterns of thinking, with attempts to help the client see connections between thoughts, emotions, and behaviors. Insights are gained through examination of the client's automatic thoughts (e.g., "It is my fault that I cannot travel to work"). Once the client can learn to challenge these automatic thoughts, he or she can begin to look at underlying assumptions and to substitute more functional thoughts and behaviors (e.g., "With adaptive equipment and public transportation that is accessible, I can work"). In later sessions, the client assumes increasing responsibility for identifying problems and solutions and for the actual development of specific homework assignments. The counselor becomes less active and serves more as an adviser and less as a teacher. Therapy is terminated when the client is able to employ appropriate coping skills and perspectives outside of therapy. The interested reader is referred to Lyddon (1995) for a thoughtful critique of CT.

Eclectic Approaches

It was once considered questionable for counselors to use techniques from two or more theories of counseling. Arguments against using an eclectic approach were based on the contention that counselors risk considerable confusion and inconsistency when they select techniques derived from differing perspectives of human development and behavior. Because different counseling theories suggest vastly different techniques, counselors should select one theory as their frame of reference. Otherwise, they might use inconsistent techniques that impede the counseling process. For this reason, some prefer the term *integration* over *eclecticism* (Bergin & Garfield, 1994).

Although this objection to eclecticism may help counselors avoid conflicts of purpose and strategy in their practice, it ignores the fact that no one counseling theory explains or provides for the remediation of all types of behavior problems. Also ignored is the fact that clients with similar problems do not always respond well to the same treatment. Therefore, by limiting their practice to one "school of counseling," counselors are assuming a universality that simply does not exist.

Consequently, the eclectic or integrative approach to counseling, which is exemplified by the work of Lazarus (1995), Beutler (1983), and Norcross (1986), has gained an increasing measure of respectability. The eclectic approach represents attempts to develop systems of counseling based on all salient scientific data and philosophical treatises on human behavior. Essentially, the integrative counselor uses techniques derived from a variety of theoretical systems, providing that these techniques can be logically integrated and are philosophically congruent.

Arnold Lazarus (1995) developed multimodal therapy to systematize the choice of counseling techniques borrowed from a variety of theories and approaches. He adhered to *technical eclecticism,* the selection of techniques based on client need regardless of the theoretical genesis of the techniques. In contrast, *theoretical eclecticism* refers to the integration of two or more theories of counseling that may be philosophically incompatible.

Lazarus conceptualized client functioning as organized around seven categories of functioning, denoted by the acronym, BASIC-ID, where B = behaviors, A = affective processes, S = sensations, I = images, C = cognitions, I = interpersonal relationships, and D = drugs, biological functioning, nutrition, and exercise. From this model, Lazarus identified 36 techniques to be partitioned by type into the seven categories. The BASIC-ID paradigm provides an organizing framework around which counselors may build their eclectic approach (Corey, 1996; Lazarus, 1995; Mahalik, 1990).

Another attempt toward synthesis and integration was made by Beutler (1983), who proposed a theoretical system derived from research and practice that differs from technical eclecticism. His model, which involves the systematic integration of basic principles from a variety of therapy schools, is an example of *systematic eclecticism.* Beutler's approach emphasizes obtaining a counselor–client match based on therapist characteristics, client characteristics, and treatment variables (Mahalik, 1990). Beutler, like Frank (1961) and Strong (1968), viewed counseling as a process of persuasion in which counselors influence clients to undergo certain changes in their lives.

The third model is that of G. S. Howard et al. (1986; Mahalik, 1990), which resembles both the models of Beutler and Lazarus. G. S. Howard presented what he terms a straightforward adaptation of the situational leadership theory developed by Hersey and Blanchard (1977) to the practice of counseling. His theory, referred to as *adaptive counseling and therapy* (ACT), posits four levels of counselor readiness and four styles of leadership. The four levels of readiness are (a) low readiness, (b) low-moderate readiness, (c) high-moderate readiness, and (d) high readiness. The four styles of direction and support (leadership) are (a) telling—high direction, low support; (b) teaching—high direction, high support; (c) supporting—low direction, high support; and (d) delegating—high direction, low support.

Howard juxtaposed the four levels of direction and four levels of support to form a 4×4 matrix containing 16 cells. Each cell represents a combination of one level of direction with one level of support. In each cell, Howard placed a major theory of counseling and its major advocates. For example, in the cell for low direction and low support, Howard placed Freudian psychoanalysis. In the cell for low direction but high support, he placed Rogerian, person-centered therapy. Thus, ACT is more an aid to conceptualizing the relationships among theories than it is an integrative approach.

Friedlander (1986), in a critique of ACT, pondered whether ACT is a descriptive or a prescriptive and operational model. Her conclusion was that ACT appears to be more descriptive than prescriptive. Nonetheless, it offers exciting possibilities for research and practice by simplifying the complex and confusing array of variables affecting the choice of a counseling intervention.

Norcross (1986) presented a comprehensive summary of the eclectic trend within counseling and psychotherapy. He provided an overview of the issues and concerns related to eclecticism and proposed the eclectic solution, that is, that eclecticism offers a solution for dealing with the bewildering array of theories and approaches of counseling and psychotherapy (Corsini, 1981). Norcross noted that the conflict between systems has begun to shift increasingly toward rapprochement. Eclecticism (integration) promises the development of a comprehensive approach to counseling that is based upon a unified, empirical body of work, which transcends the narrow boundaries of schools of counseling and psychotherapy. Finally, Norcross warned that the price of "theoretical purity" is too high because such purity invariably excludes important variables (Garfield, 1982).

The number of ways different counseling theories and techniques can be used to facilitate the attainment of positive client adjustment is extensive. For example, a counselor might combine the use of the person-centered, facilitative relationship with behavioral, operant-reinforcement techniques to improve the adjustment of a rebellious and hostile client who finds it difficult to maintain old, or establish new, friendships due to a negative self-concept. Additionally, principles of Gestalt confrontation could be combined with cognitive and trait–factor techniques to assist a client facing a difficult vocational choice requiring rigorous self-assessment and environmental assessment. The possibilities are almost endless, as long as counselors carefully explore and resolve the philosophical and value conflicts among the different theories. The influence of eclecticism on counseling in rehabilitation settings has been to provide a practical model for the selection of counseling techniques based on client needs rather than theoretical purity.

Group, Milieu, and Environmental Strategies

In addition to recognizing the efficacy of using techniques derived from various counseling theories, counselors are becoming more aware of the impact the environment may have on their clients' personal adjustment. This awareness has resulted not only in changes in the counselors' role perception, but also in the use of a broader range of counseling techniques.

The days when rehabilitation counselors could limit their practice to "cubicle counseling" are over. Rehabilitation counselors working in either agency or facility settings can, and indeed should, engineer the environment to facilitate clients' psychosocial and vocational adjustment. For example, counselors in both settings may assign clients homework that involves practicing new and more effective ways of interacting with others. Moreover, counselors may work closely with the family, school, or other social institutions to arrange cooperative reinforcement schedules, or to provide clients with more appropriate role models and greater opportunities for social interaction. Self-help or support groups, such as Alcoholics Anonymous, may also be used effectively to complement individual counseling programs. The role of environmental strategies in supported employment and a conceptual model for rehabilitation service delivery was described by Szymanski, Buckley, Parent, Parker, and Westbrook (1988). They concluded that the rehabilitation counseling process has an important role within this delivery system, one that differs radically from traditional rehabilitation service delivery.

Because of their malleability, rehabilitation workshops and supported employment placements offer particularly favorable settings for the application of environmental or milieu approaches to counseling. Rehabilitation workshops and supported employment programs possess considerable potential for helping clients to improve both psychosocial and vocational adjustment. For example, the same workshop environment used to simulate working conditions and facilitate positive work adjustment can also function as an adjunct to individual psychosocial counseling.

An obvious reason why the community milieu offers considerable potential as a therapeutic resource is that many of the client behaviors that contribute to positive work adjustment also contribute to effective interpersonal functioning. For example, the well-adjusted worker possesses good habits of personal hygiene; favorable interactions with other significant people; and characteristics of conscientiousness, dependability, and independence. Because the community-based milieu is designed to foster these worker characteristics, the counselor must work cooperatively with the client, agency, and employer to promote the generalization of these characteristics to other life areas.

Another strategy that rehabilitation counselors may use to complement one-to-one methods is the group approach. Groups can be used to provide clients with information, or as a general counseling tool. Moreover, most of the major counseling theories presented earlier in this chapter allow for the application of their techniques on both a group and an individual basis.

Use of the group approach in conjunction with one-to-one counseling may have many advantages over the use of individual methods alone. Groups offer counselors a more efficient use of their time and the potential of providing clients with feedback on their interpersonal behavior. Group members may also serve as positive role models and can provide a strong sense of support for clients learning to take risks in social situations. Because clients are often convinced that they are the only ones with particular concerns or feelings, the sharing of feelings can be an especially beneficial aspect of the group process. Although it is unlikely that the environmental, milieu, and group approaches will ever totally replace one-to-one counseling, use of these approaches augments the counselor's overall repertoire for facilitating client adjustment.

Conclusion and
Recommendations for Practice

We have presented in this chapter an overview of the major counseling theories and related techniques that rehabilitation counselors may use to facilitate positive psychosocial adjustment. A counselor's success in facilitating a client's rehabilitation necessarily depends on the interaction of a number of counselor, client, process, outcome, and contextual variables. Our conviction, however, is that the fundamental goal of rehabilitation counseling, which is to help persons with disabilities achieve their highest personal, social, and work potential, is best accomplished through the use of an eclectic, integrative model of counseling. This model is one that acknowledges both the complexity and the complementarity of varying theoretical counseling orientations, as well as the commonalities in all effective therapeutic relationships. Eclecticism incorporates findings from the research literature that suggest no one approach is distinctly superior to another. Moreover, this model takes into account counseling process and outcome studies that support the hypothesis that certain techniques fit certain client problems during certain stages of the counseling process.

To summarize, eclecticism takes into account the diverse, multisystem nature of the problems and solutions for persons with disabilities. These include internal traits; attributes and predispositions; peer support; and familial, school, work, sociopolitical, and health systems. Eclecticism also fits the active, short-term nature of rehabilitation counseling. These characteristics dictate an approach best accomplished through an eclectic, present-centered, nonpathologizing, active, egalitarian, and goal-directed orientation. In addition, eclecticism enables the counselor, through use of complementary approaches, to facilitate the increase of positive experiencing and the restoration of dormant or lost attributes (i.e., unexpected physical, attitudinal, and value resources). Importantly, eclecticism provides a means for the counselor to focus on the interactive triad of cognitions, behaviors, and affect. The rehabilitation counselor can initially focus on the specific rehabilitation problem, intervene promptly, and then address broader issues that pertain to the client's situation. This strategy enables the counselor to teach clients more adaptive behaviors and to help them achieve insight into the broader issues associated with their particular problems. Finally, eclecticism provides a method for integrating the various schools of counseling. To illustrate, existential and person-centered approaches can provide the core facilitative conditions, that is, the necessary attitudes of trust, respect, and caring; Gestalt therapy can add action techniques to enable a client to deal with inner, subjective experiences and feelings of loss, anger, and hurt; cognitive–behavioral strategies can provide the means for uncovering self-demeaning inner dialogues and the practical solutions to them through substitution of alternative views and homework assignments to teach new behaviors; and the psychoanalytic perspective can provide clients with a rich picture of how their unconscious world is organized and how their underlying personality structure may needlessly support self-defeating behaviors in their relationships with peers, significant others, and supervisors.

To further substantiate our support of eclecticism in rehabilitation counseling, eight concluding statements and their implications are presented below.

1. The complexity of rehabilitation counseling, with political, physical, language, physiological, and environmental barriers, dictates that the rehabilitation counselor must go beyond rigid adherence to any one theory. Rehabilitation counselors must assess the relevance of a complex array of factors, draw from their array of techniques and interventions, and formulate and implement a realistic rehabilitation plan. No one theory is comprehensive enough to encompass all the problems subsumed under the rubric of rehabilitation counseling. No one set of techniques from any one theory is sufficiently inclusive to cover all client variables, environmental variables, and their interrelationships. Eclecticism provides a systematic approach that offers a sound rationale and a flexible set of techniques for counseling with rehabilitation clients.

2. Because a strong counselor–client relationship is a necessary condition for client change, the core facilitative conditions constitute an essential and necessary ingredient in rehabilitation counseling. These core conditions (Patterson, 1985), constituting the "real" as contrasted with the transference relationship, have also been termed the therapeutic alliance (Bordin, 1979). The core conditions involve the counselor's offering warmth, nurturance, and genuine support through caring and encouragement sufficient to facilitate client growth and change.

3. Each stage of the rehabilitation process necessitates separate and distinctively defined sets of counselor activities. The uniqueness of each human being and his or her development requires counselors to individualize interventions.

4. The conduct of rehabilitation counseling requires the implementation of a positive, purposive, goal-directed philosophy. Rehabilitation counseling is typically a time-limited process, requiring sequencing of carefully planned services and effective management of resources.

5. Rehabilitation counselors must attend to political, social, vocational, educational, and familial variables that impinge upon the client's life. The client's total situation, or ecology, must be taken into account by the counselor. Client ecology must form the context for rehabilitation counseling.

6. Special attention must be given to the elimination of language, physical, attitudinal, and gender barriers. The reduction or elimination of all barriers is critical to effective rehabilitation counseling.

7. Client advocacy constitutes an essential part of rehabilitation counseling. Client advocacy includes political advocacy for client rights (Szymanski, Rubin, & Rubin, 1988; Thoreson & Kerr, 1978) and the counselor's commitment to work toward the reduction and elimination of barriers for persons with disabilities.

8. To ameliorate each client's unique set of problems, rehabilitation counselors must capitalize on the assets of different counseling theories and techniques. The

variability of clients' characteristics, needs, aspirations, environments, and so on, dictates that counselors must be flexible in their approach to rehabilitation counseling.

Each approach to counseling presented in this chapter has something of value to offer the rehabilitation counselor, even to the counselor who exclusively practices vocational counseling, vocational evaluation, or job placement. The professional challenge and obligation is to develop a sense of when a particular theory or technique is appropriate and then to apply it creatively and effectively.

References

Adler, A. (1963). *The practice and theory of individual psychology.* Paterson, NJ: Littlefield, Adams.

Alexander, F. M. (1963). *Fundamentals of psychoanalysis.* New York: Norton.

Allen, H. A. (1986). A Gestalt perspective. In T. F. Riggar, D. R. Maki, & A. W. Wolf (Eds.), *Applied rehabilitation counseling* (pp. 148-157). New York: Springer.

Alston, R. J., & Burkhead, J. E. (1989). Computer-assisted career guidance and the career indecision of college students with physical disabilities. *Rehabilitation Counseling Bulletin, 32,* 248-253.

Arlow, J. A. (1995). Psychoanalysis. In R. Corsini & D. Wedding (Eds.), *Current psychotherapies* (5th ed., pp. 15-50). Itasca, IL: Peacock.

Banta, H. D., & Saxe, L. (1983). Reimbursement for psychotherapy: Linking efficacy research and public policy making. *American Psychologist, 38,* 918-923.

Barrett, C., & Wright, J. (1984). Therapist variables. In M. Hersen, L. Michelson, & A. Bellack (Eds.), *Issues in psychotherapy research* (pp. 361-392). New York: Plenum.

Baruth, L., & Huber, C. (1985). *Counseling and psychotherapy: Theoretical analyses and skills applications.* Columbus, OH: Merrill.

Beck, A. T., & Emery, G. (1979). *Cognitive therapy of anxiety and phobic disorders.* Philadelphia: Center for Cognitive Therapy.

Beck, A. T., Rush, A. J., Shaw, B. F., & Emery, G. (1979). *Cognitive therapy of depression.* New York: Guilford Press.

Beck, A. T., & Weishaar, M. (1989). Cognitive therapy. In A. Freeman, K. Simon, L. E. Beuder, & H. Arkowitz (Eds.), *Comprehensive handbook of cognitive therapy* (pp. 21-36). New York: Plenum.

Bergin, A. E., & Garfield, S. L. (1971). *Handbook of psychotherapy and behavior change.* New York: Wiley.

Bergin, A. E., & Garfield, S. L. (1994). *Handbook of psychotherapy and behavior change* (4th ed.). New York: Wiley.

Bergin, A. E., & Lambert, M. J. (1978). The evaluation of therapeutic outcome. In S. L. Garfield & A. E. Bergin (Eds.), *Handbook of psychotherapy and behavior change: An empirical analysis* (2nd ed., pp. 139-190). New York: Wiley.

Bergland, M. M., & Thomas, K. R. (1991). Psychosocial issues following severe head injury in adolescence: Individual and family perceptions. *Rehabilitation Counseling Bulletin, 35,* 5–22.

Berman, J. S., & Norton, N. C. (1985). Does professional training make a therapist more effective? *Psychological Bulletin, 98,* 401–406.

Beutler, L. E. (1983). *Eclectic psychotherapy: A systematic approach.* New York: Pergamon.

Beutler, L. E., Engle, D., Mohr, D., Daldrop, R. J., Bergan, J., Meridith, K., & Merry, W. (1991). Predictors of differential response to cognitive, experiential and self-directed psychotherapeutic procedures. *Journal of Consulting and Clinical Psychology, 59,* 333–340.

Beutler, L. E., Machado, P., & Neufeldt, S. (1994). Therapist variables. In A. E. Bergin & S. L. Garfield (Eds.), *Handbook of psychotherapy and behavior change* (4th ed., pp. 229–269). New York: Wiley.

Beyrakal, S. (1975). A group experience with chronically disabled adolescents. *American Journal of Psychiatry, 132,* 1291–1294.

Bolton, B. (1974a). *Introduction to rehabilitation research.* Springfield, IL: Thomas.

Bolton, B. (1974b). Three verbal interaction styles of rehabilitation counselors. *Rehabilitation Counseling Bulletin, 18,* 34–40.

Bolton, B. (1979a). Methodological issues in the assessment of rehabilitation counselor performance. *Rehabilitation Counseling Bulletin, 21,* 190–193.

Bolton, B. (1979b). *Rehabilitation counseling research.* Austin, TX: PRO-ED.

Bolton, B. (Ed.). (1987). *Handbook of measurement and evaluation in rehabilitation* (2nd ed.). Baltimore: Brookes.

Bolton, B., & Jacques, M. E. (Eds.). (1978). *Rehabilitation counseling: Theory and practice.* Austin, TX: PRO-ED.

Bordin, E. S. (1968). *Psychological counseling* (2nd ed.). New York: Appleton-Century-Crofts.

Bordin, E. S. (1979). The generalizability of the psychoanalytic concept of working alliance. *Psychotherapy: Theory, Research and Practice, 16,* 252–260.

Bordin, E. S., Nachmann, B., & Segal, S. J. (1963). *Journal of Counseling Psychology, 10,* 107–116.

Boyle, P. S. (1976). Totally rehabilitating the physically disabled client: Recognizing the sexuality of the physically disabled individual. *Journal of Applied Rehabilitation Counseling, 7,* 176–181.

Brammer, L. M., Abrego, P. J., & Shostrom, E. L. (1993). *Therapeutic counseling and psychotherapy* (6th ed.). Englewood Cliffs, NJ: Prentice-Hall.

Brock, T., Green, M., Reich, D., & Evans, L. (1996). The Consumer Reports study of psychotherapy: Invalid is invalid. *American Psychologist, 51,* 1083.

Bryan, W. V. (1974). The effects of short-term individual and group counseling on the self-concept of physically handicapped workers in a sheltered workshop setting. *Dissertation Abstracts International* (8A, Pt. 1), 4729–4730.

Carkhuff, R. R., & Berenson, B. G. (1977). *Beyond counseling and therapy* (2nd ed.). New York: Holt, Rinehart and Winston.

Chartrand, J. M. (1991). The evolution of trait-and-factor career counseling: A person × environment fit approach. *Journal of Counseling and Development, 69,* 518–524.

Cimperman, A., & Dunn, M. (1974). Group therapy with spinal-cord–injured patients: A case study. *Rehabilitation Psychology, 21,* 44–48.

Cooper, H. M. (1984). The integrative research review: A systematic approach. *Applied Social Research Methods Series* (Vol. 2). Beverly Hills, CA: Sage.

Corey, G. (1996). *Theory and practice of counseling and psychotherapy* (5th ed.). Pacific Grove, CA: Brooks/Cole.

Corsini, R. (1981). *Handbook of innovative psychotherapies.* New York: Wiley.

Corsini, R., & Wedding, D. (Eds.). (1989). *Current psychotherapies* (4th ed.). Itasca, IL: Peacock.

Corsini, R., & Wedding, D. (Eds.). (1995). *Current psychotherapies* (5th ed.). Itasca, IL: Peacock.

Cottone, R. R. (1992). *Theories and paradigms of counseling and psychotherapy.* Boston: Allyn & Bacon.

Coven, A. B. (1977). The Gestalt approach to rehabilitation counseling. *Rehabilitation Counseling Bulletin, 20,* 167-174.

Coven, A. B. (1979). The Gestalt approach to rehabilitation of the whole person. *Journal of Applied Rehabilitation Counseling, 9*(4), 144-147.

Cubbage, M. E., & Thomas, K. R. (1989). Freud and disability. *Rehabilitation Psychology, 34,* 161-173.

Daldrup, R., Beutler, L., Greenberg, L., & Engle, D. (1988). *Focused expressive therapy: A treatment for constricted affect.* New York: Guilford.

Dawes, R. M. (1994). *House of cards: Psychology and psychotherapy built on myth.* New York: Free Press.

Dawis, R. V. (1967). The Minnesota studies in vocational rehabilitation. *Rehabilitation Counseling Bulletin, 11,* 1-10.

Dollard, J., & Miller, N. E. (1950). *Personality and psychotherapy.* New York: McGraw-Hill.

Dunn, D. (1990). Validating the master's degree in rehabilitation counseling. *Rehabilitation Counseling Bulletin, 34,* 170-174.

Eagle, M. N. (1984). *Recent developments in psychoanalysis.* New York: McGraw-Hill.

Ebra, G. (1975). Rehabilitation in end-stage renal disease. *Journal of Applied Rehabilitation Counseling, 6,* 96-105.

Ellis, A. (1989). Rational-emotive therapy. In R. Corsini & D. Wedding (Eds.), *Current psychotherapies* (4th ed., pp. 197-238). Itasca, IL: Peacock.

Ellis, A. (1995a). Coping with disabilities the Albert Ellis way. *The APA Monitor, 26*(10), 47.

Ellis, A. (1995b). Rational-emotive behavior therapy. In R. Corsini & D. Wedding (Eds.), *Current psychotherapies* (5th ed., pp. 162-196). Itasca, IL: Peacock.

Emener, W. G. (1980). Relationships among rehabilitation counselor characteristics and rehabilitation client outcomes. *Rehabilitation Counseling Bulletin, 23,* 183-192.

Erikson, E. (1950). *Childhood and society.* New York: Norton.

Fisher, S. (1976). The renal dialysis patient: A rational counseling approach. *Rehabilitation Counseling Bulletin, 19,* 556-562.

Fohs, M. W. (1991). Family systems assessment: Intervention with individuals having a chronic disability. *Career Development Quarterly, 39,* 304-311.

Frank, J. D. (1961). *Persuasion and healing.* Baltimore: Johns Hopkins University Press.

Freeman, A., Pretzer, J., Fleming, B., & Simon, K. M. (1990). *Clinical applications of cognitive therapy.* New York: Plenum.

Freud, A. (1936). *The ego and the mechanisms of defense.* New York: International Universities Press.

Freud, S. (1961). The ego and the id. In J. Strachey (Ed. and Trans.), *The standard edition of the complete psychological works of Sigmund Freud* (Vol. 19, pp. 1–66). London: Hogarth. (Original work published 1923)

Freud, S. (1964). New introductory lectures on psychoanalysis. In J. Strachey (Ed. and Trans.), *The standard edition of the complete psychological works of Sigmund Freud* (Vol. 22, pp. 1–182). London: Hogarth. (Original work published 1933)

Friedlander, M. L. (1986). Adaptive counseling theory: Description or prescription? *The Counseling Psychologist, 14,* 448–453.

Fromm, E. (1947). *Man for himself.* New York: Holt.

Garfield, S. L. (1982). Eclecticism and integration in psychotherapy. *Behavior Therapy, 13,* 610–623.

Garfield, S. L. (1994). Research on client variables in psychotherapy. In A. E. Bergin & S. L. Garfield (Eds.), *Handbook of psychotherapy and behavior change* (4th ed., pp. 190–228). New York: Wiley.

Garfield, S. L., & Bergin, A. E. (Eds.). (1986). *Handbook of psychotherapy and behavior change* (3rd ed.). New York: Wiley.

Garfield, S. L., & Kurtz, R. (1976). Clinical psychologists in the 1970's. *American Psychologist, 31,* 1–9.

Garske, G. G., & Thomas, K. R. (1992). Self-reported self-esteem and depression: Indices of psychosocial adjustment following severe traumatic brain injury. *Rehabilitation Counseling Bulletin, 36,* 44–52.

Gilliland, B. E., James, R. K., & Bowman, J. T. (1994). *Theories and strategies in counseling and psychotherapy* (3rd ed.). Needham Heights, MA: Allyn & Bacon.

Glass, G. V., McGaw, G., & Smith, M. L. (1981). *Meta-analysis in social research.* Beverly Hills, CA: Sage.

Glasser, W. (1965). *Reality therapy.* New York: Harper & Row.

Glasser, W. (1969). *Schools without failure.* New York: Harper & Row.

Glasser, W., & Wubbolding, R. (1995). Reality therapy. In R. Corsini & D. Wedding (Eds.), *Current psychotherapies* (5th ed., pp. 293–321). Itasca, IL: Peacock.

Greenberg, J. R. (1991). *Oedipus and beyond: A clinical theory.* Cambridge, MA: Harvard University Press.

Greenberg, J. R., & Mitchell, S. A. (1983). *Object relations in psychoanalytic theory.* Cambridge, MA: Harvard University Press.

Greenberg, L. S., Rice, L. N., & Elliott, R. (1993). *Process-experiential therapy: Facilitating emotional change.* New York: Guilford.

Hall, C. S., & Lindzey, G. (1987). *Theories of personality* (4th ed.). New York: Wiley.

Hedges, L. V., & Olkin, I. (1985). *Statistical methods for meta-analysis.* Orlando: Academic Press.

Hendrick, I. (1943). Work and the pleasure principle. *Psychoanalytic Quarterly, 12,* 311–329.

Hersey, P., & Blanchard, K. H. (1977). *Management of organizational behavior: Utilizing human resources* (3rd ed.). Englewood Cliffs, NJ: Prentice-Hall.

Hill, C. (1982). Counseling process research: Philosophical and methodological dilemmas. *The Counseling Psychologist, 10,* 7-20.

Horney, K. (1945). *Our inner conflicts.* New York: Norton.

Hosford, R. E., & de Visser, L. A. (1974). *Behavioral approaches to counseling:An introduction.* Washington, DC: American Personnel and Guidance Association Press.

Howard, G. S., Nance, D. W., & Myers, P. (1986). Adaptive counseling and therapy: An integrative, eclectic model. *The Counseling Psychologist, 15,* 371-447.

Howard, K. I., & Orlinsky, D. E. (1972). Psychotherapeutic processes. *Annual Review of Psychology, 23,* 615-668.

Hughes, J. M. (1989). *Reshaping the psychoanalytic domain.* Berkeley: University of California Press.

Hunt, E. (1996). Errors in Seligman's "The effectiveness of psychotherapy: The *Consumer Reports* study." *American Psychologist, 51,* 1082.

Hunter, J. E., Schmidt, F. L., & Jackson, G. B. (1982). *Meta-analysis: Cumulating research findings across studies* (Vol. 4 of Studying organizations: Innovations in methodology). Beverly Hills, CA: Sage.

Jacobson, N., & Christensen, A. (1996). Studying the effectiveness of psychotherapy: How well can clinical trials do the job? *American Psychologist, 51,* 1031-1039.

Jung, C. G. (1959). *Basic writings.* New York: Random House.

Jung, H. (1978). Gestalt therapy in rehabilitation counseling. *Psychosocial Rehabilitation Journal, 2*(3), 26-34.

Kazdin, A. E. (Ed.). (1986). Special issue: Psychotherapy research. *Journal of Consulting and Clinical Psychology, 54,* 3-118.

Kempler, W. (1973). Gestalt therapy. In R. Corsini (Ed.), *Current psychotherapies* (2nd ed., pp. 251-286). Itasca, IL: Peacock.

Kernberg, O. F. (1984). *Severe personality disorders: Psychotherapeutic strategies.* New Haven, CT: Yale University Press.

Kiesler, D. J. (1973). *The process of psychotherapy.* Chicago: Aldine.

Kohut, H. (1984). *How does analysis cure?* Chicago: University of Chicago Press.

Kosciulek, J. F. (1993). Advances in trait-and-factor theory: A person $\times$ environment fit approach to rehabilitation counseling. *Journal of Applied Rehabilitation Counseling, 24*(2), 11-14.

Krause, J. S., & Crewe, N. (1987). Prediction of long-term survival of persons with spinal cord injury: An 11-year prospective study. *Rehabilitation Psychology, 32,* 205-213.

Krieger, G. (1976). Loss and grief in rehabilitation of the severely traumatically disabled. *Journal of Applied Rehabilitation Counseling, 7,* 223-227.

Krueger, D. W. (1984). Psychological rehabilitation of physical trauma and disability. In D. W. Krueger (Ed.), *Rehabilitation psychology: A comprehensive textbook* (pp. 3-14). Rockville, MD: Aspen.

Krumboltz, J. (1966). Behavioral goals of counseling. *Journal of Counseling Psychology, 13,* 153-159.

Krumboltz, J., & Thoresen, C. E. (Eds.). (1969). *Behavioral counseling: Cases and techniques.* New York: Holt.

Krumboltz, J., & Thoresen, C. E. (Eds.). (1976). *Counseling methods.* New York: Holt.

Lambert, M. J., & Bergin, A. E. (1994). The effectiveness of psychotherapy. In A. E. Bergin & S. L. Garfield (Eds.), *Handbook of psychotherapy and behavior change* (4th ed., pp. 143-189). New York: Wiley.

Lambert, M. J., & Hill, C. E. (1994). Assessing psychotherapy outcomes and process. In A. E. Bergin & S. L. Garfield (Eds.), *Handbook of psychotherapy and behavior change* (4th ed., pp. 72-113). New York: Wiley.

Lambert, M. J., Shapiro, D. M., & Bergin, A. E. (1986). The effects of psychotherapy. In S. L. Garfield & A. E. Bergin (Eds.), *Handbook of psychotherapy and behavior change* (3rd ed., pp. 157-211). New York: Wiley.

Lazarus, A. (1995). Multimodal therapy. In R. Corsini & D. Wedding (Eds.), *Current psychotherapies* (5th ed., pp. 322-355). Itasca, IL: Peacock.

Levitsky, A., & Perls, F. S. (1970). The rules and games of Gestalt therapy. In J. Fagan & I. Shepherd (Eds.), *Gestalt therapy now* (pp. 140-149). Palo Alto, CA: Science and Behavior Books.

Light, R. J. (Ed.). (1983). *Evaluation studies review annual* (Vol. 8). Beverly Hills, CA: Sage.

Light, R. J., & Pillemer, D. B. (1984). *Summing up: The science of reviewing research.* Cambridge, MA: Harvard University Press.

Livneh, H., & Sherman, A. (1991). Application of personality theories and counseling approaches to clients with physical disabilities. *Journal of Counseling and Development, 69,* 525-538.

Luborsky, L. (1976). Helping alliances in psychotherapy: The groundwork for a study of their relationship to its outcome. In J. L. Claghorn (Ed.), *Successful psychotherapy* (pp. 92-116). New York: Basic Books.

Luborsky, L., Chandler, M., Auerbach, A. H., & Cohen, J. (1971). Factors influencing the outcome of psychotherapy: A review of quantitative research. *Psychological Bulletin, 75,* 145-185.

Luborsky, L., Crits-Christoph, P., Mintz, J., & Auerbach, A. (1988). *Who will benefit from psychotherapy? Predicting psychotherapeutic outcomes.* New York: Basic.

Lyddon, W. J. (1995). Cognitive therapy and theories of knowing: A social constructionist view. *Journal of Counseling and Development, 73,* 579-585.

Mahalik, J. (1990). Systematic eclectic models. *The Counseling Psychologist, 18,* 655-679.

Mahler, M. (1979). *The selected papers of Margaret S. Mahler* (Vols. 1, 2, & 3). New York: Jason Aronson.

Mahoney, M. J. (1980). Psychotherapy and the structure of personal revolutions. In M. J. Mahoney (Ed.), *Psychotherapy process: Current issues and future directions* (pp. 157-180). New York: Plenum.

Mahoney, M. J., & Lyddon, W. J. (1988). Recent developments in cognitive approaches to counseling and psychotherapy. *The Counseling Psychologist, 16,* 190-234.

Marsden, G. (1971). Content analysis studies of psychotherapy: 1954-1968. In A. E. Bergin & S. L. Garfield (Eds.), *Handbook of psychotherapy and behavior change* (pp. 345-407). New York: Wiley.

Matt, G. E. (1989). Decision rules for selecting effect sizes in meta-analysis: A review and reanalysis of psychotherapy outcome studies. *Psychological Bulletin, 105,* 106–115.

Meador, B., & Rogers, C. (1984). Person-centered therapy. In R. Corsini (Ed.), *Current psychotherapies* (3rd ed., pp. 142–195). Itasca, IL: Peacock.

Meltzoff, J., & Kornreich, M. (1970). *Research in psychotherapy.* New York: Atherton.

Mental health: Does therapy help? (1995, November). *Consumer Reports,* pp. 734–739.

Mintz, J. (1977). The role of the therapist in assessing psychotherapy outcome. In A. S. Gurman & A. M. Razin (Eds.), *Effective psychotherapy: A handbook of research* (pp. 590–602). New York: Pergamon.

Mintz, J., Drake, R., & Crits-Christoph, P. (1996). Efficacy and effectiveness of psychotherapy: Two paradigms, one science. *American Psychologist, 51,* 1084–1085.

Mitchell, S. A. (1988). *Relational concepts in psychoanalysis: An integration.* Cambridge, MA: Harvard University Press.

Neff, W. S. (1985). *Work and human behavior.* New York: Aldine.

Norcross, J. C. (Ed.). (1986). *Handbook of eclectic psychotherapy.* New York: Brunner/Mazel.

Orlinsky, D., Grawe, K., & Parks, B. (1994). Process and outcome in psychotherapy—Noch einmal. In A. E. Bergin & S. L. Garfield (Eds.), *Handbook of psychotherapy and behavior change* (4th ed., pp. 270–376). New York: Wiley.

Ososkie, J. N., & Turpin, J. O. (1986). Reality therapy in rehabilitation counseling. In T. F. Riggar, D. R. Maki, & A. W. Wolf (Eds.), *Applied rehabilitation counseling* (pp. 176–185). New York: Springer.

Ostby, S. (1986). A rational-emotive perspective. In T. F. Riggar, D. R. Maki, & A. W. Wolf (Eds.), *Applied rehabilitation counseling* (pp. 167–175). New York: Springer.

Passons, W. R. (1975). *Gestalt approaches in counseling.* New York: Holt, Rinehart and Winston.

Patterson, C. H. (1985). *The therapeutic relationship: Foundations for an eclectic psychotherapy* (4th ed.). New York: Harper & Row.

Patterson, C. H. (1986). *Theories of counseling and psychotherapy.* Pacific Grove, CA: Brooks/Cole.

Pavio, S. C., & Greenberg, L. S. (1995). Resolving "unfinished business": Efficacy of experiential therapy using empty chair dialogue. *Journal of Consulting and Clinical Psychology, 63,* 419–425.

Perls, F. (1969). *Gestalt therapy verbatim.* Lafayette, CA: Real People.

Perls, F., Hefferline, R. F., & Goodman, P. (1951). *Gestalt therapy.* New York: Julian.

Phillips, R., Butler, A., & Thomas, K. (1988). Rehabilitation counselor performance measures: A comparative study. *Rehabilitation Counseling Bulletin, 32,* 41–49.

Pine, F. (1990). *Drive, ego, object, and self: A clinical synthesis.* New York: Basic Books.

Polster, E. (1995). *A population of selves: A therapeutic exploration of personal diversity.* San Francisco: Jossey-Bass.

Polster, E., & Polster, M. (1973). *Gestalt therapy integrated.* New York: Brunner/Mazel.

Prochaska, J. (1984). *Systems of psychotherapy: A transtheoretical approach* (2nd ed.). Homewood, IL: Dorsey.

Rank, O. (1957). *The trauma of birth.* New York: Brunner.

Raskin, N., & Rogers, C. (1995). Person-centered therapy. In R. Corsini & D. Wedding (Eds.), *Current psychotherapies* (5th ed., pp. 128-161). Itasca, IL: Peacock.

Reagles, S. (1984). Chronic pain: Principles for rehabilitation counselors. *Rehabilitation Counseling Bulletin, 28,* 15-27.

Reppen, J. (Ed.). (1985). *Beyond Freud: A study of modern psychoanalytic theorists.* Hillsdale, NJ: Analytic.

Riggar, T. F., Maki, D. R., & Wolf, A. W. (Eds.). (1986). *Applied rehabilitation counseling.* New York: Springer.

Robbins, K. H. (1985). Traumatic spinal cord injury and its impact on sexuality. *Journal of Applied Rehabilitation Counseling, 16*(1), 24-27, 31.

Rogers, C. R. (1942). *Counseling and psychotherapy.* Boston: Houghton Mifflin.

Rogers, C. R. (1951). *Client-centered therapy.* Boston: Houghton Mifflin.

Rogers, C. R. (1957). The necessary and sufficient conditions of therapeutic personality change. *Journal of Consulting Psychology, 21,* 95-103.

Rogers, C. R. (1961). *On becoming a person: A therapist's view of psychotherapy.* Boston: Houghton Mifflin.

Rogers, C. R. (1980). *A way of being.* Boston: Houghton Mifflin.

Rogers, C. R., Gendlin, E. T., Kiesler, D. J., & Truax, C. B. (Eds.). (1967). *The therapeutic relationship and its impact: A study of psychotherapy with schizophrenics.* Madison: University of Wisconsin Press.

Rosenthal, R. (Ed.). (1980). *Quantitative assessment of research domains* (New Directions for Methodology of Social and Behavioral Science No. 5). San Francisco: Jossey-Bass.

Rotter, J. B. (1954). *Social learning and clinical psychology.* Englewood Cliffs, NJ: Prentice-Hall.

Rounds, J. B., & Tracey, T. J. (1990). From trait-and-factor to person–environment fit counseling: Theory and process. In W. B. Walsh & S. H. Osipow (Eds.), *Career counseling* (pp. 1-44). Hillsdale, NJ: Erlbaum.

Rule, W. (Ed.). (1984). *Lifestyle counseling for adjustment to disability.* Rockville, MD: Aspen Systems.

Sather, W. S., Wright, G. N., & Butler, A. J. (1968). An instrument for the measurement of counselor orientation. In G. N. Wright (Ed.), *Wisconsin studies in vocational rehabilitation* (Vol. 9, pp. 1-37). Madison: University of Wisconsin Regional Rehabilitation Research Institute.

See, J. D. (1986). A person-centered perspective. In T. F. Riggar, D. R. Maki, & A. W. Wolf (Eds.), *Applied rehabilitation counseling* (pp. 135-137). New York: Springer.

Seligman, M. E. P. (1995). The effectiveness of psychotherapy: The *Consumer Reports* study. *American Psychologist, 50,* 965-974.

Siller, J. (1988). Intrapsychic aspects of attitudes toward persons with disabilities. In H. E. Yuker (Ed.), *Attitudes toward persons with disabilities* (pp. 58-67). New York: Springer.

Siller, J., & Thomas, K. R. (1995). *Essays and research on disability.* Athens, GA: Elliott & Fitzpatrick.

Simkin, J., & Yontef, G. (1984). Gestalt therapy. In R. Corsini (Ed.), *Current psychotherapies* (3rd ed., pp. 279-319). Itasca, IL: Peacock.

Smith, D. S. (1982). Trends in counseling and psychotherapy. *American Psychologist, 37,* 802–809.

Smith, J. K., & Crisler, J. R. (1985). Variables associated with the vocational rehabilitation outcome of chronic low back pain individuals. *Journal of Applied Rehabilitation Counseling, 16*(4), 22–24.

Smith, M. L., & Glass, G. (1977). Meta-analysis of psychotherapy outcome studies. *American Psychologist, 32,* 752–760.

Smith, M. L., Glass, G., & Miller, T. (1980). *The benefits of psychotherapy.* Baltimore: Johns Hopkins University Press.

Stolorow, R. D., Brandchaft, B., & Atwood, G. E. (1987). *Psychoanalytic treatment: An intersubjective approach.* Hillsdale, NJ: Analytic.

Strong, S. R. (1968). Counseling: An interpersonal influence process. *Journal of Counseling Psychology, 15,* 215–224.

Strupp, H. (1996). The tripartite model and the *Consumer Reports* study. *American Psychologist, 51,* 1017–1024.

Sullivan, H. S. (1947). *Conceptions of modern psychiatry.* Washington, DC: William Alanson White Psychiatric Foundation.

Summers, F. (1994). *Object relations theories and psychopathology: A comprehensive text.* Hillsdale, NJ: Analytic Press.

Szymanski, E. M. (1988). *The relationship of rehabilitation client outcome to level of rehabilitation counselor education.* Unpublished doctoral dissertation, The University of Texas at Austin.

Szymanski, E. M., Buckley, J., Parent, W. S., Parker, R. M., & Westbrook, J. D. (1988). Rehabilitation counseling in supported employment: A conceptual model for service delivery and personnel preparation. In S. E. Rubin & N. M. Rubin (Eds.), *Contemporary challenges to the rehabilitation counseling profession* (pp. 111–133). Baltimore: Brookes.

Szymanski, E. M., & Parker, R. M. (1989a). Competitive closure rate of vocational rehabilitation clients with severe disabilities as a function of counselor education and experience. *Rehabilitation Counseling Bulletin, 32,* 292–299.

Szymanski, E. M., & Parker, R. M. (1989b). Relationship of rehabilitation client outcome to level of rehabilitation counselor education. *Journal of Rehabilitation, 55*(4), 32–36.

Szymanski, E. M., Parker, R. M., & Borich, G. D. (1990). Aptitude treatment interaction designs in research on the relationship between rehabilitation counselor education and rehabilitation client outcome. *Rehabilitation Education, 4,* 83–92.

Szymanski, E. M., Parker, R. M., & Butler, A. J. (1990). Sensitivity of client outcome measures in relating state vocational rehabilitation agency counselor performance to level of counselor education. *Rehabilitation Education, 4,* 103–107.

Szymanski, E. M., Rubin, S. E., & Rubin, N. M. (1988). Contemporary challenges: An introduction. In S. E. Rubin & N. M. Rubin (Eds.), *Contemporary challenges to the rehabilitation counseling profession* (pp. 1–14). Baltimore: Brookes.

Thomas, K. R. (1990). Some observations on the feasibility of establishing the superiority of rehabilitation counselors with master's degrees. *Rehabilitation Counseling Bulletin, 34,* 155–164.

Thomas, K. R., & McGinnis, J. D. (1991). The psychoanalytic theories of D. W. Winnicott as applied to rehabilitation. *Journal of Rehabilitation, 57*(3), 63–66.

Thomas, K., & Parker, R. (1986). Counseling interventions. In T. F. Riggar, D. R. Maki, & A. W. Wolf (Eds.), *Applied rehabilitation counseling* (pp. 34–44). New York: Springer.

Thoreson, R. W., & Kerr, B. (1978). Stigmatizing aspects of severe disability: Strategies for change. *Journal of Applied Rehabilitation Counseling, 9*(2), 21–26.

Thoreson, R. W., Smits, S. J., Butler, A. J., & Wright, G. N. (1968). Counselor problems associated with client characteristics. In G. N. Wright (Ed.), *Wisconsin studies in vocational rehabilitation* (Vol. 3, pp. 1–32). Madison: University of Wisconsin Regional Rehabilitation Research Institute.

Thurer, S. (1986). A psychodynamic perspective. In T. R. Riggar, D. R. Maki, & A. W. Wolf (Eds.), *Applied rehabilitation counseling* (pp. 102–111). New York: Springer.

Tichenor, D. F., Thomas, K. R., & Kravetz, S. P. (1975). Client-counselor congruence in perceiving handicapping problems. *Rehabilitation Counseling Bulletin, 19,* 299–304.

Truax, C. B., & Mitchell, K. M. (1971). Research on certain interpersonal skills in relation to process and outcome. In A. E. Bergin & S. L. Garfield (Eds.), *Handbook of psychotherapy and behavior change* (pp. 299–344). New York: Wiley.

VandenBos, G. R. (Ed.). (1986). Psychotherapy research [Special issue]. *American Psychologist, 41*(2).

VandenBos, G. R. (Ed.). (1996). Outcome assessment of psychotherapy [Special issue]. *American Psychologist, 51*(10).

VandenBos, G. R., & Pino, C. D. (1980). Research on the outcome of psychotherapy. In G. R. VandenBos (Ed.), *Psychotherapy: Practice, research, policy* (pp. 23–69). Beverly Hills, CA: Sage.

Walls, R. T., & Tseng, M. S. (1976). Measurement of client outcomes in rehabilitation. In B. Bolton (Ed.), *Handbook of measurement and evaluation in rehabilitation* (pp. 207–226). Austin, TX: PRO-ED.

Walls, R. T., & Tseng, M. S. (1987). Measurement of client outcomes in rehabilitation. In B. Bolton (Ed.), *Handbook of measurement and evaluation in rehabilitation* (2nd ed., pp. 183–201). Baltimore: Brookes.

Williamson, E. G. (1950). *Counseling adolescents.* New York: McGraw-Hill.

Williamson, E. G. (1965). *Vocational counseling.* New York: McGraw-Hill.

Winnicott, D. W. (1965). *The maturation process and the facilitating environment.* New York: International Universities Press.

Winnicott, D. W. (1975). *Through pediatrics to psychoanalysis* (2nd ed.). New York: Basic Books.

Wolpe, J. (1958). *Psychotherapy by reciprocal inhibition.* Stanford, CA: Stanford University Press.

Wolpe, J. (1969). *The practice of behavior therapy.* New York: Pergamon.

Wolpe, J. (1990). *The practice of behavior therapy* (4th ed.). Needham Heights, MA: Allyn & Bacon.

Wright, G. N. (1980). *Total rehabilitation.* Boston: Little, Brown.

Wright, G. N. (Ed.). (1987). Research on professional rehabilitation competencies. *Rehabilitation Counseling Bulletin, 31,* 81–176.

Wright, G. N., Leahy, M. J., & Riedesel, P. S. (1987). Rehabilitation education research: The importance and attainment of professional competencies. *Rehabilitation Education, 1,* 9–18.

Yates, B. T., & Newman, F. L. (1980). Approaches to cost-effectiveness analysis and cost-benefit analysis of psychotherapy. In G. R. VandenBos (Ed.), *Psychotherapy: Practice, research, policy* (pp. 103–162). Beverly Hills, CA: Sage.

Yeaton, W. H., & Wortman, P. M. (Eds.). (1984). *Issues in data synthesis* (New Directions for Program Evaluation, No. 24). San Francisco: Jossey-Bass.

Zinker, J. (1977). *Creative process in Gestalt therapy.* New York: Vintage Books.

Zinker, J. (1994). *In search of good form: Gestalt therapy with couples and families.* San Francisco: Jossey-Bass.

Chapter 8

. . . .

Rehabilitation Counseling Practice: Considerations and Interventions

. . . .

Jeanne Boland Patterson, Denise DeLaGarza,
and James Schaller

ach person is a unique individual with different interests, values, and experiences. The acquisition of a disability does not change this uniqueness, nor does the disability become the sole characteristic that identifies the individual; it simply becomes an additional attribute. Therefore, one must exercise extreme caution in generalizing about people based on their disabilities. However, just as there are general principles in counseling, there are some common experiences that *may* be shared by individuals with various types of disabilities, as well as experiences that are unique to particular types of disabilities (i.e., physical, sensory, cognitive). These common experiences can suggest interventions that may be used by rehabilitation counselors. The purpose of this chapter is to describe counseling considerations and interventions based on factors associated with the person, the environment, and the nature of the disability (Vash, 1981). Each category will be reviewed separately to focus on factors that should be considered by rehabilitation counselors. Examples of individuals with physical, sensory, and cognitive disabilities will be used to illustrate critical factors and issues. The factors discussed in each category are not meant to be exhaustive, nor are the implications for counselors. Rather, the intent is to provide tools counselors can use in organizing their efforts to assist consumers.

Counselors must keep foremost in mind the following three principles:

1. The personal meaning of a disability has considerable impact on an individual's response to disability (Wright, 1983).

2. No two individuals respond to a disability in exactly the same manner. Even twins with congenital blindness, raised in the same family, will respond differently to their disability.

3. Rehabilitation counselors must never enter the counseling relationship with rigid assumptions about how an individual *should* respond to a disability.

Disability is an individualized experience, and a number of factors influence how each individual responds. As indicated earlier, Vash (1981) grouped these factors into the following three categories: (a) the individual, (b) the environment, and (c) the nature of the disability. When the factors that comprise these three categories are considered collectively, one can better understand *why* responses to disability are so individualized.

The Individual

Personal factors are qualities inherent in the individual. These qualities define and differentiate each person from every other human, and significantly influence the meaning each individual ascribes to his or her disability. Cayleff (1986) contended that "the sex, race, class, and sexual orientation of the client must be considered, understood, and honored to prevent doing harm, serve the client's welfare, respect autonomous principles, and, ultimately, to provide effective counseling" (p. 346). To further consider personal factors, information concerning (a) personal characteristics; (b) interests, activities, and goals; (c) gender; and (d) culture is presented.

Personal Characteristics

The characteristics or qualities inherent in a person (e.g., independent, outgoing, shy, optimistic, adaptable, intelligent, attractive, mature) influence how he or she will define and come to incorporate disability in his or her life. Personal qualities also influence how an individual will deal with the changes imposed by a disability. Individual characteristics include values, attitudes, and feelings an individual holds about his or her self, life, and disability.

Vash (1981) also included the individual's spiritual and philosophical base as a personal factor that influences response to disability. She noted that an individual who perceives disability as a punishment from God will view disability differently from an individual who considers the disability as a "test or opportunity for spiritual development" (p. 18).

Muriel Jones, 43, is a high school algebra teacher. She is married and has two teenage sons, and has been diagnosed as having multiple sclerosis. She has always been an independent, optimistic, busy person. Because of the progres-

sion of her disability, her physician recently recommended that she begin using a wheelchair.[1]

As her rehabilitation counselor, you may expect Mrs. Jones to become depressed and grieve for her lost ability to walk. This "requirement of mourning," discussed by Wright (1983), may be influenced more by your expectations of Mrs. Jones than her expectations for herself. Counselors must exercise care not to impose their own values and expectations on the person with a disability. Borysenko (1987) discussed three attitudes that are essential to dealing positively with stress: "commitment, which is an attitude of curiosity and involvement in whatever is happening, . . . control, which is the belief we can influence events, . . . and challenge, which is the belief that life's changes stimulate personal growth" (p. 24). If Mrs. Jones has developed attitudes and beliefs that enable her to deal with the stress of this life change in a positive way, counseling may focus more on pragmatic considerations of managing her daily activities from a wheelchair, rather than negative feelings about using a wheelchair.

> *Daniel Young, 34, believes he has been given a raw deal in life. He was born totally blind, received very little nurturance or support from his parents, had negative experiences in school with teachers, and always had difficulty making friends. He has never had a paying job, although he has two graduate degrees. He is angry and bitter at the way he feels others treat him, and blames everything, particularly his lack of employment, on his blindness.*

Mr. Young has a long history of negative interactions with people that have probably influenced his ability to interview well and get along with others in the workplace. If the rehabilitation counselor is unable to change his generally negative orientation toward life, more in-depth counseling should be considered to help Mr. Young get the feedback and long-term support he needs to change the personal characteristics that prevent him from being employed. As a counselor, it is important to be able to assist Mr. Young in identifying his strengths, as well as his behaviors that work against him.

Counseling strategies based on a cognitive model developed by Albert Ellis (1995) may improve the development of intrapersonal skills. Confronting irrational beliefs such as "I have no control over myself and am a helpless victim of fate," "Everything painful that happens to me is the fault of someone else," or "I must be loved and approved by everyone or I am a worthless human being" may assist a consumer in developing a feeling of control over his or her life. One suggestion is to use Ellis's A-B-C-D-E model, which identifies an activating event (A), the beliefs (B) associated with that event (both rational and irrational), and the consequence (C) of the event. Developing strategies—"I am a worthwhile person based on my own strengths, and I can control my own life"—to dispute (D) the irrational beliefs and identifying the effects (E) of the disputing self talk, may result in Mr. Young's feeling better about himself, and able to more effectively pursue his work goals.

---

[1]The vignettes presented in this chapter were created for pedagogical purposes and do not represent real individuals.

Interests, Activities, and Goals

As Vash (1981) noted, "the impact of disablement is largely contingent on the extent to which it interferes with what you are doing" (p. 15) or what you plan to do. The less a disability has an impact on one's present and future activities, the fewer accommodations an individual will require. Values, interests, and goals influence people's choice of careers, friends, and leisure activities.

> *Martin Cane, 18, acquired a spinal cord injury at C4 last year. He has always been extremely athletic, and in fact, received his injury from an accident while skiing with a group of friends. His life has been centered around outdoor activities, and his career goal since he was a small child was to be a professional athlete.*

Wright (1983) pointed out that values have a major impact on one's evaluation of a disability. In Martin's case, his values are strongly oriented toward the outdoors, but because of his injury he may feel that athletic activities are no longer available to him. His comparative values, which emphasize doing something the way everyone else does, may need to be replaced with *asset values* (Wright, 1983). Through this value transformation, he can develop a focus on what he still does well. A counselor may work with Martin to increase his awareness of what he can still do, and explore job opportunities that include his long-standing interest in the outdoors. However, it is often true that people with a greater number of interests will tend to have more interests remaining following the onset of a disability than individuals with unifocal interests. Similarly, individuals with values tied to academics may have an easier time accommodating some disabilities than individuals whose values are tied more exclusively to competitive sports.

> *Sue Robins, 32, was born with a cleft palate. Numerous surgeries as a child to correct her condition left her face disfigured. She has always felt unattractive, and has avoided interactions with others as much as possible. Her goal is to obtain a job where she can work alone.*

One's body image, which is linked to self-concept, is strongly influenced by values. If one subscribes to society's value of "body beautiful," then a disability that diminishes one's physical attractiveness can create additional barriers. Ms. Robin's lifelong image of herself has shaped her interests away from interactions with others, and severely limited her experience. Her interest in working alone may be based on a lack of knowledge and experience. A skilled counselor will help her explore her interests, and help her obtain experiences, so that her choices are valid. In addition, a counselor will be sensitive to the self-esteem issues that may have resulted from her appearance.

The counselor must consider the individual's self-concept and vocational maturity. For individuals with no work history, the counselor should investigate (a) part-time jobs or leisure activities involving other people, (b) areas of responsibility in growing up, and (c) knowledge of self, as well as knowledge of the world of work. For clients with diminished or disrupted self-concepts and limited vocational maturity, the rehabilitation counselor should include activities (e.g., volunteer activities, job shadowing) in the counseling process that can enhance self-confidence and develop vocational maturity.

Both Mr. Cane and Ms. Robins may benefit from experiences in group counseling. Livneh and Sherwood-Hawes (1993) identified cognitive, affective, and behavioral goals for group counseling with individuals who have sustained myocardial infarction that may also be applicable for individuals with other disabilities. These goals are as follows:

1. *Cognitive Goals*—Providing information about the disability, including common medical complications, and encourage or reinforce compliance with treatment regimes (Jeffrey, 1986); enhancing the self-esteem of group members; and assisting individuals in understanding their strengths and limitations.

2. *Affective Goals*—Providing a supportive atmosphere in which one can comfortably self-disclose and express emotions, diminishing anxiety and tension, recognizing that others have similar responses, and reducing feelings of depression.

3. *Behavioral Goals*—Promoting independent behavior, providing the opportunity to practice new skills or behaviors, increasing coping mechanisms, and identifying future goals (see Table 8.1).

Gender

Gender differences have been noted in response to different disabilities, including spinal cord injuries, AIDS, and myocardial infarction. DeLoach and Greer (1981), in describing gender differences of individuals with spinal cord injuries, stated that women were less affected than men in terms of fertility and the ability to engage in intercourse; however, they noted that women may have problems with birth control, childbirth, and vaginal infections.

Gender differences have also been noted with people who have AIDS. As with many disabilities, more research and media attention has been focused on men with AIDS, which has contributed to the sense of isolation felt by women with AIDS (Beck, Carlton, Allen, Rosenkoetter, & Hardy, 1993). Beck and his colleagues pointed out that the counseling needs of women with HIV *are different* from those of men because of differences in the mode of transmission and clinical progression of HIV, cultural differences, and differences related to pregnancy and mothering. Research suggests that women are diagnosed later and die sooner after diagnosis, possibly because few physicians are knowledgeable about AIDS, particularly about AIDS in women. Another gender difference relates to mothering as a woman's social role. Eighty-five percent of children with AIDS contracted it from their mothers. This means that childcare services will be an important

Table 8.1

Sample Cognitive, Affective, and Behavioral Counseling Interventions
Categorized by Disability, Personal, and Environmental Variables

Variable	Cognitive	Affective	Behavioral
Disability (time and type of onset, visibility, severity, stability, functions impaired, pain)	Provide education on the nature of the disability and conditions that exacerbate the condition, treatment	Provide support services, counseling related to psychosocial issues	Follow treatment regimes; describe disability to potential employer
Person (gender, ethnicity, activities affected, interests, values, goals, remaining resources, personality variables)	Assess knowledge of self (interests)	Provide values clarification, focusing on asset instead of comparative values	Focus on adapting activities, career enhancement activities
Environment (family, friends, community and financial resources, technology, laws)	Identify community and financial resources available to consumer and family; educate family and employers	Provide family counseling	Advocate on behalf of individual with disability, participate in professional activities that can promote services and resources for individuals with a disability

consideration as the mothers' illness progresses and more medical care is required.

Lee Smith, 42, had worked as a secretary until she had a minor stroke. Because she is no longer able to read, her counselor suggested a nontraditional job training program in plumbing. Lee angrily refused.

In considering the counseling issues related to gender, rehabilitation counselors should not assume that gender stereotyping occurs only in cross-gender counseling situations (i.e., men counseling women or women counseling men). Gender stereotypes, values, and attitudes are not based solely on the gender of the counselor. Both male and female counselors are at risk when it comes to possessing stereotypic values and beliefs about women. As Cook (1990) stated, (a) "gender is a multidimensional construct that encompasses the many ways society is differentiated on the basis of sex" (p. 371); (b) "it is also important to recognize how the broader sociocultural context presents men and women with different expectations, opportunities, and rewards" (p. 371); and (c) "gender shapes our personal characteristics and views of ourselves, the experiences open to us on a daily basis, and the nature of our interactions with others" (p. 374). Therefore, not only are both male and female counselors at risk for gender stereotyping, but both men and women with disabilities may also possess gender-based expectations for the type of rehabilitation services they desire.

The first step for counselors is to evaluate their own attitudes (i.e., knowledge, feelings, and actions) and gender stereotypes that they might possess. Examining one's attitudes toward gender issues is just as important as examining one's attitudes toward people with disabilities. Counselors also need to examine their behavior. As Van Hoose and Kottler (1985) noted, there is not a perfect correlation between what one says and what one does. Some self-examination questions that counselors might consider include the following: Is it as important for a woman to have a career as it is for a man? Is it worth the extra effort to help a woman procure a nontraditional career (e.g., engineering, computer repair)? Is arranging for child care as important as arranging for transportation to an employment site? Consciously or unconsciously, rehabilitation counselors make these value-laden decisions on a daily basis. Gender issues must be considered by the counselor at each point in the process, from eligibility determination to the identification of a vocational goal, including the range of services included in the rehabilitation plan. Because bias is so often unconscious, counselors need to examine their beliefs (knowledge and feelings), as well as their actions.

> *Mary Allen, 25, has cerebral palsy, which has resulted in impaired speech and limitations in the use of her arms and hands. Her parents protected her from what they felt was cruelty from other children by not allowing her to go to school. As a result, she had very few friends and very little social interaction outside of her home and immediate family members. She knows about jobs from watching TV and listening to family members. Because she believes she cannot be a doctor, lawyer, or nurse's aide, she believes she will never be able to work. She says it would "worry her parents to death" if she ever tried to get a job.*

Restricted vocational aspirations are only one of many issues that rehabilitation counselors should consider when working with women. Restricted vocational aspirations frequently result from (a) nature and type of disability; (b) socialization, which may restrict the range of careers to traditional female jobs; and (c) limited opportunities for mentors or role models. Counselors have a special responsibility to women with disabilities to expand the range of vocational options, particularly when the consumer has a narrow range of experiences or limited knowledge. Socialization factors and disability factors may compel women to limit their vocational options to *jobs,* rather than *careers.* Therefore, it is critical for counselors to truly understand (a) the consumer's knowledge of occupations, (b) values concerning work, and (c) career aspirations, *prior* to any formal assessment. An interest inventory, for example, will not yield valid results, if a woman lacks knowledge of career opportunities or does not view a career path as a viable option. In such circumstances the counselor should use various career exploration approaches (e.g., reading about jobs, informational interviews, job shadowing, job tryouts) to assist the consumer in gaining greater career maturity.

Self-efficacy expectations—that is, "one's beliefs in one's ability to perform a given behavior successfully" (Bonett, 1994, p. 187)—have been used to explain why women may not consider themselves capable of succeeding in male-dominated occupations and why they may question their ability to successfully combine home and family responsibilities with a career. Bonett (1994), who found that both married and unmarried women had lower self-efficacy expectations than men regarding traditional male occupations, suggested that the lowered self-efficacy reflected an underestimation of capabilities by women, as well as long-term socialization.

> *Lucy Baker, 45, mother of three teenage sons and a 7-year-old daughter, had a severe heart attack 3 months ago. She has always been an active, proud, stay-at-home mom because her husband travels a great deal in his work. Just home from the hospital, she is reluctant to participate in an outpatient rehabilitation program.*

Gender differences have also been noted in the way men and women respond to coronary artery disease. Coronary artery disease has special significance for women. It is the leading cause of death in women over 40 and causes one third of the deaths of women between the ages of 20 and 40 (Wenger, 1985). Konstam and Houser (1994) summarized their review of the literature of gender differences of post–myocardial infarction adjustment by stating,

> women show an increased tendency toward experiencing more difficulties than men in their recoveries post myocardial infarction. Women tend to experience more marital and social difficulties, depression, and anxiety. Increased difficulties reported by women are consistent with an overall longer time to return to work, as well as decreased sexual activity. (p. 47)

Various explanations have been provided to explain these psychosocial differences. One theory is that women define themselves in relation to others. That is, their self-esteem is based on their assessment of their personal relationships and their competence in enhancing the lives of others. In contrast, the self-esteem of men is based largely on autonomy. This difference has been used to explain why men return to work significantly sooner than women. Men adopt an exercise regime, usually walking, to rehabilitate their hearts. Women frequently do not engage in organized exercise programs because of household responsibilities.

Research on grief and depression has also been cited to explain gender differences in engaging in exercise programs and returning to work. Men tend to respond to sadness and grief by engaging in activities that distract them, whereas women tend to be less active and more introspective. One study (Stern, 1984) found that more than half of the cardiac patients who were depressed were women, although they comprised only 20% of the group that was studied. Silverman (1981) stated that when women experience loss, the loss is more than a disruption; it is a total assault on the self. Thus, women often lose their total sense of identity.

Because of the differences in the way men and women respond to myocardial infarction, Konstam and Houser (1994) recommended that rehabilitation counselors use three types of counseling interventions to systematically address the woman's personal relationships. Using an informal interview format, the counselor can assess the responsibility she feels for the well-being of significant others in her life. Problem-solving techniques could be used to discover how she can maintain her responsibilities to others without compromising her health. In addition, family counseling may also be recommended to address relationship issues and the impact of her illness on the family system. Finally, group counseling may allow her the support and information she needs to further explore relationship issues and how those issues impact her self-definition.

Konstam and Houser (1994) also recommended that rehabilitation counselors carefully evaluate cardiac rehabilitation programs, since many are geared to men's styles of adaptations and are less compatible with women. For example, instead of focusing only on aerobic activity, the aerobic activity could be followed by small group discussions. This would address both the information and support many women need, as well as the action-oriented approach and exercise that is required in cardiac rehabilitation.

Culture

Culture may be defined as a multitude of ways to perceive and organize the world, held in common by a group of people, and passed on interpersonally and intergenerationally (Hecht, Andersen, & Ribeau, 1989). Each of us has a "personal culture" that may be influenced by a variety of factors, including age, gender, education, disability, socioeconomic status, acculturation, ethnicity, and urban versus rural geography. An individual's personal culture develops as a result of accumulated learning from a variety of sources (e.g., school, family, community); is defined through interactions with others; changes to accommodate experiences in a changing world; and provides a basis for values, beliefs, and behavior (Pedersen & Ivey, 1993).

Cultural Diversity

Cultural diversity may be conceptualized as broad constructs that represent beliefs, values, and behaviors of different cultures worldwide (Pedersen & Ivey, 1993). These constructs represent generalizations of beliefs, values, and behaviors that are found, and are present to varying degrees, in many societies around the world. An advantage to the use of broad constructs is that no one age group, gender, or ethnic group is discussed directly. Although broad constructs of culture may be generalizations of behavior and values, and therefore stereotypes, use of broad constructs to represent similarities and differences among people the world over alerts counselors to the fact that, as people, we each have varying degrees of these beliefs, values, and behaviors. It is important to remember that each broad construct represents a continuum on which an individual may lie, and is not an *either–or* representation of values and behavior. In addition, an individual may present varying degrees of a construct in different circumstances (e.g., how one communicates with others may be different at work vs. at home with family members or loved ones).

Individualism–Collectivism

In cultures that are highly individualistic, the interests of the individual prevail over the interests of the group, whereas interests of the group prevail over those of the individual in collectivist cultures (Hofstede, 1991). How one defines oneself and the role of groups to which one belongs may be influenced by this construct of culture (Gudykunst & Nishida, 1989).

Individuals who have highly individualistic values and beliefs may have a tendency to see themselves as separate and unique, and their self-definition largely does not include others. Self-realization is important, and is promoted as the highest purpose to which one can aspire. The interests of the individual are more important than those of groups they belong to, as exemplified by attachments to the nuclear family but not necessarily the extended family. Individual achievements are important, and it is felt that rewards should be distributed on an equity basis, dependent on one's contribution to the goal or objective, rather than an equality basis, dependent on one's membership in a workgroup in which all members share equally in the rewards (Cox, 1994). When asked to write 20 statements that began with "I am . . . ," individuals with an individualistic orientation used personal attributes, such as "I am hardworking" or "I am kind" (Triandis, 1990, p. 41).

On the other hand, individuals who have values and beliefs that are collectivist in orientation are more likely to value interdependence and define themselves in relation to others. Membership in stable in-groups (e.g., family, community, church) is valued. Within these groups cooperation, not competition, is stressed, for there is an awareness of how individual achievement contributes to overall in-group achievement (e.g., one feels that they represent not only themselves and their family by their actions and behavior, but their church and community as well). Relationships are important, and personal integrity within relationships is valued. When asked to write 20 statements that began with "I am . . . ," individuals with a collectivist orientation used in-group responses, such as "I am a son" or "I am a Catholic" (Triandis, 1990, p. 41).

High- Versus Low-Context Communication

Individuals with a high-context communication style value the setting or situation in which communication takes place. An individual's unarticulated moods, gestures, and speed of conversation are important and considered part of the communication process. It is expected that the listener will read the speaker's mood and gestures, and know what these behaviors mean. Therefore, the information not directly communicated through words in a conversation may be the most important part of the communication.

Individuals with a low-context communication style value direct, precise verbal communication with little attention to mood, setting, or nonverbal cues. Conveying details, time schedules, and specific instructions or information is the focus of a low-context communication style. Interpersonal relations and cooperation between individuals may not be stressed. As Hall (1977) indicated, a person with a low-context communication style, talking with a person with a high-context communication style, feels that the high-context person is not "getting to the point." The high-context person feels that the low-context person is redundant and wordy, belabors the obvious, and is possibly offensive in his or her directness.

Knowledge of cultural diversity also contributes to recognizing that disability may be defined and perceived differently among people. For example, studies have found that perceptions held by parents and individuals from minority backgrounds differ from perceptions held by professionals as to the etiology of mental retardation and mental illness and prescriptive practices (Harry, 1992; Mardiros, 1989); definitions of mental retardation and learning disabilities and the resulting labels (Harry, 1992; Harry, Allen, & McLaughlin, 1995); an emphasis on documentation rather than participation during meetings (Harry et al., 1995); and how "normalcy" is defined and testing practices (Marion, 1980).

> *A transition planning meeting is being held for Mario Izara, 18, who has spina bifida. He lives in a rural Hispanic community in a southwest state. The vocational rehabilitation counselor suggests that Mario attend college at a large state university located 300 miles away, because he certainly has the grades to be successful in college and the skills to live independently. During the conversation, the rehabilitation counselor, who has not met Mrs. Izara before, refers to Mrs. Izara by her first name in an effort to connect with her. Although Mrs. Izara smiles politely throughout the meeting, she refuses to sign a transition plan at the end of the meeting.*

The counselor must recognize that not everyone holds individualistic values, and that it may be considered inappropriate by Mario's family for Mario or any other family member to move from the family's community. Individuals may be attentive and respectful during the meeting, but that is in no way a promise to adhere to the information or rehabilitation plan discussed, especially if it is inconsistent with their belief system. It would be inappropriate for the counselor to characterize this value as "overprotective," for it may be the result of firmly held, culturally appropriate values. Individuals who hold values that are collectively oriented may feel that all respected members of the family must be part of all important decision making. In this situation, Mario's mother may take the transition plan home for consideration by both her husband and the family. In many collectively oriented cultures, families are respected and honored for taking care of each other, so it would not be out of place for the family to move to the city where the college is located if the family decides that Mario's attending college is a positive step.

Many times people come to interpersonal interactions expecting respect from professionals. Use of first names with adults during an initial meeting may violate expectations for observance of formal amenities. Informal language, casual clothes, or questions that are perceived as personal may not convey respect during an initial meeting. Using overly direct (low-context) language that contains esoteric terminology or jargon (e.g., "eligibility," "physical restoration services," or "personal adjustment counseling") and focusing on documentation or paperwork instead of participation work to establish and maintain a power imbalance. Such relationship imbalances not only may silence people but may alienate them, with the end result being withdrawal from needed rehabilitation programs and services.

Language is always an important consideration for counselors. Some consumers may prefer their primary language (e.g., Spanish), whereas others may prefer English. When working with a family, a counselor may need to use both languages, depending on the family's preference. Although it is preferable to speak to individuals in their primary language, rehabilitation counselors also must develop skills in working effectively with interpreters.

> *Tonya Jackson, who is 18 years old and African American, went with her parents to visit a rehabilitation counselor. Tonya had been in special education classes while in high school, and had recently graduated. She was looking into what the agency might provide. In reviewing the file, the counselor mentioned that since Tonya has mental retardation, she might possibly benefit from supported employment. The counselor was surprised when Tonya's parents reacted with indignation over the label of mental retardation being applied to their daughter and stated, "This agency isn't any different from the school."*

The overrepresentation of African American students in special education has been a longstanding issue for many African Americans (Harry et al., 1995; Marion, 1980). The subjectivity of the assessment and referral process of placing students into special education has been questioned (Harry & Anderson, 1995) because African American students, particularly boys, have been overrepresented, especially in the categories of mental retardation and emotional disorders. Parents have reacted with anger and dismay at schools that they feel have practiced a policy of segregation by promoting these two disability categories as the only appropriate depositories for their children (Marion, 1980).

Defining disability or creating a deviance category is based on the values and behavioral expectations of the culture creating the definition. Therefore, counselors should solicit individuals' and/or parents' perspectives of developmental and achievement levels and their interpretation of the sources of any difficulties rather than assume that perceptions and definitions of disability are universal across cultures.

Kuifen Raa is 27 years old and sustained a severe head injury as a result of a car accident 4 weeks ago. Her parents were referred to the rehabilitation counselor to discuss possibilities for Kuifen's move from the hospital to the community. The rehabilitation counselor met with Kuifen's parents and was confused because the parents did not respond to open-ended questions and attempts to reflect their feelings about their daughter. The parents also mentioned that they were going to have their daughter visit an acupuncturist. The counselor perceived the parents as cold and uncaring because of their response to her attempts to help.

Rehabilitation counselors, when working with Asian American consumers and their families, should not necessarily expect an open and public expression of feelings or emotional problems, especially during a first session (Panigua, 1994). In fact, the rehabilitation counselor may have to exhibit his or her expertise and authority during the first session through statements about having worked with many similiar individuals with traumatic brain injuries and by emphasizing concrete and tangible goals. Counselors should be aware of services specific for Asian American consumers and families and provide a listing during the first session. Suggesting short-term goals that are concrete and tangible for the next meeting demonstrates that the counselor can assist with a consumer's or family's immediate concerns and increases the likelihood that the consumer will return.

Counselors also should consider accepting the individual's use of culturally indigenous "helpers." Extended family members, healers, spiritual or religious elders, herbalists, and acupuncturists may assist in rehabilitation efforts along with formal systems of help. If the counselor expresses a lack of acceptance of these helpers, the counselor may offend the individual or the family. On the other hand, the counselor must also assess whether the helpers may harm the individual or interfere with the rehabilitation plan. This issue requires delicate handling.

Summary

Each individual's unique constellation of personal factors shapes the meaning of a disability and reaction to it. Attitudes toward disability can range from the disability's being viewed as a catastrophic event to a nuisance or inconvenience. Counselors should neither presume to know how an individual will respond to a disability nor prescribe a reaction. Basic counseling skills should be used to explore an individual's characteristics, attitudes, values, strengths, and abilities, as well as the influence of culture and gender on self-definition and expectations.

The Environment

The environment constitutes the second category of factors that influence response to disability. The environment, which includes factors external to the individual, encompasses both the immediate environment (e.g., family, friends, community resources) and the broader societal environment (e.g., technology, laws, social definition of disability). It is important to appreciate that the impact of disability can vary by environment. For example, the impact of deafness and the use of sign language is diminished when one resides in a community where sign language is the primary language. Similarly, the impact of a child with a disability on the family may be less when the family has adequate information and a range of supports (e.g., emotional, financial, social, and community).

Families

The importance of families in the rehabilitation process has been demonstrated in numerous studies (see Kelley & Lambert, 1992). As Power, Dell Orto, and Gibbons (1988) noted, "The family can become a major help to an individual's rehabilitation or adjustment, or a significant stumbling block to the attainment of treatment goals" (p. ix). The family and significant others influence the manner in which individuals respond to their disability and, in turn, families are influenced by the disabilities of a family member. For example, Kosciulek (1995) pointed out that "head injury exerts a large toll on the emotional and psychological functioning of family members" (p. 13).

Because the value of family involvement in the rehabilitation process has not been consistently recognized by rehabilitation professionals, the 1992 Amendments to the Rehabilitation Act of 1973 specifically acknowledge the family. Title I, Part A, Section 100 states, "families and natural supports can play an important role in the success of a vocational rehabilitation program, if the individual with a disability requests, desires, or needs such supports." However, it is incumbent upon rehabilitation counselors *in any circumstance* to recognize the importance of the family and involve the family in rehabilitation efforts as needed and desired by the consumer of rehabilitation services. A family that is excluded from the rehabilitation process will have more difficulty supporting rehabilitation efforts.

> *Juan Martinez, 14, was born with multiple disabilities. His deeply religious family felt that his disability was a punishment from God for sins committed by his mother. The family has limited financial, educational, and emotional resources. They keep Juan at home because of their deep feelings of shame about his condition and because they believe it is their responsibility to care for him for the rest of his life.*

The parental response is a major factor that influences a child with a congenital disability. Because most parents do not anticipate having a child with a disability, their initial reactions are typically grief, confusion, fear, anger, and dismay when they learn of the disability. Usually such feelings will abate; however, sometimes these feelings may lead to overprotection or even rejection of the child. Parental response is influenced by (a) beliefs regarding disability, (b) coping skills, (c) stress management skills, (d) child management skills, and (e) support networks (Van Hasselt, Lutzker, & Hersen, 1990).

When the onset of disability is at a very early age, as with Juan, important components of counseling are providing information to the family (Berry, 1995) and making appropriate referrals for food, housing, and entitlement benefits. They may also include coping and stress management skills, as well as information about how to positively influence Juan's growth and development. A counselor may also help the family develop networks for support (e.g., extended family members, respite care, parent support groups). A counselor should share information about the etiology of Juan's condition, without challenging the family's religious beliefs. It may also be advisable to refer them to a priest or other community service provider to discuss their feelings of being at fault for Juan's disability.

Vocational counseling from a developmental perspective is important for rehabilitation counselors because a disability, particularly a congenital disability, has a major impact on career development. Gilbride (1993), finding that parents had lowered expectations for their children with disabilities, suggested that "parents may be unknowingly reducing the vocational options of their child [with a disability]" (p. 147). Curnow (1989) suggested that limited early experiences, lack of opportunity to develop decision-making skills, and lowered self-concepts are common results of a congenital disability or the acquisition of a disability in a child. Therefore, interventions by counselors who are involved with children and their families include helping families identify opportunities for and recognize the importance of interactions with the environment outside the home that contribute to other ongoing career exploration activities. Career exploration activities include those experiences associated with developing career maturity (Conte, 1983), such as understanding one's interests, aptitudes, and various occupational environments (Curnow, 1989). Because decision making improves with practice, the counselor should help families identify opportunities for a child to learn and use decision-making skills. The counselor can help families realize that overprotectiveness and forced dependency of a child with a disability often contribute to social immaturity and impaired decision making (Chubon, 1985).

Martin Reis, 17, recently sustained a spinal cord injury. He was hospitalized for 6 months, and is now in outpatient treatment. The family believes their son will walk again, so they refuse to ramp their front door for wheelchair access.

The education and support roles of the rehabilitation counselor may vary based on the strengths and weaknesses of the family unit and points in the rehabilitation process (e.g., diagnosis, in-hospital treatment or rehabilitation, termination of in-hospital treatment or rehabilitation and return to the family unit, and outpatient treatment or rehabilitation). Power (1988) described the counseling considerations for families at different stages of the rehabilitation process. During the first stage, diagnosis and beginning of treatment, the counselor should consider the unique composition of the family. Information should be gathered on previous coping and decision-making skills, as well as the incidence of any other disability in the family, including substance abuse. Common needs of families at this time may include processing information, exploring alternatives, clarifying frustrations, receiving support, and having access to empathic listeners.

During in-hospital treatment or rehabilitation, a counselor may need to assess the accuracy of the information the family has about the disability or illness. Frequently the processing of information will need to occur outside conferences with the physician, because anxieties may be higher during those meetings. The counselor should gather information about the resource needs of the family while the family member is in the hospital. This may include counseling that focuses on identifying possible threats to family functioning, as well as assessing effective coping skills the family has used thus far.

When in-hospital treatment or rehabilitation has been terminated and the family member is returning home, Power (1988) recommended that rehabilitation counselors identify the expectations the family has for the family member with the disability or illness, the needs of the individual who will assume most of the care responsibilities, and the feelings family members have about the family member returning home. It is not unusual for family members to have intense and mixed feelings about the return of the family member; these strong feelings (e.g., anger at the behavior of the individual with the disability or a strong need to maintain the family member in a "sick" role) may have an impact on future rehabilitation efforts.

During outpatient treatment or rehabilitation, the counselor should consider whether any new disruptions have occurred within the family and whether the family's relationship to health care providers has changed. Identifying how the family has changed since the family member has been at home, any problems they feel they have in relation to the family member, and services they need, will assist the counselor in developing a plan to maintain the family member at home.

Friends

Relationships, including friendships, are at the core of living a fulfilling life. Friendships help individuals to feel a part of communities, ensure their well-being and health, and help protect them from exploitation and neglect (Strully & Strully, 1992). Friends are an important source of social support, being available to comfort a friend who needs someone to listen, congratulate a friend on successes, and acknowledge a friend's deeds.

Social support has been defined as consisting of four categories (Reid, Landesman, Treder, & Jaccard, 1989). The first, emotional support, is derived from interactions that produce feelings of being understood (e.g., receiving acknowledgment for accomplishments, and support for negative events that may have happened). Informational support from friends can be in the form of information (e.g., where to find a good grocery store, who might have a job opening, or how to get to the new clinic). Instrumental aid occurs when a friend helps to accomplish something (e.g., clean a friend's apartment, move a friend into a new home, find a lost pet). Companionship is sharing activities (e.g., going out for pizza, visiting, going to the movies). Social support contributes to emotional adjustment, life satisfaction, and physical and mental health (Sarason & Sarason, 1985).

Because all workplaces have a culture, work settings also provide opportunities for relational activities. Even workplaces with high levels of turnover evidence patterns and structures of behavior and formation of friendships between workers, and exhibit stability in their expectations for social interactions (Hagner & Dileo, 1993). Workplaces can vary in the strength of their expectations for socialization. In some workplaces, employees celebrate birthdays, know the names and ages of other employees' children, and have a strong sense of each person's needs and strengths. These workplaces have strong workplace cultures. In other workplaces, workers exchange small talk and have customary ways of doing things, but have no strong friendship bonds. These types of workplaces do not have strong cultures.

> *Edna Franklin had a history of physical abuse as a child in her family. She was born with cerebral palsy and was in a marriage that ended several years ago. She has recently been diagnosed with a degenerative nerve disorder, and is restricted to part-time work. Ms. Franklin has been doing part-time volunteer work at a municipal office as a form of job try-out, and knows that the job will lead to part-time paid work. When asked what she likes about the job, Ms. Franklin said, "Having a work-related family makes it worth going."*

The rehabilitation counselor who had been working with Ms. Franklin heard her desire and need for supportive, caring relationships in her life when talking with her about jobs and working. Ms. Franklin never directly expressed this desire to the rehabilitation counselor, but the counselor recognized the underlying need during their conversations. Ms. Franklin not only wanted to work, but also needed to be connected to people who would be sensitive and supportive. The counselor understood that Ms. Franklin had not received the emotional support that she needed during her childhood and marriage, and that trusting people would be hard. Therefore, she knew that finding a job that was consistent with Ms. Franklin's physical capabilities and skills, and had a strong workplace culture that would provide emotional support, was critical for Ms. Franklin's success on the job.

> *Bob Atkins is transitioning from school to the community. He has mental retardation and went with his parents to visit with a rehabilitation counselor about services, jobs, and working. When asked what he wanted to do, Bob replied, "I want to be able to visit my grandma."*

Bob, his parents, and the rehabilitation counselor continued to talk about what kind of community-based work experiences he had during school, what Bob had liked and not liked about those experiences, what Bob liked about his grandma and how often he visited with her, what vocational skills Bob has, and other interests and activities. The rehabilitation counselor knew that constructing a career goal with Bob should incorporate his wish to be able to visit his grandmother. He knew that for Bob, working was connected to being close to important people in his life.

Being connected to supportive people promotes a sense of acceptance. Through these relationships, a person feels accepted and a part of the workplace and communities.

Community

Individual communities have a unique combination of resources for people with disabilities. The availability of high-quality inclusive education, a variety of medical resources and facilities, inpatient and outpatient rehabilitation programs, state rehabilitation agency services, independent living services, assistive technology devices, advocacy organizations, and public transportation can influence the independence and adjustment of people with disabilities, as well as the counseling concerns they may have.

> *Roy Sauls, 27, was in a car accident 3 years ago and lives in a small town with his parents. He can use a motorized wheelchair; however, his town has very few curb cuts and only one public van that will accommodate his motorized chair. He does not know anyone else who uses a wheelchair. Mostly he watches TV and drinks at home.*

The benefits of peer groups have been well documented. However, as Ericson and Riordan (1993) noted, individuals with low-incidence disabilities, such as end-stage renal disease, may not know anyone else their age with the disability.

It is incumbent upon rehabilitation counselors to know the resources available in the communities they serve. To be effective, a counselor must make referrals to community agencies for consumers' basic needs, such as food, housing, and benefits. It is often in the counselor's best interest to make personal contacts at referral agencies. First-hand knowledge of available services not only results in more appropriate referrals *to* those agencies, but results in counselors receiving better referrals *from* those sources. A network of informed and cooperative service providers creates an effective service delivery system.

In addition, a counselor should be aware of disability-related organizations or service providers, such as centers for independent living, advocacy groups (e.g., National Federation of the Blind), and disability rights organizations. A counselor should also be aware of groups such as Deaf Clubs, Special Olympics, support groups that are specific to certain disability groups (e.g., survivors of head injury), or community groups that are accepting of members with disabilities (e.g., Boy Scout troops, or ham radio clubs). Counselors should also maintain a list of professional counselors, social workers, physicians, dentists, psychologists, and psychiatrists who have experience with and understanding of people with disabilities.

A counselor should also be aware of other types of commonly used referral sources in the community. A comprehensive list could include substance abuse treatment facilities and schedules of meetings for Alcoholics Anonymous and other 12-step programs; referral sources for women, including a rape crisis center, shelter for battered women, women's health clinics, eating disorder programs, and support groups for assault or abuse survivors; services for consumers who are gay or lesbian, such as advocacy or political organizations, support groups, and health, counseling, or religious organizations that specifically serve homosexual clients; and services for persons who are HIV positive or who have AIDS, such as emergency financial help, dental clinics, respite care, and support groups for the consumers, for family members, and for surviving partners.

Rural areas present special challenges for rehabilitation counselors because the range of services may be limited in small communities. A counselor may need to work toward developing services in more isolated areas, or developing resources for transportation to the nearest urban area where more services may be available.

> *Martha Sanford, 7, has multiple disabilities and is considered medically fragile. Her community does not have resources for respite care, so her mother has been with her every day since the day she was born.*

Community resources influence not only the individual's response but also the family's response to disability. The individual with a disability may feel that he or she is a burden, when the family is the sole caregiver and no respite care is available. Similarly, the individual able to remain in his or her home environment as a result of community support services may have an easier time adapting to a disability than an individual who is placed in an institution due to lack of community resources. Disability generally means additional costs to the individual and the family. It may be easier to have a disability when the financial resources are available to provide additional support or access to technology.

Society

The environment also includes aspects of society as a whole; of particular importance is the cultural definition of, and attitude toward, disability. The meaning that society attributes to disability also has considerable impact on an individual's response to a disability. Societal attitudes may be manifested in the laws, as well as in the images depicting, language describing, and inclusion of people with disabilities in all aspects of life. To the degree that these are negatively experienced by an individual, the disability may have a greater impact on that individual's life. A rehabilitation counselor must understand the social, political, and cultural context of disability, in order to appreciate individual experience.

Murray Stevenson, 41, has worked tirelessly on disability rights for most of his adult life. He was in Washington, D.C., when the Americans with Disabilities Act of 1990 was passed, and considered it both a personal and political victory. Six years later, he does not feel circumstances have changed much for him or his peers. He is angry and frustrated with the system, which he feels has let them all down.

The disability rights movement, led by individuals with disabilities, has forced significant positive social changes for people with disabilities in services, independence, legal protection, control, choices, and respect. By organizing, forcing confrontations, and working to change the system, many people with disabilities "gained a sense of empowerment after lives of dependency" (Shapiro, 1993, p. 135). Just as the movements for civil rights and women's rights defined and empowered disenfranchised groups, and angered other groups, the disability rights movement is not always viewed favorably by the mainstream culture, by professionals, or by some people with disabilities. Some may resent the independence and "bossiness" of consumers or feel that anger and civil disobedience is inappropriate, and that people with disabilities should work only within the existing system.

As a counselor, you must examine the attitudes toward disability you have absorbed from the mainstream culture, as well as your own feelings about independence, choice, and anger from people with disabilities. Do you want or expect gratitude and compliance from your clients? Are you aware of the environmental, legal, and social barriers that can constitute the details of the daily life of an individual with a disability?

With an appreciation of the social and political context of Mr. Stevenson's anger and frustration, a counselor may better understand its source and use it advantageously. Anger is often a response to injustice. A person may feel that maintaining an angry emotional state is the only way to right a wrong (Tavris, 1989). Anger may also feel powerful to individuals with very little power and control over their lives. Understanding and validating Mr. Stevenson's anger may help him gain distance from his fears and thoughts. In addition, a counselor can promote Mr. Stevenson's self-understanding by supporting him in exploring the social context of his anger.

A self-help group with others who have had the same experiences may also assist Mr. Stevenson. Sharing experiences can diminish isolation, reduce self-blame, and mediate strong feelings. The understanding and support of the group can generate solutions to problems. In addition, the act of helping others can be empowering, and can work to right the injustice that produced the angry feelings (Tavris, 1989). As Thompson (1985) stated,

> Those of us who are disabled must learn to cope with the anger-provoking reality that all those many barriers are not going to come tumbling down all at once, as unjust, unfair, and just plain infuriating as they are. But it is also not very helpful, to ourselves or anyone else, to just sit around and scream at the injustice of

it all. We need to find effective coping mechanisms to keep us sane and strong. For some, political action may be useful. For others a support group may help. . . . The important thing is to find a way to survive. (p. 85)

Darlene Angel, 27, is African American and has low vision. College educated and trained as an editor, she was fired from two different jobs in the last 2 years. She has no friends and she is not looking for work. After experiencing a lifetime of pity, hostility, exclusion, and dependency, she has internalized the societal attitudes about disability, gender, race, and social class, and simply feels she has nothing to contribute.

In this society, which values independence, rational intellect, and physical beauty, people with disabilities are significantly devalued (Vash, 1981). This devaluation may be manifested as pity, contempt, or exclusion. Society's generally negative attitudes toward disability may significantly impact an individual's self-concept. Curnow (1989) stated,

Lack of experience and difficulty in decision making are not solely the result of disability, but largely the outcome of social attitudes and stereotypes. Social attitudes toward disability may be as important as the disability itself in that the negative attitude of others plays a part in shaping the life role of the individual with a disability. (p. 273)

Self-esteem develops both internally and externally. During early stages of development, one's self-esteem generally is derived from the behaviors and verbalizations of others (i.e., external); as an individual matures and becomes productive, competent, and responsible, self-esteem becomes more of an internally oriented process (Tuttle & Tuttle, 1996).

Most children with disabilities grow up with messages that they are not as good as children without disabilities, that their differences make them "not okay." As a result, many people with disabilities move into adulthood with a need for approval and validation. A counselor should be aware of the negative societal attitudes toward disability, and the impact those attitudes may have on an individual's sense of self-worth. It may be helpful for an individual to explore any negative childhood messages. By encouraging the individual to think about the social context in which those messages were received, some distance from the shame may allow more self-understanding. Many times the negative messages may override any positive ones, so developing esteem-building experiences or relationships may be helpful.

Many adults with disabilities are denied opportunities to prove their competence and worth by being productive, contributing members of society; thus, they struggle to develop internal sources of self-esteem. A counselor may assist an individual in developing new opportunities, such as volunteer or work experiences, which promote an internal sense of competence and productivity. In addition, a counselor may assist individuals in evaluating other aspects of their life that prove competence and worth, but which typically are not valued as highly in this society as work. For example, an individual may be a very competent nurturer, friend, advocate, or communicator, or have a strong sense of worth developed from spiritual beliefs, but devalue those qualities because they are devalued in this society. Empowering an individual to identify and clarify measures of self-worth with personal meaning and importance, may be an important consideration in counseling an individual with low self-esteem.

Summary

The unique constellation of environmental factors for individuals necessarily influences their reactions, needs, and expectations, when disability or chronic illness becomes part of their lives. The influences of the various systems in a person's life—family, friends, the community, and even society—are interrelated; when one aspect of a system is changed, all other aspects of that system reverberate with change also. When individuals are born with or acquire a disability, they change to accommodate the disability. Inevitably family members must change in response. Social relationships are influenced by disability, and must flex to accommodate the individual. Groups of people with disabilities require communities to change and accommodate by building ramps and providing services. Larger groups of people with disabilities require society at large to recognize their humanness by enacting laws to protect individual rights and opportunities.

Nature of the Disability

Specific aspects of a disability itself influence the meaning an individual ascribes to his or her disability, and the subsequent response to that disability. The nature of the disability includes the type of disability (physical, mental, emotional), as well as factors such as the functions impaired, severity of the disability, time of onset, type of onset, visibility of the disability, stability of the disability, and pain (Vash, 1981). Each of these disability-related factors may have implications for rehabilitation counselors.

Functions Impaired

The specific sensory, motor, or cognitive functions impaired contribute to an individual's response to a disability. The disability may influence only one area of functioning, such as the ability to communicate or to problem solve. An individual may also have dual or multiple disabilities, affecting a number of functions.

The number and type of functions impaired influence an individual's response to a disability, but a more significant influence is how important an individual feels that function is in his or her daily life. A rehabilitation counselor should never make assumptions about an individual's response to a particular disability. Counselors may feel they lack information to design effective interventions, or feel frustrated at the inadequacy of resources available for persons with multiple disabilities.

> *Sara Johnson, 24, is congenitally deaf and is suspected of having mental illness. She needs to be evaluated by a psychiatrist; however, there is no psychiatrist in town who is fluent in sign language, or who understands deaf culture and will work with an interpreter.*

Individuals who have multiply impaired functions may present greater challenges to rehabilitation counselors, particularly in locating appropriate resources. Therefore, advocacy and education may be important components of the rehabilitation counselor's role. Working with other agencies to ensure that consumers with multiple disabilities do not "fall between the cracks" may mean educating other professionals about disability issues, advocating for the funding and development of appropriate resources for certain consumers (e.g., mental health professionals who sign), and clarifying the legal rights of consumers to be included in community support systems.

> *Elia Lanyard, 26, is considered to have mild mental retardation. She recently moved into a supported living apartment, but is having difficulty getting along with her roommate. She has become very isolated and seems depressed.*

The functional deficits associated with certain types of disabilities require adaptations on the part of the counselor. This is particularly true for individuals with cognitive deficits, such as mental retardation, which present numerous challenges to rehabilitation counselors in terms of the individual's understanding of counseling and choices provided. Prout and Strohmer (1995), in setting forth guidelines to assist counselors in providing more effective counseling services to individuals with mental retardation, recommended the following:

1. *Developmentally Appropriate Interventions and Goals.* Counselors should not "talk down" to clients or treat adult clients as children. The counselor should use words that can be understood by the client and focus on concrete (e.g., actual situations or current problems) rather than abstract levels of thinking. The counselor should limit the number of areas that are discussed in a counseling session. Also, because individuals with mental retardation typically lack the capacity to generalize, counseling goals should be situation specific.

2. *Style.* The counselor will be more active and directive with little or no focus on "insight" by the client. Concrete activities such as role-playing and modeling may be a major focus of the time the counselor and client spend together.

3. *Expression.* Many individuals with mental retardation lack the vocabulary to express feelings and concerns. They may also feel uncomfortable simply talking

with the counselor. Strategies that the counselor can use to facilitate expression include (a) teaching clients the difference between thoughts and feelings, as well as various feeling words (e.g., *sad, scared, nervous*), and (b) using other activities as a basis for the counseling session. For example, having the consumer draw a picture, using puppets, or talking about a picture can reduce the counselor's reliance on verbal interactions.

In considering the functions that are impaired, the counselor should never overlook the possibility of a dual disability. Ingraham, Kaplan, and Chan (1992) found that, although counselors recognize that clients may have secondary disabilities such as alcoholism, counselors tend to underestimate the prevalence of alcoholism among individuals with spinal cord injuries, traumatic brain injuries, and chronic mental illness.

Severity of the Disability

Although severity of the disability is often linked to functions impaired, there are other considerations. For example, an individual with low vision may be more independent than a person with total blindness, or vice versa. The functional limitations imposed by a disability may be influenced more by the individual's personal characteristics than by the disability itself.

> *Jeremy Silverstein, 34, has always been a computer whiz. His career, his hobby, and his life revolved around computers until he developed carpal tunnel syndrome. His hands were immobilized for 6 months, and now even simple activities result in pain. Other people tell him "It's not that bad; you still have your mind," but he remains depressed and unable to work.*

Although people often subscribe to the myth that the more severe the disability, the greater the psychological impact on the person (Patterson & Witten, 1986), there is no evidence to support this contention. Therefore, a counselor should never underestimate the impact of a disability based on severity. What is viewed as severe by one individual may not be viewed as severe by another individual. Similarly, counselors should never underestimate the psychological impact of a disability, when they view the disability as less severe. For example, Lynch and Rodriquez (1992) noted that most of the literature on carpal tunnel syndrome focuses on prevention and surgery, and that counselors may overlook the need to address fears that consumers may have about returning to the job or using a machine that initially caused the condition.

A primary counseling consideration related to severity of disability is for rehabilitation counselors to ascertain the client's view of the disability. Different types of questions or statements by the counselor may elicit this information. For example, the counselor may ask how or whether the disability has changed the individual or family interaction patterns. Or, the counselor may make a statement, such as, "Some people with [this disability] find it difficult asking for assistance with certain tasks (e.g., dressing, transportation)." This gives the consumer the opportunity to elaborate on or refute the counselor's statement.

> *Phil Miller, 43, received a closed head injury as the result of a motorcycle accident. He is both depressed and angry about his inability to support his family.*

Marmé and Skord (1993) identified a number of counseling issues, such as anger, increased awareness of deficits, overestimation of one's skills, and judgment and problem solving, that frequently arise with individuals with traumatic brain injury. In addressing issues such as these, rehabilitation counselors need to remember that all individuals experience anger and depression at some time in their lives. By recognizing this commonality, counselors are better prepared to consider the importance of timing, which means they do not let their agendas override good counseling skills. For example, if a client becomes angry, the counselor must recognize that it is generally inappropriate to present additional information that would add to the consumer's frustration. Counselors should wait until the consumer is in a calmer state of mind to present information that is threatening or contrary to what the client wants to hear. Marmé and Skord (1993), who recommended a "sandwich" technique, in which the less desirable information is preceded and followed by statements that reinforce the client's well-being, provided the following example:

> John, you are a caring and able person. You have demonstrated that you have a great deal to offer. At this time, I cannot support your goal of going to college. I do believe that there are many jobs and training programs where you could be successful and happy. I would like to work with you to find that success and happiness. (p. 23)

Other recommendations for consumers with traumatic brain injuries, as set forth by Marmé and Skord (1993), include talking with rather than at a client, allowing time for an individual to process information, using repetition, structuring the interview, limiting distractions (e.g., telephone), and focusing on the "here and now" for clients who are depressed.

Time of Onset

The period of time in an individual's life when a disability is acquired is an important counseling consideration. An individual with a congenital disability—that is, one who is born with a disability or acquires the disability before age 3—typically has different experiences than an individual with an adventitious disability—that is, one who acquires a disability after age 3. For example, consider the world of a child who is born blind, compared with that of an individual who acquires blindness at age 15, 25, 45, or 75. The child who is born without vision assumes that everyone else lacks vision, until the child is old enough to understand otherwise. In contrast, when a visual loss is acquired later in life, the individual better understands the functional limitations, because of knowledge and experiences acquired with sight. The individual is also more likely to compare what he or she could do and people's interactions before and after the vision loss. When one considers the activities in which one might be engaged at different ages, one can see the significance of time of onset. It is important for counselors to remember that time of onset of a disability does not automatically mean that adaptation to disability is more difficult earlier or later in life. It simply means that the issues an individual faces are different; thus the recommended interventions may differ.

> *Lisa Aldon, 33, is congenitally totally blind. Her family did not expect her to participate in household responsibilities, limited her social interactions, and never allowed her to consider working during adolescence. Although she has been trained as a medical transcriptionist, she has never been employed. She continues to live at home with her parents.*

As DeCowden (1990) pointed out, "the family . . . is the primary mediator of the child's development" (p. 13). However, some congenital disabilities can delay a child's development. For example, a child who is born blind usually experiences developmental lags in motor, language, and cognitive skills (Warren, 1984) and may follow a different developmental sequence from that of a child with sight (Ferrell et al., 1990). Similarly, a child who requires increased medical treatment will have less time for play or other socialization activities. It is important to note, however, that with many disabilities, development that is initially delayed does not necessarily result in long-term differences.

In early childhood, a disability may limit both the choices and the activities of a child. For example, a child with a disability may have fewer opportunities to interact with children who do not have disabilities, may be restricted in the types of activities due to physical limitations or overprotective parents, and may spend more time with treatment regimens, depending on the nature of the disability. Alexander (1990) cited diminished expectations for one's self care and encouragement to be self-initiating as "one of the leading causes of failure in the rehabilitation of children with cerebral palsy" (p. 92).

Counselors should educate family members about aspects of child development, including social, emotional, and career development, as well as the influence a particular disability may have on development. Counselors involved with family members of children with disabilities should share information about adults with similar disabilities living and working independently. It may be helpful for parents and children to meet adults with similar disabilities, as well as other parents of children with disabilities.

The importance of a developmental perspective is supported by Bibb (1990), who stated, "the initial experiences children have related to their disability casts the future for adjustment to their residual impairment, development of self-esteem, relationship potential, and future vocational choices" (p. 11). Bibb emphasized the role of rehabilitation professionals in transition activities of children from rehabilitation or medical settings to their home or school and the need for rehabilitation professionals to provide children with disabilities both information and expectations that are appropriate to their age.

> *Michaela Sampson, 18, sustained a spinal cord injury as a result of a diving accident 3 years ago. Negative experiences with her old friends resulted in her changing high schools after the accident. She has never been on a date. She is frustrated because she wants to go to college in another town so she can study to become a medical doctor, but her parents are afraid for her to move.*

Adolescence is a time that can be difficult for any child, with or without a disability. Therefore, the onset of a disability during adolescence can be extremely stressful for it is a time when young adults want to be similar to their peers, yet may find their peer group membership disrupted by disability. The presence of a disability often forces greater reliance on the family at the very time when adolescents are generally seeking greater independence from their parents (Allen & Stoltenberg, 1995). In young adulthood, a disability may have an impact on one's marriage, ability to have children, expressions of intimacy (DeLoach, 1994), and career.

Disability occurring in the middle years of one's life may also have an impact on one's family relationships and profession. Onset of disability in older individuals may result in early retirement or, for individuals who acquire disabilities after retirement, the need for alternative living arrangements, if the spouse or other family members are unable to assume the role of caregiver. It is evident, in considering the various stages of one's life, that time of onset can influence self-image, career alternatives, and interpersonal relationships.

As with all of the factors discussed in this chapter, time of onset interacts with other factors, such as functions impaired. For example, vision loss in a child can have a major impact on incidental learning, which is the learning that occurs through observation (e.g., watching a person work), whereas a visual impairment in an adult means having to unlearn some skills in which one relied on vision and replace them with skills that rely on one or more other sensory modalities.

Type of Onset

Type of onset includes sudden onset, where the disability may result from an automobile accident, as well as prolonged onset, which one might experience with a progressive disability such as multiple sclerosis. Type of onset may also be distinguished by whether the disability was self-induced, resulted from the actions of other individuals, is genetic, or has no known cause.

> *Raymond Coffey, 34, was in a car accident when intoxicated. The accident killed his wife and small child, and two teens in the other car. Mr. Coffey was*

burned over one third of his body and experiences chronic pain from a back and knee injury. He has attempted suicide twice since the accident.

In this example, an automobile accident causing a disability that could have been preventable (i.e., by not drinking) may be viewed differently from an automobile accident that is unavoidable. The actions may result in the same disability; however, an individual's response to the disability may vary, based on perceived cause of the disability. Responses to an accident may range from being grateful for being alive, to self-anger and guilt. In addition, others may view the person with the disability differently if he or she is perceived to be at fault.

Counseling considerations would include focusing on the individual's suicidal thoughts and feelings. Assessment of suicidal intent includes identifying whether the individual has a specific plan to kill himself or herself, and the means to do so. If a client has a plan, has the means to carry it out, and indicates that he or she intends to carry it out, the counselor has an ethical responsibility to protect the individual from harm. The counselor may be able to make a contract or agreement with the individual to not harm himself or herself and refer the client to a mental health professional; if the client refuses, the counselor may need to contact the police or mental health authorities so the person can obtain a psychiatric evaluation for hospitalization.

With sudden onset, the individual and his or her family have no opportunity to prepare for the disability, whereas with gradual onset, an individual may have more time to acquire information about the disability and make plans. Again, this is not to suggest that one type of onset makes adjustment easier. With a gradual onset an individual may deny the implications of a disability for a longer period of time and, thus, make no plans or learn alternative skills until forced to do so. Also, progressive disabilities can include a number of "onsets" or traumatic stages.

Rob Landers, 42, was diagnosed with Huntington's chorea 3 years ago. The disease has progressed rapidly, to the point where his wife can no longer provide the needed assistance. The move to a nursing home, although planned and anticipated, has proven to be more difficult than the initial diagnosis, for both the family and Mr. Landers.

The counselor must recognize that an individual may have adjustment issues, even if the disability has been known for some time. An individual's knowledge and feelings are not necessarily consistent. The same holds true for family members. During times of transition, the individual and/or family members may experience emotions similar in intensity to those experienced during initial diagnosis. It is important to be sensitive to a period of mourning, which may follow the acquisition of a disability, particularly a traumatic circumstance. However, counselors should not require a period of mourning, and label the reaction they see as denial if the individual does not grieve.

Individuals with adventitious disabilities often initially hold stereotypes about people with disabilities, based on their socialization experiences. Individuals often need time to reconcile previously held negative attitudes, values, and beliefs about disability with their personal experiences of having a disability. These internalized feelings can result in feelings of guilt and shame, and may be difficult for the individual to disclose.

Visibility, Stability, and Pain

Several other factors related to the nature of the disability have implications for the functioning of individuals, and for the counselor working to understand the needs and issues of those individuals. Each of these factors may interact with the other factors discussed to create unique circumstances.

The visibility of a disability, as evidenced by physical differences in the individual, or by the indicators of disability such as a wheelchair or cane, may influence how others react to a person with a disability.

> *Loretta Doren, 14, explains that other students in her school think she is "stuck up," because her hearing impairment precludes her from knowing when someone speaks to her. Bob Engles, 28, laughs at how people give him and his wheelchair a wide berth in the mall.*

Invisible disabilities such as head injuries, low vision, deafness, or chronic pain often result in misunderstanding from others. Many invisible disabilities are mistaken for cognitive disabilities or personality problems. The visibility of a disability for a wheelchair user may act as a barrier, both environmentally and in interpersonal relationships, where society often makes stereotypical assumptions about an individual, based solely on the wheelchair rather than the person. Society tends to put a high premium on physical attractiveness, which can create barriers for persons with physical disfigurement such as facial scarring. In this situation, the individual may have lost no physical functioning, but nonetheless may be treated differently because of the disability.

One counseling issue that frequently arises is the degree to which the individual chooses to conceal a hidden disability. The social stigma associated with disability may cause an individual to "pass" as able-bodied. Although such a choice should always be made by the individual with a disability, it is important for counselors to discuss the legal implications of not revealing a disability. For example, in the case of *Murphy v. Franklin Pierce Law Center* (Kincaid, 1995), the court upheld a student's dismissal from law school, because the court did not consider the school's action toward the student prior to the time she advised the school of her medical condition and requested accommodations. The same is true in employment situations. If a disability is not revealed, then the employer cannot be expected to make accommodations.

Jenny Kastner, 27, has been diagnosed with bipolar disorder. When she takes medication, her symptoms abate; however, when she feels better, she stops taking her medication and experiences severe clinical depression, with bouts of impulsive, unfocused hyperactivity.

Stability of the disability refers to the consistency of the disability. By definition, a progressive disability is not stable over time. As previously noted, slowly progressive disabilities are difficult for individuals, because various adaptations must be initiated as functioning is lost. There are other disabilities, such as mental illness or asthma, that may be unstable but not progressive. There are also disabilities that are progressive, yet fluctuations in functioning can occur over a long period of time.

In contrast to the individual with a complete spinal cord injury, who, over a period of time generally knows his or her level of functioning, an individual with mental illness or asthma can experience fluctuations in functioning on an hourly, daily, or weekly basis. The instability of some disabilities such as these can contribute to social isolation and career problems, when individuals may be hesitant to make plans not knowing whether they will have the energy or emotional stamina to follow through on the plans.

Counselors who are working with individuals with disabilities that are not stable should be vigilant to help clients identify jobs that will not exacerbate the disability, such as fumes with asthma. Counselors may also need to help clients identify vocational opportunities that will allow for more flexibility in work schedules, based on their individualized experiences with disabilities. The consumer's personal knowledge of the disability is a critical factor in planning rehabilitation programs. For example, if the consumer knows that his or her asthma is always worse in the morning, afternoon and early evening work schedules may be sought.

Terry Linden, 64, had a back injury requiring surgery 10 years ago. Unsuccessful surgery left him in constant pain in a sitting or standing position. His wife complains that his entire personality has changed as a result of his injury.

Pain is another factor that contributes to response to disability. Although an individual may have to contend with other aspects of a disability, such as joint stiffness and deformity resulting from arthritis, the pain element is usually the most difficult. Similarly, the painful treatment associated with severe burns has been well documented, and pain may also be associated with other disabilities, such as amputations. Vash (1981) stated, "Whatever the stimulus, when pain occurs, it is certain to influence a person's feelings and behavior. It is hard to be jolly, creative, or maybe even civil, when you hurt" (p. 14).

Counselors need to be sensitive to pain issues. Counseling and planning sessions may need to be shorter, and in testing situations, the client may need to take a break every 30 or 45 minutes. An understanding of pain issues can also help counselors better appreciate why one's behavior or demeanor may show great fluctuations on different days. Counselors must also be aware of the effects of pain medication (or any other medication the client may be taking) on the client's functioning.

Summary

Disability factors include the functions impaired, severity of the disability, time of onset, type of onset, visibility, stability, and pain. These factors are important for rehabilitation counselors to consider, but it is inappropriate to consider disability factors in isolation from the other factors discussed in this chapter. Disability factors interact with the individual and environmental factors to create unique and highly individualized responses to disability. A skilled counselor listens carefully to information about these and other aspects of a person's life, and thinks about the meaning of these factors to that person, in order to collaboratively formulate a service plan that truly meets the needs of the individual with the disability.

Conclusion

In this chapter, we have described counseling considerations and interventions based on factors associated with (a) the person, (b) the environment, and (c) the nature of the disability. The totality of factors from each of these three major categories results in a unique experience of disability for each individual.

To effectively use the counseling interventions that were presented, counselors must first "know thyself." If one is to truly respect the individuality and uniqueness of each person with a disability and avoid stereotyping on the basis of disability, gender, ethnicity, or any other variable, the counselor must first have self-knowledge regarding his or her values and belief systems. Without self-knowledge, one can never know the degree to which one's stereotypes, myths, attitudes, or values enter into the counseling relationship. An ongoing process on self-understanding should be a goal of every professional counselor.

In addition, counselors should assume that learning does not end with graduation from a university. For counselors, the process of learning is continuous and lifelong. Actively pursuing new information, working to integrate new ideas into one's professional practice, and staying aware of what one *does not* know are the hallmarks of effective counselors.

It is both an awesome gift and an incredible responsibility to counsel another human being. Counselors must never forget what a privilege it is to be "let in" the lives of others, to know them in a personal and profound way during some of their most difficult times. That privilege requires the highest ethical standards of professional behavior, and results in work that is both professionally and personally rewarding.

References

Alexander, M. (1990). Cerebral palsy. In M. Hersen & V. Van Hasselt (Eds.), *Psychological aspects of developmental and physical disabilities: A casebook* (pp. 87–93). Newbury Park, CA: Sage.

Allen, S., & Stoltenberg, C. (1995). Psychological separation of older adolescents and young adults from their parents: An investigation of gender differences. *Journal of Counseling and Development, 73,* 542–546.

Beck, R., Carlton, T., Allen, H., Rosenkoetter, L., & Hardy, K. (1993). Understanding and counseling special populations with HIV seropositive disease. *American Rehabilitation, 19*(3), 20–29.

Berry, J. (1995). Families and deinstitutionalization: An application of Bronfenbrenner's social ecology model. *Journal of Counseling and Development, 73,* 379–383.

Bibb, T. (1990). Planting seeds: Thoughts on pediatric rehabilitation. *Journal of Rehabilitation, 56*(3), 11.

Bonett, R. (1994). Marital status and sex: Impact on career self-efficacy. *Journal of Counseling and Development, 73,* 187–190.

Borysenko, J. (1987). *Minding the body, mending the mind.* New York: Bantam Books.

Cayleff, S. (1986). Ethical issues in counseling gender, race, and culturally distinct groups. *Journal of Counseling and Development, 64,* 345–347.

Chubon, R. (1985). Career-related needs of school children with severe physical disabilities. *Journal of Counseling and Development, 64,* 47–51.

Conte, L. (1983). Vocational development theories and the disabled person: Oversight or deliberate omission? *Rehabilitation Counseling Bulletin, 26,* 316–328.

Cook, E. (1990). Gender and psychological distress. *Journal of Counseling and Development, 68,* 371–375.

Cox, T. (1994). *Cultural diversity in organizations: Theory, research, and practice.* San Francisco: Berrett-Koehler.

Curnow, T. (1989). Vocational development of persons with disability. *Career Development Quarterly, 37,* 269–278.

DeCowden, M. (1990). Pediatric rehabilitation: Special patients, special needs. *Journal of Rehabilitation, 56*(3), 13–18.

DeLoach, C. (1994). Attitudes toward disability: Impact on sexual development and forging of intimate relationships. *Journal of Applied Rehabilitation Counseling, 25*(1), 18–25.

DeLoach, C., & Greer, B. (1981). *Adjustment to severe physical disability: A metamorphosis.* New York: McGraw-Hill.

Ellis, A. (1995). Rational–emotive behavior therapy. In R. Corsini & D. Wedding (Eds.), *Current psychotherapies* (5th ed., pp. 162–196). Itasca, IL: Peacock.

Ericson, G., & Riordan, R. (1993). Effects of psychosocial and vocational intervention on the rehabilitation potential of young adults with end-stage renal disease. *Rehabilitation Counseling Bulletin, 37,* 25–36.

Ferrell, K., Trief, E., Dietz, S., Bonner, M., Cruz, D., Ford, E., & Stratton, J. (1990). Visually impaired infants research consortium (VIIRC): First-year results. *Journal of Visual Impairment & Blindness, 84,* 404–410.

Gilbride, D. (1993). Parental attitudes toward their child with a disability: Implications for rehabilitation counselors. *Rehabilitation Counseling Bulletin, 36,* 129–150.

Gudykunst, W., & Nishida, T. (1989). Theoretical perspectives for studying intercultural communication. In M. Asante & W. Gudykunst (Eds.), *Handbook of international and intercultural communication* (pp. 17–46). Newbury Park, CA: Sage.

Hagner, D., & Dileo, D. (1993). *Working together: Workplace culture, supported employment, and persons with disabilities.* Cambridge, MA: Brookline Books.

Hall, E. (1977). *Beyond culture.* New York: Anchor.

Harry, B. (1992). *Cultural diversity, families, and the special education system: Communication and empowerment.* New York: Teachers College Press.

Harry, B., Allen, N., & McLaughlin, M. (1995). Communication versus compliance: African American parents' involvement in special education. *Exceptional Children, 61*(4), 364–377.

Harry, B., & Anderson, M. (1995). The disproportionate placement of African-American males in special education programs: A critique of the process. *Journal of Negro Education, 63*(4), 602–619.

Hecht, M., Andersen, P., & Ribeau, S. (1989). The cultural dimensions of nonverbal communication. In M. Asante & W. Gudykunst (Eds.), *Handbook of international and intercultural communication* (pp. 163–185). London: Sage.

Hofstede, G. (1991). *Cultures and organizations: Software of the mind.* London: McGraw-Hill.

Ingraham, K., Kaplan, S., & Chan, F. (1992). Rehabilitation counselors' awareness of client alcohol abuse patterns. *Journal of Applied Rehabilitation Counseling, 23*(3), 18–22.

Jeffrey, D. (1986). The hazards of reduced mobility for the person with a spinal cord injury. *Journal of Rehabilitation, 52*(2), 59–62.

Kelley, S. D., & Lambert, S. S. (1992). Family support in rehabilitation: A review of research, 1980–1990. *Rehabilitation Counseling Bulletin, 36,* 98–119.

Kincaid, J. (1995). First circuit upholds law school dismissal. *Alert, 19*(6), 4.

Konstam, V., & Houser, R. (1994). Rehabilitation of women post myocardial infarction—A new look at old assumptions. *Journal of Applied Rehabilitation Counseling, 25*(4), 46–51.

Kosciulek, J. (1995). On identifying head injury family types. *Journal of Applied Rehabilitation Counseling, 26*(3), 13–18.

Livneh, H., & Sherwood-Hawes, A. (1993). Group counseling approaches with persons who have sustained myocardial infarction. *Journal of Counseling and Development, 72,* 57–61.

Lynch, R., & Rodriquez, A. (1992). Carpal tunnel syndrome: Considerations for rehabilitation. *Journal of Applied Rehabilitation Counseling, 23*(3), 23–29.

Mardiros, M. (1989). Conception of childhood disability among Mexican-American parents. *Medical Anthropology, 12,* 55–68.

Marion, R. (1980). Communicating with parents of culturally diverse exceptional children. *Exceptional Child, 46*(8), 616–623.

Marmé, M., & Skord, K. (1993). Counseling strategies to enhance the vocational rehabilitation of persons after traumatic brain injury. *Journal of Applied Rehabilitation Counseling, 24*(1), 19–25.

Panigua, F. (1994). *Assessing and treating culturally diverse clients: A practical guide.* London: Sage.

Patterson, J., & Witten, B. (1986). Myths concerning persons with disabilities. *Journal of Applied Rehabilitation Counseling, 18*(3), 42–44.

Pedersen, P., & Ivey, A. (1993). *Culture-centered counseling and interviewing skills: A practical guide.* Westport, CT: Praeger.

Power, P. (1988). An assessment approach to family intervention. In P. Power, A. Dell Orto, & M. Gibbons (Eds.), *Family interventions throughout chronic illness and disability* (pp. 5–23). New York: Springer.

Power, P., Dell Orto, A., & Gibbons, M. (Eds.). (1988). *Family interventions throughout chronic illness and disability.* New York: Springer.

Prout, H., & Strohmer, D. (1995). Counseling with persons with mental retardation: Issues and considerations. *Journal of Applied Rehabilitation Counseling, 26*(3), 49–54.

Rehabilitation Act Amendments of 1992, 29 U.S.C. § 706 *et seq.*

Reid, M., Landesman, S., Treder, R., & Jaccard, J. (1989). "My family and friends": Six to twelve year-old children's perceptions of social support. *Child Development, 60,* 896–910.

Sarason, I., & Sarason, B. (1985). *Social support: Theory, research, and applications.* Boston: Martinus Nijhoff.

Shapiro, J. P. (1993). *No pity.* New York: Times Books.

Silverman, P. (1981). *Helping women cope with grief.* Beverly Hills, CA: Sage.

Stern, M. (1984). Psychosocial rehabilitation following myocardial infarction and coronary artery by-pass surgery. In H. Wenger & H. Hellerstein (Eds.), *Rehabilitation of the coronary patient* (2nd ed., pp. 453–471). New York: Wiley.

Strully, J., & Strully, C. (1992). The struggle toward inclusion and the fulfillment of friendship. In J. Nisbet (Ed.), *Natural supports in school, at work, and in the community for people with severe disabilities* (pp. 165–177). Baltimore: Brookes.

Tavris, C. (1989). *Anger: The misunderstood emotion.* New York: Simon & Schuster.

Thompson, D. (1985). Anger. In S. Browne, D. Connors, & N. Stern (Eds.), *With the power of each breath: A disabled women's anthology* (pp. 78–85). San Francisco: Cleis Press.

Triandis, H. (1990). Theoretical concepts that are applicable to the analysis of ethnocentrism. In R. Brislin (Ed.), *Applied cross-cultural psychology* (pp. 34–55). Newbury Park, CA: Sage.

Tuttle, D., & Tuttle, N. (1996). *Self-esteem and adjusting with blindness.* Springfield, IL: Thomas.

Van Hasselt, V. B., Lutzker, J., & Hersen, M. (1990). Overview. In M. Hersen & V. Van Hasselt (Eds.), *Psychological aspects of developmental and physical disabilities: A casebook* (pp. 11–24). Newbury Park, CA: Sage.

Van Hoose, W., & Kottler, J. (1985). *Ethical and legal issues in counseling and psychotherapy* (2nd ed.). San Francisco: Jossey-Bass.

Vash, C. (1981). *The psychology of disability.* New York: Springer.

Warren, D. (1984). *Blindness and early childhood development.* New York: American Foundation for the Blind.

Wenger, N. (1985). Coronary disease in women. *Annual Review in Medicine, 36,* 285–294.

Wright, B. (1983). *Physical disability—A psychosocial approach* (2nd ed.). New York: Harper & Row.

Chapter 9

Psychosocial Impact
of Disability

Daniel Cook

Disability can have a profound impact on many facets of a person's life, including vocational, economic, medical, psychological, and social aspects. The psychological and social consequences of disability, however, are often the most pernicious. Chronic illness and physical impairment can result not only in functional limitations in meeting basic daily needs, but also in social stigma and psychological problems. Clearly, disability can markedly affect a person's psychosocial adjustment. Indeed, a person's response to the psychosocial impact of physical or mental impairment is a universal consideration in rehabilitation counseling.

Despite extensive research efforts, the psychosocial impact of disability remains a poorly understood topic. Common beliefs among both laypersons and professionals are not supported by research. For instance, the belief that there is an epileptic, arthritic, blind, and so on, personality type is regularly conveyed in both the public media and the professional literature. Research does not support such beliefs. After reviewing over 250 studies on psychological adjustment and physical disability, Shontz (1971) concluded that specific types of disability are not associated with specific personality characteristics, and that different types of physical disability do not cause specific kinds of maladjustment. Nonetheless, disability does affect individual behavior. Unquestionably, disability can, and sometimes does, have a profound psychosocial impact on an individual (Turner & Mclean, 1989).

The study of how and why disability affects an individual's behavior is being conducted on two fronts: (a) the study of individuals' responses to their disabilities and (b) the impact of society's response to people with disabilities. Considering that personality can be defined as the enduring behavioral characteristics of an individual, theories of personality that attempt to explain human behavior should help in understanding how an individual adjusts to a disability. And because a disability can act as a social stimulus, society's views of disability must also play an important role in understanding and explaining the adjustment process.

This chapter is divided into two sections. The first section summarizes the personality theories of Sigmund Freud, Carl Rogers, and Kurt Lewin; covers each theory's contribution to the understanding of psychosocial adjustment to disability; and gives examples of research linking the theories to the study of adjustment to disability. The second section discusses the attitudes of society toward disability, the attitudes of rehabilitation professionals toward disability, and methods of fostering attitude change.

Personality Theories

Freud's Psychoanalytic Theory

Psychoanalytic theory has three main components: (a) procedures devised by Freud to study mental processes, (b) the technique for the psychological treatment practiced by Freud and his followers, and (c) the theory developed by Freud to describe and explain why people behave as they do. Because of its historical preeminence, Freud's theory undergirds many current attempts at explaining the impact of disability on the individual.

In essence, Freud (1917/1963) formulated a dynamic psychology, which postulates that psychic energy is exchanged and transferred throughout a closed system. Energy comes from basic metabolic processes and is transformed into psychic energy via the instincts. He defined instincts as internal forces that are never truly satisfied. Hence, the person is constantly subjected to these forces or tensions.

Freud hypothesized three main structural components of the mind: id, ego, and superego. The id is made up of the instinct and is the source of all psychic energy; it remains unconscious and continually strives to reduce instinctual tensions through pleasurable satisfaction of instinctual needs. The id seeks to reduce tension in any way possible, even in ways that may be socially unacceptable or detrimental to the individual. Consequently, the id is engaged in constant conflict with the ego, which seeks to channel the energies of the pleasure-seeking id into practical, reality-oriented actions to meet basic needs. The third structural construct, the superego, develops out of the ego as the child learns what society considers moral behavior. According to Freud, a child's basic personality is fixed by 5 years of age.

Freud's theory of personality represents a conflict model because there is a constant interplay of driving and restraining forces. The ego's task is to maintain a balance among these forces. When the forces become excessively unbalanced, the ego is flooded with anxiety. If the ego cannot deal with this anxiety by rational means, ego defenses come into play. These ego defenses are unconscious and serve to protect the individual by distorting reality, thus reducing anxiety. If the defenses markedly distort reality, the individual becomes maladjusted and the defenses are counterproductive.

Freud's Theory and Physical Disability

Perhaps Freud's greatest contribution to understanding the impact of disability on the individual was his conceptualization of the ego defenses. At least four defense mechanisms are continually referred to in the literature on adjustment to physical disability: repression, projection, reaction formation, and regression.

Through repression, the ego is able to keep painful memories, conflicts, and perceptions from conscious awareness. Ideas that are particularly anxiety provoking are simply put out of a person's awareness. Repression allows for an evasion of anxiety, guilt, and intrapsychic conflicts. Projection refers to the attribution of unconscious needs or conflicts to another person. A particularly unacceptable feeling, such as hostility toward a physician, may be expressed as "He hates me" rather than as "I hate him." A person with a disability who feels inadequate and is unable to tolerate that feeling might project the anxiety-producing feeling to others, such as, "Nobody knows enough to really help me." Reaction formation is the expression of feelings opposite those one would typically express. A parent with an unacceptable aversion to a child with a disability might overprotect and attempt to meet the child's every need. People with recent disabilities may resent others on whom they are dependent and paradoxically may express that resentment through excessive displays of love and affection. Both projection and reaction formation are compensation defenses. People who experience anxiety often relieve that anxiety by overdeveloping other personality traits. Regression is an escape defense in which an individual reverts to fantasy as a form of coping with psychic stress. A person using regression as a defense may revert to the childlike behavior and negativism associated with earlier developmental periods.

Although Freud recognized the influence of the mind over the body in formulating his theory, he did not specifically deal with the psychological impact of disability. One passage, however, illustrates the applicability of Freud's insights:

> A capable working-man earning his living is crippled by an accident in the course of his employment; he can work no more, but he gets a small periodical dole in compensation and learns how to exploit his mutilation as a beggar. His new life, although so inferior, nevertheless, is supported by the very thing which destroyed his old life; if you were to remove his disability you would deprive him for a time of his means of subsistence, for the question would arise whether he would still be capable of resuming his former work. When a secondary exploitation of the illness such as this is formed in a neurosis we can manage it alongside the first and call it "secondary advantage through illness." (Freud, 1917/1963, p. 344)

Like other functional psychological theories, Freud's theory allows one to make specific predictions about how disability would psychologically affect an individual. Of course, within the rehabilitation field, ego defenses have received the most attention as potential adjustment mechanisms in adapting to physical disability.

Freud's theory predicts that if an impairment occurs before the age of 5, while the personality is still developing, the person with a disability would quite likely exhibit psychological problems. English (1971a) suggested that immaturity and passive–aggressiveness are often the salient personality traits exhibited by people disabled earlier in life. Meng (1938, cited in Barker, Wright, Meyerson, & Gonick, 1953) described disability-related maladjustment as developing from hostile impulses that stem from the child's blaming the parents for the impairment. Because these hostile impulses are perceived as being unacceptable, they are likely to be repressed, and the impairment is unconsciously considered justifiable punishment for the unacceptable feelings. According to Meng, the chief task of helpers is to diminish disability-associated anxiety in the individual by bringing to consciousness the blame of parents, which is the basis of repressed hostility and guilt.

Research Evidence for Freud's Theory

Most research concerning Freud's theory has focused on interpretation of individual case studies. Indeed, one major criticism of the theory is that it is not easily empirically tested. However, at least one aspect of psychoanalytic theory, psychological defense, appears to have empirical support (Maddi, 1972).

Other facets of Freudian theory show promise in understanding the psychosocial effects of disability. In an analysis of Freud's writings, Cubbage and Thomas (1989) pointed out the importance of the concept of castration anxiety to understanding the impact of disability. A disability may represent a form of symbolic castration to the individual with a disability. To the observer, the person with a disability generates feeling of threat of castration. In this vein, Fine (1978, cited by Siller, 1984) reported a relationship between children's castration anxiety and negative attitudes toward disability. Similarly, Follensbee (1981, cited by Siller, 1984) found a relationship between castration anxiety and negative attitudes toward disability among college students.

The bulk of the research on Freud's theory, however, is at best equivocal. Even such popular notions as compensation, the concept that people with disabilities develop special compensatory abilities (e.g., that people who are blind have superior hearing), has generally not been supported (McDaniel, 1976, p. 4). Freud's original ideas remain of great importance, although most have been adapted and modified by more recent theorists with respect to the psychological consequences of disability.

Rogers's Self-Concept Theory

Carl Rogers, like Freud, developed his theory of personality largely through therapeutic relationships with clients. His theory (Rogers, 1951, 1961) is based on a phenomenological approach to personality development and change; that is, Rogers's theory relies on the client's subjective experience and defines reality as the client's perception of his or her immediate experiences. Rogers assumed that the real world exists; however, he viewed people's subjective perceptions of reality as all important.

The self-concept is the central structural construct of Rogers's theory. Various theorists have used the concept of self in different ways. Probably the most common definition of the self-concept is that it refers to those feelings, evaluations, and perceptions toward oneself that define who one is. Rogers further defined the self-concept as "the organized, consistent conceptual Gestalt composed of perceptions of the characteristics of the I or me and the perceptions of the relationship of the I or me to various aspects of life, together with the values attached to these perceptions" (Rogers, 1959, p. 200).

Contrary to Freud, who asserted that biological forces motivate the person, Rogers suggested one motivational tendency: people's need for self-actualization. Self-actualization refers to one's striving for openness, spontaneity, creativity, autonomy, independence, acceptance of self and others, and the development of deep and meaningful relationships with others. Although Rogers described other needs (e.g., the need for positive regard), they are subservient to the basic motive, the tendency toward self-actualization.

Rogers's Theory and Physical Disability

Of all the personality theorists, Rogers probably has had the most impact on the field of rehabilitation counseling. His influence stems from the fact that his system of psychotherapy broke away from the traditional disease model of maladjustment. Furthermore, his approach was refined in academic settings and popularized during the time when university-based rehabilitation counseling programs were being established.

Rogers's elaboration of the self-concept and his conceptualization of the discrepancy between real self and ideal self have contributed to understanding the psychological impact of disability on the individual. The ideal self comprises those values and meanings that the person holds in high regard. The discrepancy between the real and the ideal self becomes important when the way people view themselves differs from the way they wish to view themselves. Perhaps most important is the emphasis Rogers attached to personal experiences. Unquestionably, an individual's self-concept, values, feelings, and judgments of self-worth guide his or her behavior. It follows, then, that it is not disability per se that psychologically influences the person, but rather the subjective meaning and feelings attached to the disability. Thus, Rogers's theory explains why some individuals react catastrophically to a relatively minor physical impairment, whereas others with severe impairments are psychologically well adjusted.

Rogers's Theory and Physical Disability

Rogers defined a psychologically adjusted person as one who is self-actualized and fully functioning. Such a person is open to new experiences, possesses self-trust and self-approval, and has a self-concept that is congruent with actual experience (Rogers, 1951).

Maladjustment can occur when there is incongruence between experiences and the way individuals view themselves. This incongruence may occur when individuals are exposed to ambiguous or inconsistent conditions of worth. Because individuals seek to maintain consistent self-concepts, inconsistent evaluations (either negative or positive) may be blocked from awareness through denial or distortion—two psychological defenses recognized by Rogers's theory. Both denial and distortion falsify experiences to make them consistent with the self-concept. Defensive behavior was described by Rogers (1959) as

> the organism's response to experiences that are perceived or anticipated as threatening, as incongruent with the individual's existing picture of himself in relationship to the world. These threatening experiences are temporarily rendered harmless by being distorted in awareness, or being denied to awareness. (p. 187)

For example, consider a relatively well-adjusted lumberjack who suffers a spinal cord injury. Assume that his self-image is one of independence and physical prowess. As a result of his injury, he is placed in an extremely dependent and socially devalued position and is, in fact, unable to meet his own self-expectations. The disability represents a threat to his self-concept. In the extreme case, this individual might deny his new physical reality through such statements as "I haven't changed at all." He might distort reality by alluding to the disability as temporary: "I'll be walking and cutting trees in six months." The incongruence between the subjective reality of the person and the objective reality of the disability may impede rehabilitation. If denial or distortion of the disability is incorporated into the self-concept, the person will tend to become perceptually rigid and closed to the experiences needed for successful rehabilitation.

Rogers (1961) stated that for a maladjusted person to change, counselors must offer certain core conditions considered necessary and sufficient for change to occur. If the core conditions of congruence, warmth, and empathic understanding are present and perceived by the client, a therapeutic relationship, safe and secure from threat, is established. In the counseling relationship that is free of threat, the client can explore incongruences, experience them, and assimilate the previously distorted experiences into a reorganized self. Following successful therapy, individuals are more self-directed, responsible, and open to new experiences.

Empirical Evidence for Rogers's Theory

Hundreds of research studies have evaluated Rogers's method of facilitating client change and personal growth. Relatively fewer studies have examined the adequacy of his conceptualization of personality to describe the impact of disability. Most of the research has studied the effects of disability on self-concept. For example, Berry and Miskimins (1969) found that, compared with normal people, psychiatric patients had more negative self-concepts, but that psychiatric patients with the most positive self-concepts had better vocational outcomes than patients with negative self-concepts. Barry, Dunteman, and Webb (1968) reported that clients who had favorable self-concepts and low real-self versus ideal-self discrepancies had the most rapid recovery from disability and return to work. Roessler and Bolton (1978) reviewed 12 studies dealing with the influences of the self-concept on disability and concluded that

> (1) [People with disabilities] . . . report lower self-esteem (the evaluative component of the self-concept) than nondisabled persons, and (2) some disability conditions have greater impact on the self-concept than others. . . . [But] the data supporting the second conclusion are much more tenuous than those that support the first, because few studies have directly compared the self-concepts of persons with different types of disabilities. (p. 26)

A study conducted by Lipp, Kolstoe, James, and Randall (1968) is particularly relevant to Rogers's concept of denial as a defense. Lipp et al. tested the idea that people who have a disability are psychologically threatened by, and deny, their disability. To test for the presence of denial, Lipp et al. had subjects with and without disabilities view slides of people with and without physical disabilities. The slides were presented by a tachistoscope, a device that varies the amount of time a slide is shown. The investigators found that subjects with disabilities took significantly longer than nondisabled subjects to recognize the slides of people with disabilities. Lipp et al. concluded that "disability is unacceptable to [people with disabilities] and that they defend against this threat by the mechanism of denial" (p. 74).

Lewin and Somatopsychology

Kurt Lewin's (1935, 1936) field theory is social psychological in nature. His theory forms a bridge between personologists (e.g., Freud and Rogers), who have been primarily concerned with the developmental dynamics of the individual, and social psychologists, who have been concerned with the influence of social factors on individual behavior. Lewin's theory stressed both the importance of contemporaneity, the idea that behavior can best be understood in its immediate manifestations, and the importance of understanding the individual in relation to the larger environment. Lewin argued that to understand why people behave as they do, analysis must begin with the total situation.

By beginning analysis with the total situation, Lewin sought to go from the general to the specific. To Lewin, the most general situation was the life space, the total psychological world consisting of everything that is observed, sensed, and inferred. The life space represents the psychological environment (E) out of which the person (P) is differentiated. Thus, the life space consists of all those things that determine the behavior of an individual at any particular moment. In algebraic terms, $B = f(P,E)$, which means that behavior (B) is a function (f) of the person (P) and the environment (E). This equation represents the person $\times$ situation interaction paradigm popular in psychology today, especially as modified by Bandura (1978) to emphasize the reciprocal relationship between the person, the environment, and behavior.

Somatopsychology and Physical Disability

Lewin's theory has stimulated the most theoretical work on the psychological effects of physical disability, as exemplified in the writings of Barker et al. (1953) and Dembo, Leviton, and Wright (1956). These writers have incorporated into a point of view called somatopsychology such Lewinian ideas as the accessibility of goals and barriers to goals in the life space; here-and-now behavior; and personal–social expectations. Somatopsychology makes the assumption, largely verified (Shontz, 1971), that "there is no substantial indication that persons with an impaired physique differ as a group in their general or overall adjustment," and "there is no clear evidence of an association between types of physical disability and particular personality characteristics" (Wright, 1960, pp. 373-374). Somatopsychologists focus on the person × situation interaction, stressing that it is the personal meaning of the disability in conjunction with the stimulus value the disability holds for others in a person's life space that is important in understanding psychological adjustment to disability. Thus, somatopsychology studies "those variations in physique that affect the psychological situation of a person by influencing the effectiveness of his body as a tool for action or by serving as a stimulus to himself or others" (Barker et al., 1953, p. 1).

Somatopsychology and Adjustment to Disability

Wright (1983) has written extensively on somatopsychology, delineating how people with disabilities cope with situations that confront them. According to Wright, people with disabilities may assume an inferior status position as a result of

1. Having dual identifications with the disability group they are part of, as well as with the larger nondisabled population

2. Engaging in "as if" behavior wherein they deny or cover up their disability, acting as if they did not have a disability

3. Engaging in the idolization of normal standards by which people with disabilities strive to reach unattainable standards of "normal" performance

4. Eclipsing of behavioral possibilities in that attention is focused on deficit behaviors rather than on asset behaviors

Wright (1983) divided adjustment to disability into succumbing versus coping behaviors. She emphasized the perceptions of people with disabilities toward their disabilities and the perceptions of nondisabled people toward people with disabilities. Persons using as if behavior, idolizing normal standards, and eclipsing behavior possibilities are viewed as succumbing to disability. To the somatopsychologist, coping, or adjustment to physical disability, occurs when a person

1. Enlarges the scope of values and embraces values other than disability-related values

2. Subordinates physique, limiting the importance placed on physical appearance and physical ability

3. Contains the spread of disability by limiting disability to the impact of the actual impairment

4. Places emphasis on asset values while limiting comparative values

The emphasis on asset versus comparative values has received particular attention as a primary variable in adjustment to physical disability. Comparative values are evaluations made in reference to a standard of "normal" behavior, whereas asset values are evaluations based purely on the intrinsic qualities of the person being observed. Whereas comparative values are potentially devaluing, asset values are psychologically rewarding. The latter focus on the inherent positive qualities of a person. People exhibiting asset values toward their disability are likely to be perceived as coping with the disability. Conversely, those expressing comparative values will probably be viewed as succumbing.

Research Evidence for Somatopsychology

Barker et al. (1953) presented a detailed case analysis of two girls who had had polio. Both girls were the same age, in current excellent health, and had the same IQ and education. One, Marcia, was much more physically affected by her disability than the other, Beverley. Even though Beverley was less severely disabled and had many more social opportunities open to her, she was the more socially and psychologically maladjusted of the two.

Barker et al. (1953) interpreted Beverley's maladjustment as the result of role marginality. They saw Beverley as striving for normality and in conflict because she was caught between an underprivileged (disabled) and a privileged (normal) social position. Beverley had problems in determining what behaviors were appropriate in ambiguous social situations. Beverley, to use Wright's (1960) terminology, had dual identifications. Marcia had a rather clear understanding of her position as a person with a disability and was able to adapt her behavior to different situations. Marcia had accepted the limitations of her disability without devaluing herself. On the basis of this case analysis, Barker et al. hypothesized that role marginality would lead to conflict and social maladjustment.

Goldberg (1974) tested the somatopsychological proposition that physical disability acts as a negative stimulus and leads to social discrimination. He compared people with visible disabilities (facial burns) with a group of individuals with invisible disabilities (congenital heart disease) on 10 measures of adjustment. On all measures, the people with invisible disabilities were better adjusted. The people with invisible disabilities also had significantly better self-images. The major implication of the study was that visible disability can lead to negative social evaluations, which may, in turn, result in negative self-evaluations.

Attitudes and Disability

Of utmost importance in understanding the impact of physical disability on the person is the study of attitudes of the general public and rehabilitation professionals as they affect the adjustment of people with disabilities. Basically, attitudes are evaluations made toward an object, person, or idea. Attitudes consist of three components: feelings and cognitions, internal expressions of an attitude, and external expressions manifested as behaviors or movements toward or away from that being evaluated. The relationship between the internal and external components of an attitude is not well understood. It is generally believed that internal evaluations guide behavior, but that overt behavior depends, in part, on the situation. Thus, a person may be prejudiced, but override that prejudice depending on the situation. A well-known psychological principle is that people do not always behave in predictable ways. Attitudes are, however, considered to serve as predispositions to behave in certain ways.

Attitudes of Society Toward People with Disabilities

Because people with disabilities are often perceived by nondisabled people as "different," the prevailing theoretical view is that they tend to be classed as deviant from the majority and are forced into an inferior social position with those negative evaluations given other minority groups. Associating disability with minority group status illustrates the potential of stigmatizing the person with a disability. Certain undesirable qualities are attributed to people with disabilities, merely because they are mentally or physically impaired. Gellman (1959) suggested that when society defines a person's role as deviant, evaluation results in a self-definition of inferiority leading to adaptation of a marginal role in society.

Confounding the idea that disability is associated with negative evaluations has been the finding that, in measuring attitudes toward people with physical disabilities, publicly expressed attitudes are generally positive (Comer & Piliavin, 1975). One probable reason that public attitudes toward people with disabilities tend to be positive is that, in verbalizing public attitudes, people generally do not express negative feelings. This tendency, referred to as the social desirability bias, frequently has been found in studies of attitudes toward disability (Feinberg, 1967). Many popular attitude measurement instruments, such as the *Attitude Toward Disabled Persons Scale* (Yuker, Block, & Younng, 1966), are unidimensional; that is, they measure one dimension, typically a continuum of positive to negative effect. Because this dimension is readily apparent to most people taking these measures, they are able to, and in fact do, select the most socially desirable responses. This bias is frequently a serious difficulty in attitude measurement. Chubon (1992) noted the lack of conceptual agreement on a definition of the construct "attitude" and identified several methodological problems in research on attitudes and disability, including the prevalence of the regression to the mean phenomenon.

Siller (1976) and his associates have taken a multidimensional approach to measuring attitudes toward disability. He isolated seven dimensions that are relatively comprehensive in describing the attitudinal domain for a wide range of disabling conditions:

1. *Interaction strain*—uneasiness in the presence of [people with disabilities] and uncertainty as to how to deal with them;

2. *Rejection of intimacy*—rejection of close, particularly familial, relationships with [people with disabilities];

3. *Generalized rejection*—a pervasive negative and derogatory approach to [people with disabilities] with consequent advocacy of segregation;

4. *Authoritarian virtuousness*—ostensibly a "prodisabled" orientation, this factor is really rooted in an authoritarian context that manifests itself in a call for special treatment that is less benevolent and more harmful than it seems;

5. *Inferred emotional consequences*—intense hostile references to the character and emotions of [people with disabilities];

6. *Distressed identification*—personalized hypersensitivity to [people with disabilities] who serve as activators of anxiety about one's own vulnerability to disability;

7. *Imputed functional limitations*—devaluation of the capacities of [people with disabilities] in coping with [their] environment. (p. 72)

Siller's (1976) research suggested that attitudes toward disability are complex, but that there are underlying, essentially negative components of these attitudes. Given that attitudes toward disability are complex, they are, nevertheless, extremely important. Consequently, much research over the past 30 years has been directed toward determining the correlates of attitudes toward disability, with the goal of eventually understanding who might be expected to hold negative attitudes, how those attitudes are formed, and how such attitudes might be modified.

Extensive reviews of the literature (Altman, 1981; Antonak & Livneh, 1988; Cloerkes, 1981; English, 1971b; Livneh, 1982; McDaniel, 1976; Yuker, 1988) have attempted to summarize the theoretical determinants and empirical correlates of attitudes toward disability. For example, English (1971b) concluded that females have more favorable attitudes toward disability than do males, but that race, age, and nationality are not related to attitudes toward people with disabilities. Cloerkes (1981) and Livneh (1982) concluded that there are significant relationships between such personality characteristics as authoritarianism, ethnocentrism, and intolerance of ambiguity and unfavorable attitudes toward people with disabilities. Livneh (1982) also sought to classify the sources or root causes of negative attitudes toward disability. His categories concerning the development of negative attitudes included sociocultural influences (e.g., emphasis on the "body beautiful"), childhood influences, psychodynamic mechanisms (e.g., the requirement of mourning, whereby the person is expected by nondisabled individuals to suffer and grieve over disability-caused loss of function), aesthetic aversion, and minority group comparability.

Another important area of research has centered on the existence of a hierarchy of preference toward certain disabilities. Presumably specific disabilities that are the most negatively evaluated are also the most aversive to the general public. In ranking attitudes toward specific disabilities, mental disorders, when compared with physical disabilities, consistently receive the most negative evaluations (Furnham & Pendred, 1983; Jones, 1974; McDonald & Hall, 1969). Harasymiw, Horne, and Lewis (1976) studied the acceptance of 22 disability types by 4,459 nondisabled people. Their findings indicated a relatively stable ranking of disability according to social acceptance across various subsamples (e.g., high school students, teachers, and the general population). Similarly, Horne and Ricciardo (1988) reported that hierarchies of preferences for kinds of disabilities across children and adults were stable over time. The results of these studies suggest that the least debilitating disabilities (e.g., asthma) are most accepted, whereas those that may be termed self-imposed (e.g., drug addiction) are least accepted.

In a study of preferential ranking, Tringo (1970) found that physical disability ranked first (most preferred), sensory disability ranked second, and brain injury ranked third. Disabilities least preferred included alcoholism, emotional disturbance, and mental retardation. Other research, however, suggests that hierarchical rankings of attitudes toward disabilities are not very stable and are, in fact, complex phenomena. Schmelkin (1984) reanalyzed Tringo's (1970) data and found that preferences toward disability are multidimensional rather than unidimensional as implied in hierarchical ranking schemes. Specifically, Schmelkin found that Tringo's reported preference toward disabilities focused on the degree of ostracism, visibility, and organicity or functionality associated with each disability. However, Anderson and Antonak (1992), in a well-designed experiment, found no differences between people with favorable and people with less favorable attitudes toward disability on ratings of social acceptance of people with different disabilities (adjusted for prior contact with people with disabilities). Fichten, Robillard, Tagalakis, and Amsel (1991) also reported that nondisabled college students demonstrated no preferences in interacting with students with different disabilities; in fact, nondisabled students were negative toward interacting with disabled students in casual social situations in general. These findings support Antonak's (1979) call for a multidimensional and nonlinear approach to understanding the structure of attitudes toward disability.

Still other research (Stovall & Sedlacek, 1983; Yuker, 1983) has concluded that rankings of preference for types of disability are not stable. Rather, how people rank their preferences regarding disability depends in part on the way the disability is categorized. Yuker (1983) summarized the research as follows:

> We do not know what the differences are between the disabilities that are evaluated consistently and the ones that are evaluated in terms of the situation. We

do not know to what extent the evaluations are based on reality or pragmatism, and to what extent they are based on stereotypes. Why should evaluation of blindness be situation dependent while evaluation of deafness is comparatively consistent across situations? We do not know the source of the comparative evaluations. Why are amputees usually evaluated comparatively positively while persons with cerebral palsy tend to be evaluated negatively? There is a clear need for research that will answer such questions as these and fill in some of the gaps in our knowledge. (p. 101)

Two promising lines of research on how disabilities become categorized consider the relationship of disability and context and the causal attributions behind attitude formation. Shurka and Katz (1976) and Kravetz, Katz, and Albez (1994) found that attributions regarding the perceived responsibility for the disability were important in determining attitudes toward disability. Weiner, Perry, and Magnusson (1988) found that people with physical disabilities are viewed as not responsible for their disability, whereas people with emotional and behavioral disabilities are viewed as responsible. People with physical disabilities elicited pity and offers of help from nondisabled individuals, in contrast to people with emotional disabilities, who elicited little pity and were likely to be ignored. Also, attributions as to controllability and stability of disability were related to attitudes concerning intervention strategies. Bordieri and Drehmer (1987, 1988) reported that, in an experimental setting, both recommendations to hire and perceived coworker acceptance of people with disabilities were related to the attribution of responsibility for disability. The more the person was thought to be personally responsible for the disability, the less likely was the recommendation to hire and the less was perceived coworker acceptance. With the exception of cancer, type of disability per se was related neither to hiring nor to coworker acceptance. Thorn, Hershenson, and Romney (1994) found support for Hershenson's (1992) thesis that people use causal attribution in the formation of attitudes toward disability. Their findings suggest that people categorize causal attributions of disability to either faith, logic, or power as related to attributed personal responsibility for disability. Faith as a causal factor suggests supernatural explanations for disability, logic suggests medical explanations, and power suggests environmental barrier explanations.

Research (Gordon, Minnes, & Holden, 1990; Grand, Bernier, & Strohmer, 1982; Strohmer, Grand, & Purcell, 1984) using the *Disability Social Relationship* scale, developed by Grand et al. (1982), has pointed out the importance of considering attitudes as a function of disability and context, especially when using attitudes to predict behavior. This research has documented that attitudes toward persons with disability differ by type of disability being evaluated and by the context in which the evaluation occurs (e.g., job setting, dating). Furthermore, there is an interaction between type of disability and contextual setting. Gordon et al. (1982) concluded "that disability and situation contribute to attitudes interactively in a manner reflecting elements of social stigma, social distance, and the negatively perceived functional limitations of disabling conditions" (p. 86). However, Berry and Meyer (1995) found that in a work situation, people with negative attitudes toward disability predicted problems in a potential contact with a person with a disability but that attitudes and situation did not in fact interact.

Attitudes of Rehabilitation Professionals Toward Disability

Given that attitudes are assumed to affect behavior, the attitudes of professionals can exert a tremendous influence on the impact of disability on individuals and the professionals' interactions with them. Because professionals serve as gate-keepers to service provision, McDaniel (1976) suggested that professionals' atti-tudes are of critical importance in facilitating client success. The importance of this topic is illustrated by Chubon (1982), who cited over 100 journal articles dealing with professionals' attitudes toward disability. Generally, the research lit-erature addresses two problem areas: establishing hierarchical preferences for disabilities by professionals and linking attitudes of professionals with behavior.

Allen, Peterson, and Keating (1982) found that mental health and rehabilita-tion counselors evaluated alcoholism significantly more negatively than other types of disability. Bowman (1987) indicated that rehabilitation workers form a hierarchy of disability preference. His findings suggested that, in considering per-ceived job ability and performance, rehabilitation workers judged recovering alcoholics and facially disfigured people most capable and mentally retarded and cerebral palsied people least capable. Goodyear (1983) reported that rehabilita-tion counselors employed in a state vocational rehabilitation agency ascribed more positive attributes to clients with physical disabilities than to clients with social or emotional disabilities. Similarly, Eberly, Eberly, and Wright (1981) found that rehabilitation counseling students also ascribed more positive attributes to people with physical disabilities than to nonhandicapped individuals, but expressed a preference for working with clients who did not have disabilities. Bordieri (1993), in a study also using rehabilitation counseling students, reported that self-blame attributions, presented by potential rehabilitation clients, influ-enced the students' feelings about perceived client involvement in the rehabilita-tion process. Clients who believed they deserved their disability were rated more negatively.

Byrd, Byrd, and Emener (1977) studied how employers, rehabilitation coun-selors, and rehabilitation counseling students perceived the employability of clients with 20 different types of disability. Byrd et al. found that counselors and students were most similar in their rank ordering, whereas employers and students were the most dissimilar. However, inspection of the mean rankings per disability pre-sented by Byrd et al. clearly revealed that practicing rehabilitation counselors were the most negative in their general perceptions of employability of persons with disabilities. On the 5-point Likert scale used to rate each disability, coun-selors' average scores were 4 or above; that is, they said they would be unlikely or very unlikely to hire a person with a particular disability (e.g., blindness, cerebral palsy, paraplegia) for 8 of the 20 disabilities presented. Employers were as negative on only 1 disability—alcoholism. Students had no average rating as negative as counselors for any disability.

All the studies on professional preferences for disability assumed a unidimensional perspective. It is likely that counselor preference is at least partially situation based. For example, counselor preference or bias may be a result of experience and may represent a bona fide attempt at predicting rehabilitation outcome when only minimal information is available.

Although attitudes are thought to be linked to behavior, only a few studies have been designed to identify a link between counselor attitudes and actual behavior. For instance, Pinkerton and McAleer (1976) hypothesized that, of four chronic disabilities—renal failure, heart disease, cancer, and paraplegia—rehabilitation counselors would hold the least favorable attitudes toward cancer. They also hypothesized that counselor behavior, as measured by counselor-projected case performance, would correlate with the counselors' attitudes toward disability. Using the *Attitude Toward Disabled Persons* (ATDP) (Yuker et al., 1966) as a measure of attitudes, both hypotheses were confirmed. Counselors were most negative toward cancer as a disability and were likely to project less case service to clients with cancer than to clients with other equally severe disabilities. Pinkerton and McAleer interpreted their findings as a reflection of the counselors' own fear of cancer.

Similarly, Krauft, Rubin, Cook, and Bozarth (1976) rank ordered rehabilitation counselors' ATDP scores toward eight disabilities from most to least positive as follows: amputations, heart disease, epilepsy, orthopedic impairment, deafness, cerebral palsy, spinal cord injury, and mental retardation. Krauft et al. also found that those counselors who held less positive attitudes toward people with disabilities in general had significantly fewer of their clients with the three least favorable disabilities complete a rehabilitation program than did counselors with more favorable attitudes.

One of the most consistent findings in the literature on attitudes toward disability is that women tend to possess more favorable attitudes than do men. Cook, Kunce, and Getsinger (1976) found that gender differences in evaluating people with disabilities may be moderated by counselor effectiveness. Cook et al. asked resident hall counselors to evaluate the personality characteristics of pictures of men. Half of the sample was given additional and biasing information suggesting that some of the men depicted were disabled. When the sample was split by a supervisor's judgment of counselor effectiveness, there were no significant differences by gender for the more effective counselors given either biased or unbiased instructions. There were significant gender differences among the less effective counselors in that, with biasing instructions, women upgraded their "personality" ratings and men downgraded their ratings. If rating personality characteristics from pictures of people can be construed as an ambiguous task, then it is apparent that the more effective counselors tended to suspend judgment when given a biasing set, whereas the less effective counselors may have added structure to the task by relying on stereotypical and/or prejudiced attitudes; perhaps men downgraded people with disabilities by taking a "hard-nosed, make-them-face-reality" approach, and possibly women upgraded disability because of a nurturing attitude.

As with the general population, rehabilitation professionals obviously are not immune to having negative or potentially biasing attitudes. Counselors can, and sometimes do, hold negative attitudes toward people with a specific disability. These attitudes might be formed or moderated by many variables, including counselor-projected fears (Pinkerton & McAleer, 1976), negative experiences (Byrd et al., 1977), or counselor ineffectiveness (Cook et al., 1976; Krauft et al., 1976). Given the power of attitudes to set expectations and influence actual behavior, methods to modify attitudes have drawn increasing attention.

Changing Attitudes Toward Disability

Within the literature of social psychology, there are many competing theories of how attitudes may be changed. Whereas some theories assume that attitudes change to become more congruent with behaviors, others assert that behavioral change leads to attitudinal change. Nonetheless, research suggests that attitudes toward disability (a) are related to situational determinants, (b) vary according to type of disability, and (c) are generally resistant to change. Research also suggests that attitudes toward people with disabilities are complex; individuals demonstrating overt neutral, or even positive, attitudes may covertly hold negative attitudes that are manifested in subtle ways, for instance, through job discrimination and aversiveness in interpersonal interactions.

It is paradoxical that, in stigmatizing people with disabilities, nondisabled individuals may attribute some positive trait to those with disabilities. Occasionally, nondisabled individuals even attribute special powers, enhanced awareness, or heightened sensitivity to people who have experienced a disability. For example, a number of studies (D. C. Mitchell & Frederickson, 1975; J. Mitchell, 1976; J. Mitchell & Allen, 1975) have found that counselors with physical disabilities are preferred by people without physical disabilities. In these studies, clients perceived the counselors with disabilities as possessing an enhanced ability to understand and empathize. It is a pragmatic concern as to whether attempts should be made to modify these positive, yet stereotypical, attitudes.

Several studies suggest that interpersonal interactions with people with disabilities produce anxiety, uncertainty, and discomfort in able-bodied people. This anxiety is called interaction strain. Kleck, Ono, and Hastorf (1966), for instance, reported that nondisabled people experienced interaction strain that was reflected in their maintaining greater physical distance and terminating the interaction more quickly with people who had disabilities. In addition, Marinelli and Kelz (1973) found that subjects who interacted with a person with a visible disability experienced significant anxiety. Furthermore, Davis (1961) explored various strategies adopted by people with visible disabilities to reduce interaction strain.

If, as Synder, Kleck, Strenta, and Mentzer (1979) suggested, nondisabled people avoid people with disabilities in social situations because of negative attitudes, then strategies to combat this social handicap must be developed. Investigators have speculated that there are several possible reasons for these negative attitudes, including (a) the nondisabled person's fear of becoming disabled, (b) conflicting social norms concerning showing kindness without appearing to be condescending, (c) assuming people have strong emotional reactions to their disabilities, and (d) simply not knowing how to act in the presence of people with disabilities. In fact, Albrecht, Walker, and Levy (1982) found that 83% of the people they surveyed felt that ambiguity or uncertainty in social interaction was the main reason for not engaging people with disabilities. Consequently, much of the research on attitudes and disability has focused on understanding the uncertainty felt by the nondisabled when they interact with individuals who have disabilities. Langer, Fiske, Taylor, and Chanowitz (1976) conducted a series of experiments in which they tested the hypothesis that people with visible disabilities are avoided because of the conflict over a desire to stare at such persons despite the norm against staring at people. Langer et al. found support for their hypothesis and also discovered that, when disability as a novel stimulus was reduced, interaction avoidance was reduced. However, Thompson (1982) found that Langer et al.'s hypothesis holds only when verbal interaction is unlikely to occur. When interaction such as conversation is required, people tend to avoid eye contact with persons with visible disabilities.

Understanding the dynamics of social interaction is the first step to developing methods to combat interaction strain. Several successful strategies have been developed. The experimental approach, when used in the study of interpersonal interaction between people with and without disabilities, is a powerful method of isolating ways to modify attitudes. Traditional attempts to modify attitudes toward people with disabilities have focused on direct persuasion, providing information about physical disability, and instigating direct contact with people who have disabilities. The use of direction persuasion—for example, the slogan, "Hire the handicapped . . . It's good business"—has done little to open employment opportunities for people with disabilities. In some cases, merely providing information about physical disability can reduce misconceptions and ignorance, thus changing the cognitive component of an attitude. On the other hand, contact with people with disabilities may invoke the aforementioned interaction strain and modify attitudes in a negative direction. This unfortunate outcome was observed by Cowen, Underberg, and Verrillo (1958).

Apparently, it is not contact or information alone, but the contact between people without disabilities and people with disabilities when both are of equal status, combined with information about disability, that is the most powerful strategy for changing attitudes (Anthony, 1972). For example, in an experimental study, Evans (1976) demonstrated that contact alone did not affect the attitudes of able-bodied people. Contact in which the person with a disability specifically provided information to put the nondisabled person at ease significantly increased the positive attitudes of the nondisabled person. A major implication of this study was that, in providing relevant information about physical disability, people with disabilities themselves can minimize interaction strain.

Other research has refined the information-contact strategy by focusing on the way information about disability is expressed. In a series of well-designed experiments, Hastorf, Wildfogel, and Cassman (1979) found that acknowledging one's disability is a good tactic to reduce discomfort and uncertainty in nondisabled people. Significantly, Royse and Edwards (1989) presented evidence that individuals with disabilities are open to discussing their disabilities. Belgrave and Mills (1981) reported that, when a male with a disability made a general comment concerning his disability following a request for help, he was viewed more positively than when he did not mention his disability. These authors concluded that mentioning the disability in the context of a natural response to a plausible situation indicates a nonemotional response to disability. Such a response allays the nondisabled person's fear of interaction. In a second study, Belgrave (1984) found that an effective way for a person with a physical disability to increase a nondisabled person's willingness to engage in social interaction was to demonstrate nonpreoccupation with the disability by showing an interest in others. Barrett and Pullo (1993) reported that a classroom program designed to provide contact with people with disabilities, accurate information about disability, and a disability simulation, did positively influence undergraduates' attitudes toward disability.

To summarize, the measurement of attitudes presents formidable methodological problems to the study of attitudes toward disability. Research suggests that (a) even seemingly positive attitudes may have negative underlying components; (b) there are important correlates of attitudes that may lead to a better understanding of how attitudes are formed; and (c) some disabilities seem to be consistently evaluated positively, whereas others tend to be evaluated negatively, depending on the situational context. Other research stresses that rehabilitation professionals can, and do, develop negative attitudes toward clients with disabilities. Although attitudes may be related to situational determinants, they are assumed to act as predispositions to behavior and, once formed, are likely to be resistant to change. Effective methods of modifying negative attitudes toward disability include having a person with a disability who is of equal status provide information about the disability to people who are not impaired. Demonstrating a nonemotional response to the impairment is thought to lessen interaction strain in the nondisabled and provide an impetus for social interaction.

Trends and Conclusions

How people adapt to the effects of a disability continues to be a perplexing question. Basically, there are three broad schools of thought concerning the adjustment process. Some theorists believe that individuals are the primary determinant of their actions; others regard the environment as the determining factor of people's behavior; and still others believe that the interaction of the individual and the environment largely determines the adjustment process. In rehabilitation, this latter viewpoint, as expressed by Lewin (1935) and Bandura (1978), is currently popular among theorists and researchers.

Developmental psychology continues to exert influence on rehabilitation psychology, primarily as a method to predict adaptation to the adjustment process. Generally, the developmental approach suggests that there are clearly defined reaction stages (e.g., shock, denial, depression, adaptation, adjustment) that people go through during the adjustment process. Because these stages are thought to be necessary to successful treatment, proponents of the developmental approach believe they can predict behavior according to the expected progression through the stage hierarchy. Consequently, stage theories remain very popular among practitioners, even though research (Cook, 1979; Trieschmann, 1978, 1988) does not support the accuracy and usefulness of this approach. After an exhaustive review of the literature on adjustment to spinal cord injury, Trieschmann (1988) indicated that stage models of adjustment are based predominantly on clinical impressions. Furthermore, she stated that there is "no data . . . to demonstrate reliably and validly the existence, sequence, or duration of these stages" (p. 69).

Research on attitudes toward disability has moved from describing those attitudes and their correlates to trying to discover the determinants of attitudes and the conditions necessary to foster attitude change. Certainly, the recognition that professionals can and sometimes do hold negative attitudes toward disability has important ramifications. Given the trend for vocational rehabilitation to engage employers in a partnership, one area of increased emphasis will be a revitalization of research on employer attitudes toward disability, such as the now classic study by Rickard, Triandis, and Patterson (1963).

Since passage of the Rehabilitation Act of 1973, there have been tremendous changes in the ability of people with disabilities to become an effective political force. Certainly, the Americans with Disabilities Act of 1990 has drawn more attention to discrimination on the basis of disability in the United States. The emphasis on empowerment of people with disabilities will have a profound influence on attitudes toward disability. One area of attitude research that has received little attention is research on the attitudes people with disabilities hold toward other people with disabilities. Studies by Fichten et al. (1991) and Gordon et al. (1990) on the structure and context of attitude formation and the conceptual approach of Hershenson (1992) suggest that this may be a fruitful area of future research. Indeed research on the attitudes of people with disabilities might shed light on strategies to enhance positive attitudes toward disability. For example, Makas (1988) reported results suggesting there are different perceptions among persons as to what makes up positive attitudes toward disability. Specifically, her results suggest that interaction strain between people with disabilities and nondisabled individuals may stem from misunderstanding of each others' expectations and not necessarily negative intent. Misunderstandings are correctable.

References

Albrecht, G. L., Walker, V. G., & Levy, J. A. (1982). Social distance from the stigmatized. *Social Science Medicine, 16,* 1319-1327.

Allen, H. A., Peterson, J. S., & Keating, G. V. (1982). Attitudes of counselors toward the alcoholic. *Rehabilitation Counseling Bulletin, 25,* 162-163.

Altman, B. (1981). Studies of attitudes toward the handicapped: The need for a new direction. *Social Problems, 25,* 321-337.

Americans with Disabilities Act of 1990, 42 U.S.C. § 12101 *et seq.*

Anderson, R. J., & Antonak, R. F. (1992). The influence of attitudes and contact on reactions to persons with physical and speech disabilities. *Rehabilitation Counseling Bulletin, 35,* 240-247

Anthony, W. A. (1972). Societal rehabilitation: Changing society's attitudes toward the physically and mentally disabled. *Rehabilitation Psychology, 29,* 117-126.

Antonak, R. F. (1979). An ordering-theoretic analysis of attitudes. *Rehabilitation Psychology, 26,* 136-144.

Antonak, R. F., & Livneh, H. (1988). *The measurement of attitudes toward people with disabilities.* Springfield, IL: Thomas.

Bandura, A. (1978). The self system in reciprocal determinism. *American Psychologist, 33,* 344-358.

Barker, R. G., Wright, B. A., Meyerson, L., & Gonick, M. R. (1953). *Adjustment to physical handicap: A survey of the social psychology of physique and disability* (2nd ed.). New York: Social Science Research Council.

Barrett, K. E., & Pullo, R. E. (1993). Attitudinal change in undergraduate rehabilitation students as measured by the attitudes toward disability scale. *Rehabilitation Education, 7,* 119-126.

Barry, J. R., Dunteman, G. H., & Webb, M. H. (1968). Personality and motivation in rehabilitation. *Journal of Counseling Psychology, 15,* 237-244.

Belgrave, F. Z. (1984). The effectiveness of strategies for increasing social interaction with a physically disabled person. *Journal of Applied Social Psychology, 14,* 147-161.

Belgrave, F. Z., & Mills, J. (1981). Effect upon desire for social interaction with a physically disabled person of mentioning the disability in different contexts. *Journal of Applied Social Psychology, 11,* 44-57.

Berry, J. O. & Meyer, J. A. (1995). Employing people with disabilities: Impact of attitude and situation. *Rehabilitation Psychology, 40,* 211-222.

Berry, K. L., & Miskimins, R. W. (1969). Concept of self and post-hospital vocational adjustment. *Journal of Consulting and Clinical Psychology, 33,* 103-108.

Bordieri, J. E. (1993). Self blame attributions for disability and perceived client involvement in the vocational rehabilitation process. *Journal of Applied Rehabilitation Counseling, 24*(2), 3-7.

Bordieri, J. E., & Drehmer, D. E. (1987). *Rehabilitation Counseling Bulletin, 30,* 218-226.

Bordieri, J. E., & Drehmer, D. E. (1988). Causal attribution and hiring recommendations for disabled job applicants. *Rehabilitation Psychology, 33,* 239-247.

Bowman, J. T. (1987). Attitudes toward disabled persons: Social distance and work competence. *Journal of Rehabilitation, 53*(1), 41–44.

Byrd, E. K., Byrd, P. D., & Emener, W. G. (1977). Student, counselor, and employer perceptions of employability of severely retarded. *Rehabilitation Literature, 38,* 42–44.

Chubon, R. A. (1982). An analysis of research dealing with the attitudes of professionals toward disability. *Journal of Rehabilitation, 48*(1), 25–30.

Chubon, R. A. (1992). Attitudes toward disability: Addressing fundamentals of attitude theory and research in rehabilitation education. *Rehabilitation Education, 6,* 301–312.

Cloerkes, G. (1981). Are prejudices against disabled persons determined by personality characteristics? *International Journal of Rehabilitation Research, 4,* 35–46.

Comer, R. C., & Piliavin, J. A. (1975). As others see us: Attitudes of physically handicapped and normals toward own and other groups. *Rehabilitation Literature, 36,* 206–221, 225.

Cook, D. W. (1979). Psychological adjustment to spinal cord injury: Incidence of denial, depression, and anxiety. *Rehabilitation Psychology, 56,* 97–104.

Cook, D. W., Kunce, J. T., & Getsinger, S. H. (1976). Perceptions of the disabled and counseling effectiveness. *Rehabilitation Counseling Bulletin, 19,* 470–475.

Cowen, E. L., Underberg, R., & Verrillo, R. T. (1958). The developmental and testing of an attitude to blindness scale. *Journal of Social Psychology, 48,* 297–304.

Cubbage, M. E., & Thomas, K. R. (1989). Freud and disability. *Rehabilitation Psychology, 34,* 161–173.

Davis, F. (1961). Deviance disavowed: The management of strained interaction by the visibly handicapped. *Social Problems, 9,* 121–132.

Dembo, T., Leviton, G. L., & Wright, B. A. (1956). Adjustment to misfortune: A problem of social–psychological rehabilitation. *Artificial Limbs, 3,* 4–62.

Eberly, C., Eberly, B., & Wright, K. (1981). Mental health professional attitudes toward physically handicapped groups in attributionally ambiguous and nonambiguous situations. *Journal of Counseling Psychology, 25,* 276–278.

English, R. W. (1971a). The application of personality theory to explain psychological reactions to physical disability. *Rehabilitation Research and Practice Review, 3,* 35–47.

English, R. W. (1971b). Correlates of stigma towards physically disabled persons. *Rehabilitation Research and Practice Review, 2,* 1–18.

Evans, J. H. (1976). Changing attitudes toward disabled persons: An experimental study. *Rehabilitation Counseling Bulletin, 59,* 572–579.

Feinberg, L. B. (1967). Social desirability and attitudes toward the disabled. *Personnel and Guidance Journal, 46,* 373–381.

Fichten, C. S., Robillard, K., Tagalakis, V., & Amsel, R. (1991). Causal interaction between college students with various disabilities and their nondisabled peers: The internal dialogue. *Rehabilitation Psychology, 36,* 3–20.

Freud, S. (1963). *A general introduction to psychoanalysis.* New York: Liveright. (Original work published 1917)

Furnham, A., & Pendred, J. (1983). Attitudes towards the mentally and physically disabled. *British Journal of Medical Psychology, 56,* 179–187.

Gellman, W. (1959). Roots of prejudice against the handicapped. *Journal of Rehabilitation, 25*(1), 4-6, 25.

Goldberg, R. T. (1974). Adjustment of children with invisible and visible handicaps: Congenital heart disease and facial burns. *Journal of Counseling Psychology, 25,* 428-432.

Goodyear, R. K. (1983). Patterns of counselors' attitudes toward disability groups. *Rehabilitation Counseling Bulletin, 26,* 181-184.

Gordon, E. D., Minnes, P. M., & Holden, R. R. (1990). The structure of attitudes toward persons with a disability, when specific disability and context are considered. *Rehabilitation Psychology, 35,* 79-90.

Grand, S. A., Bernier, J. E., & Strohmer, D. C. (1982). Attitudes toward disabled persons as a function of social context and specific disability. *Rehabilitation Psychology, 27,* 165-174.

Harasymiw, S. J., Horne, M. D., & Lewis, S. C. (1976). A longitudinal study of disability group acceptance. *Rehabilitation Literature, 37,* 98-102.

Hastorf, A. H., Wildfogel, J., & Cassman, T. (1979). Acknowledgment of handicap as a tactic in social interaction. *Journal of Personality and Social Psychology, 37,* 1790-1797.

Hershenson, D. B. (1992). Conceptions of disability: Implications for rehabilitation. *Rehabilitation Counseling Bulletin, 35,* 154-160.

Horne, M. D., & Ricciardo, J. L. (1988). Hierarchy of response to handicaps. *Psychological Reports, 62,* 83-86.

Jones, R. L. (1974). The hierarchical structure of attitudes toward the exceptional. *Exceptional Children, 40,* 430.

Kleck, R., Ono, H., & Hastorf, A. H. (1966). The effects of physical deviance on face-to-face interaction. *Human Relations, 19,* 425-436.

Krauft, C. C., Rubin, S. E., Cook, D. W., & Bozarth, J. D. (1976). Counselor attitudes toward disabled persons and client program completion: A pilot study. *Journal of Applied Rehabilitation Counseling, 7,* 50-54.

Kravetz, S., Katz, S., & Albez, D. (1994). Attitudes toward Israeli war veterans with disabilities: Combat versus noncombat military service and responsibility for the disability. *Rehabilitation Counseling Bulletin, 37,* 371-379.

Langer, E. J., Fiske, S., Taylor, S. E., & Chanowitz, B. (1976). Stigma, string and discomfort: A novel-stimulus hypothesis. *Journal of Experimental Social Psychology, 12,* 451-463.

Lewin, K. (1935). *A dynamic theory of personality.* New York: McGraw-Hill.

Lewin, K. (1936). *Principles of topological psychology.* New York: McGraw-Hill.

Lipp, L., Kolstoe, R., James, W., & Randall, H. (1968). Denial of disability and internal control of reinforcement: A study using a perceptual defense paradigm. *Journal of Consulting and Clinical Psychology, 32,* 72-75.

Livneh, H. (1982). On the origins of negative attitudes toward people with disabilities. *Rehabilitation Literature, 43,* 338-347.

Maddi, S. (1972). *Personality theories: A comparative analysis.* Homewood, IL: Dorsey.

Makas, E. (1988). Positive attitudes toward disabled people: Disabled and nondisabled persons' perspectives. *Journal of Social Issues, 44,* 49-61.

Marinelli, R., & Kelz, J. (1973). Anxiety and attitudes toward visibly disabled persons. *Rehabilitation Counseling Bulletin, 16,* 198-205.

McDaniel, J. W. (1976). *Physical disability and human behavior* (2nd ed.). New York: Pergamon Press.

McDonald, A. P., & Hall, J. (1969). Perception of disability by the nondisabled. *Journal of Consulting and Clinical Psychology, 33,* 654–660.

Mitchell, D. C., & Frederickson, W. A. (1975). Preferences for physically disabled counselors in hypothetical counseling situations. *Journal of Counseling Psychology, 25,* 477–482.

Mitchell, J. (1976). Disabled counselors: Perceptions of their effectiveness in a therapeutic relationship. *Archives of Physical Medicine and Rehabilitation, 57,* 348–352.

Mitchell, J., & Allen, H. (1975). Perception of a physically disabled counselor in a counseling session. *Journal of Counseling Psychology, 22,* 70–73.

Pinkerton, S. S., & McAleer, C. A. (1976). Influences of client diagnosis of cancer on counselor decisions. *Journal of Counseling Psychology, 53,* 575–578.

Rehabilitation Act of 1973, 29 U.S.C. § 791 *et seq.*

Rickard, T., Triandis, H., & Patterson, C. (1963). Indices of employer prejudice toward disabled applicants. *Journal of Applied Psychology, 47,* 52–55.

Roessler, R., & Bolton, B. (1978). *Psychosocial adjustment to disability.* Austin, TX: PRO-ED.

Rogers, C. R. (1951). *Client-centered therapy: Its current practice, implications, and theory.* Boston: Houghton Mifflin.

Rogers, C. R. (1959). A theory of therapy, personality, and interpersonal relationships as developed in the client-centered framework. In S. Koch (Ed.), *Psychology: A study of a science* (Vol. 3, pp. 184–256). New York: McGraw-Hill.

Rogers, C. R. (1961). *On becoming a person.* Boston: Houghton Mifflin.

Royse, D., & Edwards, T. (1989). Communicating about disability: Attitudes and preferences of persons with physical handicaps. *Rehabilitation Counseling Bulletin, 32,* 203–209.

Schmelkin, L. P. (1984). Hierarchy of preferences toward disabled groups: A reanalysis. *Perceptual and Motor Skills, 59,* 151–157.

Shontz, F. C. (1971). Physical disability and personality. In W. S. Neff (Ed.), *Rehabilitation psychology* (pp. 33–73). Washington, DC: American Psychological Association.

Shurka, E., & Katz, J. (1976). Evaluations of persons with disability: The influence of disability context and personal responsibility for the disability. *Rehabilitation Psychology, 23,* 65–71.

Siller, J. (1976). Attitudes toward disability. In H. Rusalem & D. Malikin (Eds.), *Contemporary vocational rehabilitation* (pp. 67–79). New York: New York University Press.

Siller, J. (1984). Personality and attitudes toward physical disabilities. In C. J. Golden (Ed.), *Current topics in rehabilitation psychology* (pp. 201–227). New York: Grune & Stratton.

Stovall, C., & Sedlacek, W. E. (1983). Attitudes of male and female university students toward students with different physical disabilities. *Journal of College Student Personnel, 24,* 325–330.

Strohmer, D. C., Grand, S. A., & Purcell, M. J. (1984). Attitudes toward persons with a disability: An examination of demographic factors, social context, and specific disability. *Rehabilitation Psychology, 29,* 131–145.

Synder, M. L., Kleck, R. E., Strenta, A. C., & Mentzer, S. J. (1979). Avoidance of the handicapped: An attributional ambiguity analysis. *Journal of Personality and Social Psychology, 37,* 2297–2306.

Thompson, T. (1982). Gaze toward the avoidance of the handicapped: A field experiment. *Journal of Nonverbal Behavior, 6,* 188–196.

Thorn, K. R., Hershenson, D. B., & Romney, A. K. (1994). Causal attribution factors in conceptions of disability. *Rehabilitation Counseling Bulletin, 37,* 315–331.

Trieschmann, R. B. (1978). *The psychological, social, and vocational adjustment in spinal cord injury.* Los Angeles: Easter Seal Society.

Trieschmann, R. B. (1988). *Spinal cord injuries: Psychological, social, and vocational rehabilitation* (2nd ed.). New York: Demos.

Tringo, J. L. (1970). The hierarchy of preference toward disability groups. *Journal of Special Education, 4,* 295–306.

Turner, R. J., & Mclean, P. D. (1989). Physical disability and psychological distress. *Rehabilitation Psychology, 34,* 225–242.

Weiner, B., Perry, R. P., & Magnusson, J. (1988). An attributional analysis of reactions to stigmas. *Journal of Personality and Social Psychology, 55,* 738–748.

Wright, B. A. (1960). *Physical disability:A psychological approach.* New York: Harper & Row.

Wright, B. A. (1983). *Physical disability:A psychosocial approach* (2nd ed.). New York: Harper & Row.

Yuker, H. (1983). The lack of stable order of preference for disabilities: A response to Richardson and Ronald. *Rehabilitation Psychology, 28,* 93–103.

Yuker, H. (1988). *Attitudes toward persons with disabilities.* New York: Springer.

Yuker, H., Block, J., & Younng, J. (1966). *The measurement of attitudes toward disabled persons.* Albertson, NY: Human Resources Center.

Chapter 10

Career Development of People with Disabilities: An Ecological Model

Edna Mora Szymanski and David B. Hershenson

ork is a central force in people's lives. In addition to providing economic support, an occupation reflects an individual's social status (Roe, 1969; Rothman, 1987) and self-concept (Super, 1969, 1990). Unfortunately, people with disabilities have dramatically high rates of unemployment and under-employment (Louis Harris & Associates, 1994), which can adversely affect not only economic and social status, but also self-image.

Rehabilitation counselors, as specialists in the vocational implications of disability (Hershenson, 1988), are key professionals in addressing the employment problems of people with disabilities. A major focus of rehabilitation counseling is the special application of theories and models of career development to people with disabilities (Super, 1969). Topics covered in this chapter highlight the vocational focus of rehabilitation counseling and include (a) history and context; (b) theories of vocational behavior and career development; (c) an ecological model for organization of the theories; (d) general issues regarding theory application and career development of people with disabilities, including members of racial and ethnic minority groups; and (e) career interventions with people with disabilities.

Note. Preparation of this manuscript was supported, in part, by Grant H133B30052 from the National Institute on Disability and Rehabilitation Research of the U.S. Department of Education. However, the views expressed are those of the authors and not necessarily those of the funding agency.

History and Context

Theories of career development address a number of interrelated constructs, including occupational choice, career development, and work adjustment. *Occupational choice* is the process of choosing a specific job at one point in time; *career development* focuses on the developmental process of one's lifelong sequence of occupationally relevant choices and behaviors (D. Brown, 1990b; Herr & Cramer, 1992); and *work adjustment* addresses adjustment to the work process itself, independent of the occupation in which it is performed.

Occupational choice was the initial focus of the study of vocational behavior. Parsons (1909) assumed that once the choice of an occupation was made in late adolescence or early adulthood, it would remain unchanged for one's lifetime. Subsequent studies, however, indicated that people average about four major job changes over the course of their working life, thus invalidating Parsons's focus on a single event and suggesting the need to employ the longitudinal, developmental concept of career. The subsequent evolution of career development theories addressed the "lifelong process of getting ready to choose, choosing, and typically continuing to choose from among the many occupations available in our society" (D. Brown & Brooks, 1984, p. ix). The last group of theories to evolve, work adjustment theories, resulted from studies of work behavior (Neff, 1985) and were specifically designed to be broadly applicable to persons either with or without disabilities (Hershenson, 1981; Lofquist & Dawis, 1969). At the present time, work adjustment theories coexist with theories of occupational choice and career development. Furthermore, although theories may have begun with one focus (e.g., career development), many have expanded to include additional focuses (e.g., occupational choice) (see, e.g., Super, 1994).

Today, there are many career development theories relating to a variety of disciplines, including counseling, psychology, and sociology. Interestingly, "each academic discipline happily develops its own concepts but does not feel obligated to connect them to the concepts that flow from other disciplines" (Schein, 1986, pp. 315–316). To further complicate matters, most of these theories are still at a relatively early stage of scientific development (D. Brown, 1990b).

Recently, leaders in vocational psychology explored the possibility of theory convergence (Savickas & Lent, 1994a). The theories contain similarities, and some convergence has occurred naturally (Osipow, 1994). However, current theories address different aspects of vocational behavior (Dawis, 1994; Krumboltz, 1994) and diverse audiences (Holland, 1994). For example, organizational career theories (e.g., Hall, 1990) focus on the interplay of individuals and businesses, whereas developmental theories (e.g., Super, 1990) focus on the course of career through individual lifespans. In addition, "the theories need each other in order to comprehensively address the complexity of career development. Furthermore, the results of research studies acquire deeper meaning when they are viewed from the perspectives of two or more theories" (Savickas & Lent, 1994b, p. 2).

The application of career development theories to people with disabilities has been an issue of concern during recent years. Rehabilitation counseling has a long history of adopting theories and practices developed on populations of persons without disabilities. This was the case in the area of vocational behavior, as well as in many other content areas (e.g., assessment, strategies of counseling). However, some authors (e.g., Conte, 1983; Curnow, 1989) have questioned the applicability of these theories to people with disabilities. Recently, however, Szymanski, Hershenson, Enright, and Ettinger (1996) suggested that the wide variability among people with disabilities means that theories, by their very nature, cannot be fully applicable or nonapplicable. The heterogeneity of the population mitigates against the possibility of any one theory's either explaining or failing to explain the behavior of all individuals.

Theories of Vocational Behavior and Career Development

Although the theories are not fully applicable or nonapplicable, they are associated with valuable interventions that can assist people with disabilities. Thus, by gaining familiarity with the theories, rehabilitation counselors will be able to selectively apply specific facets of various theories to individual consumers. To this end, brief reviews of the following major theories or approaches are provided in this chapter: Super's Life-Span, Life-Space Theory; Holland's theory; trait–factor theory; Miller-Tiedeman's Theory of Career Decision Making; Roe's Theory of Personality Development and Career Choice; Krumboltz's Social Learning Theory; the Minnesota Theory of Work Adjustment; Hershenson's Model of Work Adjustment Development; sociocognitive approaches; developmental contextualism; organizational career theory; and sociological approaches. Readers wishing further information concerning theories of career development, occupational choice, and work adjustment may consult D. Brown, Brooks, and Associates (1990, 1996), Herr and Cramer (1992), Osipow (1983), and Savickas and Lent (1994a).

Super's Life-Span, Life-Space Theory

Super's career development theory, known as Life-Span, Life-Space Theory, is the most comprehensive theory to date (D. Brown, 1990b). It combines elements of developmental, differential, social, personality, and phenomenological psychology with self-concept and learning theory, and includes some consideration of trait and factor congruence (Super, 1990, 1994). This multifaceted view of career development, which yields testable hypotheses for each facet (Super, 1990), has had profound impact on theory, research, and practice (Savickas, 1994).

Key Elements

Super (1990) conceptualized his model as a "life-career rainbow," which combined situational and personal determinants with life roles and life stages. Life roles are child, student, leisurite, citizen, worker, and homemaker (Super, 1990). Life stages (and corresponding ages) are growth (birth to 14), exploration (15 to 24), establishment (25 to 44), maintenance (45 to 64), and decline (65+) (Zunker, 1986). "The ages of transitions [from one stage to the next] are very flexible . . . [and] each transition involves a recycling through one or more of the stages—a minicycle" (Super, 1990, p. 215).

Basic Propositions

Super (1990) formulated 14 basic propositions to undergird his model:

1. People differ in their abilities and personalities, needs, values, interests, traits, and self-concepts.
2. People are qualified, by virtue of these characteristics, each for a number of occupations.
3. Each occupation requires a characteristic pattern of ability and personality traits, with tolerances wide enough to allow both some variety of occupations for each individual and some variety of individuals in each occupation.
4. Vocational preferences and competencies, the situations in which people live and work, and, hence their self-concepts change with time and experience, although self-concepts, as products of social learning, are increasingly stable from late adolescence until late maturity, providing some continuity in choice and adjustment.
5. This process of change may be summed up in a series of life stages (a "maxicycle") characterized as a sequence of growth, exploration, establishment, maintenance, and decline, and these stages may in turn be subdivided into (a) the fantasy, tentative, and realistic phases of the exploratory stage and (b) the trial and stable phases of the establishment stage. *A small (mini) cycle takes place in transitions from one stage to the next or each time an individual is destabilized by a reduction in force, changes in type of manpower needs, illness or injury, or other socioeconomic or personal events. Such unstable or multiple-trial careers involve new growth, reexploration, and reestablishment (recycling)* [italic added].
6. The nature of the career pattern, that is, the occupational level attained and the sequence, frequency, and duration of trial and stable jobs—is determined by the individual's parental socioeconomic level, mental ability, education, skills, personality characteristics (needs, values, interests, traits, and self-concepts), and career maturity and by the opportunities to which he or she is exposed.
7. Success in coping with the demands of the environment and of the organism in that context at any given life-career stage depends on the readiness of the individual to cope with these demands (that is, on his or her career maturity). Career maturity is a constellation of physical, psychological, and social characteristics; psychologically, it is both cognitive and affective. It includes the

degree of success in coping with the demands of earlier stages and substages of career development, and especially with the most recent.

8. Career maturity is a hypothetical construct. Its operational definition is perhaps as difficult to formulate as that of intelligence, but its history is much briefer and its achievement even less definitive. . . . It does not increase monotonically, and it is not a unitary trait.

9. Development through the life stages can be guided, partly by facilitating the maturing of abilities and interests and partly by aiding in reality testing and in the development of self-concepts.

10. The process of career development is essentially that of developing and implementing occupational self-concepts. It is a synthesizing and compromising process in which the self-concept is a product of the interaction of inherited aptitudes, physical makeup, opportunity to observe and play various roles, and evaluations of the extent to which the results of role playing meet with the approval of superiors and fellows (interactive learning).

11. The process of synthesis of or compromise between individual and social factors, between self-concepts and reality, is one of role playing and learning from feedback, whether the role is played in fantasy, in the counseling interview, or in such real-life activities as classes, clubs, part-time work, and entry jobs.

12. Work satisfactions and life satisfactions depend on the extent to which the individual finds adequate outlets for abilities, needs, values, interests, personality traits, and self-concepts. They depend on establishment in a type of work, a work situation, and a way of life in which one can play the kind of role that growth and exploratory experiences have led one to consider congenial and appropriate.

13. The degree of satisfaction people attain from work is proportional to the degree to which they have been able to implement self-concepts.

14. Work and occupation provide a focus for personality organization for most men and women, although for some persons this focus is peripheral, incidental, or even non-existent. The other foci, such as leisure activities and homemaking, may be central. (Social traditions, such as sex-role stereotyping and modeling, racial and ethnic biases, and the opportunity structure, as well as individual differences, are important determinants of preferences for such roles as worker, student, leisurite, homemaker, and citizen.) (Super, 1990, pp. 206–208)[1]

Common Applications

Super's work has been used frequently in career counseling (D. Brown, 1990b; Osipow, 1983). His life-career rainbow (Super, 1990) has been applied to the practice of career counseling in a multitude of ways, including Bowlsby's computerized *DISCOVER* program (American College Testing Program, 1984). Super's work on career maturity has also been used in career counseling and has been the focus of instruments developed by Super and associates, for example, the *Career Development Inventory* (Thompson & Lindeman, 1984), the *Career Maturity*

---

[1]From "A Life-Span, Life-Space Approach to Career Development," by D. E. Super, 1990, in *Career Choice and Development: Applying Contemporary Theories to Practice* (pp. 206–208), by D. Brown, L. Brooks, and Associates, San Francisco: Jossey-Bass. Copyright 1990 by Jossey-Bass. Reprinted with permission.

Inventory (Crites, 1978), and the *Adult Career Concerns Inventory* (Super, Thompson, & Lindeman, 1988). Two additional instruments, *The Salience Inventory* (Super & Nevill, 1986a) and *The Values Scale* (Super & Nevill, 1986b), also address important aspects of career development. In fact, Super's most recent work on life-role saliency also has been applied in a number of international settings (Super & Sverko, 1995) and shows considerable promise for flexible application across cultures, ages, and socioeconomic statuses.

Special Concerns for People with Disabilities

Super's theory is particularly applicable to rehabilitation counseling. It offers a framework for addressing the career development needs of persons with congenital disabilities, whose career development may have been restricted, and those with acquired disabilities, whose career development may have regressed (Thomas & Parker, 1992).

People with congenital disabilities may have limited early experiences, including opportunities for play, work-role fantasies, and career-related role playing (Conte, 1983; Curnow, 1989; Szymanski, Dunn, & Parker, 1989). Such early experiences are likely to be vital to normal career development of nondisabled persons (Osipow, 1983) and persons with congenital disabilities (Turner & Szymanski, 1990). In fact, in discussing the progression of career development through life stages, Super (1990) suggested that "skipping a stage in the normal cycle can result in difficulties at a later stage (for example, failure to explore often leads to a poor choice of occupation or job)" (p. 215).

Super's construct of career maturity has considerable utility with persons with congenital disabilities or those who have acquired disabilities early in their career development. This construct can help counselors to recognize the extent to which experiential deficiencies hinder the full participation of clients in career planning and decision making. In addition, counselors can identify critical areas of experiential or knowledge deficiency and develop rehabilitation plans to remediate these deficiencies and facilitate the client's full and informed participation in career planning.

For people with acquired disabilities, career development can be destabilized, as noted in Super's Proposition 5, and result in the need for reexploration and reestablishment. Although Super's model suggests an individually oriented focus for addressing career development of persons with midcareer disabilities, one critical element appears to be missing, that is, the interaction of limitations resulting from an acquired disability with the individual's current or previous career and job skills.

The limitations of disabilities are not inherent within individuals, but rather in individuals' interactions with their environments (Szymanski, Hershenson, & Power, 1988). Although Super's theory addresses this issue in congenital disabilities by allowing for the effects of limitations in early experiences, the theory appears to fall short in this regard for persons with acquired disabilities. In addition, the theory does not adequately integrate the impact of chance, which frequently is a critical factor in career development (Cabral & Salomone, 1990). Nonetheless, many aspects of Super's theory are applicable to individuals with disabilities (Thomas & Parker, 1992). Such application, however, must be individually designed, with consideration of individual ability and disability, early experiences, work history, and functional limitations.

Holland's Theory

In contrast to Super's theory, which is developmental in nature, Holland's (1985a) theory is a typology that links six broad personality types to occupational environments (Osipow, 1983). The theory builds upon and extends the trait and factor tradition (Weinrach & Srebalus, 1990). Holland's theory is among the most prominent in career counseling practice (D. Brown, 1990b).

Key Elements

Holland's theory is based on a division of U.S. work environments into the following six categories: realistic (R), investigative (I), artistic (A), social (S), enterprising (E), and conventional (C) (Osipow, 1983). Similarly, personality types, which develop under the influence of heredity, culture, and individual forces, can be categorized using combinations of the same six broad personality categories. Table 10.1 gives a brief description of Holland's six personality types and corresponding potential occupational environments.

The six personality types described in Table 10.1 have relationships to each other, as represented in a hexagonal form with the following order: RIASEC. Types that are next to each other on the hexagon are more closely related than types that are on opposite sides. Combinations of an individual's three personality types are commonly used to characterize their modal personality styles (e.g., ISE, SEI), thus indicating their primary repertoire of coping strategies and the relative predominance of these strategies (Weinrach & Srebalus, 1990).

Basic Propositions

Holland's (1985a) theory is based on the following assumptions:

1. In our culture, most persons can be categorized as one of six types: realistic, investigative, artistic, social, enterprising, or conventional. . . .
2. There are six model environments: realistic, investigative, artistic, social, enterprising, and conventional. . . .
3. People search for environments that will let them exercise their skills and abilities, express their attitudes and values, and take on agreeable problems and roles. . . .
4. Behavior is determined by an interaction between personality and environment. (pp. 2–4)

Table 10.1
Holland's Personality Types and Corresponding Occupational Examples

Personality Type	Description	Occupational Examples
Realistic	Prefers concrete, hands-on activities: may lack social skills	Skilled trades, technician
Investigative	Is analytical, methodological; may lack leadership skills	Scientist, computer programmer
Artistic	Is self-expressive, original; may lack clerical skills	Musician, writer
Social	Likes to work with and help others: may lack mechanical or scientific ability	Counselor, teacher
Enterprising	Uses verbal skills for goal achievement or dominance; may lack scientific ability	Lawyer, salesperson, manager
Conventional	Likes to manipulate data; has concern for rules	Secretary, bookkeeper

Note. The contents of this table were adapted from *Theories of Career Development* by S. H. Osipow, 1983, Englewood Cliffs, NJ: Prentice-Hall; "Holland's Theory of Careers," by S. G. Weinrach and D. J. Srebalus, 1990, in *Career Choice and Development: Applying Contemporary Theories to Practice* (pp. 37–67), by D. Brown, L. Brook, and Associates, San Francisco: Jossey-Bass; and *Career Counseling: Applied Concepts in Life Planning,* by V. G. Zunker, 1986, Monterey, CA: Brooks/Cole.

Common Applications

Holland's theory is prominent in current career counseling approaches due to its relative ease of use (D. Brown, 1990b; Osipow, 1983). Two instruments that operationalize the typology and facilitate consideration of possible occupations are the *Vocational Preference Inventory* (Holland, 1985c) and the *Self-Directed Search* (Holland, 1985b). Another instrument, *My Vocational Situation* (Holland, Daiger, & Power, 1980), addresses vocational identity and has been used to measure the effectiveness of career interventions on people with and without disabilities (see, e.g., Conyers & Szymanski, in press; Farley, Bolton, & Parkerson, 1992). Finally, the recently developed *Career Attitudes and Strategies Inventory* (Holland & Gottfredson, 1994) shows some promise as a career counseling tool for people with some work experience.

Special Concerns for People with Disabilities

Holland's theory may have limitations in application to people with mental retardation and severe mental illness (Hagner & Salomone, 1989). In addition, the theory has been criticized as not readily applicable to persons with disabilities due to its emphasis on individual traits, and its relative lack of consideration of societal factors, chance factors, and environmental variables, other than those depicted in the occupational types (Conte, 1983). Environmental factors are known to be important considerations in career development of persons with disabilities (Szymanski, Hershenson, & Power, 1988), and chance is likely to play an important role, especially for persons with acquired disabilities (Cabral & Salomone, 1990). Interestingly, however, as noted in recent reviews, Holland's typology has been quite robust in application to various minority populations (see, e.g., Arbona, 1995; M. Brown, 1995). Further research is needed to address applicability to various populations of people with disabilities.

Limitations of some of the assessment instruments can be conceptualized in terms of individual adaptations and job modifications. For example, individuals responding to items of the *Self-Directed Search* (Holland, 1985b) might rule out interesting occupations, because they do not believe they can perform the required tasks due to physical or mental limitations. Possibilities for adaptive devices or job modifications typically do not enter into the assessment process, thus limiting the expressed interest of the individual. Another problem with application of Holland's typology results from limitations in the early experiences of persons with congenital disabilities (Conte, 1983; Curnow, 1989; Turner & Szymanski, 1990). Experiential limitations restrict the ability of these individuals to make informed choices among items on the instruments.

Nevertheless, the ease of use of the instruments related to Holland's theory may make them valuable for career counseling. The use of these instruments with people with disabilities, however, should be accompanied by appropriate caution, supplemental assessments of career maturity, and consideration of potential adaptive devices and job modifications.

Trait–Factor Theory

Trait-factor theory, which underlies much of the current practice in career counseling, has laid the foundation for other prominent theories, including Holland's theory and the Minnesota Theory of Work Adjustment. The theory involves the matching of specific individual traits to job requirements (D. Brown, 1990c). It is thus fitting that the theory is often referred to as *person-environment fit* (Chartrand, 1991; Rounds & Tracey, 1990).

Key Elements

Traits (e.g., interests, aptitudes, intelligence) and assessment instruments, which measure the traits, make up one major set of ingredients of trait-factor theory (Zunker, 1986). The second major set of ingredients comprises job factors or requirements, which are often gleaned from job analyses. Individual traits are then matched with job factors to determine potential matches (Zunker, 1986).

Key Propositions

The key propositions of trait-factor theory include the following:

1. Each individual has a unique set of traits that can be measured reliably and validly.

2. Occupations require that workers possess certain very specific traits for success, although a worker with a wide range of characteristics can still be successful in a given job.

3. The choice of an occupation is a rather straightforward process, and matching is possible.

4. The closer the match between personal characteristics and job requirements, the greater the likelihood of success (productivity and satisfaction). (D. Brown, 1990c, p. 17)

Common Applications

Vocational tests are based on the trait–factor assumption that traits can be measured (D. Brown, 1990c). In addition, most of the increasingly popular computerized career guidance systems are based on a traditional trait–factor approach (e.g., *System of Interactive Guidance and Information* [SIGI], Katz, 1975), as is Bolles's (1995) popular book, *What Color Is Your Parachute?*

Special Concerns for People with Disabilities

Trait–factor theory has been criticized in its application to people with disabilities (Conte, 1983). The focus of the theory on current individual traits obscures (a) the capability of people with severe disabilities to perform most jobs with appropriate assistive devices and job modifications and (b) the impact of limited early experiences on the career development of people with congenital disabilities. Nonetheless, the foundation of trait–factor theory can be found in most current rehabilitation practices in the public and private sectors. Job matching systems and analyses of transferable skills (Weed & Field, 1994) are obvious manifestations of trait–factor theory in current rehabilitation practice. Similarly, the ecological assessment practices of supported employment depend on identification of individual traits, job analyses, task analyses, and discrepancy analyses (Parker, Szymanski, & Hanley-Maxwell, 1989). Clearly, these components are obvious descendants of trait–factor theory, with one important extension. In the ecological model of rehabilitation in supported employment and rehabilitation, discrepancies between individual traits and job requirements are addressed by supports or modifications to the ecological dimensions, that is, supports to the individual, the environment, interactions, and perceptions. Supports can include such interventions as empowerment of coworkers as support givers, functional mediators (e.g., assistive devices), job modifications, and individual skill training (Szymanski & Parker, 1989).

Miller-Tiedeman's Theory of Career Decision Making

The early development of the Miller-Tiedeman decision-making model relied on concepts of Erikson's approach to ego development (Zunker, 1986) to "link person to career through the concepts of personality and individual responsibility" (Miller-Tiedeman & Tiedeman, 1990, p. 310). The Miller-Tiedeman model can be applied in conjunction with other theories of career development, work adjustment, and career choice. Essentially, it offers a framework from which to examine and reexamine human development in the broad context of one's career. The flexible essence of this theory is captured in the following quote from Miller-Tiedeman and Tiedeman (1990), in which they used the analogy of a ship at sea to describe what they refer to as the life-career process:

> Just as the horizons are seemingly infinite at sea, . . . the career process [is] . . . an ongoing process of growth and change, of evolution that is limitless. Just as a ship's captain can map navigational routes, using the stars, the wind, and sea currents, the individual can make career choices based on nature, social opportunities, and personal inclinations. Just as the sea currents and winds present unforeseen changes so that the captain must make navigational adaptations . . . , so must individuals adapt to changing natural circumstances and remain flexible. (pp. 309–310)

Key Elements

The core of the theory is the process of differentiation and reintegration of the self (Osipow, 1983; Zunker, 1986). The necessity of making a choice is one way that the differentiation–integration process is triggered. There are two major phases of decision making: (a) anticipation or preoccupation and (b) implementation or accommodation. Anticipation includes the following steps: exploration, crystallization, choice, and clarification. Implementation may include the following steps: induction, reformation, and reintegration (Miller-Tiedeman & Tiedeman, 1990).

Basic Propositions

As the Miller-Tiedeman model evolved from its initial conceptualization, it added basic philosophical tenets that guided the consideration of the elements of the decision-making model. The following are some of these tenets:

1. "Life is a self-organizing system" (Miller-Tiedeman & Tiedeman, 1990, p. 332).

2. "Objectivity is mostly a subjective experience" (Miller-Tiedeman & Tiedeman, 1990, p. 332).

3. Language represents individual experience; "the language people use about their careers mirrors the self, as both a reactor and an actor, and discloses personal assumptions about the career" (Miller-Tiedeman & Tiedeman, 1990, p. 320).

4. Personal reality differs from common reality. "Personally authoritative reality is defined as an act, thought, behavior, or direction that the individual feels is right for her or him" (Miller-Tiedeman & Tiedeman, 1990, p. 320). It is contrasted with common reality, which is what others believe the individual

should do, and is considered an often overlooked cornerstone of career decision making.

5. Actual investment of time is seen as tangible evidence of the broad process of career development (Miller-Tiedeman & Tiedeman, 1990).

Common Applications

The complexity and subjective frame of reference that are characteristic of the Miller-Tiedeman model limit the potential of commercial applications and the relevance of empirical theory testing studies (D. Brown & Brooks, 1990; Miller-Tiedeman & Tiedeman, 1990). Nonetheless, there have been some applications, including the computer-based *Information System for Vocational Decisions* (Tiedeman, 1979) and Miller-Tiedeman's curriculum for adolescents (Miller-Tiedeman & Tiedeman, 1990). Although the theory has had few practical applications (Osipow, 1983), it has made a significant contribution by increasing the focus on self-awareness (Zunker, 1986) and the subjective frame of reference as critical elements of career development.

Special Concerns for People with Disabilities

The Miller-Tiedeman model has been recognized for its potential application to people with disabilities (McDaniel, 1963). Since its recent evolution, as presented by Miller-Tiedeman and Tiedeman (1990), the theory may be even more applicable, but at the same time even more difficult to apply. The subjective frame of reference, contextual consideration, and consideration of adaptation that characterize the current Miller-Tiedeman model are particularly appropriate for people with disabilities who (a) have different frames of reference and different experiences than persons without disabilities (Wright, 1983); (b) require careful consideration of current, past, and future environments, perceptions, and interactions in rehabilitation planning (Szymanski, Dunn, & Parker, 1989); and (c) have career development patterns that may have been affected by chance (Cabral & Salomone, 1990). The evolved model of Miller-Tiedeman and Tiedeman (1990) does not provide an easy to use instrument or a clearly defined series of steps for rehabilitation counselors. It does, however, offer a useful philosophical framework and some concepts to use in understanding career decisions. This may be particularly compatible with qualitative research, which also takes into consideration subjective and contextual frames of reference and is increasingly recognized as an important tool in the study of career development of people with disabilities (see, e.g., DeLaGarza, in press; Ferguson, Ferguson, & Jones, 1988; Treviño & Szymanski, 1996).

Roe's Theory of Personality Development and Career Choice

Roe's theory of "occupational choice assumes a relationship between certain childhood environments, need development, personality, and ultimately, job choice" (D. Brown, 1990b, p. 350). Early interactions of children and parents were seen as vital forces in career development. Roe's theory is based in part on Maslow's need hierarchy and the interaction of needs and occupations. The theory was operationalized through a system of classification of occupations (Roe & Lunneborg, 1990). The foundation philosophy of Roe's theory can be seen in the following quotation:

> In our society, no single situation is potentially so capable of giving some satisfaction, at all levels of basic needs, as the occupation. . . . I would contend that, in our culture, social and economic status depend more on the occupation (of the individual, the father, or less frequently now, the husband) than on any other one thing—even wealth. (Roe & Lunneborg, 1990, p. 69)

Key Elements

There are two types of key elements to Roe's theory: factors involved in occupational choice and classification of occupations. The factors involved in occupational choice are sex (S), the general state of the economy (E), family background (B), learning and education (L), special acquired skills (A), physical appearance and abilities (P), chance (C), friends (F), marital situation (M), cognitive ability (G), temperament and personality (T), and interests and values (I). These factors are related according to the following equation: $S[(eE + bB + cC) + (fF, mM) + (lL + aA) + (pP \times gG \times tT \times iI)]$. "The lower case letters represent coefficients indicating the weight to be attached to the factor; they may vary with time and circumstances" (Roe & Lunneborg, 1990, p. 87). The comma joining F and M in the equation indicates that usually only one or the other is relevant.

Classification of occupations, the second key element of Roe's theory, is accomplished with eight occupational groups and six levels of responsibility or difficulty. The eight occupational groups are service, business contact, organization, technology, outdoor, science, general culture, and arts and entertainment. The six levels, which are applicable across groups, are professional and managerial 1 (e.g., top management), professional and managerial 2 (e.g., middle management), semiprofessional and small business, skilled, semiskilled, and unskilled (Roe & Lunneborg, 1990).

Basic Propositions

Roe's theory has five basic propositions on the origin of interests and needs:

1. Genetic inheritance sets limits on the potential development of all characteristics. . . .

2. The degrees and avenues of development of inherited characteristics are affected not only by experience unique to the individual but also by aspects of the general cultural background and the socioeconomic position of the family. . . .

3. The pattern of development of interests, attitudes, and other personality variables with relatively little or nonspecific genetic control is primarily determined by individual experiences, through which involuntary attention becomes channeled in particular directions. . . . These directions are first determined by the pattern of early satisfactions and frustrations. . . . The modes and degrees of need satisfaction determine which needs will become the strongest motivators. . . .

4. The eventual pattern of psychic energies, in terms of attention-directedness, is the major determinant of interests.

5. The intensity of these needs and their satisfaction . . . and their organization are the major determinants of the degree of motivation that reaches expression in accomplishment. (Roe & Lunneborg, 1990, pp. 74, 75, 78)

Common Applications

The *Career Occupational Preference System* (COPS) (Knapp & Knapp, 1984), a commonly used vocational guidance instrument, is based on Roe's classification system and is linked with occupational information in the *Dictionary of Occupational Titles* (U.S. Department of Labor [U.S. DOL], 1977) and the *Occupational Outlook Handbook* (U.S. DOL, 1990). *The Vocational Interest Inventory* (Lunneborg, 1981), *Ramak* (Meir, 1975), and *Courses* (Meir, 1975) are other interest inventories that have been developed from Roe's framework. Another dimension of application, addressing the core of Roe's theory, is *The Parent–Child Relations Questionnaire* (Siegelman & Roe, 1979), which provides scores on the following factors of parent–child relations: loving–rejecting, casual–demanding, and overt attention.

Special Concerns for Persons with Disabilities

Roe's theory has been described as particularly inapplicable to persons with disabilities due to its dependence on inherent personal factors (e.g., genetic inheritance, family interactions), the effect of which may have been altered by the presence of a congenital or acquired disability (Conte, 1983). However, certain aspects of Roe's theory, especially the classification of occupations by group and level, may be helpful to rehabilitation counselors. From a conceptual standpoint some of the other aspects of the theory may be useful, if one remembers that disability may significantly alter the potential effect of normal determinants of occupational choice. Congenital disability, for example, may have significant impact on early parent–child interactions, peer interactions, and many other factors (Turner & Szymanski, 1990). Acquired disability may alter the relationship of past experiences to current occupational choices (Conte, 1983). Thus, it is suggested that Roe's theory be applied with the same caution as other theories, that is, on an individual basis with full recognition of the potential impact of disability on all factors of the theory.

Krumboltz's Social Learning Theory

Krumboltz extended Bandura's social learning theory into the realm of career development (D. Brown, 1990b; Osipow, 1983). Krumboltz's theory addresses "how career interests develop, how the environment influences one's career decision making, and the manner in which career decision-making skills are developed" (National Occupational Information Coordinating Committee [NOICC], 1986, p. 31).

Key Elements

Krumboltz's theory suggests that four factors influence career decisions: (a) genetic endowment and special abilities, (b) environmental conditions and events, (c) learning experiences, and (d) task approach skills. The complex interaction of these factors leads individuals to form beliefs about themselves (self-observation generalizations) and about the world around them (world-view generalizations).

Basic Propositions

Krumboltz's theory stresses that "interests are a consequence of learning, and learning, not interests, is what leads people to make occupational choices. . . . [Thus], we need to provide individuals with a wide variety of learning experiences" (NOICC, 1986, p. 31). Decision making and future learning are related to past learning; one's beliefs about oneself and the world "influence one's approach to learning new skills and ultimately one's aspirations and actions" (Mitchell & Krumboltz, 1990, p. 156). Problematic views of oneself and the world that may impede career development include the following:

1. Persons may fail to recognize that a remediable problem exists. . . .
2. Persons may fail to exert the effort needed to make a decision or solve a problem. . . .
3. Persons may eliminate a potentially satisfying alternative for inappropriate reasons. . . .
4. Persons may choose poor alternatives for inappropriate reasons. . . .
5. Persons may suffer anguish and anxiety over perceived inability to achieve goals. . . . (Mitchell & Krumboltz, 1990, pp. 179–180)

Common Applications

Although Krumboltz's theory does not have a long history of commonly used instruments, as do Holland's and Super's theories, it does have direct applicability to the process of career counseling. "The theory provides a basis for identifying difficulties in the career decision making process, and, because of its relationship to cognitive behaviorism, techniques for remediating deficiencies are identified"

(D. Brown, 1990b, pp. 356–357). The *Career Beliefs Inventory* (Krumboltz, 1988) may also be of assistance in surfacing "presuppositions that may block people from achieving their career goals" (Mitchell & Krumboltz, 1990, p. 181).

Krumboltz's theory is also applicable in business and industry. Its focus on the interaction of individuals and their environments (Mitchell & Krumboltz, 1990) is similar to ecological approaches in rehabilitation (see, e.g., Parker et al., 1989; Szymanski & Hanley-Maxwell, 1996). The ecological focus "suggests that for organizations to promote optimal staff development, they need to examine both recruitment and job-analysis strategies carefully" (Mitchell & Krumboltz, 1990, p. 192).

Special Concerns for People with Disabilities

Krumboltz's theory appears to be particularly applicable for career counseling with people with disabilities due to its ecological nature and its focus on learning. People with congenital disabilities, for example, face numerous obstacles in career development (Turner & Szymanski, 1990). Limited early experiences, underdeveloped decision-making skills, and negative self-concept are frequent attributes of such individuals (Curnow, 1989). Thus, a wide variety of learning experiences (e.g., career education, job shadowing, work tryouts) should be encouraged for preparation of persons with congenital disabilities. Similarly, Krumboltz's principles can be used to assist persons with acquired or congenital disabilities to make informed career decisions and to identify dysfunctional career-related beliefs. Also, perhaps, the learning-based concepts of career education and work tryout experiences should be considered for those people with acquired disabilities who face changes of both employer and occupation.

Minnesota Theory of Work Adjustment

Although all the theories presented thus far were developed by focusing primarily or exclusively on individuals without disabilities, the Minnesota Theory of Work Adjustment and other work adjustment theories were developed by authors whose initial concern was directed at least equally toward persons with disabilities. These approaches have tended to be cast in terms of work behavior and work adjustment, rather than in terms of occupational choice or career development, because the latter concepts are considered of dubious applicability to many persons with severe disabilities.

Work personality is a key construct in work adjustment theories, although definitions of work personality vary widely. Neff, a pioneer in the study of work personality, based his definition on his work with persons with disabilities in Chicago and New York. He concluded that the work personality was "the concrete set of interrelated motives, coping styles, defensive maneuvers, and the like with which a given individual confronts the demand to work" (Neff, 1985, p. 156). Neff (1985) further concluded that work personality constitutes a semi-autonomous area of the personality. As such, a person may be well adjusted in that area but poorly adjusted in some other areas (e.g., psychopathology, social relationships), or vice versa. Implicit in this conception is that treatment of problems in one area (e.g., marriage) may not improve functioning in another area (e.g., work). Conversely, the presence of an emotional disability does not preclude immediate vocational rehabilitation.

The Minnesota Theory of Work Adjustment was one of the earliest work adjustment theories, with development beginning in 1959 and continuing over the next decade. It was developed by Lofquist and Dawis and their associates at the University of Minnesota (1969; Dawis & Lofquist, 1984) with support from the Rehabilitation Services Administration. Recently, the theory was extended to a person–environment correspondence theory in order to "go beyond the adjustment to work to address the whole gamut of problems presented to counselors" (Lofquist & Dawis, 1991, p. 1).

Key Elements

Lofquist and Dawis also used the term *work personality,* but defined it differently from Neff. For Lofquist and Dawis, the work personality consists of the person's abilities and work-related needs. These individual abilities and needs are matched with the ability requirement and reinforcer system of the work environment. The match between the person's abilities and the ability requirements of the work environment determines satisfactoriness (i.e., the extent to which the person is able to perform the job). The match between the person's needs and the reinforcer system of the work environment determines the person's satisfaction with the job. Tenure (length of time the person stays on the job) is a function of both satisfactoriness and satisfaction. Work adjustment is defined as "the continuous and dynamic process by which the individual seeks to achieve and maintain correspondence with . . . [the] work environment" (Lofquist & Dawis, 1969, p. 46).

Basic Propositions

Lofquist and Dawis (1969) proposed the following set of formal propositions:

1. An individual's work adjustment at any point in time is indicated by his concurrent levels of satisfactoriness and satisfaction. . . .
2. Satisfactoriness is a function of the correspondence between an individual's abilities and the ability requirements of the work environment, provided that the individual's needs correspond with the reinforcer system of the work environment. . . .
3. Satisfaction is a function of the correspondence between the reinforcer system of the work environment and the individual's needs, provided that the individual's abilities correspond with the ability requirement of the work environment. . . .
4. Satisfaction moderates the functional relationship between satisfactoriness and ability–requirement correspondence. . . .

5. Satisfactoriness moderates the functional relationship between satisfaction and need–reinforcer correspondence. . . .

6. The probability that an individual will be forced out of the work environment is inversely related to his satisfactoriness. . . .

7. The probability that an individual will voluntarily leave the work environment is inversely related to his satisfaction. . . .

8. Tenure is a joint function of satisfactoriness and satisfaction. . . .

9. Work personality–work environment correspondence increases as a function of tenure. (pp. 50–53)

These propositions and corollaries derived from them were used to suggest hypotheses for testing. Research based on these propositions has generally supported the utility of the model (Betz, Fitzgerald, & Hill, 1989). The theory continues to be the focus of considerable research. In fact, a special issue of the *Journal of Vocational Behavior* (Tinsley, 1993), which was devoted to the theory, contained articles that provided additional empirical support for some of the theory's propositions.

Common Applications

Abilities are typically measured by the U.S. Department of Labor's (1979) *General Aptitude Test Battery* (GATB), and needs are assessed by the *Minnesota Importance Questionnaire* (MIQ) (Rounds, Henly, Dawis, Lofquist, & Weiss, 1981), which was developed for this purpose. Ability requirements are included in a system of occupational aptitude patterns (OAPs); the system is keyed to the GATB and was also developed by the Department of Labor. The *Minnesota Job Description Questionnaire* is used to assess the kinds and levels of reinforcers in different types of jobs. Based on responses from workers in a given type of job, an occupation reinforcer pattern (ORP) is developed to profile the reinforcer system for that job. Thus, congruence between GATB scores and OAPs and between MIQ scores and ORPs is examined. These objective measures of worker–environment congruence are complemented by subjective measures; satisfactoriness is measured by the supervisor's rating on the *Minnesota Satisfactoriness Scales,* and satisfaction is measured by a self-report on the *Minnesota Satisfaction Questionnaire* (Weiss, England, Dawis, & Lofquist, 1966).

Special Concerns for People with Disabilities

Because the Minnesota Work Adjustment Project was supported primarily by federal rehabilitation funds, considerable attention was given to the applicability of the materials and concepts to persons with disabilities. Lofquist, Siess, Dawis, England, and Weiss (1964) indicated that the Minnesota theory focuses more on work adjustment potential of persons being evaluated for rehabilitation than does any other theory to date. They also suggested that the ease of administration of their measures can free rehabilitation counselor time for more individual counseling with the client (Lofquist & Dawis, 1969).

Conte (1983) criticized the Minnesota theory for having too restricted a range of focus, thereby limiting its utility for persons with disabilities. Although the theory focuses on the relationship between a particular person and a particular job, it fails to address the lifelong process of career development. This criticism may not be fully warranted, in that the theory set out to address work adjustment and made no claims to account for career development.

The Minnesota theory, being based largely on a trait–factor model, is susceptible to the same criticisms presented earlier for trait–factor theories in general and Holland's theory in particular, which is also essentially a trait–factor congruence model. Trait–factor approaches do nothing to compensate for the limited early experiences of persons with congenital disabilities or to suggest supportive interventions that can permit persons with disabilities to enter, function, and sustain themselves in the work environment.

Hershenson's Model of Work Adjustment Development

Hershenson's theory of work adjustment combined features of career development and work adjustment theories. This theory, which was developed after the Minnesota theory, is applicable both to persons with congenital disabilities (Szymanski, Hershenson, & Power, 1988; Turner & Szymanski, 1990) and to persons with acquired disabilities (Hershenson, 1981).

Key Elements

The two essential elements in this model are the person and the person's environment. Within the person, three domains develop in sequence. The first, the work personality, is composed of three elements, the person's self-concept as a worker, the person's system of motivation for work, and the person's work-related needs and values. (It should be noted that Hershenson, Lofquist and Dawis, and Neff all used the term work personality, but each defined it differently.) The next domain to develop is work competencies, which is composed of three elements: work habits, physical and mental skills applicable to jobs, and work-related interpersonal skills. The third domain to develop is appropriate, crystallized work goals (Hershenson, 1981, 1996). As they develop and continue to function, these three domains interact with each other and with the environment. The product of the interaction of these domains with the work environment is called work adjustment. (Again, this definition of work adjustment differs from Lofquist and Dawis's use of the term.)

Work adjustment, as used by Hershenson, has three components: task performance (i.e., quality and quantity of work output), work-role behavior (i.e., behavior appropriate to the work setting, such as wearing suitable clothes, taking responsibility, following directions, getting along with supervisors and coworkers), and work satisfaction (i.e., the person's own degree of gratification resulting from work). Of these three components of work adjustment, task performance is linked primarily with work competencies and secondarily with work personality, work-role behavior is linked primarily to work personality and secondarily to the work habits component of work competencies, and work satisfaction is linked primarily to work goals and secondarily to work personality. Although task performance can be completely defined by objective standards (e.g., industrial norms) and work-role behavior is largely objectively defined, work satisfaction is subjective.

Basic Propositions

Each of the three domains within the person—work personality, work competencies, and work goals—becomes the focus of development in the sequence indicated above; however, each domain also reciprocally influences the development of the other two. Thus, the development of work adjustment is a dynamic process in which each domain develops only to a level that is supported by its predecessor. However, the next focal domain to develop can reciprocally affect the predecessor and thereby change the limit of its own further development. For instance, although the basic work personality domain is fairly well established before the development of work competencies assumes primacy, as work habits and skills develop or fail to develop, the configuration of the individual's self-concept as a worker and motivational system (i.e., the components of work personality) is necessarily affected. Likewise, the development of work goals influences the configuration of the other two domains. Skills not relevant to these goals may atrophy, and the individual's motivational system must become consistent with the goals that have been developed.

The Hershenson model posits that, throughout an individual's lifetime, all domains will continue to develop, although not as rapidly or dramatically as at the time they are focal. The three domains establish a dynamic, reciprocal balance, so that any change in one domain will necessitate changes in the other two to restore balance.

According to this model, work personality develops focally during the pre-school years, primarily under the influence of the family, the principal environmental influence on the child at this point in life. Work competencies have their focal development during the school years, largely as a result of successes and failures encountered in meeting the physical, mental, and social demands of the school setting. To the extent that these environmental expectations are exceeded or are not met, the child may have to revise the work personality that was formed before the demands of the outside world were confronted. Thus, failures at school may stimulate revision of an unrealistically omnipotent self-concept, and successes at school may lead to an upward revision of an unrealistically negative self-concept. Finally, work goals reflect the influences of peer or reference groups as the person goes through the process of preparing to leave school and enter the world of work.

It must be recognized that these three factors—home, school, and reference groups—are not completely independent of each other, since the family largely determines the school that the child will attend, and the school, in turn, often provides a reference group. It must also be noted that in developing work adjustment, the child undergoes two major transitions, the first from home to school and the second (and currently more focused upon) from school to work. It must further be recognized that the first of these transitions has a potentially significant effect on the shape and outcome of the second transition.

Common Applications

Several rating scales, both self-rating and observer rating, have been developed to assess the status of the three domains within the person (Hershenson & Langbauer, 1973; Hershenson & Lavery, 1978). These scales, as reported in these studies, have consistently supported the existence of the developmental sequence postulated by the theory in nondisabled persons and in both persons with congenital or precareer disabilities and those with acquired, midcareer disabilities.

Special Concerns for People with Disabilities

As has been indicated, this theory was designed to be applicable specifically to persons with disabilities. According to the theory (Hershenson, 1981), disability initially has an impact on work competencies, although the impact of disability rapidly spreads to the interconnected domains of work personality and work goals. For persons with acquired disabilities, this means that the initial impact of disability on work adjustment results from the interaction of established work competencies with the functional limitations resulting from the disability, the specific job tasks of the current or desired position, and the possibilities for job modification. Thus, rheumatoid arthritis may have a more devastating effect on the work adjustment of a garment worker than on that of an attorney.

For persons with congenital disabilities, the situation is somewhat different, because work personality generally develops before disability has its major impact on work competencies. The child with a disability is particularly likely to experience a conflict between preschool work personality and work competencies shown at school. Thus, the transition from home to school is more likely to be discontinuous, providing a negative set for the second transition, from school to work. An example of this phenomenon is specific learning disability in a child of above average intelligence. During the preschool years, the child may have developed a strong, positive work personality. When confronted with tasks at school that other, apparently less bright students can master easily but that are overwhelming for this child, the work personality can be thrown into disarray. This, in turn, may be reflected in unrealistically high or unnecessarily low work goals (Hershenson, 1984).

Conte (1983) criticized Hershenson's model on the same grounds that he criticized the Minnesota theory, for having too restricted a range of focus on the specific person–job relationship, and hence for not accounting enough for the developmental process. Because Hershenson, unlike the Minnesota group, set out to present a developmental model, this criticism may be more justified in his case.

The theories or approaches presented in the remainder of this section are either recently emergent or not frequently applied in rehabilitation counseling. Thus the section on common applications is omitted. Nonetheless, we believe that these theories have very important potential application to rehabilitation counseling practice.

Sociocognitive Approaches

Individual beliefs and social structures add important dimensions to the study of career development, which may be particularly salient for people with disabilities and racial and ethnic minorities. In this section, we summarize a recent approach by Lent and Hackett (1994).

Key Elements

The key elements of this approach are cognitive processes (e.g., self-efficacy, outcome expectations) that mediate the impact of individual, environmental, and performance factors.

Basic Propositions

According to Lent and Hackett (1994), work performance is influenced by the interrelationship of the following factors: personal inputs (i.e., predispositions, gender, race/ethnicity, disability, health status), background (i.e., context), learning experiences, self-efficacy, outcome expectations, interests, goals, choice actions, contextual influences proximal to choice behavior, and performance outcomes. Self-efficacy and outcome expectations are particularly important elements of the sociocognitive approach. Self-efficacy addresses individual beliefs about the abilities related to specific tasks (Bandura, 1982). Outcome expectations, a separate but related construct, address the anticipated results of actions (Lent & Hackett, 1994).

Possible Applications for People with Disabilities

Sociocognitive approaches have particularly good potential for addressing career development of people with disabilities for at least a few reasons. First, disability is a complex phenomenon. The sociopolitical definition of disability (Hahn, 1985) places its impact in the relationship of individuals with their environments. Second, disability is socially and culturally constructed (Whyte, 1995). Thus, both meanings and impacts of disability are affected not only by individual, environmental, and social conditions but also by the interactions among these conditions and the belief structures of individuals.

In addition, both self-efficacy and outcome expectations are important constructs to consider in career planning with individuals with disabilities. Self-efficacy (see Strauser, 1995) has considerable potential in explaining the varying results of the same disability. Similarly, outcome expectations are quite important in light of potential financial disincentives related to social security (Szymanski, 1988) and other benefits, as well as the anticipated impacts of discrimination.

Developmental Contextualism

Developmental contextualism has emerged in the last decade as an important addition to other career development models. It has been used in addressing career development of minorities (see, e.g., Vondracek & Fouad, 1994) and has good potential for application to people with disabilities.

Key Elements

Developmental contextualism includes many of the individual and environmental elements of other theories. However, it adds emphasis on the context in which individuals live and have lived and on the changing nature of that context (Vondracek, Lerner, & Schulenberg, 1986). In addition, the approach addresses nonnormative events, including chance (Vondracek & Schulenberg, 1992), which have been considered important, albeit often overlooked, contributors to career development (Cabral & Salomone, 1990).

Basic Propositions

Developmental contextualism "recognizes the changing character of the individual's social, physical, and cultural milieus" (Vondracek et al., 1986, p. 5). It is exemplified by the following propositions.

1. "Both the individual and the context . . . [change] interdependently over time, which thus requires a *dynamic interactional* view of career development" (Vondracek et al., 1986, p. 8).

2. Contextual factors, which are broadly constructed, include influences related to age (e.g., maturity, graduating from school), history (e.g., war, the 1960s), and nonnormative events (e.g., winning the lottery, inheriting the family business) (Vondracek & Schulenberg, 1992).

3. Similar to Bronfenbrenner (1988), the developmental contextual approach addresses the embeddedness of phenomena:

   Key phenomena of human life exist at multiple levels of analysis (e.g., biological, individual–psychological, dyadic, organizational, social, cultural, physical–ecological, historical). At any time, these variables and processes from any and all of these multiple levels may contribute to human functioning. . . . These levels do not act independently; rather each level reciprocally interacts with others, resulting in dynamic interaction. (Vondracek & Fouad, 1994, p. 212)

Possible Applications for People with Disabilities

The important contributions of developmental contextualism to rehabilitation counseling cannot be underestimated. The context in which people with disabilities live may include poverty, financial disincentives for working or living independently, or a host of other situations that are quite relevant to career planning. In addition, acquired disabilities, which are themselves nonnormative events, may be associated with other such events (e.g., war, accident), which are quite relevant to vocational behavior. Both context and nonnormative factors are often overlooked in individual assessment.

Organizational Career Theories

Organizational theories build on and extend other approaches to address the behavior of individuals in the workplace. Thus, this group of theories is particularly useful in human resource planning and employee assistance programs. Our overview includes elements of the work of Moos (1986) and Hall (1986, 1990, 1996).

Key Elements

Key ingredients of these approaches are individual characteristics and organizational needs. The focus is both on the development of the individual and that of the organization.

Basic Propositions

The following propositions provide a glimpse at this approach to career development:

1. Individual adaptation (i.e., work morale and performance, overall well-being and health) is interrelated with the personal system (e.g., demographic and personal factors; type of job and work role) and the environmental system (organizational and work context, nonwork stressors and resources) (Moos, 1986).

2. Organizational career development is "a planned effort to link the individual's career needs with the organization's workforce requirements" (Gutteridge, Leibowitz, & Shore, 1993, p. 1). Key elements include career planning and career management.

3. Career planning is a "deliberate process of (1) becoming aware of self, opportunities, constraints, choices, and consequences; (2) identifying career-related goals, and (3) programming work, education, and related developmental experiences to provide the direction, timing, and sequence of steps to attain a specific goal" (Hall, 1986, p. 3).

4. "Career management is an ongoing process of preparing, implementing, and monitoring career plans undertaken by the individual alone or in concert with the organization's career systems" (Hall, 1986, p. 3).

5. Individual and organizational flexibility and planning will be keys to future survival and success (Gutteridge, 1986).

Possible Applications for People with Disabilities

Assisting people with disabilities in becoming employed requires consideration of both individual and organizational perspectives (see Millington, Butterworth, Fesko, & McCarthy, Chapter 11, this text). Organizational career theory provides a framework for uniting these perspectives.

Sociological Approaches

Work is the "activity performed by individuals to produce goods and services of value to others. . . . It is typically performed in a socially structured context" (Hotchkiss & Borow, 1990, p. 262). Sociological perspectives (see, e.g., Erikson & Vallas, 1990; Hotchkiss & Borow, 1990; Rothman, 1987) focus on this social context.

Key Elements

Key elements of this group of theories include occupational and educational attainments, socialization, and allocation.

Basic Propositions

Sociological approaches usually incorporate the following propositions:

1. Occupational attainment results from the combined forces of socialization and allocation.

2. Socialization is influenced by parental occupation, gender, social class, race, and ethnicity.

3. Allocation is a process in which gatekeepers (i.e., parents, teachers, vocational counselors, school administrators, and personnel directors) funnel people in specific directions based on external criteria (Rothman, 1987).

Possible Applications for People with Disabilities

Socialization and allocation are external forces, which are often overlooked in rehabilitation counseling. Allocation is particularly important because professionals in rehabilitation counseling and special education can, either knowingly or unknowingly, reduce the occupational opportunities available for people with disabilities.

In summary, a wide variety of theories have been presented in this section. Although the theories have varying degrees of empirical support (D. Brown, 1990b), they all add some illumination to career development and have potential applications for people with disabilities. In addition, the theories, which are designed for different audiences, present multiple frames of reference from which to design and interpret career development research (Savickas & Lent, 1994b). Nonetheless, the sheer number of such theories presents a challenge for rehabilitation counselors seeking to address the career-related concerns of consumers. To this end, an organizational framework is presented in the next section.

An Ecological Model for Organization of the Theories

As theories of vocational behavior have proliferated, various attempts have been made to categorize them (e.g., Herr & Cramer, 1988; Roth, Hershenson, & Hilliard, 1970). Because we believed that the existing classification systems were not adequate, we added a new system in the last edition of this text (Hershenson & Szymanski, 1992). Since that time, theories have continued to evolve as has our understanding of their intricacies.

In a recent work (Szymanski, Hershenson, Enright, & Ettinger, 1996), we developed a new approach to organization of theories through the constructs that they address. In the following paragraphs we describe that model and extend it by adding career development processes. The model is described as ecological because, like other models in rehabilitation and related disciplines (see, e.g., Parker et al., 1989; Szymanski, in press; Szymanski, Hershenson, & Power, 1988), it follows the traditions of Bronfenbrenner (1988) and Lewin (1936) in addressing the interactions of individuals and their environments. Additionally, it is important to note that the current model was developed both to classify theories and to aid in planning assessment and interventions.

Constructs

Constructs are concepts used to explain phenomena (Kerlinger, 1986). Each career theory uses a variety of constructs—for example, work personality and individual traits—to explain behavior. All of the constructs addressed by the multiple career development theories presented in the previous section can be classified into at least one of the following five groups: individual, contextual, mediating, environmental, and outcome (Szymanski, Hershenson, Enright, & Ettinger, 1996); some constructs (e.g., discrimination) can be classified into more than one group (i.e., mediating, environment).

Before we proceed, it should be noted that parts of the current discussion are adapted from the original source (Szymanski, Hershenson, Enright, & Ettinger, 1996), and from discussion of the application of the construct portion of the model to school-to-work transition (Szymanski, in press), to individuals with developmental disabilities (Szymanski & Hanley-Maxwell, 1996), and to training rehabilitation counselors (Szymanski, Fernandez, Koch, & Merz, 1996).

Individual

Individual constructs, which are part of most career development theories, are attributes directly connected to the person. They include gender, race (Fitzgerald & Betz, 1994), physical and mental abilities, interests (Lofquist & Dawis, 1991), and the aspect of disability that is an individual (rather than social) attribute (Szymanski, Hershenson, Enright, & Ettinger, 1996).

Contextual

Contextual constructs relate to the situations in which individuals live or have lived. They are external to the individual and include opportunity structures, socioeconomic status, family, education, nonnormative influences (e.g., floods, war), and relevant legislation (e.g., the Americans with Disabilities Act of 1990) (Szymanski, Hershenson, Enright, & Ettinger, 1996). Contextual constructs have long been included in sociological theories (see, e.g., Rothman, 1987) and have recently received more prominence in vocational and counseling psychology (see, e.g., Fitzgerald & Betz, 1994; Vondracek, Lerner, & Schulenberg, 1986).

Mediating

Mediating constructs are individual, cultural, or societal beliefs that affect the interaction of individuals with environments (Szymanski, Hershenson, Enright, & Ettinger, 1996). On the individual level, mediating constructs include work personality (see, e.g., Hershenson, 1981), self-efficacy (see, e.g., Bandura, 1982), and outcome expectations (see, e.g., Lent & Hackett, 1994). Cultural mediating constructs include cultural and religious beliefs (see, e.g., Trueba, Rodriguez, Zou, & Cintron, 1993), acculturation (see, e.g., LaFramboise, Coleman, & Gerton, 1993), and racial identity (Rowe, Behrens, & Leach, 1995). Societal mediating constructs include discrimination (see, e.g., James, 1994) and castification, which is a way in which one group systematically marginalizes another group (Szymanski & Trueba, 1994).

Human behavior is known to be influenced by belief structures (Bronfenbrenner, 1988). The mediating impact of belief structures is reflected in developmental (see, e.g., Super, 1990), sociocognitive (see, e.g., Lent & Hackett, 1994), and developmental contextualism (see, e.g., Vondracek & Fouad, 1994) approaches to career development.

Environmental

Environmental constructs include elements and structures in work and other environments that influence the behavior of individuals (Szymanski, Hershenson, Enright, & Ettinger, 1996). Organizational culture of work (see, e.g., Rothman, 1987) and other environments, such as schools, is particularly important. Other such constructs include task requirements and reinforcement systems (Dawis, 1994; Lofquist & Dawis, 1991), the characteristics of workers in the environment as operationalized by Holland's (1985a, 1994) modal work environments, and physical characteristics of the environment that may limit or promote access to people with disabilities. Trait and factor type theories (see, e.g., D. Brown, 1990c; Holland, 1985a; Lofquist & Dawis, 1991) have long included the environment. In fact, as previously stated, this group of theories recently has been referred to by the term *person–environment interaction* (Rounds & Tracey, 1990). Additionally, organizational career theories emphasize these constructs.

Outcome

Outcome constructs describe the behaviors or states resulting from the interaction of the other groups of constructs (Szymanski, Hershenson, Enright, & Ettinger, 1996). They include job satisfaction and satisfactoriness (Lofquist & Dawis, 1991), job stress (Landy, 1992), occupational attainment (Rothman, 1987), and organizational productivity and competitiveness (Hall, 1990). Most career development theories include some type of outcome construct.

Processes

In addition to constructs, theories also address processes. The major processes in career theories are congruence, decision making, development, socialization, allocation, and chance.

Congruence (Holland, 1985a), also described as correspondence (Lofquist & Dawis, 1991), is the process of relative match or mismatch of individuals with their environments. *Decision making,* for the purposes of this chapter, is the process by which individuals consider career-related alternatives and formulate decisions (D. Brown, 1990a). The *developmental* process involves systematic changes over time (Vondracek et al., 1986), which are interwoven with characteristics and perceptions of the individual (see, e.g., Super, 1990) and reciprocally influenced by the environment (Bronfenbrenner, 1988). *Socialization* is the process by which people learn work and life roles. It is influenced by parental occupation, gender, social class, race, and ethnicity (Rothman, 1987). *Allocation* is the process by which societal gatekeepers (i.e., parents, teachers, vocational counselors, school administrators, and personnel directors) use external criteria to channel individuals into or exclude them from specific directions. *Chance* is the occurrence of unforeseen events or encounters (Cabral & Salomone, 1990).

Three of the processes, congruence, decision making, and development, are primarily internal to the individual, although they are influenced by external factors. The other three are primarily external to the individual, although they also interact with internal factors and processes.

Model

The constructs and processes present a framework to understand career development, classify theories, and plan assessment and interventions. Specifically, according to this model, *career development is determined by the dynamic interaction of individual, contextual, mediating, environmental, and outcome constructs with congruence, decision-making, developmental, socialization, allocation, and chance processes.* A major evolution of the model presented in this section is that classification does not result in mutually exclusive categories. This is particularly important because, as noted by many authors in the convergence project (Savickas & Lent, 1994a), the theories have continued to evolve and expand.

Table 10.2 illustrates the constructs and processes addressed by each of the theories covered in this chapter. As is evident from the table, the theories complement each other. Although there is some overlap, they tend to differ somewhat as to which groups of constructs and which processes they address.

General Issues Regarding Theory Application and Career Development of People with Disabilities, Including Members of Racial and Ethnic Minority Groups

As we noted earlier, no theory can be fully applicable or nonapplicable to any diverse group, including people with disabilities and racial and ethnic minorities (Szymanski, Hershenson, Enright, & Ettinger, 1996). Nonetheless, both disability (Rojewski, 1994) and minority status (Leong, 1995) pose *risk factors* for career development. In addition, disabilities are overrepresented in minority populations (Storck & Thompson-Hoffman, 1991). Therefore, in the following paragraphs, we address general issues relating to people with disabilities, including minorities, and their career development, according to the constructs and processes introduced in the previous section.

Individual Constructs

Both people with disabilities and members of racial and ethnic minority groups are very diverse. This diversity limits the degrees of theory applicability or

Table 10.2
Multiple Construct and Process System of Theory Classification

Theory	Types of Constructs					Types of Process					
	Individual	Contextual	Mediating	Environment	Outcome	Development	Decision Making	Congruence	Socialization	Allocation	Chance
Super's Theory	X	X	X	X	X	X		X			
Holland's Theory	X			X	X			X			
Trait-Factor Theory	X		X	X	X			X			
Miller-Tiedeman's Theory	X		X				X				
Roe's Theory	X	X		X	X	X			X		X
Krumboltz's Theory	X	X	X		X	X	X		X		X
Minnesota Theory	X			X	X			X			
Hershenson's Model	X		X	X	X	X			X		X
Sociocognitive Approach	X	X	X	X	X	X			X		X
Developmental Contextualism	X	X	X	X	X	X		X	X		X
Sociological Theories	X	X	X	X	X				X	X	
Organizational Career Theories	X			X	X					X	X

nonapplicability (Szymanski, Hershenson, Enright, & Ettinger, 1996). Both groups include individuals with widely different life experiences, abilities, and interests. Thus, a given theory can be applicable to one member of a group and not applicable to another member of the same group.

In addressing the needs for career development of people with disabilities, it is important to recognize the existence of two different populations: people with congenital disabilities and people with acquired disabilities. These populations frequently have very different life experiences and career counseling needs (Conte, 1983; Super, 1969). However, as with the general population, considerable variation exists within both groups of people with disabilities. Consider, for example, the full range of cognitive and physical abilities and limitations. Thus, one would not expect to find a distinct theory of occupational choice, career development, or work adjustment that could be applied to all people with disabilities. Perhaps it was this realization of diversity that led Super to suggest over two decades ago that rehabilitation counseling relied on special applications of existing theories rather than formulations of new theories (Super, 1969).

Similarly, there is considerable within-group and across-group variability among members of racial and ethnic minority groups (see, e.g., Lee & Richardson, 1991; Leong, 1995; Sue & Sue, 1990). For example, Hispanics or Latinos include people from Mexico, Cuba, Puerto Rico, and Central and South America. These groups vary widely along cultural beliefs and their history of disadvantage (Arbona, 1995). Similar variability exists within and across Native American populations (Johnson, Swartz, & Martin, 1995). Thus, although an early criticism of many career development theories was their limitations in applicability to members of different racial and ethnic minorities (see, e.g., D. Brown, 1990b), it would not be reasonable to expect full applicability of any theory to such a diverse population.

Once this diversity is considered, the constructs and instruments of various theories can be used appropriately to assist consumers in understanding their individual abilities. Such self-understanding is key to successful career planning (Phillips, 1992).

Contextual Constructs

Contextual constructs can be particularly potent risk factors to the career development of minorities and people with disabilities. Certain contexts can constrain positive career development and may suggest remedial or enrichment experiences to facilitate career planning. Two areas that bear special consideration are (a) socioeconomic status and opportunity structures and (b) socialization patterns.

People with disabilities and members of racial and ethnic minority groups are overrepresented among persons living in poverty (Szymanski, Ryan, Merz, Treviño, & Johnston-Rodriguez, 1996). Further, background characteristics, including socioeconomic status and parental education, have potent influences on educational and occupational attainment (Haveman & Wolfe, 1994). In addition, frequent limitations in opportunity structures and beliefs about the centrality of work in individual lives have called into question the assumptions of many career theories in application to minorities (Osipow & Littlejohn, 1995). Similar concerns would seem warranted for people with disabilities.

Two areas of concern relating to socialization, which may contribute to mediating beliefs (e.g., self-efficacy, outcome expectations), are plausible role models and chores. The presence of work role models who are similar in important characteristics (e.g., gender, race, disability) has been considered important in career development of people with disabilities (see, e.g., Szymanski, 1994) and racial and ethnic minorities (see, e.g., Bowman, 1995). In addition, frequency of chores during childhood has been associated with employment of young adults with physical disabilities (Victor, McCarthy, & Palmer, 1986).

It is important to note that a full range of contexts exists for people with disabilities and members of racial and ethnic minority groups. Thus, although contextual limitations may pose risk factors, their relative importance for any one individual cannot be assumed. Rather, contextual constructs introduce another dimension of diversity that must be considered in career assessment and intervention.

Mediating Constructs

Mediating structures are also important to addressing the career development of people with disabilities and minorities. Individual belief systems can affect career development (see, e.g., Lent & Hackett, 1994). Self-efficacy and outcome expectations are particularly important considerations (Fitzgerald & Betz, 1994; Leong, 1995), which may be affected by contextual factors.

In considering mediating structures, it is important to note that a person's racial and ethnic background or the nature of his or her disability cannot reliably predict the barriers the person will face in career development. Acculturation, which is the degree of identification with the culture of origin and the majority culture, mediates the effect of ethnicity (LaFromboise et al., 1993). Similarly, adjustment processes (see, e.g., Cook, Chapter 9, this text), self-concept (Wright, 1983), and work personality (Hershenson, 1981) can mediate the impact of disability.

Societal beliefs also mediate career development and the application of career theories to people with disabilities and minorities. "Social attitudes toward disability may be as important as the disability itself in that the negative attitude of others plays a part in shaping the life role of the individual with disability" (Curnow, 1989, p. 273). Similarly, discrimination remains a problem in the workplace. "The limited empirical evidence available supports the idea that discrimination and prejudice on the job contribute to minority stress and stress-related disturbances" (James, 1994, p. 128).

The theories provide a number of constructs and a few instruments that can assist counselors and consumers in understanding and considering mediating constructs that may have an impact on career development. Examples of potential instruments include the *Career Decision Making Self-Efficacy Scale* (Taylor & Betz, 1983), *My Vocational Situation* (Holland et al., 1980), the *Salience Inventory* and the *Values Scales* (Super & Nevill, 1986a, 1986b), *The Career Attitudes and Strategies Inventory* (Holland & Gottfredson, 1994), and the *Career Beliefs Inventory* (Krumboltz, 1988).

Environmental Constructs

A variety of environmental constructs are important to career planning with people with disabilities and minorities. Of obvious importance are social and monetary reinforcements (Lofquist & Dawis, 1991), especially wage levels that can offset social security or welfare and Medicaid assistance. Organizational culture is an important yet often overlooked consideration. Not fitting in to the culture can be as detrimental as lacking requisite skills (see Millington et al., Chapter 11, this text).

Physical accessibility and potential support services for people with disabilities may be important concerns in choosing among potential educational and work environments. Similarly, the cultural composition and relative absence of discrimination are potential concerns for minorities.

Outcome Constructs

Work adjustment (Hershenson, 1981), performance (Moos, 1986), job tenure (Lofquist & Dawis, 1991), and satisfaction (Lofquist & Dawis, 1991) are important outcome considerations in career planning. Simply getting a job is not sufficient for most people. The job must be within their abilities and fulfill important needs (e.g., money, social support).

Job stress is a very important area of career planning for both people with disabilities and minorities. Job stress appears to be increasing and is particularly associated with jobs in which individuals have little control or in which there is monotony and high demand (Landy, 1992). Unfortunately, good jobs are decreasing, and minorities and people with disabilities often find themselves in jobs that can produce unhealthy levels of stress. Therefore, in addition to stress avoidance, counselors should consider stress inoculation. Possible interventions might include development of social supports, which have been shown to mediate the impact of job stress (Landy, 1992), regular exercise, and healthy lifestyles.

Finally, job tenure may not be a reliable output indicator for people with limited options. Persons with developmental disabilities may be required to remain in jobs that are stressful or unpleasant due to constraints associated with their living situations (Szymanski, Johnston-Rodriguez, Millington, Rodriguez, & Lagergren, 1995). Similarly, economic constraints or lack of qualifications (Kozol, 1991) may keep minorities from leaving problematic employment.

Congruence (or Correspondence) Processes

The process of congruence or correspondence provides an important area of consideration in career planning with people with disabilities and minorities. The validity of the process can be compromised by limitations in measurement of either the person or the environment. Disabilities and language proficiency can interfere with the construct validity of ability measures. For example, a person whose physical limitations make writing difficult might test poorly on a written test of math ability even though his or her true abilities were superior (Parker et al., 1989). Language can present a similar problem for people with limited English proficiency (Szymanski & Trueba, 1994). Thus, counselors need to carefully evaluate the validity of instruments used in the matching process for individual consumers.

Similarly, on the environment side, job matching approaches that do not consider possible job accommodations or assistive technology can incorrectly limit the options considered by people with disabilities. To counter this possibility, it is important for counselors to assist consumers in learning about a wide range of possible accommodations and consider these in preliminary evaluations of potential occupations.

In addition, social class and self-efficacy may mediate the relationship between interests and occupations for minorities (Arbona, 1995). Counselors may need to consider enrichment experiences in order to expand the range of occupations considered.

Decision-Making Processes

Decision-making processes and career goals are of particular concern in career planning with both people with disabilities and minorities. Consumer choice (see, e.g., West & Parent, 1992) and self-determination (Wehmeyer, 1992) have been important areas of concern in rehabilitation and special education. Due to limited experiences, people with developmental disabilities may need assistance in order to fully participate in career planning. Hagner and Salomone (1989) recommended "(a) guided job experiences, (b) decision-making training, (c) technical assistance within the decision-making process, and (d) longitudinal career services" (p. 155).

Both decision-making processes and goals are important concerns for racial and ethnic minorities, including those with disabilities. For European-type cultures, like the majority in the United States, independence is a valued goal, and independent approaches to decision making are the norm. In contrast, for many minority cultures, interdependence, community membership, and family contributions are important goals, and collectivist approaches to decision making are the norm (Betz & Fitzgerald, 1995). Of course, as noted earlier, acculturation mediates the impact of the culture of origin. Thus, rehabilitation counselors need to carefully consider the cultural preferences of consumers in decision making and career goals.

Developmental Processes

Developmental disabilities, which are often present during childhood and adolescence, can influence developmental processes (Anastasiow, 1986) and thus affect career development. Particular areas of concern are play, chores, and interest development.

Play and chores can contribute to the development of work personality and work competencies (Hershenson, 1981). Children with disabilities may have limited opportunities to learn critical social skills through play, especially play with peers without disabilities, or to learn responsibility through chores.

Interests are not innate. Rather, they are learned (Mitchell & Krumboltz, 1990). Limitations in early experiences as a result of disability or poverty can restrict interest development. Adolescents or young adults with disabilities and those who have grown up in poverty may exhibit flat profiles on interest inventories. Rehabilitation counselors should be cognizant of the potential interactions of development and disabilities. Enrichment or remedial experiences may be necessary for consumers to gain the requisite experiences for informed career planning.

Socialization Processes

Socialization is the process by which behavior is shaped and life roles are learned and implemented. As noted by Rothman (1987), it is influenced by the contextual constructs of parental occupation and social class, as well as the individual constructs of race, gender, and ethnicity.

Disability can affect socialization. In addition to the roles played by family, friends, coworkers, and other people with disabilities (Albrecht, 1976), rehabilitation professionals may exert pressure for people with disabilities to accept a sick or disabled role (Salifos-Rothschild, 1976; Scott, 1969). Similarly, ethnicity and gender affect socialization (Fitzgerald & Betz, 1994).

The key point in consideration of socialization is that both people with disabilities and members of racial and ethnic minority groups can be socialized into deviant or inferior life or work roles. Rehabilitation counselors must be aware of this socialization process and work to empower consumers rather than reinforce acquiescence or marginalized roles.

Allocation Processes

As noted earlier, allocation is a process in which gatekeepers provide or restrict access to critical opportunities according to specified criteria (Rothman, 1987). For both minorities and people with disabilities, the allocation process may restrict career development.

Minorities have a long history of exclusion from educational and work opportunities (Trueba et al., 1993). Similar processes operate for people with disabilities.

In fact, the very processes and services that have been established to serve people with disabilities can isolate them or otherwise restrict their opportunities (Gove, 1976; McKnight, 1977; Szymanski & Trueba, 1994).

Help giving can have disempowering consequences for marginalized populations, such as people with disabilities and minorities (McWhirter, 1994; Mithaug, 1996). Thus, rehabilitation counselors must consider previous restrictions imposed by allocation processes (e.g., special education placement). In addition, they must guard against compounding these barriers through their own actions as gatekeepers. Periodic self-assessment is an important professional responsibility for counselors seeking to empower rather than disempower (Fetterman, Kaftarian, & Wandersman, 1996; McWhirter, 1994).

Chance Processes

Chance events and encounters can contribute to career development (Salomone & Slaney, 1981). By its very nature, chance cannot be fully controlled. Nonetheless, it can be used to positive advantage. The context of chance events and their timing in relation to individual development are particularly important. "The ability to cope successfully with unforeseen events or encounters depends, in large part, on the strength of the individual's self-concept and sense of internal (or enabling) control" (Cabral & Salomone, 1990, p. 14).

In some situations acquired disability can result from chance events. Hershenson's (1981, in press) theory suggests that both work personality and contextual factors contribute to the extent to which the disability disrupts career development.

Both disability and minority status are risk factors that may impede positive use of chance in career development through self-efficacy (Fitzgerald & Betz, 1994), work personality (Hershenson, 1981), and the context of individual lives (Vondracek & Fouad, 1994). In this respect, the role of chance in career development might contribute to the operation of the Matthew Principle. Specifically, in ecological research there is considerable evidence that the interplay of context and development often demonstrate the biblical principle that those who have get and those who have not lose (Bronfenbrenner, 1988). Although current legislation (e.g., the Americans with Disabilities Act of 1990, Affirmative Action) may limit the potential negative impact of disability and minority status, the interplay of these risk factors with self-efficacy, work personality, and context may either impede or facilitate the positive use of chance.

Career Interventions with People with Disabilities

As we indicated earlier, the ecological model introduced in previous sections was designed to facilitate assessment and intervention. In this section, therefore, we cover the following topics: (a) a brief overview of career development interventions, (b) considerations for planning interventions, and (c) the use of the ecological model to plan assessment and interventions.

Brief Overview of Interventions

Here we present a very brief discussion of possible career interventions. For more complete discussions of career interventions with people with disabilities, readers should consult a recent chapter on the topic, such as that by Szymanski, Hershenson, Ettinger, and Enright (1996).

A wide range of career interventions are available. General interventions include (a) career planning systems (Taylor, 1988); (b) assessment tools (Kapes, Mastie, & Whitfield, 1994); (c) career classes and workshops (Isaacson & Brown, 1993), including those specially designed for people with disabilities (e.g., see Farley et al., 1992); and (d) career portfolios (Ettinger, Conyers, Merz, & Koch, 1995). Career interventions, which may accompany school-to-work transition, include apprenticeship; cooperative education; school-based enterprises/entrepreneurship; internships and practica; community-based volunteerism; technical preparation; and simulations, shops, and labs. After-school and part-time jobs are also important (Smith & Rojewski, 1993).

Meta-analyses have demonstrated that interventions including individual and group counseling, workshops, semester-long classes, and brief, consumer-directed interventions are effective for the general population (Oliver & Spokane, 1988) and that specially designed workshops are effective for rehabilitation center consumers (Bolton & Akridge, 1995). In addition, Ericson and Riordan (1993) demonstrated the effectiveness of a psychoeducational intervention on the career development of adolescents and young adults with end-stage renal disease. Similarly, Powers, Sowers, and Stevens (1995) showed that mentorship had a positive impact on the career development of adolescents with severe physical disabilities. Finally, in a study of an integrated intervention, Conyers and Szymanski (in press) demonstrated that a 10-hour workshop increased vocational identity and career decision-making self-efficacy for college students with and without disabilities.

Although the summary of intervention studies reviewed here by no means represents a comprehensive review, it is nonetheless illustrative. A variety of career interventions have been demonstrated to be effective for people with and without disabilities.

Considerations for Planning Interventions

Career planning is an active process, which must be done in an empowering context. To that end, we present the following considerations for planning interventions.

Active Consumer Involvement

Successful interventions require active consumer involvement in all phases of the process. Career planning is an active process in which individuals take responsibility for (a) gathering and integrating information about themselves, occupations, and the labor market; (b) generating and evaluating alternatives; (c) making decisions and formulating plans of action; (d) implementing career plans; and (e) evaluating their results (Phillips, 1992; Szymanski, Hershenson, Ettinger, & Enright, 1996).

Unfortunately, current processes often put consumers in passive positions. Consider the very term, *service delivery,* which tends to imply doing something *to* or *for* someone, and the common practices of sending consumers *for* vocational evaluation or *giving someone* a job match printout. Passive approaches may work against consumer ownership, which is critical to successful career planning. In addition, "regardless of intention, any form of help giving that places the receiver in a passive role, that supplants his or her existing capabilities, or that postpones the acquisition of necessary skills, is, ultimately, disempowering" (McWhirter, 1994, p. 4).

Independence (or Interdependence), Consumer Control, and Planning for Future Career Changes

Career planning is not merely about the current goal but also about future job transitions. As noted in previous publications (see, e.g., Parker, Szymanski, & Hanley-Maxwell, 1989; Szymanski, 1994), interventions should be designed to (a) facilitate independence or interdependence, depending on cultural identification; (b) promote maximum possible consumer control; and (c) be the most natural and least restrictive, effective alternatives for the given environment. Similarly, Blustein (1992) recommended that interventions should enhance consumers' sense of control and abilities in self and environmental exploration.

> It is important to remember that . . . any particular career decision . . . is merely a single instance in a lifetime of career choice points. Unless we plan to work with an increasingly dependent client again and again across the decades, *our professional responsibility is to assure that each person learns the* [career planning] *process.* (Mastie, 1994, p. 37)

Avoidance of Premature Restriction of Career Options

The recommendation of Blustein (1992) to avoid premature restriction of career options is particularly important for students in transition from school to work. Career development is a lifelong process that does not begin to stabilize until late adolescence or early adulthood (Lent, Brown, & Hackett, 1994). Unfortunately, current practices in transition and rehabilitation tend toward the narrowing of options during the high school years. These practices work against what is known about the developmental nature of career development and the potential risks incurred with developmental disabilities. It is important to assist students in considering a range of goals rather than prematurely foreclosing on one specific career path (Blustein, 1992).

Use of the Ecological Model To Plan Assessment and Interventions

One of the strangest phenomena in the field of counseling (a field with no dearth of strange phenomena) is the way in which career development theory and research and career counseling theory, practice, and research have developed relatively independently of each other, while generally acknowledging each other's existence in an obligatory, perfunctory way. Most career development studies proclaim that they are relevant to career counseling, albeit frequently in an unspecified way. Most books on career counseling devote an early chapter to career development theories, but once that has been done, rarely refer to them again. The approaches suggested in the literature for career counseling have tended to mirror the dominant approaches to therapeutic counseling rather than to reflect the current work in career development.

In the current chapter, we break with tradition by using the conceptual model introduced earlier to plan assessment and intervention. As illustrated in Table 10.3, the five constructs and six processes of the model present an ecological method of planning assessment and considering potential interventions. The constructs and processes are neither mutually exclusive nor exhaustive. Therefore, some questions and potential interventions appear with more than one construct or process. The constructs and processes provide the framework of a picture that depicts past, current, and potential career development influences.

To apply the model, counselors should consider the questions listed with each construct and process. Additional questions should be added in order to assure adequate understanding of the consumer's career development according to the constructs and processes. The idea is to facilitate consumer self-awareness along the multiple constructs and processes of career development and to plan interventions, along those same constructs and processes, in order to advance career development.

Conclusion

As persons with disabilities are a heterogeneous population, no single career development approach will be applicable to all persons with disabilities, or even to all of those with either congenital or acquired disabilities. Therefore, as with all career counseling clients, the focus should be eclectic, that is, on identifying and meeting individual needs, removing specific barriers, expanding the person's range of options, and supporting the person through his or her transition to work. Most important, the counselor must be sure that the interventions that are used offer a solution rather than compound the problem.

Table 10.3
Assessment Questions and Interventions According to the Constructs
and Processes of the Ecological Model of Career Development

Questions	Possible Interventions
Individual Constructs	
What are current abilities, interests, and limitations?	Active involvement in self-assessment
How are these perceived by the consumer and family?	Career portfolio
What skills have been learned as a result of education or work experience?	Career portfolio
What values are considered important to career planning by the consumer and by the family?	Career portfolio
Has the consumer had sufficient experiences to foster interest development?	Volunteer and paid work experience
How can individual abilities be enhanced?	Skill training, Further education, Job supports
How can limitations be lessened?	Assistive technology, Job accommodation
Contextual Constructs	
How have family background and neighborhood influenced perception of opportunities and responsibilities?	Work role models, Mentors, Chores, Work experience, Community empowerment
How has education facilitated or impeded realization of potential?	Remedial education
What are the financial incentives or disincentives perceived by the individual and family as associated with work?	Inclusion of financial considerations in career planning
Mediating Constructs	
How does the consumer perceive her or his work-related abilities?	Career counseling, Successful work experiences
What outcomes does the consumer expect from employment preparation or rehabilitation?	Appropriate role models, Mentors
What are the consumer's abilities in career planning?	Career classes and workshops, Career counseling

(Continues)

Table 10.3 *Continued.*

Questions	Possible Interventions
What are the consumer's and family's cultural and religious beliefs that relate to education and work?	Culturally sensitive career planning, Culturally sensitive career portfolios
How has the consumer been impacted by discrimination or stereotypes?	Advocacy

Environmental Constructs

How physically accessible are various target environments?	Consultation on barrier removal, Assistive technology, Job accommodation, Consideration of alternate environments
What is the organizational culture of the target work environment? Does the consumer understand how to get along in such a culture?	Job analysis, Social skills training
How has the consumer gotten along in previous work or school environments?	Social skills training, Job coaching
What are the tasks of the environment?	Job analysis
What are the reinforcements?	Job analysis, Planning for career advancement

Outcome Constructs

How well do the consumer's skills and behaviors meet the requirements of possible work environments?	Additional training, On-the-job training, Social skills training
How well do the reinforcements of the work environment meet the consumer's needs?	Additional training for career advancement, Possible job change
Has the consumer experienced job-related stress? How well is the consumer equipped to cope with job-related stress?	Stress reduction techniques, Wellness planning, Encouragement to use social support, Leisure and lifestyle planning

Congruence or Correspondence Processes

Is the consumer aware of potential job accommodations or assistive devices? Have these possibilities been considered?	Discussion and exploration of accommodation possibilities and assistive devices

(Continues)

Table 10.3 *Continued.*

Questions	Possible Interventions
Have ability scores been lowered by problems of construct validity?	Ecological or qualitative approaches to measurement
Are social class or self-efficacy limiting the types of occupations considered?	Enrichment experiences, Role models

Decision-Making Processes

What are the cultural practices of the consumer and her or his family relating to decision making and independence?	Incorporate the consumer's culture into interventions and goals, Involve family members if appropriate
What are the consumer's skills and experiences related to making choices or decisions?	Decision-making training, assistance with identifying alternatives and making choices, Multiple trial work experiences

Developmental Processes

Has disability limited developmental experiences?	Longitudinal approach to career planning, Cautious approach to interpretation of interest measures
Has social skill development been limited?	Social skills training
Has work personality and work competency development been impeded?	Chores, Supervised work experiences

Socialization Processes

How have socialization processes affected the consumer's current role or consideration of future roles?	Enrichment experiences, Role models, Psychoeducational interventions

Allocation Processes

Have opportunities been limited by gatekeeping functions in education, rehabilitation, or other service delivery systems?	Remedial education, Mentoring, Enrichment programs, Special recruitment programs
Do the requirements or processes of current service delivery programs restrict options, create dependency, or otherwise disempower?	Empowerment evaluation, Capacity building interventions

(Continues)

Table 10.3 *Continued.*

Questions	Possible Interventions
Chance Processes	
Is the consumer prepared to recognize and capitalize on chance opportunities?	Career planning workshops, Career portfolio

Note. Some content adapted from "Career Development Theories, Constructs, and Research: Implications for People with Disabilities," by E. M. Szymanski, D. B. Hershenson, M. S. Enright, and J. M. Ettinger, 1996, in E. M. Szymanski and R. M. Parker (Eds.), *Work and Disability: Issues and Strategies in Career Development and Job Placement,* Austin, TX: PRO-ED. Copyright 1996 by PRO-ED, Inc. Adapted with permission. Content also was adapted from *Career Development: Planning for Placement,* by E. M. Szymanski, D. Fernandez, L. Koch, and M. A. Merz, 1996, University of Wisconsin–Madison, Rehabilitation Research and Training Center on Career Development and Advancement.

References

Albrecht, G. L. (1976). Socialization and the disability process. In G. L. Albrecht (Ed.), *The sociology of physical disability and rehabilitation* (pp. 3–38). Pittsburgh: University of Pittsburgh Press.

American College Testing Program. (1984). *DISCOVER: A computer-based career development and counselor support system.* Iowa City: Author.

Americans with Disabilities Act of 1990, 42 U.S.C. § 12101 *et seq.*

Anastasiow, N. J. (1986). *Development and disability: A psychobiological analysis for special educators.* Baltimore: Brookes.

Arbona, C. (1995). Theory and research on racial and ethnic minorities: Hispanic Americans. In F. T. L. Leong (Ed.), *Career development and vocational behavior of racial and ethnic minorities* (pp. 37–66). Mahwah, NJ: Erlbaum.

Bandura, A. (1982). Self-efficacy mechanism in human agency. *American Psychologist, 37,* 122–147.

Betz, N. E., & Fitzgerald, L. F. (1995). Career assessment and intervention with racial and ethnic minorities. In F. T. L. Leong (Ed.), *Career development and vocational behavior of racial and ethnic minorities* (pp. 263–279). Mahwah, NJ: Erlbaum.

Betz, N. E., Fitzgerald, L. F., & Hill, R. E. (1989). Trait–factor theories: Traditional cornerstone of career theory. In M. B. Arthur, D. T. Hall, & B. S. Lawrence (Eds.), *Handbook of career theory* (pp. 26–40). Cambridge, England: Cambridge University Press.

Blustein, D. L. (1992). Applying current theory and research in career exploration to practice. *The Career Development Quarterly, 41,* 174–184.

Bolles, R. N. (1995). *The 1995 what color is your parachute?* Berkeley, CA: Ten Speed.

Bolton, B., & Akridge, R. L. (1995). A meta-analysis of skills training programs for rehabilitation clients. *Rehabilitation Counseling Bulletin, 38,* 262–273.

Bowman, S. L. (1995). Career intervention strategies and assessment issues for African Americans. In F. T. L. Leong (Ed.), *Career development and vocational behavior of racial and ethnic minorities* (pp. 137–164). Mahwah, NJ: Erlbaum.

Bronfenbrenner, U. (1988). *Foreword.* In A. R. Pence (Ed.), *Ecological research with children and families: From concepts to methodology* (pp. ix–xix). New York: Teachers College Press.

Brown, D. (1990a). Models of career decision making. In D. Brown, L. Brooks, & Associates, *Career choice and development: Applying contemporary theories to practice* (2nd ed., pp. 395–421). San Francisco: Jossey-Bass.

Brown, D. (1990b). Summary, comparison, and critique of the major theories. In D. Brown, L. Brooks, & Associates, *Career choice and development: Applying contemporary theories to practice* (2nd ed., pp. 338–363). San Francisco: Jossey-Bass.

Brown, D. (1990c). Trait and factor theory. In D. Brown, L. Brooks, & Associates, *Career choice and development: Applying contemporary theories to practice* (2nd ed., pp. 13–36). San Francisco: Jossey-Bass.

Brown, D., & Brooks, L. (1984). Preface. In D. Brown, L. Brooks, & Associates, *Career choice and development: Applying contemporary theories to practice* (pp. ix–xii). San Francisco: Jossey-Bass.

Brown, D., & Brooks, L. (1990). Introductions to career development: Origins, evolution, and current approaches. In D. Brown, L. Brooks, & Associates, *Career choice and development: Applying contemporary theories to practice* (2nd ed., pp. 1–12). San Francisco: Jossey-Bass.

Brown, D., Brooks, L., & Associates. (1990). *Career choice and development: Applying contemporary theories to practice* (2nd ed.). San Francisco: Jossey-Bass.

Brown, D., Brooks, L., & Associates. (1996). *Career choice and development* (3rd ed.). San Francisco: Jossey-Bass.

Brown, M. (1995). Career development of African Americans: Theoretical and empirical issues. In F. T. L. Leong (Eds.), *Career development and vocational behavior of racial and ethnic minorities* (pp. 7–36). Mahwah, NJ: Erlbaum.

Cabral, A. C., & Salomone, P. R. (1990). Chance and careers: Normative versus contextual development. *The Career Development Quarterly, 39,* 5–17.

Chartrand, J. M. (1991). The evolution of trait-and-factor career counseling: A person × environment fit approach. *Journal of Counseling and Development, 69,* 518–524.

Conte, L. (1983). Vocational development theories and the disabled person: Oversight or deliberate omission. *Rehabilitation Counseling Bulletin, 26,* 316–328.

Conyers, L., & Szymanski, E. M. (in press). The effectiveness of an integrated career intervention for college students with and without disabilities. *Journal of High Education and Disability.*

Crites, J. O. (1978). *Career Maturity Inventory.* Monterey, CA: McGraw-Hill.

Curnow, T. C. (1989). Vocational development of persons with disability. *Vocational Guidance Quarterly 37,* 269–278.

Dawis, R. V. (1994). The theory of work adjustment as convergent theory. In M. L. Savickas & R. W. Lent (Eds.), *Convergence in career development theories: Implications for science and practice* (pp. 33–43). Palo Alto, CA: CPP.

Dawis, R. V., & Lofquist, L. H. (1984). *A psychological theory of work adjustment.* Minneapolis: University of Minnesota Press.

DeLaGarza, D. (in press). *Women and disability: Relationships and work. Findings from a qualitative study.* In A. Leal-Idrogo, J. Gonzales-Calvo, & V. Krenc (Eds.), *Multicultural women's issues in health, disabilities, and rehabilitation.* Dubuque, IA: Kendall-Hunt.

Ericson, G. D., & Riordan, R. J. (1993). Effects of a psychosocial and vocational intervention on the rehabilitation potential of young adults with end-stage renal disease. *Rehabilitation Counseling Bulletin, 37,* 146–162.

Erikson, K., & Vallas, S. P. (Eds.). (1990). *The nature of work: Sociological perspectives.* New Haven, CT: Yale University Press.

Ettinger, J., Conyers, L., Merz, M. A., & Koch, L. (1995). *Strategies and tools for counselors, educators, and employers* (RRTC Working Paper No. 3). Madison: University of Wisconsin—Madison, Rehabilitation Research and Training Center on Career Development and Advancement.

Farley, R. C., Bolton, B., & Parkerson, S. (1992). Effects of client involvement in assessment on vocational development. *Rehabilitation Counseling Bulletin, 35,* 146–153.

Ferguson, P. M., Ferguson, D. L., & Jones, D. (1988). Generations of hope: Parental perspectives on the transitions of their children with severe disabilities from school to adult life. *Journal of The Association for Persons with Severe Handicaps, 13,* 177–187.

Fetterman, D. M., Kaftarian, S. J., & Wandersman, A. (Eds.). (1996). *Empowerment evaluation: Knowledge and tools for self-assessment and accountability.* Thousand Oaks, CA: Sage.

Fitzgerald, L. F., & Betz, N. E. (1994). Career development in cultural context: The role of gender, race, class, and sexual orientation. In M. L. Savickas & R. W. Lent (Eds.), *Convergence in career development theories: Implications for science and practice* (pp. 103–117). Palo Alto, CA: CPP.

Gove, W. R. (1976). Social reaction theory and disability. In G. L. Albrecht (Ed.), *The sociology of physical disability and rehabilitation* (pp. 57–71). Pittsburgh: University of Pittsburgh Press.

Gutteridge, T. G. (1986). Organizational career development systems: The state of the practice. In D. T. Hall & Associates, *Career development in organizations* (pp. 50–94). San Francisco: Jossey-Bass.

Gutteridge, T. G., Leibowitz, Z. B., & Shore, J. E. (1993). *Organizational career development: Benchmarks for building a world-class workforce.* San Francisco: Jossey-Bass.

Hagner, D., & Salomone, P. (1989). Issues in career decision making for workers with developmental disabilities. *Career Development Quarterly, 38,* 148–159.

Hahn, H. (1985). Changing perception of disability and the future of rehabilitation. In L. G. Perlman & G. F. Austin (Eds.), *Social influences in rehabilitation planning: Blueprint for the 21st century* (pp. 53–64). A report of the Ninth Mary E. Switzer Memorial Seminar. Alexandria, VA: National Rehabilitation Association.

Hall, D. T. (1986). Introduction: An overview of current career development theory, research, and practice. In D. T. Hall & Associates, *Career development in organizations* (pp. 1–20). San Francisco: Jossey-Bass.

Hall, D. T. (1990). Career development theory in organizations. In D. Brown, L. Brooks, & Associates, *Career choice and development: Applying contemporary theories to practice* (pp. 422-454). San Francisco: Jossey-Bass.

Hall, D. T., & Associates. (1996). *The career is dead: Long live the career: A relational approach to careers.* San Francisco: Jossey-Bass.

Haveman, R., & Wolfe, B. (1994). *Succeeding generations: On the investment in children.* New York: Russell Sage Foundation.

Herr, E. L., & Cramer, S. H. (1988). Career guidance and counseling through the lifespan (3rd ed.). Glenview, IL: Scott, Foresman.

Herr, E. L., & Cramer, S. H. (1992). *Career guidance and counseling through the lifespan: Systematic approaches* (4th ed.). New York: Harper Collins.

Hershenson, D. B. (1981). Work adjustment, disability, and the three R's of vocational rehabilitation: A conceptual model. *Rehabilitation Counseling Bulletin, 25,* 91-97.

Hershenson, D. B. (1984). Vocational counseling with learning disabled adults. *Journal of Rehabilitation, 50,* 40-44.

Hershenson, D. B. (1988). Along for the ride: The evolution of rehabilitation education. *Rehabilitation Counseling Bulletin, 31,* 204-217.

Hershenson, D. B. (1996). A systems reformulation of a developmental model of work adjustment. *Rehabilitation Counseling Bulletin, 40,* 2-10.

Hershenson, D. B., & Langbauer, W. R. (1973). Sequencing of intrapsychic stages of vocational development. *Journal of Counseling Psychology, 20,* 519-521.

Hershenson, D. B., & Lavery, G. J. (1978). Sequencing of vocational development stages: Further studies. *Journal of Vocational Behavior, 12,* 102-108.

Hershenson, D., & Szymanski, E. M. (1992). Career development of people with disabilities. In R. M. Parker & E. M. Szymanski (Eds.), *Rehabilitation counseling: Basics and beyond* (2nd ed., pp. 273-303). Austin, TX: PRO-ED.

Holland, J. L. (1985a). *Making vocational choices: A theory of vocational personalities and work environments.* Englewood Cliffs, NJ: Prentice-Hall.

Holland, J. L. (1985b). *The Self-Directed Search professional manual.* Odessa, FL: Psychological Assessment Resources.

Holland, J. L. (1985c). *Vocational Preference Inventory.* Odessa, FL: Psychological Assessment Resources.

Holland, J. L. (1994). Separate but unequal is better. In M. L. Savickas & R. W. Lent (Eds.), *Convergence in career development theories: Implications for science and practice* (pp. 45-51). Palo Alto, CA: CPP.

Holland, J. L., Daiger, D. C., & Power, P. G. (1980). *My vocational situation.* Palo Alto, CA: Consulting Psychologists Press.

Holland, J. L., & Gottfredson, G. D. (1994). *The Career Attitudes and Strategies Inventory.* Odessa, FL: Psychological Assessment Resources.

Hotchkiss, L., & Borow, H. (1990). Sociological perspectives on work and career development. In D. Brown, L. Brooks, & Associates, *Career choice and development: Applying contemporary theories to practice* (2nd ed., pp. 262-307). San Francisco: Jossey-Bass.

Isaacson, L. E., & Brown, D. (1993). *Career information, career counseling and career development* (5th ed.). Boston: Allyn & Bacon.

James, K. (1994). Social identity, work stress, and minority worker's health. In G. P. Keita & J. J. Hurrell, Jr. (Eds.), *Job stress in a changing workforce: Investigating gender, diversity, and family issues* (pp. 127–145). Washington, DC: American Psychological Association.

Johnson, M. J., Swartz, J. L., & Martin, W. E. (1995). Application of psychological theories for career development with Native Americans. In F. T. L. Leong (Ed.), *Career development and vocational behavior of racial and ethnic minorities* (pp. 103–133). Mahwah, NJ: Erlbaum.

Kapes, J. T., Mastie, M. M., & Whitfield, E. A. (Eds.). (1994). *A counselor's guide to career assessment instruments* (3rd ed., pp. 31–40). Alexandria, VA: The National Career Development Association.

Katz, M. R. (1975). *SIGI: A computer-based system of interactive guidance and information.* Princeton, NJ: Educational Testing Service.

Kerlinger, F. N. (1986). *Foundations of behavioral research* (3rd ed.). New York: Holt, Rinehart & Winston.

Knapp, R. R., & Knapp, L. (1984). *COPS Interest Inventory Technical Manual.* San Diego: EdITS.

Kozol, J. (1991). *Savage inequalities: Children in America's schools.* New York: Crown.

Krumboltz, J. D. (1988). *Career Beliefs Inventory.* Palo Alto, CA: Consulting Psychologists Press.

Krumboltz, J. D. (1994). Improving career development theory from a social learning perspective. In M. L. Savickas & R. W. Lent (Eds.), *Convergence in career development theories: Implications for science and practice* (pp. 9–31). Palo Alto, CA: CPP.

LaFromboise, T., Coleman, H. L. K., & Gerton, J. (1993). Psychological impact of biculturalism: Evidence and theory. *Psychological Bulletin, 114,* 395–412.

Landy, F. J. (1992). Work design and stress. In G. P. Keita & S. L. Sauter (Eds.), *Work and well being: An agenda for the 1990s* (pp. 119–158). Washington, DC: American Psychological Association.

Lee, C. C., & Richardson, B. R. (Eds.). (1991). *Multicultural issues in counseling: New approaches to diversity.* Alexandria, VA: American Counseling Association.

Lent, R. W., Brown, S. D., & Hackett, G. (1994). Toward a unifying social cognitive theory of career and academic interest, choice, and performance. *Journal of Vocational Behavior, 45,* 79–122.

Lent, R. W., & Hackett, G. (1994). Sociocognitive mechanisms of personal agency in career development: Pan theoretical prospects. In M. L. Savickas & R. W. Lent (Eds.), *Convergence in career development: Implications for science and practice* (pp. 77–101). Palo Alto, CA: CPP.

Leong, F. T. L. (Ed.). (1995). *Career development and vocational behavior of racial and ethnic minorities.* Mahwah, NJ: Erlbaum.

Lewin, K. (1936). *Principles of topological psychology.* New York: McGraw-Hill.

Lofquist, L. H., & Dawis, R. V. (1969). *Adjustment to work: A psychological view of man's problems in a work-oriented society.* New York: Appleton-Century-Crofts.

Lofquist, L. H., & Dawis, R. V. (1991). *Essentials of person–environment correspondence counseling.* Minneapolis: University of Minnesota Press.

Lofquist, L. H., Siess, T. F., Dawis, K. V., England, G. W., & Weiss, D. J. (1964). *Disability and work.* [Monograph]. *Minnesota Studies in Vocational Rehabilitation, 17.*

Louis Harris and Associates, Inc. (1994). *N.O.D./Harris Survey of Americans with Disabilities.* Washington, DC: National Organization on Disability.

Lunneborg, P. W. (1981). *The Vocational Interest Inventory (VII) Manual.* Los Angeles: Western Psychological Services.

Mastie, M. M. (1994). Using assessment instruments in career counseling: Career assessment as compass, credential, process and empowerment. In J. T. Kapes, M. M. Mastie, & E. A. Whitfield (Eds.), *A counselor's guide to career assessment instruments* (3rd ed., pp. 31–40). Alexandria, VA: The National Career Development Association.

McDaniel, J. W. (1963). Disability and vocational redevelopment. *Journal of Rehabilitation, 29*(4), 16–18.

McKnight, J. (1977). Professionalized service and disabling help. In I. Illich, I. K. Zola, J. McKnight, J. Caplan, & H. Shaiken, *Disabling professions* (pp. 69–91). London: Marion Boyars.

McWhirter, E. H. (1994). *Counseling for empowerment.* Alexandria, VA: American Counseling Association.

Meir, E. L. (1975). *Manual for the Ramak and Courses Interest Inventories.* Tel Aviv: Tel Aviv University, Department of Psychology.

Miller-Tiedeman, A., & Tiedeman, D. V. (1990). Career decision making: An individualistic perspective. In D. Brown, L. Brooks, & Associates, *Career choice and development: Applying contemporary theories to practice* (2nd ed., pp. 308–337). San Francisco: Jossey-Bass.

Mitchell, L. K., & Krumboltz, J. D. (1990). Social learning approach to career decision making: Krumboltz's theory. In D. Brown, L. Brooks, & Associates, *Career choice and development: Applying contemporary theories to practice* (2nd ed., pp. 145–196). San Francisco: Jossey-Bass.

Mithaug, D. E. (1996). Fairness, liberty, and empowerment evaluation. In D. M. Fetterman, S. J. Kaftarian, & A. Wandersman (Eds.), *Empowerment evaluation: Knowledge and tools for self-assessment and accountability* (pp. 234–255). Thousand Oaks, CA: Sage.

Moos, R. H. (1986). Work as a human context. In M. S. Pallak & R. Perloff (Eds.), *Psychology and work: Productivity, change, and employment* (pp. 9–52). Washington, DC: American Psychological Association.

National Occupational Information Coordinating Committee. (1986). *Using labor market information in career exploration and decision making: A resource guide.* Garrett Park, MD: Garrett Park Press.

Neff, W. S. (1985). *Work and human behavior* (3rd ed.). New York: Aldine.

Oliver, L. W., & Spokane, A. R. (1988). Client-intervention outcome: What contributes to client gain? *Journal of Counseling Psychology, 35,* 447–462.

Osipow, S. H. (1983). *Theories of career development* (3rd ed.). Englewood Cliffs, NJ: Prentice-Hall.

Osipow, S. H. (1994). Moving career theory into the twenty-first century. In M. L. Savickas & R. W. Lent (Eds.), *Convergence in career development theories: Implications for science and practice* (pp. 217–224). Palo Alto, CA: CPP.

Osipow, S. H., & Littlejohn, E. M. (1995). Toward a multicultural theory of career development: Prospects and dilemmas. In F. T. L. Leong (Ed.), *Career development and vocational behavior of racial and ethnic minorities* (pp. 251–261). Mahwah, NJ: Erlbaum.

Parker, R. M., Szymanski, E. M., & Hanley-Maxwell, C. (1989). Ecological assessment in supported employment. *Journal of Applied Rehabilitation Counseling, 20*(3), 26-33.

Parsons, F. (1909). *Choosing a vocation.* Boston: Houghton Mifflin.

Phillips, S. D. (1992). Career counseling: Choice and implementation. In S. D. Brown & R. W. Lent (Eds.), *Handbook of counseling psychology* (2nd ed., pp. 513-547). New York: Wiley.

Powers, L. E., Sowers, J., Stevens, T. (1995). An exploratory, randomized study of the impact of mentoring on the self-efficacy and community-based knowledge of adolescents with severe physical challenges. *Journal of Rehabilitation, 61*(1), 33-41.

Roe, A. (1969). The meaning of work. In D. Malikin & H. Rusalem (Eds.), *Vocational rehabilitation of the disabled: An overview* (pp. 63-74). New York: New York University Press.

Roe, A., & Lunneborg, P. W. (1990). Personality development and career choice. In D. Brown, L. Brooks, & Associates, *Career choice and development: Applying contemporary theories to practice* (2nd ed., pp. 68-101). San Francisco: Jossey-Bass.

Rojewski, J. W. (1994). Applying theories of career behavior to special populations: Implications for secondary vocational transition programming. *Issues in Special Education and Rehabilitation, 9*(1), 7-26.

Roth, P. M., Hershenson, D. B., & Hilliard, T. (1970). *The psychology of vocational development: Readings in theory and practice.* Boston: Allyn & Bacon.

Rothman, R. A. (1987). *Working: Sociological perspectives.* Englewood Cliffs, NJ: Prentice-Hall.

Rounds, J. B., Henly, G. A., Dawis, R. V., Lofquist, L. H., & Weiss, D. J. (1981). *Manual for the Minnesota Importance Questionnaire: A measure of vocational needs and values.* Minneapolis: University of Minnesota, Center for Interest Measurement Research.

Rounds, J. B., & Tracey, T. J. (1990). From trait-and-factor to person–environment fit counseling: Theory and process. In W. B. Walsh & S. H. Osipow (Eds.), *Career counseling: Contemporary topics in vocational psychology* (pp. 1-44). Hillsdale, NJ: Erlbaum.

Rowe, W., Behrens, J. T., & Leach, M. M. (1995). Racial/ethnic identity and racial consciousness: Looking back and looking forward. In J. G. Ponterotto, J. M. Casas, L. A. Suzuki, & C. M. Alexander (Eds.), *Handbook of multicultural counseling* (pp. 218-235). Thousand Oaks, CA: Sage.

Salifos-Rothschild, C. (1976). Disabled persons' self-definitions and their implications for rehabilitation. In G. L. Albrecht (Ed.), *The sociology of physical disability and rehabilitation* (pp. 39-56). Pittsburgh: University of Pittsburgh Press.

Salomone, P. R., & Slaney, R. B. (1981). The influence of chance and contingency factors on the vocational choice process of non-professional workers. *Journal of Vocational Behavior, 19,* 25-35.

Savickas, M. L. (Ed.). (1994). From vocational guidance to career counseling: Essays to honor Donald E. Super [Special issue]. *Career Development Quarterly, 43*(1).

Savickas, M. L., & Lent, R. W. (Eds.). (1994a). *Convergence in career development theories: Implications for science and practice.* Palo Alto, CA: CPP.

Savickas, M. L., & Lent, R. W. (1994b). Introduction: a convergence project for career psychology. In M. L. Savickas & R. W. Lent (Eds.), *Convergence in career development theories: Implications for science and practice* (pp. 1-6). Palo Alto, CA: CPP.

Schein, E. H. (1986). A critical look at current career development theory and research. In D. T. Hall & Associates, *Career development in organizations* (pp. 310–331). San Francisco: Jossey-Bass.

Scott, R. A. (1969). *The making of blind men: A study of adult socialization.* New York: Russell Sage Foundation.

Siegelman, M., & Roe, A. (1979). *Manual: The Parent–Child Relations Questionnaire II.* Tucson, AZ: Simroe Foundation.

Smith, C. L., & Rojewski, J. W. (1993). School-to-work transition: Alternatives for educational reform. *Youth and Society, 25,* 222–250.

Storck, I. F., & Thompson-Hoffman, S. (1991). Demographic characteristics of the disabled population. In S. Thompson-Hoffman & I. F. Storck (Eds.), *Disability in the United States: A portrait from national data* (pp. 15–33). New York: Springer.

Strauser, D. R. (1995). Applications of self-efficacy theory in rehabilitation counseling. *Journal of Rehabilitation, 61*(1), 7–11.

Sue, D. W., & Sue, D. (1990). *Counseling the culturally different: Theory and practice* (2nd ed.). New York: Wiley.

Super, D. E. (1969). The development of vocational potential. In D. Malikin & H. Rusalem (Eds.), *Vocational rehabilitation of the disabled: An overview* (pp. 75–90). New York: New York University.

Super, D. E. (1990). A life-span, life-space approach to career development. In D. Brown, L. Brooks, & Associates, *Career choice and development: Applying contemporary theories to practice* (2nd ed., pp. 197–261). San Francisco: Jossey-Bass.

Super, D. E. (1994). A life span, life space perspective on convergence. In M. L. Savickas & R. W. Lent (Eds.), *Convergence in career development theories: Implications for science and practice* (pp. 63–74). Palo Alto, CA: CPP.

Super, D. E., & Nevill, D. D. (1986a). *The Salience Inventory.* Palo Alto, CA: Consulting Psychologists Press.

Super, D. E., & Nevill, D. D. (1986b). *The Values Scale.* Palo Alto, CA: Consulting Psychologists Press.

Super, D. E., & Sverko, B. (Eds.). (1995). *Life roles, values, and careers: International findings of the work importance study.* San Francisco: Jossey-Bass.

Super, D. E., Thompson, A. S., & Lindeman, R. H. (1988). *Adult Career Concerns Inventory: Manual for research and exploratory use in counseling.* Palo Alto, CA: Consulting Psychologists Press.

Szymanski, E. M. (1988). Rehabilitation planning with Social Security Work Incentives: A sequential guide for the rehabilitation professional. *Journal of Rehabilitation, 54*(2), 28–32.

Szymanski, E. M. (1994). Transition: Life-span, life-space considerations for empowerment. *Exceptional Children, 60,* 402–410.

Szymanski, E. M. (in press). School to work transition: Ecological considerations for career development. In W. E. Martin & J. L. Swartz (Eds.), *Applied ecological psychological for schools within communities: Assessment and intervention.* Mahwah, NJ: Erlbaum.

Szymanski, E. M., Dunn, C., & Parker, R. M. (1989). Rehabilitation of persons with learning disabilities: An ecological framework. *Rehabilitation Counseling Bulletin, 33,* 38–53.

Szymanski, E. M., Fernandez, D., Koch, L., & Merz, M. A. (1996). *Career development: Planning for placement* (training materials). Madison: University of Wisconsin—Madison, Rehabilitation Research and Training Center on Career Development and Advancement.

Szymanski, E. M., & Hanley-Maxwell, C. (1996). Career development of people with developmental disabilities: An ecological model. *Journal of Rehabilitation, 62*(1), 48-55.

Szymanski, E. M., Hershenson, D. B., Enright, M. S., & Ettinger, J. M. (1996). Career development theories, constructs, and research: Implications for people with disabilities. In E. M. Szymanski & R. M. Parker (Eds.), *Work and disability: Issues and strategies in career development and job placement* (pp. 79-126). Austin, TX: PRO-ED.

Szymanski, E. M., Hershenson, D. B., Ettinger, J., & Enright, M. S. (1996). Career development interventions for people with disabilities. In E. M. Szymanski & R. M. Parker (Eds.), *Work and disability: Issues and strategies in career development and job placement* (pp. 255-276). Austin, TX: PRO-ED.

Szymanski, E. M., Hershenson, D. B., & Power, P. W. (1988). Enabling the family in supporting transition from school to work. In P. W. Power, A. E. Dell Orto, & M. B. Gibbons (Eds.), *Family interventions throughout chronic illness and disability* (pp. 216-233). New York: Springer.

Szymanski, E. M., Johnston-Rodriguez, S., Millington, M. J., Rodriguez, B. H., & Lagergren, J. (1995). The paradoxical nature of disability services: Illustrations from supported employment and implications for rehabilitation counseling. *Journal of Applied Rehabilitation Counseling, 26*(2), 17-22.

Szymanski, E. M., & Parker, R. M. (1989). Rehabilitation counseling in supported employment. *Journal of Applied Rehabilitation Counseling, 20*(3), 65-72.

Szymanski, E. M., Ryan, C., Merz, M. A., Treviño, B., & Johnston-Rodriguez, S. (1996). Psychosocial and economic aspects of work: Implications for people with disabilities. In E. M. Szymanski & R. M. Parker (Eds.), *Work and disability: Issues and strategies in career development and job placement* (pp. 9-38). Austin, TX: PRO-ED.

Szymanski, E. M., & Trueba, H. T. (1994). Castification of people with disabilities: Potential disempowering aspects of classification in disability services. *Journal of Rehabilitation, 60*(3), 12-20.

Taylor, K. M. (1988). Advances in career-planning systems. In W. B. Walsh & S. H. Osipow (Eds.), *Career decision making* (pp. 137-211). Hillsdale, NJ: Erlbaum.

Taylor, K. M., & Betz, N. E. (1983). Applications of self-efficacy theory to the understanding and treatment of career indecision. *Journal of Vocational Behavior, 22,* 63-81.

Thomas, K. T., & Parker, R. M. (1992). Applications of theory to rehabilitation counselling practice. In S. E. Robertson & R. I. Brown (Eds.), *Rehabilitation counselling: Approaches in the field of disability* (pp. 34-78). London: Chapman & Hall.

Thompson, A. S., & Lindeman, R. H. (1984). *Career Development Inventory: Technical manual.* Palo Alto, CA: Consulting Psychologists Press.

Tiedeman, D. V. (1979). *Career development: Designing our career machines.* Schenectady, NY: Character Research Press.

Tinsley, H. E. A. (Ed.). (1993). Special issue on the Theory of Work Adjustment [special issue]. *Journal of Vocational Behavior, 43*(1).

Treviño, B., & Szymanski, E. M. (1996). A qualitative study of the career development of Hispanics with disabilities. *Journal of Rehabilitation, 62*(3), 5-13.

Trueba, H. T., Rodriguez, C., Zou, Y., & Cintron, J. (1993). *Healing multicultural America: Mexican immigrants rise to power in rural California.* London: Falmer.

Turner, K. D., & Szymanski, E. M. (1990). Work adjustment of people with congenital disabilities: A longitudinal perspective from birth to adulthood. *Journal of Rehabilitation, 56*(3), 19–24.

U.S. Department of Labor. (1977). *Dictionary of occupational titles* (4th ed.). Washington, DC: U.S. Government Printing Office.

U.S. Department of Labor. (1979). *Guide to the use of the General Aptitude Test Battery.* Washington, DC: U.S. Government Printing Office.

U.S. Department of Labor. (1990). *Occupational outlook handbook.* Washington, DC: U.S. Government Printing Office.

Victor, J., McCarthy, H., & Palmer, J. T. (1986). Career development of physically disabled youth. In E. L. Pan, S. Newman, T. Becker, & C. Vash (Eds.), *Annual review of rehabilitation* (Vol. 5, pp. 97–150). New York: Springer.

Vondracek, F. W., & Fouad, N. A. (1994). Developmental contextualism: An integrative framework for theory and practice. In M. L. Savickas & R. W. Lent (Eds.), *Convergence in career development: Implications for science and practice* (pp. 207–214). Palo Alto, CA: CPP.

Vondracek, F. W., Lerner, R. M., & Schulenberg, J. E. (1986). *Career development: A life-span developmental approach.* Hillsdale, NJ: Erlbaum.

Vondracek, F. W., & Schulenberg, J. (1992). Counseling for normative and nonnormative influences on career development. *Career Development Quarterly, 40,* 291–301.

Weed, R. O., & Field, T. F. (1994). *Rehabilitation consultant's handbook* (rev. ed.). Athens, GA: E & F.

Wehmeyer, M. L. (1992). Self-determination and the education of students with mental retardation. *Education and Training in Mental Retardation, 27,* 303–314.

Weinrach, S. G., & Srebalus, D. J. (1990). Holland's theory of careers. In D. Brown, L. Brooks, & Associates, *Career choice and development: Applying contemporary theories to practice* (pp. 37–67). San Francisco: Jossey-Bass.

Weiss, D. J., England, M. E., Dawis, R. V., & Lofquist, L. H. (1966). *Instrumentation on the Theory of Work Adjustment.* Minnesota Studies in Vocational Rehabilitation (No. 21). Minneapolis: University of Minnesota, Center for Interest Measurement Research.

West, M. D., & Parent, W. S. (1992). Consumer choice and empowerment in supported employment services: Issues and strategies. *Journal of the Association of Persons with Severe Handicaps, 17,* 47–52.

Whyte, S. R. (1995). Disability between discourse and experience. In B. Ingstad & S. R. Whyte (Eds.), *Disability and culture* (pp. 267–291). Berkeley: University of California Press.

Wright, B. A. (1983). *Physical disability: A psychosocial approach* (2nd ed.). New York: Harper & Row.

Zunker, V. G. (1986). *Career counseling: Applied concepts in life planning* (2nd ed.). Monterey, CA: Brooks/Cole.

Chapter 11

The Constructs and Practices of Job Placement

Michael J. Millington, John Butterworth,
Sheila Lynch Fesko, and Henry McCarthy

ob placement is central to the professional role of the rehabilitation counselor. Job placement ties counseling efforts to real-world outcomes for the
client: finding, getting, and keeping a job with financial, social, and psychological
value. Without job placement and related employment constructs, there is little
legislative rationale or market demand for the existence of rehabilitation counseling as a unique and viable profession (Parent & Everson, 1986; Stensrud, Millington, & Gilbride, 1996).

The cultivation of a strong theoretical base for placement research and the
development of counselor competencies in placement activities are arguably two
of the most important pursuits of the rehabilitation counseling profession. The
purpose of this chapter is to reconcile the practice of job placement with constructs
of the employment selection process. In this chapter we provide an overview of
the employment process in a rehabilitation context by explaining and discussing
(a) a systems framework, (b) job search, (c) job acquisition, (d) job entry and stabilization, and (e) stakeholder definitions of success in job placement.

A Systems Framework

From a systems perspective (see Geist & Calzaretta, 1982; Vandergoot, 1987; Vandergoot & Swirsky, 1980), placement services may be defined as any professional
intervention that facilitates or supplements the naturally occurring employment
selection process (see Millington, Szymanski, & Johnston-Rodriguez, 1995). The

employment selection process is a labor market transaction between the applicant and the employer motivated by a mutual need to change current employment status (see Figure 11.1). The applicant and the employer bring a unique set of intentions and expectations to the transaction—that is, what they plan to do and what outcomes they predict their actions will precipitate. Expectations are the medium of the transaction, perhaps best described for both parties as expectations of satisfaction and satisfactoriness (see Dawis, 1994; Dawis & Lofquist, 1984). The arrow between the applicant and the business organization in Figure 11.1 indicates the communication of expectations between the stakeholders. The stages of employment selection identify three discrete objectives: (1) job search, (2) acquisition, and (3) entry and stabilization. This complex stage process is supported (or impeded) by the contextual influences of family, work organization, and labor market factors (Millington et al., 1995).

Placement services intervene in the employment selection process when either of the primary stakeholders—the applicant or the employer—is dissatisfied with the outcomes, or requests brokering services or other assistance from a third-party placement professional. Placement interventions have traditionally focused on the applicant with a disability, helping the person to develop the skills and motivation to successfully search for, acquire, and keep a satisfactory job. However, placement interventions could just as easily focus on developing the skills and motivation of the employers to recruit, hire, and integrate workers with disabilities. From a systems perspective, the competencies of the placement professional are ultimately determined by his or her ability to effect positive change

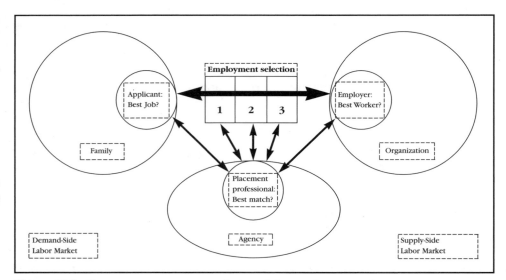

Figure 11.1. Placement as an accommodation of the employment selection process. See text for explanation.

in the applicant, the employer, or the process of selection that binds them. Each satisfactory placement outcome (i.e., "best match") is created rather than simply identified.

Job Search

The transactions between the applicant market and the employer market begin with an exchange of job-relevant information, for the purpose of generating options. Information flows between the stakeholder groups through formal and informal social structures. Applicants may refer to this as job search. Employers refer to this as recruitment. In the following sections we discuss (a) the job applicant's perspective and activities in this transactional process, (b) the employer's recruitment interests, and (c) job search roles for placement professionals.

The Job Applicant's Perspective and Activities

Applicants engage in job search activities designed to identify potential employment targets within their chosen markets. Activities may include perusing classified advertisements, circulating resumes, contacting employers, attending job fairs, soliciting leads and support from family and other social contacts, and engaging placement agencies. Some job search activities are more effective than others. Findings have consistently shown that tapping informal social networks is the preferred and most effective means of generating job leads among employed blue collar, managerial, and even doctoral-level workers (Gottfredson & Swatko, 1979; Rosenfeld, 1975; Schwab, 1982; Schwab, Rynes, & Aldag, 1987).

Motivation is an important factor in the relative success of job search activities. Financial need is the primary situational motivator linked to intensity of search (Schwab et al., 1987). Research suggests that the intensity of search behaviors also increases with the expected probability of success (Harrel & Stahl, 1986; Rynes & Lawler, 1983) and increased levels of self-esteem (Ellis & Taylor, 1983). Indicators of motivation include level of procrastination, number of employment contacts (Sheppard & Belitsky, 1966), time spent in search activities (Barron & Mellow, 1981), and number of placement professionals involved (Kanfer & Hulin, 1985). Motivation and effective use of social networks in the job market maximize the efficacy of search efforts.

The Employer's Recruitment Interests

Employers engage in recruitment strategies devised to attract an applicant pool of likely candidates from employer-recognized labor markets (Bedeian, 1989; Millington et al., 1995). Strategies may include the use of advertising and public events (e.g., job fairs, career days), orientation sessions that present realistic job previews (Premack & Wanous, 1985), internal and external postings, contracting professional recruiters, and informal word-of-mouth networking (Arthur, 1991). A good recruitment process helps potential applicants to self-select by aligning their work expectations with the realities of the job (Wanous, 1980). The salient outcome goals of recruitment are linked to the objectives of the employment selection process, which are (a) to maximize job performance and satisfaction and (b) to minimize turnover (Premack & Wanous, 1985).

Employer motivation is an important factor in the recruitment of applicants with disabilities. The fundamental employer motivator is profit. Employers wish to attract the highest qualified applicants for the lowest possible cost. When unemployment is low and traditional labor markets are shrinking, employers are more likely to recruit and hire nontraditional workers (see Millington, Asner, Der-Stepanian, & Linkowski, 1996). Conversely, when unemployment is high and traditional markets are plentiful, employers tend to rely on the traditional, economically conservative recruitment strategies. Profit is not the only motivator, however. Other motivational factors affecting employer recruitment of workers with disabilities include ancillary business objectives, community relations, compliance with federal and state mandates, and organizational values (Pitt-Catsouphes & Butterworth, 1995).

Changing demographics in the workforce present a challenge to employer recruitment strategies. Current trends indicate that the workforce is becoming older, more ethnically diverse, and more balanced in terms of gender (Kiernan & Lynch, 1992). Some authors believe that employers will have to surpass minimal standards set by Equal Employment Opportunity Commission (EEOC) guidelines and affirmative action programs simply to maintain their workforce. The nontraditional labor markets of today will be the target of future recruitment efforts (Arthur, 1991).

Job Search Roles for Placement Professionals

Job search skills may be more problematic than satisfactory job performance for applicants with disabilities. Poor job seeking skills limit access to job markets (Rubin & Roessler, 1995) and exacerbate the economic hardships experienced by applicants with disabilities (Levitan & Taggert, 1982). Proper assessment and planning are important precursors to job search. While planning job search strategies with a client, placement professionals may engage in person-centered planning approaches that focus on the needs of the client first and also solicit input from family and friends in planning and implementation of the job search (O'Brien & Lovett, 1993). Placement professionals may also assess the applicant's employability competencies (Bolton, 1982; Rubin & Roessler, 1995), including knowledge of the job market, ability to develop job leads (Gilbride & Burr, 1993), and ability to self-promote and identify reasonable accommodations (Roessler & Gottcent, 1994).

Job seeking–skills training has been an effective intervention with a range of populations (Walker, 1987). It usually includes the development of applied skills, such as writing a resume, filling out applications, and obtaining interviews. Self-instructional training packages are available (Seifker, 1989; Wesolowski, 1981), but the most effective and most replicated format (Hagner, Fesko, Cadigan, Kiernan, & Butterworth, 1996) is that of the "job club" (Azrin & Besalel, 1980; Azrin, Flores, & Kaplan, 1975). Job clubs use a behaviorally based, group-oriented approach to train, support, and motivate job seekers in their search efforts. Participants in job clubs meet daily or weekly to develop and pursue job leads, practice search techniques, and receive encouragement and feedback on their performance from group members. Both individualized (Zadny & James, 1979) and group (Azrin & Philip, 1979; Matkin, 1989; Wesolowski, Zawlocki, & Dowdy, 1986) approaches have been shown to be successful in achieving applicant employment goals. When properly trained in job seeking skills, many people with disabilities find their own jobs.

When applicants cannot negotiate a job search without support, placement professionals engage in job development services. In job development, the professional assumes partial or total responsibility for contacting and negotiating with the employer. Traditional services identify an existing job opening, and then seek a match among available client applicants. This job-centered model (Hagner & Daning, 1993) has a tendency to usurp client choice unnecessarily, limiting the variety and quality of jobs (Mank, 1994; West & Parent, 1992). More recently, there has been increased emphasis on job creation and job restructuring, methods that rely on a company-centered approach to job development. A company-centered approach looks broadly at the needs of a company rather than at existing job openings and emphasizes alternative ways of meeting those needs.

By examining how vocational rehabilitation is practiced, a wide range of strategies can be identified that reveal the scope of potential roles of placement professionals in the job search. Hagner et al. (1996) identified 31 different activities that relate to the job search (see Table 11.1). These strategies represent distinct approaches to the job search process that may be combined in a number of ways to respond to individual support needs and preferences.

Fesko and Temelini (in press) surveyed 370 placement professionals who worked for community rehabilitation providers or independent living centers that use the practices identified in Table 11.1. A principal components analysis of their data yielded five clusters of practices that represent alternative approaches to the job development process. The approaches are distinguished primarily by whether employer contacts are targeted for the benefit of a specific individual, for several job seekers, or simply as a generic network-building exercise. The generic approach emphasizes traditional job search. Activities may include reviewing classified advertisements, developing contact lists through the yellow pages and business directory, making "cold calls," walk-in solicitation, researching business and labor market trends, and hosting a job fair. The agency-marketing approach emphasizes raising awareness and generating support within the business community for

Table 11.1
Job Search Activities

Planning and Preparation

1. Implement a formal vocational assessment of applicant knowledge, skills, abilities, and interests.

2. Involve family in informal assessment of interests and abilities.

3. Teach job seeking skills.

4. Provide counseling support.

5. Facilitate job club.

Employer Contact

6. Host an agency or program business advisory committee.

7. Sponsor public relations events with employers.

8. Develop list of employer contact information.

9. Join and present in business-oriented community groups.

10. Research business and/or labor trends.

11. "Cold call" employers to solicit job leads.

12. Use placement professional network to identify job leads.

13. Use job-seekers' social network to develop job leads.

14. Employer account: Develop relationship with local employers.

15. Participate in local job bank.

16. Host or attend a career fair or job fair.

17. Give informational seminars and workshops for local business.

18. Review traditional job listings.

19. Provide brochure or written proposal to employer.

Employer Negotiation

20. Identify appropriate jobs and/or restructuring options.

21. Explain job–applicant match to the employer.

22. Guarantee applicant production rates.

(Continues)

Table 11.1 *Continued.*

23. Provide consultation to employer on disability-related issues.

24. Assist employer to obtain financial remuneration.

25. Facilitate employer subminimum wage certification.

26. Facilitate alternate work agreements (i.e., work under contract).

27. Address job seeker's disability and job accommodation needs.

28. Restructure job station, work schedule, or assistive devices.

29. Train applicant as volunteer or on subsidized wage basis.

30. Consult with employer on generic vocational issues.

31. Arrange applicant interviews with employer.

Note. Adapted from "Securing Employment: Job Search and Employer Negotiation Strategies in Rehabilitation," by D. Hagner, S. L. Fesko, M. Cadigan, W. Kiernan, and J. Butterworth, 1996, in *Work and Disability: Issues and Strategies for Career Counselors and Job Placement,* by E. M. Szymanski and R. M. Parker (Eds.), Austin, TX: PRO-ED.

the placement agency. This approach may involve establishing an employer advisory board, participating in business-oriented community groups, organizing public relations events, and sponsoring a job club. The networking approach is similar to the agency-marketing approach, emphasizing the development of placement service relationships in the business community. Activities may include canvassing personal networks to establish job leads, identifying advocates within the business community (Nietupski, Verstegen, Hamre-Nietupski, & Tanty, 1993), and maintaining an intra-agency job bank for sharing job leads. Individually focused placement emphasizes the creation of a good match between a specific individual and employer. Among the ways that this approach is implemented are assessing the job match, restructuring the job as needed, and strategizing job accommodation with the employer. Finally, the traditional job placement approach emphasizes the needs of the employer by guaranteeing the satisfactoriness of the worker. Activities include offering contract or subminimum wage options and providing technical assistance to the employer.

Although all employer-contact activities tended to be relatively effective at helping people become employed, the networking approach demonstrated better quality of outcomes in terms of salary and hours (Fesko & Temelini, in press). As noted previously, networking is the most frequently used approach to access jobs in the labor market (Silliker, 1993). However, the effectiveness of job search is largely a function of the intensity of the search rather than adherence to a particular model. When it comes to employer contact, more is usually better (Bortnick & Ports, 1992).

Job Acquisition

The second objective of employment selection is job acquisition. The employer gathers applicant information and makes screening and hiring decisions accordingly. The applicant is in competition for the job with other applicants, who are all trying to make the most positive impression on the employer. Acquisition concludes with the negotiation of the terms of employment. The role of the placement professional is to support the process such that the needs of both parties are met. We discuss the following features of job acquisition: (a) differences between screening and hiring, (b) issues in employers' use of applicant information, (c) applicants' impression management and disclosure of disability, and (d) negotiating employment.

Differences Between Screening and Hiring

Millington et al. (1995) described how the employer decision-making process consists of two contingent and convergent subprocesses: screening and hiring. Screening is a negatively weighted, criterion-referenced removal of undesirable applicants from the applicant pool (Bills, 1990). The purpose of screening is to minimize the cost of employment selection, which is a particularly important objective when the applicant pool is large. Individuals with severe disabilities in particular may have difficulty surviving a negatively weighted screening process, and the role of the placement professional is to seek opportunities to bypass or inform the screening process. Hiring is the final narrowing of the employer options to a single choice, in which the applicants are ranked according to the employer's perception of "best fit," generally based on positively weighted criteria (Kiernan & Rowland, 1989). The objective of hiring is to achieve the best match between applicant and employer.

Screening and hiring may or may not appear as discrete activities in the employment selection process, depending on the employer's information gathering strategy. Both may take place in the course of a simple interview, or be formally identified in a complex, multistaged selection process that may include the use of biographical review, tests, and interviews. The underlying assumptions of employment selection are that, in the decision-making process, employers are looking for reasons to reject an applicant as well as reasons to hire, and that screening tends to occur early in the process.

Implied in the screening and hiring components of the employment selection process is a schema against which applicants are to be compared. Typically, employers believe they define positions generically and create job descriptions without regard to an individual, and then attempt to find prospects in the labor market who match the job description (Cole & Bragman, 1985). Accordingly, they tend to rely on labor markets with which they are familiar, in order to fill job vacancies. Such rationality and routine, however, encourage them (rather unaware) to form a singular and stereotypical schema for the "ideal worker" (Hagner & Dileo, 1993). This can be problematic for applicants with disabilities because they have been significantly underrepresented in the workforce and, therefore, underrepresented among the images and information contributing to the ideal worker schema.

Issues in Employers' Use of Applicant Information

The decision-making outcomes of screening and hiring are based on employer assessment of applicant information. A fair outcome requires that the information be job related and appropriately used. Different issues emerge with respect to the use of applicant information derived from (a) biographical data review, (b) employment tests, and (c) interviews.

Biographical Data Review

Application forms, letters of reference, and resumes provide a great deal of information about the applicant that may be used to make screening and hiring decisions. The intentional use of this information is called biographical data review. The quality of a biographical data review depends upon (a) job relatedness of the criteria, (b) method by which the criteria are measured (direct vs. inferred), and (c) method by which the criteria are evaluated (rational vs. statistical). Biographical data reviews that have demonstrated good reliability and validity (Shackleton & Anderson, 1987), such as training and experience (T&E) review, focus on documented past work performance (Hunter & Hunter, 1984), achievement, and educational history (Ash, Levine, & McDaniel, 1989).

T&E evaluation is perhaps the most popular method of review. T&E review uses a functional profile of the target job based on job analysis (Levine, 1983) and standardized collection and rating protocols (Ash et al., 1989) to establish a statistically defensible minimal standard for work competencies. Information obtained from a written application tends to be a more accurate indicator of competency than information remembered and reported by the applicant during the dynamics of a job interview where the applicant is under stress and driven to maximize a favorable impression (Cascio, 1987). Ash et al. (1989) cautioned that T&E evaluations are not the best predictors of knowledge, skills, and abilities, but are effective as screening tools for estimating an applicant's general education development and specific vocational preparation. In addition to estimating skill level, employers frequently use T&E review for inferring work motivation of an applicant by noting the consistency and length of the applicant's involvement in a specific line of training or experience (Ash et al., 1989). To the extent that the listed work history information captures the complete picture of the applicant's situation, such inferences are less subject to misinterpretation.

Employment Tests

Many employers use standardized or criterion-referenced instruments to screen applicants from the applicant pool or to place applicants into specific job categories (Aiken, 1994). These instruments tend to be special aptitude tests, such as tests of clerical skill or mechanical aptitude, that measure job-specific skills and ability. Measures of personality and interest may be used in some situations, as in screening for sales or management positions (Bittel, 1989). To be safely and effectively used in personnel selection, the test must be reliable, valid, fair (free from bias), and cost-effective (Muchinsky, 1986). For these reasons, formal testing approaches to selection have been relatively job specific (see Cesare, Blankenship, Giannetto, & Mandel, 1993) and conservatively applied.

Interviews

Despite being labor intensive and weak on reliability, interviews remain the most widely used employment selection procedure. This paradox, given employers' penchant for otherwise favoring the most economic path to a goal, suggests that reliance on human interface surfaces in even the most formal and pragmatic of work organizations. Dipboye (1989) pointed out that interviews may serve other organizational functions, such as counseling, increasing worker involvement in the process, and improving public relations. Herriot (1989) indicated that employers believe that they can gauge the cultural fit of the applicant best through a face-to-face encounter, and that they find the format useful in "selling" the organization to particularly desirable applicants. We suggest that, work being a human endeavor, it is not unreasonable to assume that the most natural closure on the selection process would be person centered, regardless of the statistical or logical arguments to the contrary.

The two basic approaches to interviewing may be described as unstructured and formally structured. The unstructured interview is a free-flowing, two-way exchange of information; "the interviewer may have an overall agenda of areas he or she wishes to cover, but the order in which they are covered and the questions which are framed depend upon the responses of the interviewee" (Herriot, 1989, p. 433). The formally structured process does not deviate from a preestablished set of job-related questions. The structured format is often based on a job analysis and focused on surfacing biographical information thought to be directly job relevant.

The outcomes of these two approaches may be further differentiated in terms of reliability, validity, and fairness. Unstructured interviews are historically lacking in all three indices (see Arvey, 1979; Hunter & Hunter, 1984; Reilly & Chao, 1982; Schmitt, Gooding, Noe, & Kirsch, 1984). Unstructured interviews are guided by the social encounter, and thus are open to the influence of stereotypes and the intrusion of interpersonal judgments. Structured interviews have exhibited more acceptable outcomes. The common reliance on job analysis data for designing most structured interviews has demonstrated a strong improvement in validity (Arvey & Campion, 1982).

Dipboye (1989, pp. 48–49) outlined a three-stage information-processing interview model: the preinterview phase, when the interviewer has an opportunity to form impressions of the applicant based on paper credentials such as test scores and the completed application form; the face-to-face interview; and the postinterview phase, when the interviewer synthesizes a conclusion about the applicant's qualifications and renders a decision to hire, not hire, or to seek more information. Although this sequence of events does not describe all interviews, it does seem descriptive of the typical or modal interview. Using this model, Dipboye has called the incremental validity of the interview into question. If interviewing does not add to the specificity of the selection process, then it is at best unnecessary and perhaps susceptible to confirmatory bias (Dipboye, 1989).

Confirmatory bias refers to a primacy effect of early information, either positively or negatively charged, mediating the way in which subsequent information is gathered or interpreted. Macan and Dipboye (1988) identified conditions that may encourage the development of confirmatory bias: (a) interviewers are very sure of their early impressions, (b) applicants are unsure of their ability to perform in interview situations, (c) interviewers have made their initial (biased) impressions explicitly known to significant others, (d) the interview format is unstructured, and (e) the interviewer has not been trained in interviewing techniques. Confirmatory bias may change the nature of the interviewer's information gathering interactions with the applicant. If the interviewer harbors a negative bias against an applicant, the interviewer may exhibit verbal behavior (e.g., closed-ended questions, focusing on applicant weaknesses) and nonverbal cues (e.g., increased physical distance, lack of congeniality) that discourage positive interaction. In response, the applicant may withdraw or react negatively to what is perceived as a hostile transaction, particularly when he or she is characterized by low self-esteem (Liden, Martin, & Parsons, 1993). This behavioral confirmation of expectations becomes a self-fulfilling prophecy acted out in the interview (Dipboye, 1982). Confirmatory bias may affect recall and interpretation of information in the postinterview phase (Dipboye, Stramler, & Fontenelle, 1984; Macan & Dipboye, 1988). Interviewers may remember or attach more significance to information that reinforces their initial impressions, even in the presence of information that refutes those impressions.

The process of evaluating job applicants who have a disability is considered to be especially vulnerable to confirmatory bias. For example, Farina and Felner's (1973) study suggested that application information indicating an episode of mental illness resulted in less congenial interaction with the interviewer and lowered interviewer expectations for employment. Type of disability and causal attribution of disability have been suggested as potential biasing agents in job acquisition (Bordieri, 1988; Bordieri & Drehmer, 1986, 1987; Drehmer & Bordieri, 1985). These information-processing biases may effectively negate the validity and fairness of the most well-designed interview.

Applicants' Impression Management and Disclosure of Disability

Applicant verbal and nonverbal behaviors in the employment selection process are generally directed toward making the most favorable impression on the employer (Schlenker, 1980). The degree of desirability of the job drives the intentional behaviors of impression management (Schlenker & Weigold, 1992; Stevens & Kristof, 1995). Applicants can move toward or withdraw from an organization and its selection process by consciously (or unconsciously) manipulating the image of them that the employer is developing. Employers are attracted to applicants who accentuate and promote their potential fit within the organization (Rynes & Gerhart, 1990) by stressing similarities, motivation, and competence, and by exhibiting an interpersonal warmth in the interview. Research suggests that verbal (D. C. Gilmore & Ferris, 1989; Kacmar, Delery, & Ferris, 1992; Stevens & Kristof, 1995) and nonverbal (Imada & Hakel, 1977; Parsons & Liden, 1984; Washburn & Hakel, 1973) communication congruent with employer predilections may positively influence the selection process and outcomes.

In a summary of impression management strategies, Stevens and Kristof (1995) suggested that verbal behaviors may be classified as assertive (accentuating the positive) or defensive (diminishing the effect of negative information). Assertive tactics can be either ingratiating or self-promoting. Ingratiating behaviors are designed to build liking and congruence with the interviewer. The applicant may praise the interviewer or express opinions and attitudes that conform with those of the interviewer (or the organization) to create greater interpersonal attraction. Ingratiating behavior may become grating, if overdone (Jones, Stires, Shaver, & Harris, 1968; Stevens & Kristof, 1995). Self-promoting behaviors that emphasize positive personal qualities, past achievements, and future goals engender favorable attributions by the interviewer concerning salient applicant work characteristics (Godfrey, Jones, & Lord, 1986; Stevens & Kristof, 1995). Defensive tactics can be either excusing or justifying (Schlenker & Weigold, 1992; Stevens & Kristof, 1995). They are designed to defuse negative information about the applicant during the course of the interview. Applicants may explain why they should not be linked to the negative information, or why the information should not be interpreted in a negative fashion.

An applicant with a disability may encounter problems with impression management when deciding whether, when, and how to disclose the presence of a "hidden" disability that may affect job performance. The manner in which an individual's disability is discussed affects both the chances of being offered a job and the eventual inclusion into the workplace. Disclosure allows for open negotiation of accommodation needs, but may make impression management more difficult. Findings from a survey of human resource managers suggested that an individual should disclose a disability at or after the interview (Rutherford, Merrier & Parry, 1993). Although there was not consensus on this issue, the majority said that they prefer the individual to be direct about the nature of a disability rather than refer to it indirectly. Hagner and Daning (1993) found that mention of disability gradually, indirectly, or in a specific planned context was the preferred strategy of most job developers.

Negotiating Employment

The central objective for the placement professional in this stage of placement is to help the employer correctly match the worker and the job. This requires that the placement professional be well versed in the nature of the job and the culture of the workplace (Vandergoot, 1984). Once the demands of the job are known, a fit can be made by referring an appropriate, work-ready applicant or by creating accommodations for an otherwise work-ready applicant. Negotiation is the art of convincing the employer that the accommodated worker is a desirable (profitable) addition to the workplace. Much depends on the quality of the information gleaned from the workplace and the communication skills of the placement professional (Culver, Spencer, & Gliner, 1990). One approach that emphasizes the relationship and communication between the placement professional and the employer is the "employer accounts" arrangement (Hagner et al., 1996; Research Utilization Laboratory, 1976). In this approach, placement professionals are assigned to particular employers. Over time, they develop a thorough knowledge of the business, establish trust, and nurture a working relationship with the employer.

Job matching, job accommodation, and job creation all require developing a clear understanding of both the work tasks and company culture in a business. Job analysis is a process of systematically identifying the essential job functions, which then serve as the basis for establishing an applicant's competence for the job, with or without potential accommodations (see Roberts, Zimbrick, Butterworth, & Hart, 1993). On the basis of a completed job analysis, the rehabilitation counselor may explain the appropriateness of a job match to an employer and address any misgivings. Furthermore, job analysis is a fruitful avenue for learning a lot of specifics about working in a particular business organization (Hagner & Daning, 1993).

Job accommodation is a term that describes a wide range of interventions that may be used during job negotiation or after job entry. Job accommodation may include changes in work schedule, task sequences, or work area organization; provision of assistive technology; or modifications to the nature of the work performed. This latter option, known as job restructuring, involves modifying a job by eliminating nonessential tasks or reassigning tasks to others who have the relevant skills and interests. Job restructuring falls within the range of accommodations that a business is expected to consider under the Americans with Disabilities Act of 1990 (ADA), which requires that businesses provide reasonable accommodation (Witt, 1992). Although there is no specific definition of reasonable, employers are not required to suffer "undue hardship" in providing an accommodation. The definition of undue hardship varies according to individual company circumstances. In general, an applicant or worker with a disability is expected, under the guidelines of the ADA, to perform the essential job functions, either with or without accommodation, but employers may elect to negotiate reassignment or restructuring of essential job tasks.

One alternative to job negotiation is job creation, which involves using a marketing approach to customize a job to an individual worker. Through this approach, a position is created by identifying unmet or poorly met needs in a company and combining them to create a new position (Bissonette, 1994; Jackson, 1991). This is a proactive approach to negotiation in which the placement professional works with employers to create an opening where one did not previously exist. The placement professional analyzes the potential for match between applicant and workplace based on an analysis of market and workplace factors, seeking a "win–win" business solution. This entrepreneurial approach requires a great many skills (communication, business knowledge, problem solving, etc.) on the part of the placement professional (Bissonnette, 1994). Both job creation and job restructuring are strategies that demand a skillful, synthesizing approach to job development. Sometimes, however, they may provide the best opportunity to establish jobs for workers who have specific interests or needs that are not well matched to jobs typically available in the labor market.

Several ancillary benefits can be used to sway the decision in favor of the placement client. Tax credits, on-the-job training funds, or other monetary incentives have been used, though they are not as important to employers as one might think (Sitlington & Easterday, 1992). Employers are more concerned about productivity than cheap labor; thus, agency guarantees of applicant productivity can be an effective bargaining chip. If a working relationship exists between the rehabilitation professional and the employer, other services that benefit employers may be offered, such as inservice training or counseling services or disability management, depending upon the expertise of the placement professional.

An offer of employment signals a shift to the applicant as the locus of decision making (see Schwab et al., 1987). The employer approaches the applicant with a proposal, and the applicant decides whether to accept, decline, or counteroffer. Specific job attributes are important considerations in negotiating the acceptance of a job offer. Considerations include security, type of work, benefits, coworker and supervisor characteristics, pay, and working conditions (Jurgensen, 1978). The job market also exerts a powerful influence on the applicant negotiations (Liden & Parsons, 1986). It is not surprising that applicants are more likely to accept a job, even an undesirable one, when the job market is tight (Herriot, 1989).

Job Entry and Stabilization

Negotiation brings closure to the acquisition stage of the employment selection process. Ideally, the expectations of the applicant and employer have been communicated, and the terms of the transaction are amenable to both. Expectations form the implicit contract between them, and are now tested on the job. The employment selection process extends into that of job entry and stabilization, as the new worker and the work organization decide whether the job match measures up to expectations. We discuss the following issues related to job entry and stabilization: (a) integration into the work setting, (b) evaluating the worker-environment fit, and (c) postemployment roles for the placement professional.

Integration into the Work Setting

Once the new worker is hired, the employment selection process continues via organizational socialization (Louis, 1980; Schein, 1987). As Schein noted, organizational socialization is the "price of membership" the new worker must be willing to pay in order to stay employed. New employees begin to form an identity within the organization upon arrival, as they attempt to meet normative criteria of the work culture as well as work demands of the job. Acclimation and adaptation into the work culture are critical to the worker's inclusion in the work group (Louis, 1980). To make an effective transition into the organization, the newcomer must be able to recognize and interpret cultural values and norms that surface through group interaction. Increasing integration through socialization is evidenced by positive changes in the new worker's position in the workplace network of informal information and influence (Louis, 1980). Unsuccessful socialization often has sanctions attached, primarily in the form of withdrawal of support by the group (Rothman, 1989) and isolation of the deviant worker. The purpose of these sanctions may be to discourage socially unacceptable behavior through punishment or to protect the work culture from an "outsider" through rejection and eventual expulsion from the job.

Brett (1984) conceptualized occupational socialization as a process of personal development. The new worker takes on new knowledge, skills, values, beliefs, and expectations that approximate the ideal worker conceived by supervisors and coworkers. In Brett's model, intervening and exogenous variables interact in complex ways to mediate the socialization process.

Intervening variables describe internal characteristics of the new worker that mediate socializing behavior. Brett suggested three types of intervening variables: (a) behavior–outcome uncertainty, (b) effort–behavior uncertainty, and (c) learning expectations. Behavior–outcome uncertainty refers to knowledge and skill deficits. It occurs when the new worker either does not know what to do or does not see the connection between job performance and desired outcomes. Lack of information concerning appropriate work behavior and the contingent outcomes interferes with adjustment of the new worker, creating task uncertainty (Mansfield, 1972). Effort–behavior uncertainty refers to the level of "conviction that one can successfully execute the behaviors required to produce contingent outcomes" (Brett, 1984, p. 168). Poor perceptions of self-efficacy interfere with motivation to adapt to new surroundings. Learning expectations are beliefs concerning future access to job-related training. Lowered learning expectations may have a negative effect upon self-efficacy as well.

Exogenous variables describe external "causes of expectations, uncertainty, and development" (Brett, 1984, p. 169) in the employment selection process. Skill-based social support refers to an external validation of competence. Knowledge of incumbent performance provides the new worker with a schema for approximating the ideal worker. Formal socialization refers to the procedure for disseminating general information to a number of new workers. Informal socialization refers to information concerning required tasks, contingencies, and feedback from the perspective of other employees or customers. Goal setting refers to the "explicit discussion between supervisor and subordinate concerning tasks, behaviors which may be used to accomplish those tasks, and expected levels of task performance" (p. 176). These external forces delineate the context for decision-making transactions.

Evaluating Worker–Environment Fit

The new worker evaluates worker–environment fit in terms of role satisfaction. The satisfaction of the new work role depends on five factors (Vroom, 1964): (a) financial remuneration, (b) effort required to remain a satisfactory employee, (c) value of productivity, (d) characteristics of social interaction, and (e) the social status of the position. Muchinsky and Morrow (1980) described three classes of variables that affect job motivation and tenure: individual, work related, and economic. Individual variables include "age, length of service, family size, vocational interests, aptitude, personality, and biographical indices" (p. 270). The authors found a consistent though modest relationship between individual variables and voluntary turnover. Work-related variables include recognition and feedback, autonomy and responsibility, nature of supervision, organizational commitment, salary, role clarity, provisions for seniority, integration into the organization, size of the organization, repetitiveness of tasks, and size of the work unit. Economic variables include labor market characteristics and the geographic location of the organization. According to Muchinsky and Morrow, economic variables are the strongest determinants for voluntary turnover.

The employer evaluates worker–environment fit in terms of worker performance. Performance evaluation is a formal, periodic organizational process for making future employment decisions concerning the worker (DeNisi, Cafferty, & Meglino, 1984). The satisfactoriness of the new worker depends on employer perception of worker performance with respect to such work-related criteria as productivity, safety, reliability, social competence, and adaptability. This model emphasizes that what is remembered and how it is interpreted may be mediated by personality variables of the rater, attitudes in particular. That such a schema may be resistant to change in the face of contradictory evidence (DeNisi et al., 1984) provides a logical rationale for investigating the effect of disability status on performance appraisals (see Smith, Edwards, Heinemann, & Geist, 1984). Other potential contextual effects on performance evaluations include purpose of the appraisal (e.g., support, tenure, advancement, or deployment of worker within the organization), rater time constraints, nature of the rating instrument (DeNisi et al., 1984), and potential bias within the rater (Bernardin & Pence, 1980; Bernardin & Walter, 1977) or the instrument (Landy & Farr, 1980).

Postemployment Roles for the Placement Professional

Although some traditional approaches to placement end with the acquisition of employment, experience has shown that, for many people with disabilities, further support is necessary for them to keep their new positions (Housman & Smith, 1975). Interventions focus on helping the worker adapt to the workplace or helping the workplace adapt to the worker.

As the worker begins the transition from the role of new hire to member of the workforce, the rehabilitation counselor may assess progress and intervene as necessary. In a *client-centered* approach, the counselor uses indirect means by talking to the employee, assessing satisfaction with job and agency services (Schwartz, 1985), and providing peripheral counseling or training off-site. The rehabilitation counselor may coordinate ancillary support services in a case management fashion, such as transportation to and from work, or personal and medical care. A *selective* approach will use direct means by involving the supervisor in assessment and training strategies (Anderson, 1990) or having the counselor serve as a surrogate supervisor for a time and provide training on-site.

Hanley-Maxwell and Millington (1992) identified three important workplace interventions: self-management, maximizing generalizability and maintenance skills, and developing external adaptations. Self-management interventions include problem solving (Mithaug, Martin, Husch, Agran, & Rusch, 1988), self-monitoring, and reinforcement (Berg, Wacker, & Flynn, 1990). These may be taught in job clubs or in transitional employment programs (MacDonald-Wilson, Mancuso, Danley, & Anthony, 1989). The goal of maximizing the generalizability and maintenance of skills is to facilitate long-term independence. Some of the strategies employed involve training clients how to recognize and use natural cues, providing numerous examples during training, and teaching individuals to generalize experience across settings. External adaptations include picture cues, to-do lists, check sheets, audio cues, and peer assistance (Wacker & Berg, 1986). Support services typically offered are training in job, community, and social skills; advocacy; crisis intervention; and job modification (Hanley-Maxwell & Millington, 1992).

Selected interventions should be based on the needs of both the worker and the employer and utilize the employer's current resources, including natural supports (Hagner, Butterworth, & Keith, 1995). Available natural supports vary widely among businesses, some formal, others more informal in nature. Supports may be encouraged by targeting supervisor and coworker interventions, such as disability awareness training; teaching techniques for training, evaluation, and support (Fabian, Edelman, & Leedy, 1993; Gardner, Chapman, Donaldson, & Jacobson, 1988); or simply reinforcing positive coworker interaction with the new employee.

Defining Success in Job Placement from Stakeholders' Perspectives

How successful is job placement as a professional endeavor? As the above systems framework suggests, the answer depends on whom you ask. Job placement services are evaluated differently by each stakeholder group, based on the particular and sometimes conflicting expectations of each. In this section we address current placement evaluation issues and outcomes from the perspective of (a) workers with a disability, (b) employers, and (c) rehabilitation agency personnel.

Perspective of the Worker with a Disability

Defining successful placement of workers with disabilities need not be restricted to the quantitative measures of hours worked, wages, and length of job retention (Moseley, 1988). Beyond satisfaction and satisfactoriness on the job, placement has implications for career development and quality of life.

Career Development

For a variety of reasons covered elsewhere in this text, disability is identified as a risk factor that may (or may not) have an impact on career development (see Syzmanski & Hershenson, Chapter 10, this text; Szymanski, Hershenson, Ettinger, & Enright, 1996). The systems framework for placement provides a clear understanding of the relationship between career development and job placement:

- Employment status over time is the functional outcome of career development. Changing jobs is the essence of a dynamic career path.

- Employment selection governs employment status.

- Placement services attempt to surmount or circumvent barriers to the employment selection process.

- To the degree that past employment experience has not remediated barriers to employment selection, placement services will be useful in future changes in employment status.

From a developmental perspective, job placement can be seen as the achievement of a single step in the career path of the worker: entry into the job market. Once employed, the worker influences the workplace, and the workplace changes the worker. Work experience allows for the refinement of interests, which may increase satisfaction or draw the worker toward other employment options. Work experience allows for the development of skills, increasing worker satisfactoriness and adding labor market value to the worker. In this way, satisfaction and satisfactoriness are fluid constructs: Successful placement is a temporary condition from the perspective of career development.

Quality of Life

A broader view of placement outcomes addresses the relationship between employment and individual quality of life, a difficult concept to determine because of its inherently personal meaning (Taylor & Bogdan, 1995). Quality of life has been described as a multidimensional construct that includes factors such as life conditions, personal satisfactions (e.g., quality of social network, friendships), and personal values (Felce & Perry, 1995; Hughes & Hwang, 1995). It involves the interaction of multiple domains in an individual's life, including work, living environment, family, health care, relationships, and leisure (Stark & Faulkner, 1995). Test, Hinson, Solow, and Keul (1993) found that consumers with experience in both sheltered and community employment preferred the latter, and that friendships were an important part of that preference. Yet, there is evidence that workers with severe disabilities often have fewer non–work-related social interactions in the workplace, initiate fewer interactions, and form fewer friendships that extend beyond the workplace (Chadsey-Rusch, Gonzalez, Tines, & Johnson, 1989; Ferguson, McDonnell, & Drew, 1993; Rusch, Wilson, Hughes, & Heal, 1994; Storey & Horner, 1991).

To enhance quality-of-life outcomes in placement may be a daunting task for rehabilitation counselors. They have to be able to identify the intangible and highly personal motivations for work, as well as the concrete and practical. They have to be adept at identifying stressors and facilitating social support (House, 1981; Kiernan, Schalock, Butterworth, & Sailor, 1993) both on and off the job. In short, they must bring counseling activities into a more holistic model of placement and career planning.

Perspective of the Employer

Data suggest that, overall, employers have been very satisfied with the performance and potential of workers with disabilities (Kregel & Unger, 1993; Levy, Jessop, Rimmerman, Francis, & Levy, 1993). The National Organization on Disability/Harris survey of employers found that 82% of managers feel there were no differences between employees with disabilities and those without, and 75% of respondents indicated that they will likely increase their efforts to hire individuals with disabilities (Louis Harris and Associates, 1995). Coworkers and supervisors may have positive attitudes toward employees with disabilities (Butterworth & Strauch, 1994), even when the employee is characterized by severe developmental disabilities and behavior problems (Belcher & Datlow-Smith, 1994).

Whereas some astute employers may find economic motivation to recruit and hire workers with disabilities, others are more reluctant. Employers may expect more problems with employees with disabilities than with their nondisabled counterparts (Rubin & Roessler, 1995), including higher insurance premiums (Greenwood & Johnson, 1985), higher absenteeism, and lower productivity (Ellner & Bender, 1980). Employers may doubt their own capacity to train and supervise employees with disabilities, because of actual or anticipated barriers to comfortable communication. Employers are also concerned about the impact of the ADA (Gilbride, Stensrud, & Connolly, 1992) and many are doubtful of its worth (Satcher & Hendren, 1992).

In their efforts to accommodate the employment selection process, rehabilitation personnel may affect employers' willingness to hire in positive or negative ways. Several studies suggest that employers view services provided by rehabilitation staff as a positive influence, including the availability of on-the-job training (job coaching), follow-along support services, and consultant resources (Kregel & Unger, 1993; Shafer, Hill, Seyfarth, & Wehman, 1987; Sitlington & Easterday, 1992). Greenwood, Johnson, and Schriner (1988) found that employers valued training and technical assistance from rehabilitation staff, including referrals, consultation on job modification and affirmative action, disability awareness training, and advice on architectural barrier removal.

Research also has raised concerns, however, about the negative perceptions employers may harbor concerning the consonance between the work environment and the way some rehabilitation personnel deliver their services (Gilbride & Stensrud, 1992). Pitt-Catsouphes and Butterworth (1995) found that managers viewed rehabilitation personnel's advocacy efforts during hiring to be intrusive. Similarly, Bullis et al. (1994) found that some employers identified on-the-job support to be too obtrusive, and Kregel and Unger (1993) found some concern about the reliability and quality of supported employment services. It is clear that employers and rehabilitation personnel may have different assumptions and priorities in the placement process, and the ensuing conflict can sour a working relationship between the two. This was clearly illustrated by Arthur (1991), who noted,

> While government agencies can be helpful, they are frequently known to refer unqualified job applicants in spite of the requirements stipulated. In addition, they often challenge the reasons given for rejecting the candidate. Therefore, it is important that recruiters learn appropriate rejection language. (p. 62)

That employers should learn "appropriate rejection language" to deflect a counselor's "challenge" is a revealing comment on Arthur's perception of the tenuous relationship between the placement professional and the employer.

Greater attention needs to be paid to understanding the structure and priorities of the workplace, as well as dealing with counterproductive employer attitudes. For example, many of the supports that workers with disabilities receive in the workplace are provided informally by coworkers. It is important that supports provided by rehabilitation personnel enhance and encourage those supports, rather than impede or replace them (Fabian et al., 1993; Pitt-Catsouphes & Butterworth, 1995).

Perspective of Rehabilitation Agency Personnel

Placement services are available through public and private service providers, for-profit and nonprofit organizations, and disability-specific or generic services. Placement services are funded by state–federal vocational rehabilitation (VR) programs, state mental retardation/developmental disability (MR/DD) agencies, state mental health (MH) agencies, private insurers, state departments of employment and training, regional employment boards, or private industry councils via the Job Training Partnership Act of 1982. Placement services may be received directly from a government agency or upon referral to a contracting rehabilitation service provider. The particulars of successful placement from an agency perspective are a function of who pays and who delivers services, but the fundamental measure of success common to all is consumer employment.

There has been increasing attention in the profession to providing access to employment for all individuals with disabilities. However, successful placement outcomes vary significantly according to type of disability. In fiscal year 1991 (FY91), the percentage of closures designated as rehabilitated ranged from 33% for individuals with psychiatric disabilities to 59% for individuals with hearing disabilities. These data also indicate differences in the quality of the outcome. For example, although 50% of the cases involving individuals with mental retardation were successful closures, 29% of these individuals were closed into sheltered employment. Between FY85 and FY91, closures into sheltered employment decreased from 18.8% to 13.5% for individuals with mild mental retardation and from 66.5% to 48.6% for individuals with severe mental retardation (D. S. Gilmore, Butterworth, Schalock, & Kiernan, 1995). Much of the reduction in sheltered workshop closures is due directly to a professional ideological shift to supported employment models. The introduction of supported employment in the mid-1980s has had an impact on the structure of employment supports by emphasizing job training and support at the job site after job entry and continuing for the life of the job, if necessary. This approach, sometimes referred to as "place–train–support," implies that a worker can enter employment without meeting the prerequisites assumed by a more traditional "train–place–support" approach (Rusch & Hughes, 1990). Since FY85, there has been an increase in the use of supported work as training for persons with moderate and severe mental retardation, with a concurrent decrease in the use of work adjustment training across disability groups (D. S. Gilmore et al., 1995).

Despite these initiatives, the effectiveness of state and federal rehabilitation and human service systems in supporting access to employment remains a professional concern (Mank, 1994; United States General Accounting Office, 1993). There was little change in the national employment rate of people with disabilities between 1986 and 1994, despite passage of the Americans with Disabilities Act in 1990 (Louis Harris and Associates, 1995). Fully 68% of the work-age population of people with disabilities remained unemployed in 1994. According to the Harris poll, two thirds of the unemployed are actively interested in finding a job. Also, the percentage of consumers who achieved a successful placement outcome (status 26) remained fairly stable from FY85 through FY91 at between 38% and 42% of referrals (D. S. Gilmore et al., 1995).

Limited access to employment has also been an issue with community-based rehabilitation service providers. Nationally, over 6,000 community-based agencies provide day treatment and employment services to people with severe disabilities. These are primarily people with developmental disabilities such as mental retardation. Of the projected 1 million consumers served in 1991, 70% were placed in facility-based work and nonwork programs, 21% in individual competitive or supported jobs, and 10% in group supported employment options (McGaughey, Kiernan, McNally, Gilmore, & Keith, 1994).

Conclusion

Given the complex transactional nature of employment selection, it is easy to understand why integrating the spectrum of possible placement practices into a unified model has been such a challenge for the profession. We conclude this chapter by briefly explaining a few of the dimensions of this persistent challenge to the field of placement, dimensions that are likely to shape theory development, research, and practice in the next decade.

Just as the ideology and implementation of *increasing consumer control* are changing the shape of rehabilitation services in general, so too are they affecting the delivery of job placement services. Consider the accepted role of the stakeholders in defining practice. Traditional models first conceptualized a continuum of involvement and control over the process with the individual with a disability and the placement professional at opposite poles. The selective placement model designates an intensive role for the rehabilitation counselor in assessing relevant applicant characteristics, matching them to jobs, developing employer contacts and job leads, and even intervening in the interview (Geist & Calzaretta, 1982). Client-centered placement represents the other end of the spectrum, in which the client assumes responsibility for nearly all placement-related activities and the counselor assumes a supportive role (Vandergoot, 1984). Recent introduction of demand-side placement models suggests that employers may also dictate service delivery in some respects (Gilbride & Stensrud, 1992).

Another aspect of the complexity that both enriches and complicates placement practice is the *expanding scope of services.* Vandergoot (1984) identified the following service categories for placement practice: counseling; work readiness assessment; development of labor market information; job seeking skills training; placement and career planning; job development; job analysis; referral of prescreened, job-ready applicants to employers; job modification and accommodation; follow-up; and coordination with other resources. In a more recent review of the placement literature by Hagner et al. (1996), 31 unique practice options were identified. Services continue to expand over the life span as well. Specifically, the supported employment movement has argued for normalizing the notion of providing follow-along and support services for life if necessary, rather than dictated by a time limit set by a bureaucratic calendar. The influences of career development and career education theories have resulted in heightened concern for preparing even early elementary schoolchildren for the world of work by emphasizing computer literacy, group cooperation through teamwork assignments, and problem-solving skills in the curriculum.

One of the major changes in the employment sector that has been occurring over the past three decades is the *diversification of the labor force and place-ment clientele.* Workers with disabilities are among the previously underrepre-sented groups that are entering the labor market in increasing numbers with increased expectations and legal protections for equal opportunity to employ-ment. Even within the disabled community, there is a diversification in the sub-groups who have obtained or desire employment. Whereas in the past the preponderance of rehabilitants who secured mainstream employment had ortho-pedic or sensory impairments, the job candidates of today are as often repre-sented by people with a variety of cognitive and chronic health impairments. It is very important that service programs demonstrate, in their design and imple-mentation, appropriate sensitivity to and adequate representation of the scope of cultural and disability subgroups. This issue should be examined not merely as a response to the current consciousness about multiculturalism, but because the basic, implicit foundations of vocational rehabilitation counseling were devel-oped on a clientele that in terms of demographic characteristics, work-related experience, and service needs is quite different from many of today's placement candidates. Given the cognitively compromised or socially disadvantaged status of many of today's clients, counselors need to seriously scrutinize the appropri-ateness and adequacy of the strategies and tools for vocational rehabilitation assessment, counseling, and training.

Although placement has often been deemphasized in rehabilitation counsel-ing, it is central to achieving the fundamental objectives of the rehabilitation sys-tem. All rehabilitation counselors will practice placement at some level, whether as direct providers of training and support or simply as purchasers of placement services for their clients. Achieving skills and experience in the art and science of placement should be a requirement for all qualified rehabilitation counselors.

References

Aiken, L. R. (1994). *Psychological testing and assessment* (8th ed.). Needham Heights, MA: Allyn & Bacon.

Americans with Disabilities Act of 1990, 42 U.S.C. § 12101 *et seq.*

Anderson, B. (1990). *Creating diversity: Organizing and sustaining workplaces that support employees with disabilities.* Sitta, AL: Center for Community.

Arthur, D. (1991). *Recruiting, interviewing, selecting, and orienting new employees* (2nd ed.). New York: AMACOM.

Arvey, R. D. (1979). Unfair discrimination in the employment interview: Legal and psychological aspects. *Psychological Bulletin, 86,* 736-765.

Arvey, R. D., & Campion, J. E. (1982). The employment interview: A summary and review of recent research. *Personnel Psychology, 35,* 281-322.

Ash, R. A., Levine, E. L., & McDaniel, M. A. (1989). Job applicant training and work experience evaluation in personnel selection. In G. R. Ferris & K. M. Rowland (Eds.), *Research in personnel and human resources management: A research annual* (Vol. 7, pp. 183-225). Greenwich, CT: Jai Press.

Azrin, H. N., & Besalel, V. A. (1980). *The job club counselor's manual: A behavioral approach to vocational counseling.* Baltimore: University Park Press.

Azrin, N. H., Flores, T., & Kaplan, S. J. (1975). Job-finding club: A group-assisted program for obtaining employment. *Behavior Research and Therapy, 13,* 17-27.

Azrin, N. H., & Philip, R. A. (1979). Job club method for the job handicapped: A comparative outcome study. *Rehabilitation Counseling Bulletin, 23,* 144-155.

Barron, J. M., & Mellow, W. (1981). Changes in labor force status among the unemployed. *Journal of Human Resources, 16,* 427-441.

Bedeian, A. (1989). *Management.* New York: Dryden Press.

Belcher, R. G., & Datlow-Smith, M. (1994). Coworker attitudes toward employees with autism. *Journal of Vocational Rehabilitation, 4*(1), 29-36.

Berg, W. K., Wacker, D. P., & Flynn, T. H. (1990). Teaching generalization and maintenance of work behavior. In F. R. Rusch (Ed.), *Supported employment: Models, methods, and issues* (pp. 145-160). Sycamore, IL: Sycamore.

Bernardin, H. J., & Pence, E. C. (1980). Effects of rater training: Creating new response sets and decreasing accuracy. *Journal of Applied Psychology, 65,* 60-66.

Bernardin, H. J., & Walter, C. S. (1977). Effects of rater training and diary keeping on psychometric errors in rating. *Journal of Applied Psychology, 62,* 64-69.

Bills, D. (1990). Employers' use of job history data for making hiring decisions: A fuller specification of job assignment and status attainment. *The Sociological Quarterly, 31*(1), 23-35.

Bissonnette, D. (1994). *Beyond traditional job development: The art of creating opportunity.* USA: Milt Wright & Associates.

Bittel, L. R. (1989). *The McGraw-Hill 36-hour management course.* New York: McGraw-Hill.

Bolton, B. (1982). *Vocational adjustment of disabled persons.* Austin, TX: PRO-ED.

Bordieri, J. E. (1988). Disability cause and predicted work adjustment for job applicants with low back pain. *Journal of Job Placement, 4*(1), 12-15.

Bordieri, J. E., & Drehmer, D. E. (1986). Hiring decisions for disabled workers: Looking at the cause. *Journal of Applied Social Psychology, 16,* 197-208.

Bordieri, J. E., & Drehmer, D. E. (1987). Attribution of responsibility and predicted social acceptance of disabled workers. *Rehabilitation Counseling Bulletin, 30,* 218-226.

Bortnick, S. M., & Ports, M. H. (1992). Job search methods and results: Tracking the unemployed, 1991. *Monthly Labor Review, 115*(2), 29-35.

Brett, J. M. (1984). Job transitions and personal and role development. In K. M. Rowland & G. R. Ferris (Eds.), *Research in personnel and human resources management* (Vol. 2, pp. 155-185). Greenwich, CT: Jai Press.

Bullis, M., Fredericks, H. D. B., Lehman, C., Paris, K., Corbitt, J., & Johnson, B. (1994). Description and evaluation of the job designs project for adolescents with emotional or behavioral disorders. *Behavioral Disorders, 19,* 254–268.

Butterworth, J., & Strauch, J. (1994). The relationship between social competence and success in the competitive work place for persons with mental retardation. *Education and Training in Mental Retardation, 29,* 118–133.

Cascio, W. F. (1987). *Applied psychology in personnel management* (3rd ed.). Englewood Cliffs, NJ: Prentice-Hall.

Cesare, S. J., Blankenship, M. H., Giannetto, P. W., & Mandel, M. Z. (1993). A predictive validation study of the methods used to select eligibility technicians. *Public Personnel Management, 22*(1), 107–122.

Chadsey-Rusch, J., Gonzalez, P., Tines, J., & Johnson, J. R. (1989). Social ecology in the workplace: Contextual variables affecting social interactions of employees with and without mental retardation. *American Journal on Mental Retardation, 94,* 141–151.

Cole, J. C., & Bragman, R. (1985). Guidelines for improving employer effectiveness in interviewing disabled applicants. *Journal of Rehabilitation, 51*(1), 46–49, 79.

Culver, J. B., Spencer, K. C., & Gliner, J. A. (1990). Prediction of supported employment placements by job developers. *Education & Training in Mental Retardation, 25,* 237–242.

Dawis, R. V. (1994). The theory of work adjustment as convergent theory. In M. L. Savickas & R. W. Lent (Eds.), *Convergence in career development theories* (pp. 33–43). Palo Alto, CA: CPP.

Dawis, R. V., & Lofquist, L. (1984). *A psychological theory of work adjustment.* Minneapolis: University of Minnesota Press.

DeNisi, A. S., Cafferty, T. P., & Meglino, B. M. (1984). A cognitive view of the performance appraisal process: A model and research propositions. *Organizational Behavior and Human Performance, 33,* 360–396.

Dipboye, R. L. (1982). Self-fulfilling prophecies in the selection recruitment interview. *Academy of Management Review, 7,* 579–587.

Dipboye, R. L. (1989). Threats to the incremental validity of interviewer judgments. In R. W. Eder & G. R. Ferris (Eds.), *The employment interview: Theory, research, and practice* (pp. 45–60). Beverly Hills, CA: Sage.

Dipboye, R. L., Stramler, C. S., & Fontenelle, G. A. (1984). The effects of the application on recall of information from the interview. *Academy of Management Journal, 27,* 561–575.

Drehmer, D. E., & Bordieri, J. E. (1985). Hiring decisions for disabled workers: The hidden bias. *Rehabilitation Psychology, 30,* 157–164.

Ellis, R. A., & Taylor, M. S. (1983). Role of self-esteem within the job search process. *Journal of Applied Psychology, 68,* 632–640.

Ellner, J. R., & Bender, H. E. (1980). *Hiring the handicapped: A research study.* New York: AMACOM.

Fabian, E. S., Edelman, A., & Leedy, M. (1993). Linking workers with severe disabilities to social supports in the workplace: Strategies for addressing the barriers. *Journal of Rehabilitation, 58,* 29–34.

Farina, A., & Felner, R. D. (1973). Employment interviewer reactions to former mental patients. *Journal of Abnormal Psychology, 82,* 268–272.

Felce, D., & Perry, J. (1995). Assessment of quality of life. In R. Schalock (Eds.), *Quality of life: Perspectives and issues* (pp. 63-72). Washington, DC: American Association on Mental Retardation.

Ferguson, B., McDonnell, J., & Drew, C. (1993). Type and frequency of social interactions among workers with and without mental retardation. *American Journal on Mental Retardation, 97,* 530-540.

Fesko, S. L., & Temelini, D. (in press). What consumers and staff tell us about effective job placement strategies. In R. Schalock & W. Kiernan (Eds.), *Integrated employment.* Washington, DC: American Association on Mental Retardation.

Gardner, J. F., Chapman, M. S., Donaldson, G., & Jacobson, S. G. (1988). *Toward supported employment: A process guide for planned change.* Baltimore: Brookes.

Geist, C. S., & Calzaretta, W. A. (1982). *Placement handbook for counseling disabled persons.* Springfield, IL: Thomas.

Gilbride, D. D., & Burr, F. (1993). Self-directing labor markets survey: An empowering approach. *Journal of Job Placement, 9*(2), 13-17.

Gilbride, D. D., & Stensrud, R. (1992). Demand-side job development: A model for the 1990s. *Journal of Rehabilitation, 58*(4), 34-39.

Gilbride, D. D., Stensrud, R., & Connolly, M. (1992). Employers' concerns about the ADA: Implications and opportunities for rehabilitation counselors. *Journal of Applied Rehabilitation Counseling, 23*(3), 45-46.

Gilmore, D. S., Butterworth, J., Schalock, R., & Kiernan, W. E. (1995). *Vocational rehabilitation outcomes: Analysis of the 1985, 1988, and 1991 RSA data tapes.* Boston: Institute for Community Inclusion, Children's Hospital.

Gilmore, D. C., & Ferris, G. R. (1989). The effects of applicant impression management tactics on interviewer judgments. *Journal of Management, 15,* 557-564.

Godfrey, D. K., Jones, E. E., & Lord, C. G. (1986). Self-promotion is not ingratiating. *Journal of Personality and Social Psychology, 50,* 106-115.

Gottfredson, C. D., & Swatko, M. K. (1979). Employment, unemployment, and the job search in psychology. *American Psychologist, 34,* 1047-1060.

Greenwood, R., & Johnson, V. (1985). *Employer concerns regarding workers with disabilities.* Fayetteville: Arkansas Research and Training Center in Vocational Rehabilitation.

Greenwood, R., Johnson, V. A., & Schriner, K. F. (1988). Employer perspectives on employer–rehabilitation partnerships. *Journal of Applied Rehabilitation Counseling, 19*(1), 8-12.

Hagner, D. C., Butterworth, J., & Keith, G. (1995). Strategies and barriers in facilitating natural supports for employment of adults with severe disabilities. *Journal of the Association for Persons with Severe Handicaps, 20,* 110-120.

Hagner, D. C., & Daning, R. (1993). Opening lines: How job developers talk to employers. *Career Development for Exceptional Individuals, 16,* 123-124.

Hagner, D. C., & Dileo, D. (1993). *Working together: Workplace culture, supported employment, and persons with disabilities.* Cambridge, MA: Brookline.

Hagner, D., Fesko, S. L., Cadigan, M., Kiernan, W., & Butterworth, J. (1996). Securing employment: Job search and employer negotiation strategies in rehabilitation. In E. M. Szymanski

& R. M. Parker (Eds.), *Work and disability: Issues and strategies for career counselors and job placement* (pp. 309-340). Austin, TX: PRO-ED.

Hanley-Maxwell, C., & Millington, M. J. (1992). Enhancing independence in supported employment: Natural supports in business and industry. *Journal of Vocational Rehabilitation, 2*(4), 51-58.

Harrel, A., & Stahl, M. (1986). Additive information processing and the relationship between expectancy of success and motivational force. *Academy of Management Journal, 29,* 429-433.

Herriot, P. (1989). The selection interview. In P. Herriot (Ed.), *Assessment and selection in organizations* (pp. 433-438). New York: Wiley.

House, J. S. (1981). *Work stress and social support.* Reading, MA: Addison-Wesley.

Housman, R., & Smith, D. (1975). Placement for persons with severe physical disabilities. *Rehabilitation Counseling Bulletin, 17*(6), 245-252.

Hughes, C., & Hwang, B. (1995). Attempts to conceptualize and measure quality of life. In R. Schalock (Ed.), *Quality of life: Perspectives and issues* (pp. 51-61). Washington, DC: American Association on Mental Retardation.

Hunter, J. E., & Hunter, R. F. (1984). The validity and utility of alternative predictors of job performance. *Psychological Bulletin, 96,* 72-98.

Imada, A. S., & Hakel, M. D. (1977). Influence of nonverbal communication and rater proximity on impressions and decisions in simulated employment interviews. *Journal of Applied Psychology, 62,* 295-300.

Jackson, T. (1991). *Guerrilla tactics in the new job market.* New York: Doubleday.

Jones, E. E., Stires, L. K., Shaver, K. G., & Harris, V. A. (1968). Evaluation of an ingratiator by target persons and bystanders. *Journal of Personality, 36,* 349-385.

Jurgensen, C. E. (1978). Job preferences (What makes a job good or bad?). *Journal of Applied Psychology, 63,* 267-276.

Kacmar, K. M., Delery, J. E., & Ferris, G. R. (1992). Differential effectiveness of applicant IM tactics on employment interview decisions. *Journal of Applied Social Psychology, 22,* 1250-1272.

Kanfer, R., & Hulin, C. L. (1985). Individual differences in successful job searches following layoff. *Personnel Psychology, 38,* 835-847.

Kiernan, W. E., & Lynch, S. A. (1992). Employment opportunities for people with disabilities in the years to come. *American Rehabilitation, 18*(3), 12-19.

Kiernan, W., & Rowland, S. (1989). Factors contributing to success and failure in the work environment. In W. Kiernan & R. Schalock (Eds.), *Economics, industry, and disability: A look ahead* (pp. 253-263). Baltimore: Brookes.

Kiernan, W. E., Schalock, R. L., Butterworth, J., & Sailor, W. (1993). *Enhancing the use of natural supports for people with severe disabilities.* Boston: Training and Research Institute for People with Disabilities, Children's Hospital.

Kregel, J., & Unger, D. (1993). Employer perceptions of the work potential of individuals with disabilities. *Journal of Vocational Rehabilitation, 3*(4), 17-25.

Landy, F. S., & Farr, J. L. (1980). Performance rating. *Psychological Bulletin, 87,* 72-107.

Levine, E. L. (1983). *Everything you always wanted to know about job analysis.* Tampa, FL: Mariner.

Levitan, S., & Taggert, R. (1982). Rehabilitation employment and the disabled. In J. Rubin & V. LaPorte (Eds.), *Alternatives in rehabilitating the handicapped: A policy analysis* (pp. 89–149). New York: Human Sciences Press.

Levy, J. M., Jessop, D. J., Rimmerman, A., Francis, F., & Levy, P. H. (1993). Determinants of attitudes of New York state employers towards the employment of persons with severe handicaps. *Journal of Rehabilitation, 59*(1), 49–54.

Liden, R. C., Martin, C. L., & Parsons, C. K. (1993). Interviewer and applicant behaviors in employment interviews. *Academy of Management Journal, 36*(2), 372–386.

Liden, R. C., & Parsons, C. K. (1986). A field-study of job applicant interview perceptions, alternative opportunities, and demographic characteristics. *Personnel Psychology, 39*, 109–122.

Louis Harris and Associates. (1995). *National Organization on Disability/Harris survey on employment of people with disabilities.* New York: Author.

Louis, M. R. (1980). Surprise and sense-making: What newcomers experience in entering unfamiliar organizational settings. *Administrative Science Quarterly, 25*, 226–251.

Macan, T. H., & Dipboye, R. L. (1988). The effects of interviewers' initial impressions on information gathering. *Organizational Behavior and Human Decision Making Process, 42*, 364–387.

MacDonald-Wilson, K. L., Mancuso, L. L., Danley, K. S., & Anthony, W. A. (1989). Supported employment for people with psychiatric disability. *Journal of Applied Rehabilitation Counseling, 20*(3), 50–57.

Mank, D. (1994). The underachievement of supported employment: A call for reinvestment. *Journal of Disability Policy Studies, 5*(2), 1–24.

Mansfield, R. (1972). The initiation of graduates into industry. *Human Relations, 25*, 77–86.

Matkin, R. E. (1989). Overcoming disincentives for job seekers with mental illness through mini-counseling and job club methods. *Journal of Job Placement, 5*(1), 11–15.

McGaughey, M. J., Kiernan, W. E., McNally, L. C., Gilmore, D. S., & Keith, G. R. (1994). *Beyond the workshop: National perspectives on integrated employment.* Boston: Institute for Community Inclusion.

Millington, M. J., Asner, K., Der-Stepanian, J., & Linkowski, D. (1996). Employers and job development: The business perspective. In E. M. Szymanski & R. Parker (Eds.), *Work and disability: Issues and strategies for career counselors and job placement* (pp. 277–308). Austin, TX: PRO-ED.

Millington, M. J., Szymanski, E. M., & Johnston-Rodriguez, S. (1995). A contextual-stage model for employment selection. *Journal of Job Placement, 11*(1), 31–36.

Mithaug, D. E., Martin, J. E., Husch, J. V., Agran, M., & Rusch, F. R. (1988). *When will persons in supported employment need less support?* Colorado Springs, CO: Ascent.

Moseley, C. R. (1988). Job satisfaction research: Implications for supported employment. *Journal of the Association for Persons with Severe Handicaps, 13*(3), 211–219.

Muchinsky, P. M. (1986). Personnel selection methods. In C. L. Cooper & I. Robertson (Eds.), *International review of industrial and organizational psychology* (pp. 37–70). New York: Wiley.

Muchinsky, P. M. & Morrow, P. C. (1980). A multidisciplinary model of voluntary employee turnover. *Journal of Vocational Behavior, 17*(3), 263–290.

Nietupski, J., Verstegen, D., Hamre-Nietupski, S., & Tanty, S. (1993). Leveraging community support in approaching employers: The referral model of job development. *Journal of Vocational Rehabilitation, 3*(4), 38–45.

O'Brien, J., & Lovett, H. (1993). *Finding a way toward everyday lives: The contribution of person centered planning.* Harrisburg, PA: Pennsylvania Office of Mental Retardation.

Parent, W. S., & Everson, J. M. (1986). Competencies of disabled workers in industry: A review of business literature. *Journal of Rehabilitation, 52*(4), 16–23.

Parsons, C. K., & Liden, R. C. (1984). Interviewer perceptions of applicant qualifications: A multivariate field study of demographic characteristics and nonverbal cues. *Journal of Applied Psychology, 69,* 557–568.

Pitt-Catsouphes, M., & Butterworth, J. (1995). *Different perspectives: Workplace experience with the employment of individuals with disabilities.* Boston: Center for Work and Family, Boston University.

Premack, S. L., & Wanous, J. P. (1985). A meta-analysis of realistic job preview experiments. *Journal of Applied Psychology, 70,* 706–719.

Reilly, R. R., & Chao, G. T. (1982). Validity and fairness of some alternative employee selection procedures. *Personnel Psychology, 35,* 1–62.

Research Utilization Laboratory. (1976). *Job placement and job development.* Chicago: Jewish Vocational Service.

Roberts, G., Zimbrick, K., Butterworth, J., & Hart, D. (1993). *Job Accommodation System.* Boston: Training and Research Institute for People with Disabilities, Children's Hospital.

Roessler, R. T., & Gottcent, J. (1994). The work experience survey: A reasonable accommodation/career development strategy. *Journal of Applied Rehabilitation Counseling, 25*(3), 16–21.

Rosenfeld, C. (1975, August). Job seeking methods used by American workers. *Monthly Labor Review,* pp. 39–42.

Rothman, R. (1989). *Working: Sociological perspectives.* Englewood Cliffs, NJ: Prentice-Hall.

Rubin, S. E., & Roessler, R. T. (1995). *Foundations of the vocational rehabilitation process* (4th ed.). Austin, TX: PRO-ED.

Rusch, F. R., & Hughes, C. (1990). Historical overview of supported employment. In F. R. Rusch (Eds.), *Supported employment: Models, methods, and issues.* Sycamore, IL: Sycamore.

Rusch, F. R., Wilson, P. G., Hughes, C., & Heal, L. (1994). Matched-pairs analysis of co-worker interactions in relation to opportunity, type of job, and placement approach. *Mental Retardation, 32,* 113–122.

Rutherford, L., Merrier, P., & Parry, L. (1993, Fall). To disclose or not to disclose? *Careers and the DisAbled,* pp. 36–39.

Rynes, S. L., & Gerhart, B. (1990). Interviewer assessments of applicant "fit": An exploratory investigation. *Personnel Psychology, 43,* 13–35.

Rynes, S. L., & Lawler, S. (1983). A policy-capturing investigation of the role of expectancies in decisions to pursue job alternatives. *Journal of Applied Psychology, 68,* 620–631.

Satcher, J., & Hendren, G. R. (1992). Employer agreement with the Americans with Disabilities Act of 1990: Implications for rehabilitation counseling. *Journal of Rehabilitation, 58*(3), 13–24.

Schein, E. (1987). *Process consultation. Vol. 2: Lessons for managers and consultants.* Reading, MA: Addison-Wesley.

Schlenker, B. R. (1980). *Impression management: The self-concept, social identity, and interpersonal relations.* Monterey, CA: Brooks/Cole.

Schlenker, B. R., & Weigold, M. F. (1992). Interpersonal processes involving impression regulation and management. *Annual Review of Psychology, 43,* 133–168.

Schmitt, N., Gooding, R. Z., Noe, R. A., & Kirsch, M. (1984). Meta-analyses of validity studies published between 1964 and 1982 and the investigation of study characteristics. *Personnel Psychology, 37,* 407–422.

Schwab, D. P. (1982). Recruiting and organizational participation. In K. M. Rowland & G. R. Ferris (Eds.), *Personnel management* (pp. 103–128). Boston: Allyn & Bacon.

Schwab, D. P., Rynes, S. L., & Aldag, R. J. (1987). Theories and research on job search and choice. In K. M. Rowland & G. R. Ferris (Eds.), *Research in personnel and human resources management* (Vol. 5, pp. 129–161). Greenwich, CT: Jai Press.

Schwartz, P. (1985). *Employment incentives manual: How to motivate businesses to hire individuals with disabilities.* Bellingham, WA: American Council on Rural Special Education.

Seifker, J. (1989). The placement problem-solver. *Vocational Evaluation and Work Adjustment Bulletin, 22*(3), 121–122.

Shackleton, V., & Anderson, N. (1987). Personnel recruitment and selection. In B. M. Bass & P. J. Drenth (Eds.), *Advances in organizational psychology* (pp. 68–82). Newbury Park, CA: Sage.

Shafer, M. S., Hill, J., Seyfarth, J., & Wehman, P. (1987). Competitive employment and workers with mental retardation: Analysis of employers' perceptions and experiences. *American Journal of Mental Retardation, 92,* 304–311.

Sheppard, H. L., & Belitsky, A. H. (1966). *The job hunt.* Baltimore: Johns Hopkins University Press.

Silliker, S. A. (1993). The role of social contacts in the successful job search. *Journal of Employment Counseling, 30*(1), 25–34.

Sitlington, P. L., & Easterday, J. R. (1992). An analysis of employer incentive rankings relative to the employment of persons with mental retardation. *Education and Training in Mental Retardation, 27,* 75–80.

Smith, C. H., Edwards, J. E., Heinemann, A. W., & Geist, C. (1984). Attitudes toward and performance evaluations of workers with disabilities. *Journal of Applied Rehabilitation Counseling, 16*(1), 39–41.

Stark, J., & Faulkner, E. (1995). Quality of life across the lifespan. In R. Schalock (Ed.), *Quality of life: Perspectives and issues* (pp. 23–32). Washington, DC: American Association on Mental Retardation.

Stensrud, R., Millington, M., & Gilbride, D. (1997). Professional practice: Placement. In D. R. Maki & T. F. Riggar (Eds.), *Rehabilitation Counseling: Profession and practice* (pp. 197–213). New York: Springer.

Stevens, C. K., & Kristof, A. L. (1995). Making the right impression: A field study of applicant impression management during job interviews. *Journal of Applied Psychology, 80,* 587–606.

Storey, K., & Horner, R. (1991). Social interactions in three supported employment options: A comparative analysis. *Journal of Applied Behavior Analysis, 24*(2), 349–360.

Szymanski, E. M., Hershenson, D. B., Enright, M. S., & Ettinger, J. M. (1996). Career development theories, constructs, and research: Implications for people with disabilities. In E. M. Szymanski & R. M. Parker (Eds.), *Work and disability: Issues and strategies in career development and job placement* (pp. 79–126). Austin, TX: PRO-ED.

Taylor, S., & Bogdan, R. (1995). Quality of life and the individual's perspective. In R. Schalock (Eds.), *Quality of life: Perspectives and issues* (pp. 11–22). Washington, DC: American Association on Mental Retardation.

Test, D. W., Hinson, K. B., Solow, J., & Keul, P. (1993). Job satisfaction of persons in supported employment. *Education and Training in Mental Retardation, 28*(1), 38–46.

United States General Accounting Office. (1993). *Vocational rehabilitation: Evidence for federal program's effectiveness is mixed.* Washington, DC: Author.

Vandergoot, D. (1984). Placement practices in vocational rehabilitation. *Journal of Applied Rehabilitation, 15*(3), 24–28.

Vandergoot, D. (1987). Review of placement research literature: Implications for research and practice. *Rehabilitation Counseling Bulletin, 30,* 243–272.

Vandergoot, D., & Swirsky, J. (1980). Applying a systems view of placement career services in rehabilitation. *Journal of Applied Rehabilitation Counseling, 11,* 149–155.

Vroom, V. H. (1964). *Work and motivation.* New York: Wiley.

Wacker, D. P., & Berg, W. K. (1986). Generalizing and maintaining work behavior. In F. R. Rusch (Ed.), *Competitive employment: Issues and strategies* (pp. 129–140). Baltimore: Brookes.

Walker, G. (1987). A job seeking behaviors training program for mentally retarded persons. *Journal of Rehabilitation, 53*(1), 37–40.

Wanous, J. P. (1980). *Organizational entry: Recruitment, selection and socialization of newcomers.* Reading, MA: Addison-Wesley.

Washburn, P. V., & Hakel, M. D. (1973). Visual cues and verbal content as influences on impressions formed after simulated employment interviews. *Journal of Applied Psychology, 58,* 137–141.

Wesolowski, M. D. (1981). Self-directed job placement in rehabilitation: A comparative review. *Rehabilitation Counseling Bulletin, 25,* 80–89.

Wesolowski, M. D., Zawlocki, R., & Dowdy, C. A. (1986). Job obtaining behavior strategies (JOBS) in rehabilitation. *Journal of Job Placement, 2*(1), 13–16.

West, M. D., & Parent, W. S. (1992). Consumer choice and empowerment in supported employment services: Issues and strategies. *Journal of The Association for Persons with Severe Handicaps, 17,* 47–52.

Witt, M. A. (1992). *Job strategies for people with disabilities.* Princeton, NJ: Peterson's Guide.

Zadny, J. J., & James, L. F. (1979). Job placement in state vocational rehabilitation agencies: A survey of technique. *Rehabilitation Counseling Bulletin, 22,* 361–378.

Chapter 12

Rehabilitation Client Assessment

Brian Bolton

he purpose of client assessment in rehabilitation is to develop a factual basis for the provision of rehabilitation services to people with disabilities. The specific objective of the assessment process is to develop the foundation for the individualized rehabilitation service plan for each client. The goal of the rehabilitation service plan is the preparation of the client for suitable employment and community living in the least restrictive environment that is feasible. Rehabilitation client assessment may be described as the application of measurement principles to the unique problems of people with disabilities. Although many appraisal techniques designed for use with the general population are applicable to people with disabilities, some areas of functioning require special approaches and these receive special attention in this chapter. Consequently, the primary focus of this chapter is the presentation of an assessment model consisting of a series of standardized procedures for determining each client's assets and limitations that will establish a basis for the development of an optimal program of rehabilitation services.

The rehabilitation counselor is responsible for coordinating the client assessment process. However, most of the diagnostic procedures, whether medical, psychiatric, psychological, vocational, or social, are usually purchased from specialized professionals or organizations. Once the necessary assessment reports have been received, the rehabilitation counselor integrates all diagnostic information into a comprehensive portrait of the client and then, in collaboration with the client, develops a plan of services that will maximize the probability of a successful rehabilitation outcome. Thus, although the counselor will seldom administer the appraisal instruments or conduct the actual diagnostic examinations, the counselor does have to possess the skills for interpreting assessment findings and translating the results into implications for client service.

This chapter provides a thorough introduction to the principles, methods, and strategies that are essential in the assessment of people with disabilities who are clients in vocational rehabilitation (VR) programs. The emphasis is on practical, useful knowledge and techniques. The following topics are covered: terminology and technical issues, components of the assessment process, the initial interview, assessment instruments, situational assessment, assessment interpretation, and sources of additional information.

Terminology and Technical Issues

As stated in the introductory section, rehabilitation client assessment is the application of measurement principles to the unique problems of people with disabilities. In this section, some basic terminology and a few technical issues are briefly reviewed. I begin by defining *measurement* as the assignment of numbers to the attributes of people according to rules. A synonym for measurement is *quantification,* which means simply to reduce to numerical form. The rules that are referred to in the definition of measurement are the stipulated procedures for administering and scoring the examinee's performance on a test or inventory. These rules constitute the *standardization* of the instrument; this is the most fundamental feature of an assessment device. Test users can have confidence in scores derived from carefully standardized instruments, if there is accompanying evidence supporting the reliability and validity of the scores. The latter characteristics are discussed below.

The terms *assessment, appraisal,* and *evaluation* are used interchangeably in this chapter. They refer to standardized approaches or techniques for gathering psychosocial and vocational information that is essential for developing an in-depth understanding of a client. The goal of all assessment procedures is to predict or make inferences about the examinee's behavior beyond the confines of the test situation. In other words, the conclusions, implications, and recommendations that derive from the assessment process should be generalizable to the client's future behavior and circumstances. The vehicle for communicating assessment results, the written report, should provide conclusions that can be translated by the rehabilitation counselor into a plan for service delivery. Strategies for interpreting assessment instruments and techniques are presented later in the chapter.

In the remainder of this section, two essential features of scientifically reputable assessment instruments are briefly summarized. These important features are reliability and validity. It should be noted that the following discussion has direct relevance to standardized psychosocial and vocational appraisal instruments. The medical and psychiatric examinations conducted in rehabilitation emanate from a somewhat different professional tradition, although the scientific concepts of reliability and validity apply in principle to these assessment techniques, too. The same can be stated for the diagnostic interview, which is discussed in a separate section. A slightly longer presentation about reliability and validity is provided in Chapter 13 in this text. Readers desiring detailed treatments of these important topics are referred to the handbook by Bolton (1987a) or to the popular textbook by Cronbach (1990).

The *reliability* of a test score indicates the precision with which the trait or attribute is measured. Reliability is usually reported as a reliability coefficient, which may range from .00 to 1.00. However, scores with reliabilities below .70 should be used cautiously in the assessment process. The reliability coefficient is interpreted as a proportion of variance; for example, a reliability coefficient of .82 indicates that 82% of the variability among clients on the test trait reflects true or real individual differences, and only 18% of the differences among respondents is due to errors of measurement. The higher the reliability coefficient, the more confidence the counselor can have in the score. However, it is important to emphasize that, although reliability or precision of measurement is a necessary condition for validity, it is not a sufficient condition. That is to say, high reliability does not imply or guarantee a valid measurement process.

Validity is a critical issue in client assessment because it determines the meaning that can be conferred on test scores, and this meaning establishes the foundation for interpretation in the assessment process. Validity is an easy property to define but a complex subject to explain. In straightforward language, a valid test measures what it purports to measure. However, the determination of validity involves an overall evaluative judgment of the extent to which the evidence supports the interpretation of test scores. Three types of validity evidence (content, criterion related, and construct) are described in Chapter 13. Validity is never finally established for a test instrument; validation is an ongoing process of collecting and evaluating relevant evidence. Fortunately, test authors have the obligation to provide up-to-date comprehensive surveys of validity evidence in their test manuals. These validity summaries enable counselors to determine which score interpretations are warranted by the validity evidence.

Components of the Assessment Process

The ultimate objective of the diagnostic evaluation in rehabilitation is to determine the nature and scope of services that will enable the client to function as independently as possible. Independent functioning includes both employment and community living circumstances. Therefore, the assessment process must be comprehensive and thorough, encompassing medical, psychosocial, and vocational components. As noted above, the rehabilitation counselor typically does not actually conduct the examinations or administer the required test procedures; however, the counselor must understand the assessment process so that he or she can translate the diagnostic information into a plan of services. Because every agency and facility has detailed procedures for conducting the diagnostic study, this section provides only a general overview of the components of the assessment process.

The most basic component of the rehabilitation assessment is the general medical examination. In addition to establishing the nature of the disabling condition, the general medical examination should specify the functional limitations that result from the disability, as well as the examinee's residual functional capacities, meaning what the examinee can *still do.* The medical examination, which should include diagnosis, prognosis, limitations, and recommendations, is conducted by a licensed physician. Sometimes a specialized medical examination is warranted and may be obtained, if recommended by the general physician. For clients with behavioral disorders, an examination by a licensed psychiatrist may be necessary. In cases where mental retardation or learning disabilities are central issues, diagnosis by a licensed psychologist is required. The diagnosis of mental retardation must be based on an evaluation of intellectual functioning and adaptive behavior, whereas the determination of a learning disability requires that the cause of the learning problems be demonstrated to involve central nervous system dysfunction.

Medical, psychiatric, and psychological examinations are always conducted by specially trained professionals, after the client is referred by the rehabilitation counselor. Before requesting these diagnostic evaluations, the counselor collects relevant personal history information from the client. Almost all rehabilitation assessments begin by obtaining personal data from the client using a standard questionnaire that solicits information about the disabling condition, educational background, family situation, work history, and so forth. It is important to realize that personal history data not only have value in reaching a thorough understanding of the client but also are predictive of successful rehabilitation outcomes (Bellini, Neath, & Bolton, 1995). The completed personal history questionnaire provides the starting point for the initial interview that the rehabilitation counselor conducts with the client. The length and scope of the interview vary widely, depending on the resources available and the assessment philosophy of the agency.

After the initial interview is completed and the required medical and psychological examinations are conducted, the focus of the rehabilitation assessment process becomes the client's vocational and psychosocial status. The selection of tests, inventories, and other standardized appraisal techniques reflects the particular mission of the service delivery program. *To reiterate:* The goal of the assessment process is to establish a foundation for the development of an individualized program of services. Vocational preparation, job placement, and independent living objectives involve different combinations of services to produce optimal client outcomes. It follows that different assessment batteries are required to design different service programs. Still, a standard battery of instruments is usually desirable. At a minimum, the assessment battery should include measures of general intellectual ability, readiness for vocational planning, occupational interests, work temperaments, normal personality functioning, and independent living capabilities. In some situations, a multiple aptitude test, a psychopathology inventory, or a work skills test may be desirable. In all situations, the selection of assessment procedures should be guided by the goals of the rehabilitation service program. Capsule descriptions of eight especially suitable tests and inventories are included later in this chapter.

The Initial Interview

The initial interview that the rehabilitation counselor conducts with the client is the first major appraisal activity in the assessment process. The personal history questionnaire (or application form) may be regarded as the first phase of the interview. It can be argued reasonably that the intake interview constitutes the basis for all subsequent assessment decisions. Although authorities disagree on the importance of the interview as an appraisal technique, everybody agrees that it is a critical step in the rehabilitation service delivery sequence. This is because the interview entails getting acquainted with the client and building a relationship, as well as obtaining relevant information. Moreover, a preliminary understanding of the client's strengths and weaknesses usually results and the overall level of case difficulty can be estimated. Only a quick overview of some essential considerations of the initial interview can be given here.

The remainder of this section is adapted from a self-directed learning module for acquiring and enhancing interview skills that was developed by Farley (1983). More than 200 specific interview behaviors are included in this comprehensive approach to interviewing skills. The major categories of interview performance are planning the interview, structuring the setting, disseminating information, collecting information, facilitating information exchange, observing nonverbal communication, listening actively, organizing and processing information, using specific responses, facilitating client exploration, and monitoring interview skills.

Because the initial interview establishes the foundation for the interpretation of the tests and inventories that are administered subsequently, it is imperative that the interview be comprehensive in scope. The best way to assure that all critical topics are discussed with the client is to conduct a carefully structured interview. The outline that follows lists the issues that should be covered (Farley, 1983):

- *Referral*—referral source, client expectations, previous rehabilitation services, current services from other agencies

- *Disability/Medical*—reported disabilities, duration and stability, previous/current treatment, functional limitations, client's feelings about disabilities

- *Social*—living arrangements, family members' attitudes, support from others, social/leisure activities

- *Economic*—sources of support, medical insurance, client's feelings about economic situation

- *Work History*—employment status, information about most recent job, reason for leaving, ability to get along with supervisors and coworkers, job seeking behavior

- *Vocational Goals*—vocational motivation, vocational goals, client's perceived ability to achieve goals, long-range planning

- *Education*—educational status, attitude toward school, favorite subjects/ courses, grades, previous vocational training, client's feelings about educational status

This section concludes with a series of practical guidelines for conducting the initial interview. Interested readers are referred to the manual by Farley (1983) for details.

1. Develop specific interview objectives for the client and share these with the client.

2. Provide a meeting place that is accessible and comfortable and where confidentiality can be assured.

3. Follow a systematic interview plan that consists of a series of topics to be discussed with the client.

4. Communicate at the client's level of understanding and avoid confusing terminology, jargon, and so on.

5. Observe the client's personal appearance, gestures, movement, posture, and facial expressions.

6. Provide the client with information that serves the goals of promoting independence and involvement.

7. Ask focused questions only to obtain specific items of information or to appropriately restrict the discussion.

8. Give the client opportunities for expression by using open-ended questions and statements.

9. Listen carefully for the client's major concerns and the common themes expressed.

10. Explore the client's thoughts and feelings that relate to the facts being gathered.

11. Be attentive to inconsistencies in the client's communication, especially between verbal and nonverbal expression.

12. Communicate understanding of what the client expresses by rephrasing statements.

13. Summarize for the client the significant content of the discussion at the end of the interview.

Assessment Instruments

This section presents capsule summaries of eight instruments that are especially appropriate for use in rehabilitation assessment. Many other excellent tests and inventories also may be helpful in evaluating people with disabilities. Sources of information about other instruments are described in the last section of this chapter. Work behavior rating scales are discussed briefly in the next section on situational assessment. Each of the standard summaries presents descriptions of the instrument format, the traits or behaviors measured, applications in rehabilitation, and validity evidence. References that provide technical details are also given. Seven of the eight instruments have accompanying computer-generated reports that greatly extend the utility of the assessment data.

The first two instruments are general purpose tests. The *Functional Assessment Inventory* (Crewe & Athelstan, 1984) is a comprehensive observer rating scale that may be used to summarize the strengths and limitations of the client. Requiring 1 hour of individual testing, the *Preliminary Diagnostic Questionnaire* (Moriarty, 1981) produces estimates of abilities and personal characteristics in eight areas of functioning. The other six instruments focus on specific areas. The *Employability Maturity Interview* (Roessler & Bolton, 1987) is a brief structured interview that measures readiness for vocational planning. The *USES Interest Inventory (U.S. Department of Labor, 1982)* generates a profile of the client's salient vocational interests. Based on an assessment of the 12 work temperaments defined in the Department of Labor's occupational research, the *Work Temperament Inventory* (Bolton & Brookings, 1993) lists a dozen worker trait groups for which the respondent is temperamentally suited. The *Sixteen Personality Factor Questionnaire—Form E* (Institute for Personality and Ability Testing, 1985) generates a profile of the client's trait structure in the normal personality sphere. The *Rehabilitation Indicators* (M. Brown, Diller, Fordyce, Jacobs, & Gordon, 1980) constitute a comprehensive resource for assessing the independent living skills of people with disabilities. The *General Aptitude Test Battery* (U.S. Department of Labor, 1970) measures nine occupational aptitudes that can be used with the USES–II to identify suitable occupations for the examinee.

Functional Assessment Inventory

The *Functional Assessment Inventory* (FAI; Crewe & Athelstan, 1984) is a 42-item rating instrument designed for use by vocational rehabilitation counselors. All FAI items are focused on vocationally relevant behaviors and capabilities and provide data essential in rehabilitation service planning. The FAI consists of 30 behaviorally anchored rating items that assess the client's vocational capabilities and deficiencies, 10 items that identify unusual assets, and 2 global items judging severity of disability and probability of vocational success. The Personal Capacities Questionnaire (PCQ) is a self-report version of the FAI that can be used in conjunction with the observer rating form or independently.

Seven subscales are the primary organizing scheme for reporting FAI results: Adaptive Behavior, Motor Functioning, Physical Condition, Communication, Cognition, Vocational Qualification, and Environmental Orientation. The FAI can be hand scored easily. Percentile equivalents for three categories of disability (physical, behavioral, and blind) are available for items, subscale scores, and the total Functional Limitation score. The Functional Assessment Rating System (FARS) computer program generates the best score report, however, because it incorporates the largest and most representative normative samples. The FARS is a comprehensive eligibility determination and case planning program that enables the counselor to complete a functional assessment using the FAI, from which a series of normative functional profiles are calculated, and guides him or her in designing a service plan that links functional deficits to needed services.

The available validity evidence strongly supports the objective of the FAI, which is to assess vocationally relevant functional capabilities of applicants for VR services. Scores on FAI items, subscales, and total limitations and strengths distinguish between disability groups in logically expected ways, identify applicants for services who are judged to have substantial vocational handicaps, correlate with global evaluations of severity of disability and probability of employment, and predict rehabilitation outcome criteria such as work status, earnings, and service costs. Readers interested in statistical details and references are referred to Bolton (1990).

Preliminary Diagnostic Questionnaire

The *Preliminary Diagnostic Questionnaire* (PDQ; Moriarty, 1981) was developed to assess the functional capacities of persons with disabilities in the context of employability. Implicit in the construction of the PDQ was the assumption that a preliminary assessment of work-relevant characteristics should be possible without special tools and equipment and should take about an hour to administer. The PDQ was designed to assess four broad areas of functioning relevant to the employability of persons with disabilities: cognitive (measured by Work Information, Preliminary Estimate of Learning, Psychomotor Skills, and Reading Retention subtests), motivation or disposition to work (measured by Work Importance and Internality subtests), physical (measured by the Personal Independence subtest), and emotional (measured by the Emotional Functioning subtest).

The 148 PDQ items are administered in a structured interview format using a self-contained, consumable 12-page booklet. All examinee responses and examiner notes are recorded in the booklet. Item scoring is accomplished simultaneously with test administration by the experienced examiner, and the profile of standard scores can be calculated in a few minutes. The normative sample that constitutes the basis for converting raw scores on the eight PDQ subtests to stanine scores consists of 2,972 VR clients from 30 state agencies. A computerized PDQ report is available on floppy disk, and a computer-based decision support system for rehabilitation counselors incorporates PDQ results as client database elements.

Because the PDQ purports to assess the employment potential of persons with disabilities, evaluation of its validity should be based on the prediction of employment outcomes. Two subtests were significant predictors of earnings after case closure for a sample of former clients, whereas three subscales were predictive of minimum wage attainment. Additional evidence supportive of the validity of the PDQ includes the careful scale construction procedures and expected convergent and divergent relationships with standard aptitude, intelligence, and achievement tests. Readers interested in statistical details and references are referred to Bolton (1991).

Employability Maturity Interview

The *Employability Maturity Interview* (EMI; Roessler & Bolton, 1987) is a structured interview consisting of 10 questions designed to assess readiness for the VR planning process. The EMI is useful as a brief screening instrument to identify clients needing additional vocational exploration and employability services. Readiness for vocational planning is operationalized by the EMI in terms of level of self-knowledge and extent of occupational information.

The 10 questions that compose the EMI represent four areas: occupational choice, self-appraisal of abilities, orientation to work, and self-appraisal of personality characteristics. The rationale for including these questions is that clients who have a good understanding of self in relation to the world of work, and have used this knowledge in vocational exploration to obtain information about relevant occupations, are ready to participate in the formulation of a VR plan.

The EMI takes between 10 and 15 minutes to administer and another 5 minutes to score using detailed guidelines that result in a score of 0, 1, or 2 for each question. Three factor scores are calculated: general maturity, specificity of goals, and variety of interests. Two normative comparisons are available: rehabilitation center clients and Veterans Administration clients. The EMI computer-generated report (Neath & Bolton, 1995) produces a score profile, a normative interpretation, and a series of recommendations for further vocational exploration.

Reliability of the EMI is high, especially for a scoring procedure that requires subjective judgment. The construct validity of the EMI was confirmed by predicted relationships with intelligence, achievement, vocational interest differentiation, general interest in work, and an independent measure of employment potential. Readers interested in statistical details and references are referred to Morelock, Roessler, and Bolton (1987).

USES Interest Inventory

The *USES Interest Inventory* (USES–II; U.S. Department of Labor, 1982) is a self-report instrument that measures the respondent's relative strength of interests in 12 broad categories of occupational activity. The 12 occupational interest areas constitute the primary organizing theme of the U.S. Department of Labor's (1979a) *Guide for Occupational Exploration.* The USES–II consists of 162 items of three types: job activity statements, occupational titles, and life experiences. The 12 interest areas measured are Artistic, Scientific, Plants and Animals, Protective, Mechanical, Industrial, Business Detail, Selling, Accommodating, Humanitarian, Leading–Influencing, and Physical Performing.

The USES–II can be appropriately used with the general adult population aged 16 years and above. The reading level required is about third grade, but an audiotape version for administration to poor readers is easily prepared. After a profile of 12 raw scores is obtained by counting the number of "liked" items for each of the 12 interest areas, the raw scores are translated into standard *T*-scores using a geographically and racially representative normative sample consisting of 6,530 students, job applicants, and employed workers.

The USES–II is the product of a careful program of developmental research. Although the inventory was not developed specifically for use with persons with disabilities, several psychometric studies of the instrument have been carried out with rehabilitation client samples. For example, the USES–II predicted with substantial accuracy graduation from various vocational training curricula at a comprehensive rehabilitation center.

The USES–II is the only interest inventory designed to be used with the most thoroughly occupationally validated multiaptitude test available, the *General Aptitude Test Battery* (described later), and is directly linked with an occupational exploration system that encompasses all jobs in the U.S. economy. Readers interested in statistical details and references are referred to Bolton (1994a).

Work Temperament Inventory

The *Work Temperament Inventory* (WTI; Bolton & Brookings, 1993) is a self-report measure of 12 work temperaments that were originally identified and defined by the U.S. Department of Labor. Work temperaments are the adaptability requirements made on the worker by specific types of jobs or, analogously, the "personal traits" required of the worker by the job situation. An employee's inability to adapt to the work situation may be the cause of dissatisfaction or failure to perform adequately on the job.

The WTI consists of 134 items requiring a simple "like" or "dislike" response and a seventh-grade reading level. The WTI can be completed in 20 minutes or less by the respondent using a consumable booklet or direct input to the WTI Computer Report. The 12 WTI scales are Directing Others, Performing Repetitive

Work, Influencing People, Variety of Duties, Expressing Feelings, Making Judgments, Working Alone, Performing Under Stress, Attaining Precise Tolerances, Working Under Specific Instructions, Dealing with People, and Decisions Based on Measurable Data.

The use of the WTI in counseling is greatly facilitated by the availability of a computer-generated report. The WTI Computer Report (Neath & Bolton, 1993) generates a percentile score profile on the 12 work temperament scales and then lists up to 12 worker trait groups for which the respondent is temperamentally suited. The 12 (or fewer) worker trait groups are selected by matching the client's profile with the groups that require the same work temperaments.

The WTI normative group includes students, employees, and rehabilitation center clients. The typical scale reliability coefficient is in the mid .70s. The validity of the WTI is supported by the original developmental analysis, the factor structure of the 12 temperaments, convergent and divergent relationships with measured occupational interests, and the differential temperamental requirements of 91 worker trait groups. Readers interested in statistical details and references are referred to Bolton, Brookings, and Neath (1994).

Sixteen Personality Factor Questionnaire—Form E

The *Sixteen Personality Factor Questionnaire—Form E* (16PF–E; Institute for Personality and Ability Testing, 1985) is a special-purpose personality inventory that was designed for use with persons with limited educational and cultural backgrounds. In particular, it is appropriate for individuals whose reading level is no more than third grade. As its name indicates, the 16PF–E measures 16 primary characteristics of the normal personality sphere: Warmth, Intelligence, Stability, Dominance, Impulsivity, Conformity, Boldness, Sensitivity, Suspiciousness, Imagination, Shrewdness, Insecurity, Radicalism, Self-Sufficiency, Self-Discipline, and Tension. In addition, five second-order dimensions are also scored: Extraverted, Adjusted, Tough-Minded, Independent, and Disciplined.

The 16PF has been used in at least 20 investigations designed to identify the unique personality traits associated with various types of disability, thus to better understand reactions to disablement (Roessler & Bolton, 1978). Furthermore, several basic psychometric studies of the 16PF–E have been conducted on samples of rehabilitation clients. Each of the 16 primary scales is represented by eight items. The five secondary scales are scored according to formulas derived from the results of a factor analysis of the protocols of more than 10,000 respondents. Norms are available for a heterogeneous sample of almost 1,000 rehabilitation clients, subdivided by sex and age.

The 16PF–E rehabilitation client norms are incorporated into a computer-generated report, the *Vocational Personality Report* (Bolton, 1987c), which provides scores on the five second-order personality scales, two psychopathology dimensions (Anxiety and Depression, Sociopathic Tendency), three general vocational interest scales, (Humanitarian/Interpersonal, Productive/Creative, Managerial/Leadership), and Holland's six occupational types (Realistic, Investigative, Artistic, Social, Enterprising, Conventional).

Rehabilitation Indicators

The *Rehabilitation Indicators* (RIs; M. Brown et al., 1980) constitute a comprehensive assessment system for describing the functional capabilities of rehabilitation clients. RIs focus on observable elements of client behavior, using lay terminology to characterize a broad range of content (e.g., vocational, educational, self-care, communication, mobility, household, recreation, and transportation) at varying levels of detail from specific to general. There are three types of RIs. Status Indicators (SIs) describe categorical statuses or roles that are crucial to clients' functioning. Activity Pattern Indicators (APIs) describe clients' daily living activities in terms of frequency, duration, social interaction, and assistance needed. Skill Indicators (SKIs) describe the behavioral tools that clients need to attain their rehabilitation goals.

The RI materials were devised to provide maximum flexibility for users, with each component (SIs, APIs, and SKIs) being administrable by interview, by independent observation, or by self-report. Furthermore, the user selects only those items from the SIs and SKIs that are relevant to the purpose for which the RIs are being used. The SIs consist of 48 indicators that represent six role categories; the APIs include 106 items organized into 15 categories of activities; and the SKIs consist of more than 700 skills that represent 78 skill areas organized under 14 categories of functioning.

RIs were developed for the explicit purpose of describing rehabilitation clients' statuses or life roles, daily living activities, and behavioral competencies or skills in ways that are especially helpful in the provision and evaluation of rehabilitation services. Depending on the mode of administration (interview, observation, or self-report), the RIs can be administered in almost any setting, ranging from the examiner's office to the client's home. Readers interested in statistical details and references are referred to Bolton (1994b).

General Aptitude Test Battery

The *General Aptitude Test Battery* (GATB; U.S. Department of Labor, 1970) is the most extensively researched occupational aptitude test in existence. First published in 1947, the GATB has been the central instrument in an ongoing program of validity research that has established linkages between aptitude scores and vocational proficiency for 97% of the nonsupervisory jobs in the U.S. labor market. An overview of the USES testing system is provided by Droege (1987).

The GATB measures nine aptitude factors with eight paper-and-pencil tests and four apparatus tests. The nine aptitudes measured by weighted combinations of the tests are General learning ability (G), Verbal aptitude (V), Numerical aptitude (N), Spatial aptitude (S), Form perception (P), Clerical perception (Q), Motor coordination (K), Finger dexterity (F), and Manual dexterity (M). The entire battery, which is available to nonprofit organizations through licensing agreements with the USES, can be administered to small groups of examinees by trained test administrators in about 2¼ hours. The GATB is a carefully standardized instrument with detailed directions for test administration.

The GATB is the centerpiece of the most elaborate and detailed career assessment and exploration system available to counselors. Used in conjunction with the USES–II or the *Interest Check List* (U.S. Department of Labor, 1979b) and the *Guide for Occupational Exploration* (GOE), the counselor and counselee have access to the most thoroughly researched occupational data file ever assembled for the U.S. labor market. In addition to translating aptitude and interest profiles into potential occupations for the counselee to consider, the GOE and related documents provide data on a variety of critical job features, such as physical demands, working conditions, specific vocational preparation required, and mathematical and language skills needed.

Conversion of the individual's GATB and USES–II profiles into an ordered list of suitable job families and representative jobs can be easily accomplished by computer. The *Occupational Report* (Bolton, 1987b) is a computer-generated report that summarizes an examinee's interest and aptitude levels for the 66 work groups (job families) in the GOE. The report includes graphic presentations of interest and aptitude results, followed by lists of suitable work groups and sample occupations ordered from high-interest and high-aptitude combinations to average areas.

The GATB is the most extensively researched multiaptitude instrument available for use in career assessment and occupational exploration. Four notable strengths of the GATB are as follows: (a) the reliability and especially the stability of the aptitude scores are exceptional, although there is a small to moderate practice effect due to retesting; (b) validity generalization studies have demonstrated that the battery is a valid predictor of job performance for all jobs in the U.S. economy; (c) aptitude scores are translated directly into three levels of qualification for 66 work groups and composite percentile scores for 179 job groups; and (d) the battery assesses the aptitudes of racial/ethnic minority examinees fairly. A review of the GATB and its uses, sponsored by the National Research Council, was more critical of the instrument (Hartigan & Wigdor, 1989). Readers interested in statistical details and references are referred to Bolton (1994a).

Situational Assessment

Situational assessment has a long and successful history as an appraisal strategy in rehabilitation. This is because people with disabilities sometimes do not perform well on standardized tests and inventories. Furthermore, common sense suggests that the optimal approach to the evaluation of work behavior involves observing the client in a simulated or actual job for an extended period of time. Although this is not feasible for most clients, there are assessment strategies that approximate in varying degrees the ideal circumstance. This section provides an overview of three approaches to situational assessment: work samples, workshop evaluation, and on-the-job evaluation. It is important to stress that situational approaches are not substitutes for traditional psychological and vocational testing, but rather are supplemental appraisal strategies.

The work sample is an assessment approach that stands between the psychometric test and the workshop evaluation on the continuum from high control to less control. The work sample is abstracted from an actual job task—it is a "mock-up" or miniature version of a common job. Because the work sample is simpler in format, it is amenable to standardization. All work samples should have manuals that give directions for administration, scoring, and interpretation, as well as technical details about reliability and validity. Individual work samples are usually organized into a series or a system that measures performance across a range of basic job tasks. The first widely used work sample system is known by the acronym TOWER (for *Testing, Orientation, and Work Evaluation in Rehabilitation*) and was developed almost four decades ago at the Institute for the Crippled and Disabled (1959). For thorough descriptions of 18 work sample systems used in rehabilitation, the reader is referred to the guide by C. Brown, McDaniel, and Couch (1994).

Workshop evaluation and on-the-job evaluation are closely related assessment strategies. They both focus on the client's work personality, which refers to the work attitudes, values, and behaviors that the individual has developed. Can the client adapt to the work role? Respond appropriately to supervision? Get along harmoniously with coworkers? Come to work on time? Evaluative workshops simulate the typical environment in the competitive job market. Clients perform various types of repetitive assembly-line tasks for which they are paid modest piece rates. Professionally trained work evaluators observe client–workers as they perform different tasks and interact with peers and supervisors. They assess the client's work personality, with deficits identified and carefully described so that an individualized, remedial work-adjustment program can be implemented.

Although the more controlled setting of the evaluative workshop is usually best for assessing the work personality, some clients can be evaluated through trial employment: such jobs as kitchen help, custodial duties, and grounds maintenance may be substituted for the workshop. The critical consideration in selecting an on-the-job evaluation setting is whether adequate opportunities for observation of relevant work behaviors are available. The primary advantage of the on-the-job evaluation is its realism and authenticity, which means that the appraisal has high generalizability and therefore fosters more accurate predictions of future work behavior. In contrast, the evaluative workshop sacrifices some generalizability for the opportunity to experimentally manipulate the work context. For example, supervisory attitudes, coworker relationships, work pressure, and type and level of work may all be experimentally modified in the evaluative workshop. Readers interested in the actual conduct of situational work appraisals are referred to the relevant articles in Bolton and Cook (1980).

Regardless of the nature of the setting and its location and the work assessment strategy used, all situational work evaluations should include a structured observational rating form. Numerous vocational rating scales have been constructed, and most of these instruments fulfill the designated purpose. The most recently developed instrument, the *Work Personality Profile* (WPP; Bolton & Roessler, 1986), consists of 58 items that assess 11 dimensions of work behavior that are directly relevant to employment success: Acceptance of Work Role, Ability to Profit from Instruction or Correction, Work Persistence, Work Tolerance, Amount of Supervision Required, Extent Trainee Seeks Assistance from Supervisor, Degree of Comfort or Anxiety with Supervisor, Appropriateness of Personal Relations with Supervisor, Teamwork, Ability to Socialize with Co-workers, and Social Communication Skills. Each item is rated on a 4-point scale ranging from *employability strength* (4) to *employability deficit* (1); completion of the WPP takes between 5 and 10 minutes. The WPP Computer Report generates a profile on the 11 primary work behavior scales and five second-order factor scales.

There are other situational assessment approaches that focus on specific aspects of the job search and acquisition process. One critical area that merits the attention of the rehabilitation counselor is that of job application and interviewing. A comprehensive assessment approach is presented in the *Manual for the Job Seeking Skills Assessment* (Hinman, Means, Parkerson, & Odendahl, 1988). In general, situational assessment procedures are expensive and time-consuming to develop, validate, administer, and interpret. However, the higher costs may be justified when conducting assessments of clients with severe disabilities. The interested reader is referred to Roessler and Greenwood (1987) for more information about situational vocational evaluation techniques.

Assessment Interpretation

Assessment interpretation refers to the process of translating the results of examinations, tests, questionnaires, and other appraisal techniques into a coherent written report. The interpretation of assessment data is a task that requires clinical judgment and expertise with assessment instruments. Clinical expertise is based on experience conducting assessments and knowledge about the research foundations of the instruments used. Although there are no simple systems of assessment interpretation and no fixed rules, there are basic principles for evaluating and synthesizing assessment data into a coherent, useful report. In this section, principles and strategies for interpreting assessment data are outlined and then illustrated with a brief case study.

There are three basic strategies for translating test scores into conclusions about the client's performance or trait structure. Domain-referenced score interpretation depends on the adequacy of the sample of test content. The client's status typically is reported as a proportion of the test tasks mastered. This is a common approach in independent living assessment. Criterion-referenced score interpretation depends on empirically established relationships between the score and the measured outcomes. The test score is often translated into an estimated probability of success or a goodness-of-fit index with a modal profile. Norm-referenced score interpretation involves comparison to a representative sample of people, called the normative group. The client's status is usually reported as a derived score, such as a percentile (1st through 99th) or a *T*-score (mean of 50 and standard deviation of 10). It should be emphasized that all score interpretation is trait referenced, meaning that the foundation for the interpretation is the construct validity evidence that indicates that the test score measures what it purports to measure.

The goal of assessment interpretation is to organize and synthesize interview and test information into a comprehensive, integrated portrait of the client's rehabilitation potential. To accomplish this goal, it is necessary to become intimately familiar with the client, and the best approach is to use a battery of procedures that encompass all relevant areas of the client's history and functional status. The composition of the assessment battery depends to some extent on the specific focus of the rehabilitation agency or program that has sponsored the client.

Still, there are several overarching principles that apply in the interpretation of rehabilitation assessment data. The following principles of interpretation are discussed in more detail in Bolton (1987a) and Moriarty, Minton, and Spann (1981).

1. Use one or more models or theories for organizing the assessment data. Assessment interpretation is more meaningful when it reflects the framework of a well-grounded model of vocational adjustment, such as Gellman's (1953) Chicago Jewish Vocational Service Theory, Holland's (1985) well-known typology of vocational personalities, or Neff's (1985) typology of maladaptive work patterns.

2. Look for convergence across scales, instruments, work groups, work history, and interview data. Interpretation of scale scores should be based on construct validity evidence and examination of instrument content, that is, the scale items. Remember that test scores are estimates of the client's performance potential, so allowance should be made for unreliability of test scores.

3. Begin by listing the client's strengths and deficits in selected relevant areas. Do the strengths offset the deficits? Can the deficits be remediated? Start with the simpler, more straightforward explanations, before moving to complex interpretations. Describe test results in functional terms in relation to employment and independent living. Translate test results into implications for client service planning.

4. When in doubt, consult the expert: the client. There are three reasons for involving the client in the test interpretation process: (a) explaining the purpose of assessment to clients encourages them to become active participants; (b) sharing assessment results with clients gives them some responsi-

bility for acting upon the results; and (c) because clients are lifelong experts on themselves, they bring a wealth of self-knowledge to assessment interpretation (Vash, 1981).

5. Providing clients with feedback about their results is the final requirement of a comprehensive rehabilitation assessment. The feedback interview has four goals: (a) presenting information in a nonthreatening manner, (b) interpreting results so that the client understands the implications, (c) eliciting the client's response to test results, and (d) developing alternative courses of action. A step-by-step manual for conducting the feedback interview is available (Farley, Parkerson, Farley, & Martin, 1993).

It is obviously impossible to explain the assessment interpretation process in a few paragraphs. Furthermore, learning how to interpret assessment instruments and write the assessment report requires extensive supervised practice. In the remainder of this section, some general guidelines for interpreting and synthesizing assessment data are outlined and then illustrated with a case example. First, interpretation begins by becoming thoroughly immersed in the raw data—the examinations, the interview, and the score profiles from the various tests and inventories. A helpful approach that facilitates the analytic process is "mapping" the client on a large piece of drawing paper. The objective of the mapping exercise is to get all relevant information diagrammed into a visual representation of the client. The ultimate goal of the client map is to capture the central organizing themes of the individual's personality and life circumstances.

The salient results that derive from each examination, test, questionnaire, and other appraisal technique should be summarized in brief notes and phrases located around the perimeter of the map. The objective is to reduce the client's history, examination results, and test scores to a manageable set of information. The next step is to connect, with lines drawn across the center space, those findings that converge to build a consistent portrait of the client. Red lines may be drawn to link results that appear to be inconsistent or contradictory with the emerging picture of the client. Counselors should use a variety of interpretative resources at this stage, including the test manuals and handbooks that have been assembled to accompany the instruments. From the map of the client, the assessor should be able to write a series of six to eight conclusions that establish the framework for the assessment report. The final step is actually writing the report. The following topics should be covered: background information; disability factors; abilities and skills; interests, temperaments, and personality; vocational exploration; and summary and recommendations.

One especially important facet of the interpretative process concerns the analysis of multiscore profiles. Most aptitude, achievement, personality, and interest measures used in psychological and vocational assessment generate a series of scores that should be interpreted simultaneously. The most efficient strategy for interpreting a profile of scores involves three distinct steps. First, examine the overall level of the profile. Do the scores tend to be above average, average, or below average? Second, note the overall variability of the scores in the profile. Do the scores tend to be about the same, or is there substantial intraindividual variation or differentiation? Third, identify the highest and lowest scores in the profile for further review. Carefully interpreted, multiscore profiles can provide a wealth of information about the organization of the client's traits. A fourth step that applies to all assessment instruments is to examine the responses that produced each score. This requires that the scoring key be used to locate and review the client's answers. This step is essential in resolving apparent contradictions in assessment results for a complicated case.

The following case study is abstracted from a longer written report. The main facts and the interpretation of test data are emphasized. The abbreviated presentation, which was prepared for teaching purposes, illustrates the sequence of topics reviewed and the analysis and synthesis of assessment data. The examinee's name and basic identifying information have been changed; "Mr. Gray" gave his permission to use the report here. Finally, it should be stressed that diagnostic assessment and report writing can be learned only through supervised practice.

 ## ASSESSMENT REPORT FOR EDWARD GRAY

Introduction

Mr. Gray arrived early for the assessment on April 29, and participated readily in the assessment process. He conducted himself in a congenial and cooperative manner, appeared to understand all directions, and applied himself well to completing each task.

Family And Social Background

Mr. Gray is 38 years old and married with two children, a son age 14 and a daughter age 10. He stated that it is not necessary for his family to be involved in decisions concerning his vocational future. However, he said that his family would be supportive and understanding in helping him to achieve his goal. Hobbies listed by Mr. Gray were hunting, fishing, and woodworking. He noted that, until his disability interfered, he enjoyed golf and tennis.

Education

Mr. Gray reported that he attended Memorial High School until the 10th grade. He said that he then joined the navy and obtained a GED. He stated that while in the military he received training in aviation operations, familiarization and supply, and training and recruitment methods. He said that while in school his favorite subjects were accounting, self-defense courses, law enforcement courses, and foreign language.

Employment History

Mr. Gray stated that after his discharge from the navy he was employed for brief periods of time as a carpenter, a dispatcher for a truck company, an accident specialist, and a delivery person. He said that he is currently employed as a jailer (DOT 372.367-014). He stated that his last duty in the military was as an operations manager for an airfield (DOT 184.117-050). He stated further that prior to that duty he worked in aviation supply performing the duties of a shipping and receiving clerk (DOT 222.387-050) and a stock clerk (DOT 222.387-058).

Disability Factors

According to information in the referral file, Mr. Gray has service-connected disabilities including cluster headaches, a fracture of the left jaw with loss of sensation of the fifth and seventh cranial nerves, and tinnitus. Mr. Gray explained that the injury to his jaw occurred in a physical altercation with another soldier, and that the tinnitus was a result of working around jet engines. He added that he thought a hearing aide might be helpful, but that he is a "can doer" who does not allow anything to stop him.

Transferable Skills

An analysis of worker trait factors present in Mr. Gray's work history was conducted. In his present and previous work, he has demonstrated the ability to work around hazards and he has shown above-average reasoning, math, and language skills. Mr. Gray has demonstrated above-average intelligence, verbal and numerical aptitudes, and spatial and form perception. In work activities and situations, he has shown the ability to do business with people, perform routine organized tasks, work with machinery, receive prestige and esteem, keep control over tasks, work in stressful situations, meet precise standards, and evaluate information subjectively and objectively. Mr. Gray possesses valuable transferable skills related to his previous experience in the military, especially in his work as the operations chief of an airfield.

Interests, Aptitudes, and Abilities

The *Wonderlic Personnel Test* (Wonderlic Personnel Test, Inc., 1992) is a short-form test of general cognitive ability. Mr. Gray scored at the 54th percentile, which reflects the job potential for a routine office worker who could run office equipment and perform jobs with lengthy routinized steps. His education potential indicates that he would do better in classes on a less academic track. His interest scores on the USES–II were generally low. (See Figure 12.1 for score profiles.). However, he did indicate a strong interest in protective work activities. On the *Work Temperament Inventory*, Mr. Gray indicated strong temperaments for 8 of the 12 factors, indicating an adaptability for a variety of work demands. Mr. Gray's scores on the Vocational Planning Report (VPR) suggest a careful and controlled person who has internalized society's rules and abides by them. His scores also describe a person who is rational, objective, and introverted, preferring his own decisions to those of others. His scores on the VPR general interest scales indicate that he has personality traits consistent with expressed interests and activities that involve leadership and direction of other people. Associated motivating personality traits are friendly support, responsibility, and confidence. Mr. Gray's scores on the VPR occupational scales suggest that he has personality characteristics similar to people who are in realistic, conventional, and enterprising occupations. Persons in these occupations may be described as self-reliant, efficient, conscientious, and ambitious. Mr. Gray scored at the 99th percentile on the *Employability Maturity Interview,* indicating that he is highly motivated for rehabilitation.

	Score	Percentile Score				
		1	25	50	75	99
USES Interest Inventory						
Artistic	1	•				
Scientific	15	----•				
Plants and Animals	20	--------•				
Protective	90	-----------------------------------•				
Mechanical	11	---•				
Industrial	59	---------------------•				
Business Detail	23	---------•				
Selling	1	•				
Accommodating	1	•				
Humanitarian	1	•				
Leading–Influencing	16	------•				
Physical Performing	72	--------------------------•				
Work Temperament Inventory						
Directing Others	98	--•				
Repetitive Work	87	-----------------------------------•				
Influencing People	40	--------------•				
Variety of Duties	84	----------------------------------•				
Feelings/Creativity	11	---•				
Sensory Judgments	38	--------------•				
Working Alone	99	--•				
Working Under Stress	96	---•				
Precise Tolerances	93	---------------------------------------•				
Specific Instructions	99	--•				
Dealing with People	38	--------------•				
Objective Judgments	94	--•				
Vocational Personality Report						
Extroversion	22	---------•				
Adjustment	44	-----------------•				
Tough Mindedness	87	-----------------------------------•				
Independence	33	-----------•				
Discipline	88	------------------------------------•				
Anxiety and Depression	67	-----------------------•				
Sociopathic Tendency	23	---------•				
Humanitarian Commitment	7	--•				
Productivity Creativity	13	----•				
Managerial Attitude	75	---------------------------•				
Realistic	99	---•				
Investigative	46	------------------•				
Artistic	12	---•				
Social	3	-•				
Enterprising	74	-------------------------•				
Conventional	99	---•				

Figure 12.1. Score profiles for Edward Gray.

Vocational Exploration

Mr. Gray stated that he would like to take some college-level criminology courses to qualify for a position as a field deputy in the area of police work. He explained that while in the military he held a position of great prestige and esteem and he realizes now that he prefers a work position that involves authority and responsibility and respect from others. He noted that he would also like a job with stability and benefits, and one that would allow him more time with his family. He listed some of his qualities as reliability, dependability, good self-discipline, and being able to instill discipline in others.

Summary

Assessment results indicate that Mr. Gray has the ability to function well in jobs that involve responsibility, self-sufficiency, decisive action, and the direction of others. He could also work well alone or in stressful situations. He has temperaments, personality traits, and abilities consistent with his current position and with his stated vocational goal. Mr. Gray's score on the Wonderlic does not predict academic success, and he has not taken any college courses in the past. However, his interest in the subject matter combined with personality traits such as conscientiousness may enable him to do well in college courses. Mr. Gray explained that police work provides him with respect and prestige, which he has discovered are necessary for him in the workplace. Mr. Gray appears to be highly motivated toward rehabilitation, stating that he is willing to do what is asked of him in the rehabilitation program, has determination to get a job, and considers himself to have good common sense. He stated that, although he considers himself to be moderately to severely disabled, he thinks his chances of getting and holding a job are good.

Sources of Additional Information

The final section of this chapter includes short descriptions of a variety of resources that are concerned with rehabilitation assessment instruments and appraisal procedures. It should be emphasized, however, that the best source of information about a test, inventory, or other standardized appraisal technique is the test manual. The manual gives detailed directions for the administration, scoring, and interpretation of the instrument. Technical information about the normative groups and the reliability and validity of the scores should be presented in considerable detail.

Because authors naturally have positive biases toward their own tests and inventories, and thus present strong cases in favor of their instruments, it is important for counselors to become knowledgeable about the reference volumes that publish independent test reviews. In the late 1930s Oscar Buros recognized the need for "frankly critical" reviews of psychological and educational tests to assist users in selecting the most appropriate instruments for their purposes. To serve this need, Buros established the *Mental Measurements Yearbooks* (MMYs), a cumulative series of reference volumes. *The Twelfth Mental Measurements*

Yearbook (Conoley & Impara, 1995) was published recently. Another useful compilation of expert test reviews is the *Test Critiques* (TC) series (Keyser & Sweetland, 1994), which now contains 10 volumes. Rehabilitation counselors should be familiar with both of these test review series.

A handy collection of reviews of tests and instruments with special relevance to the work of vocational counselors is *A Counselor's Guide to Career Assessment Instruments* (Kapes, Mastie, & Whitfield, 1994). Most of the reviews are reprinted in full or abridged form from the MMYs, the TC series, or other sources. Another useful volume of reprinted reviews is *Special Education and Rehabilitation Testing* (Bolton, 1988a). This reference book includes reviews of about 60 instruments that are appropriately used with adults and adolescents with disabilities. All of the reviews were originally published in the TC series.

Several books and chapters address topics that are directly relevant to rehabilitation assessment. The introductory textbook *A Guide to Vocational Assessment* (Power, 1991) includes capsule descriptions of many tests and discussions of how they might be used in rehabilitation. *Improving Assessment in Rehabilitation and Health* (Glueckauf, Sechrest, Bond, & McDonel, 1993) consists of 12 chapters written by experts in rehabilitation assessment and covering a variety of issues such as theory, validity, utility, training, and applications. The most comprehensive volume available on assessment in vocational rehabilitation is the *Handbook of Measurement and Evaluation in Rehabilitation* (Bolton, 1987a), which contains 20 chapters that review basic psychometric concepts, describe tests and inventories in eight areas, and discuss the assessment process with several special populations, such as visually impaired clients and persons with mental retardation. *Rehabilitation Client Assessment* (Bolton & Cook, 1980) reprints a number of classic articles in rehabilitation assessment. A chapter by Bolton (1988b) discusses vocational assessment of clients with psychiatric disabilities, and another chapter by Bolton (1986) provides a general description of clinical testing principles and strategies.

Conclusion

Rehabilitation client assessment is a complex professional activity that requires both extensive knowledge about instruments and supervised experience in administering tests and writing reports to become skillful. It is essential that the rehabilitation counselor become familiar with the development and technical characteristics of instruments, because this information constitutes the scientific basis for the process of assessment interpretation. It is especially important for the counselor to learn how to use the psychometric tools in assessing clients; this skill can be acquired only through supervised practice in a clinic or agency setting. Mastery of the materials presented in this chapter will establish a foundation for the development of competence in the critical area of client assessment.

References

Bellini, J., Neath, J., & Bolton, B. (1995). Development of a Scale of Social Disadvantage for vocational rehabilitation. *Journal of Rehabilitation Administration, 19,* 107–118.

Bolton, B. (1986). Clinical diagnosis and psychotherapeutic monitoring. In R. B. Cattell & R. Johnson (Eds.), *Functional psychological testing* (pp. 348–376). New York: Brunner/Mazel.

Bolton, B. (Ed.). (1987a). *Handbook of measurement and evaluation in rehabilitation* (2nd ed.). Baltimore: Brookes.

Bolton, B. (1987b). *Manual for the Occupational Report.* Fayetteville: Arkansas Research and Training Center in Vocational Rehabilitation.

Bolton, B. (1987c). *Manual for the Vocational Personality Report.* Fayetteville: Arkansas Research and Training Center in Vocational Rehabilitation.

Bolton, B. (1988a). *Special education and rehabilitation testing: Current practices and test reviews.* Austin, TX: PRO-ED.

Bolton, B. (1988b). Vocational assessment of persons with psychiatric disorders. In J. A. Ciardiello & M. D. Bell (Eds.), *Vocational rehabilitation of persons with prolonged psychiatric disorders* (pp. 165–180). Baltimore: Johns Hopkins University Press.

Bolton, B. (1990). Functional Assessment Inventory. In D. J. Keyser & R. C. Sweetland (Eds.), *Test critiques* (Vol. 8, pp. 209–215). Austin, TX: PRO-ED.

Bolton, B. (1991). Preliminary Diagnostic Questionnaire. In D. J. Keyser & R. C. Sweetland (Eds.), *Test critiques* (Vol. 9, pp. 405–410). Austin, TX: PRO-ED.

Bolton, B. (1994a). The General Aptitude Test Battery and the USES Interest Inventory. In J. T. Kapes, M. M. Mastie, & E. Whitfield (Eds.), *A counselor's guide to career assessment instruments* (3rd ed., pp. 116–123). Alexandria, VA: American Counseling Association.

Bolton, B. (1994b). Rehabilitation Indicators. In D. J. Keyser & R. C. Sweetland (Eds.), *Test critiques* (Vol. 10, pp. 581–592). Austin, TX: PRO-ED.

Bolton, B., & Brookings, J. (1993). *Manual for the Work Temperament Inventory.* Fayetteville: Arkansas Research and Training Center in Vocational Rehabilitation.

Bolton, B., Brookings, J., & Neath, J. (1994). The Work Temperament Inventory: A computer-generated report for career planning in rehabilitation. *Assessment in Rehabilitation and Exceptionality, 1,* 28–39.

Bolton, B., & Cook, D. (Eds.). (1980). *Rehabilitation client assessment.* Baltimore: University Park Press.

Bolton, B., & Roessler, R. (1986). *Manual for the Work Personality Profile.* Fayetteville: Arkansas Research and Training Center in Vocational Rehabilitation.

Brown, C., McDaniel, R., & Couch, R. (1994). *Vocational evaluation systems and software: A consumer's guide.* Menomonie: University of Wisconsin–Stout.

Brown, M., Diller, L., Fordyce, W., Jacobs, D., & Gordon, W. (1980). Rehabilitation Indicators: Their nature and uses for assessment. In B. Bolton & D. Cook (Eds.), *Rehabilitation client assessment* (pp. 102–117). Baltimore: University Park Press.

Conoley, J. C., & Impara, J. (Eds.). (1995). *The twelfth mental measurements yearbook.* Lincoln: University of Nebraska Press.

Crewe, N. M., & Athelstan, G. T. (1984). *Functional Assessment Inventory manual.* Menomonie: University of Wisconsin–Stout.

Cronbach, L. J. (1990). *Essentials of psychological testing* (5th ed.). New York: HarperCollins.

Droege, R. C. (1987). The USES testing program. In B. Bolton (Ed.), *Handbook of measurement and evaluation in rehabilitation* (2nd ed., pp. 169–182). Baltimore: Brookes.

Farley, R. C. (1983). *Developing and enhancing interview skills: A supplemental manual for the interviewing skills training workshop.* Hot Springs: Arkansas Research and Training Center in Vocational Rehabilitation.

Farley, R. C., Parkerson, S., Farley, O., & Martin, N. (1993). *Know thyself: An empowerment strategy for involving consumers in the vocational evaluation and planning process.* Hot Springs: Arkansas Research and Training Center in Vocational Rehabilitation.

Gellman, W. (1953). Components of vocational adjustment. *Personnel and Guidance Journal, 31,* 536–539.

Glueckauf, R. L., Sechrest, L. B., Bond, G. R., & McDonel, E. C. (Eds.). (1993). *Improving assessment in rehabilitation and health.* Newbury Park, CA: Sage.

Hartigan, J. A., & Wigdor, A. K. (Eds.). (1989). *Fairness in employment testing: Validity generalization, minority issues, and the General Aptitude Test Battery.* Washington, DC: National Academy Press.

Hinman, S., Means, B., Parkerson, S., & Odendahl, B. (1988). *Manual for the Job Seeking Skills Assessment.* Hot Springs: Arkansas Research and Training Center in Vocational Rehabilitation.

Holland, J. L. (1985). *Making vocational choices: A theory of vocational personalities and work environments.* Englewood Cliffs, NJ: Prentice-Hall.

Institute for the Crippled and Disabled. (1959). *TOWER: Testing, Orientation, and Work Evaluation in Rehabilitation.* New York: Author.

Institute for Personality and Ability Testing. (1985). *Manual for Form E of the 16PF.* Champaign, IL: Author.

Kapes, J. T., Mastie, M. M., & Whitfield, E. (1994). *A counselor's guide to career assessment instruments* (3rd ed.). Alexandria, VA: American Counseling Association.

Keyser, D. J., & Sweetland, R. C. (Eds.). (1994). *Test critiques: Volume 10.* Austin, TX: PRO-ED.

Morelock, K., Roessler, R., & Bolton, B. (1987). The Employability Maturity Interview: Reliability and construct validity. *Vocational Evaluation and Work Adjustment Bulletin, 20,* 53–59.

Moriarty, J. B. (1981). *Preliminary Diagnostic Questionnaire.* Dunbar: West Virginia Rehabilitation Research and Training Center.

Moriarty, J. B., Minton, E. B., & Spann, V. (1981). *Preliminary Diagnostic Questionnaire, module 4—Feedback and interpretation.* Dunbar: West Virginia Rehabilitation Research and Training Center.

Neath, J., & Bolton, B. (1993). *Work Temperament Inventory Computer Report.* Fayetteville: Arkansas Research and Training Center in Vocational Rehabilitation.

Neath, J., & Bolton, B. (1995). *Employability Maturity Interview Computer Report.* Fayetteville: Arkansas Research and Training Center in Vocational Rehabilitation.

Neff, W. S. (1985). *Work and human behavior* (3rd ed.). New York: Aldine.

Power, P. W. (1991). *A guide to vocational assessment* (2nd ed.). Austin, TX: PRO-ED.

Roessler, R., & Bolton, B. (1978). *Psychosocial adjustment to disability.* Baltimore: University Park Press.

Roessler, R., & Bolton, B. (1987). *Manual for the Employability Maturity Interview.* Fayetteville: Arkansas Research and Training Center in Vocational Rehabilitation.

Roessler, R., & Greenwood, R. (1987). Vocational evaluation. In B. Bolton (Ed.), *Handbook of measurement and evaluation in rehabilitation* (pp. 151–168). Baltimore, MD: Brookes.

U.S. Department of Labor. (1970). *Manual for the General Aptitude Test Battery, Section III: Development.* Washington, DC: U.S. Government Printing Office.

U.S. Department of Labor. (1979a). *Guide for occupational exploration.* Washington, DC: U.S. Government Printing Office.

U.S. Department of Labor. (1979b). *Instructions for administering and using the Interest Check List.* Washington, DC: U.S. Government Printing Office.

U.S. Department of Labor. (1982). *Manual for the USES Interest Inventory.* Minneapolis: Intran Corporation.

Vash, C. L. (1981). *The psychology of disability.* New York: Springer.

Wonderlic Personnel Test, Inc. (1992). *User's manual for the Wonderlic Personnel Test and Scholastic Level Exam.* Libertyville, IL: Author.

Chapter 13

Research in Rehabilitation Counseling

Brian Bolton and Randall M. Parker

R ehabilitation counselors and students in rehabilitation training programs often question the value of much of the research reported in professional journals. There are several reasons underlying this skeptical, if not negative, attitude toward rehabilitation research. First, the language is often unfamiliar to practitioners. Second, reliance on quantitative analyses and presentation of statistical data are typically viewed by counselors as remote from the goals of client service. Third, researchers often fail to translate their findings into clear implications for rehabilitation counseling practice.

It can be reasonably stated, however, that enhanced utilization of rehabilitation research is the responsibility of both practitioners and researchers. Practitioners, as the ultimate consumers (although not the intended beneficiaries) of rehabilitation research, must acquire some familiarity with research terminology and statistical procedures. Rehabilitation researchers, for their part, need to be more sensitive to practitioners' concerns with the immediate problems of service provision and should strive to report research results in a format that emphasizes strategies for improved counseling practice. Although this sounds simple enough, all available evidence suggests that the distance (chasm some would say) between practitioners and researchers is substantial and that the difficulties involved are complicated. Furthermore, complex problems are often not amenable to simple solutions.

Howard (1985) postulated that the reason counselors tend to ignore research results is that very little research investigates final causes of behavior (i.e., causes of behavior within the client, such as motives, goals, and purpose in life). He further alleged that research studies typically examine one or two variables of particular interest and disregard everything else, especially the social context in which the observed behavior occurs. In other words, much counseling research is atomistic in conception, emphasizing precision and control at the expense of meaning and generalizability to counseling practice. Gelso (1985) disagreed with this position, however, arguing that the critical issue in research utility is simply whether counselors perceive the research to be relevant to their counseling practice.

Although there is some truth to Howard's (1985) position, this chapter was written on the premise that rehabilitation counselors cannot perceive research as relevant to their professional needs unless they understand it. Hence, the chapter presents an overview of research principles, strategies, and methods, with examples taken from recent rehabilitation literature to illustrate the various points. It is important to emphasize that the practitioner's role in research is more than merely that of a consumer or user. Because no individual (except possibly the client) has better opportunities to identify needed research, counselors have a professional responsibility to communicate their ideas to researchers. Informed practitioners can also participate in and contribute to the conduct of research investigations in rehabilitation agencies and facilities.

This chapter is designed to provide current and future practitioners of rehabilitation counseling with an orientation to the philosophy and methods of research. The chapter contains separate sections on (a) the scientific method, (b) measurement and statistics, (c) principles of research design, (d) multivariate strategies, (e) single-subject research, (f) integrative reviews, and (g) research utilization in rehabilitation.

Scientific Method

The term *science* refers literally to a method of knowing. It is an enterprise whose purpose is to produce knowledge that leads to the understanding of natural phenomena. Science is not only a method for producing knowledge but a process of inquiry that requires continuous self-correction and elaboration. Thus, scientific research, which is based on hypotheses and theories, leads to further hypothesis and theory formulation, which in turn leads to further scientific research. From this description, science appears to be a circular process. The scientific process, however, is more than simply circular in nature; it is a process of evolution of knowledge built upon an ever-increasing base of previous findings (Babbie, 1979; Christensen, 1988; Kerlinger, 1986).

The scientific method is frequently described as consisting of five separate steps (Christensen, 1988; Mason & Bramble, 1978): (a) problem identification, (b) research question and hypothesis formulation, (c) designing and conducting the research, (d) hypothesis testing, and (e) interpretation and theory development and evaluation. A clear, unambiguous statement of the problem is required before one can proceed with the scientific process. Statement of the problem leads to the development of research questions, which are interrogative statements amenable to empirical testing. Unlike research questions, hypotheses are written as declarative sentences. An hypothesis is a speculative statement about the relationship between two or more variables. The variables must be open to operational definition, which specifies how variables will be measured or manipulated. Following these formative stages of the scientific process, the study is designed and conducted, and data collected in the study are analyzed. Statistical analysis culminates in hypothesis testing, which assists in the development or evaluation of theories.

As previously stated, the scientific method was devised to produce an evolving body of knowledge. However, there are four more immediate objectives of the scientific approach: description, prediction, explanation, and control of natural phenomena. Description, the most elemental objective, is attained by systematic observation and recording of natural phenomena. The second objective, prediction, may be derived directly from description. Observable phenomena that are orderly in nature can be rendered predictable through careful description. For example, comprehensive observations of individuals who are adjusting to a physical disability suggest that many people will experience value changes (B. A. Wright, 1983), which include enlarging the scope of values, subordinating physique, containing the spread of disability, and placing emphasis on asset values rather than comparative values (see Cook, Chapter 9, this text). Rigorous descriptions may lead to relatively accurate predictions of the occurrence, if not the sequence, of the value changes.

Once a set of behaviors is described and predicted, one may wish to explain or understand the behavior. Explanation typically involves the identification of the mechanism or process underlying the behavior and is frequently achieved through the development of models, paradigms, and theories. The final objective of science is the control of the phenomena being studied. Control typically requires the attainment of the three preceding objectives. For example, research leading to the description, prediction, and explanation of learning has identified variables that allow one to manipulate or control to varying degrees the rate and amount of learning.

Some readers may reject the notion that control of human behavior should be an ultimate goal of science. They may find the implied restriction of freedom of choice antithetical to their values. Most assuredly, humanistic psychologists would find the goal of allowing individuals greater control over their own behavior more acceptable. In fact, research has yielded various strategies, including biofeedback, for use by individuals to control their behaviors (e.g., pain). Aside from aiding in the formulation of effective treatment strategies, the ability to control a behavior suggests an understanding of the variables that cause the target behavior. Causality, and the role it plays in contemporary science, however, is a topic of considerable controversy.

The disputable role of causality in attaining the goals of science just enumerated is expressed by this question: To describe, predict, explain, and control behavior, don't the underlying causes have to be revealed? The answer to this rather straightforward question is problematic. Current thought on causation is represented by what T. Cook and Campbell (1979) referred to as a "productive state of near chaos" (p. 10). The complexity of this issue begins to surface when one realizes that there may be several types of cause. Rychlak (1977), for instance, identified four different types of causes:

1. *Material causes* reflect the basic nature of the material in question; for example, the molecular structure of iron causes it to be hard.

2. *Efficient causes* refer to the energy or forces behind events, for example, the action of a football when it is kicked.

3. *Formal causes* refer to the mental strategies that influence behavior in human encounters, such as chess, football, or even war.

4. *Final causes* relate to the internal motivations or influences that result in a person's taking a particular course of action, for example, a woman's becoming a physician because she had a great desire to help others.

As previously mentioned, Howard (1985) suggested that surprisingly little counseling research has been directed toward uncovering final causes; most studies appear to be focused upon efficient causes of human behavior. Ignoring final causes while pursuing efficient causes of human behavior presents a curious situation. Researchers in counseling apparently prefer to investigate variables that are mechanistically related rather than those that are generated by human volition. This preference tends to exclude from consideration constructs that uniquely characterize human beings. Motivations, for example, are final causes that are regarded by many as critical to understanding human behavior, yet motivations cannot be studied if researchers are restricted solely to exploring observable, efficient causes (De Charms, 1968).

To complicate matters, a number of philosophers, including Bertrand Russell (1913), have argued that the notion of causation is unnecessary. Considering that mathematical formulas and proofs are regarded as the most precise and elegant method of depicting functional relationships, one is struck by the realization that well-known mathematical formulas (e.g., $E = mc^2$) do not explicitly or implicitly rely upon the concept of causation. Although there are obvious differences in points of view, many authorities favoring the use of the notion of causality, particularly those in the social and behavioral sciences, will likely concede that direct causation is impossible to specify and that the usage of probabilistic causation is a more meaningful and practical construct. Interested readers are referred to T. Cook and Campbell (1979) for a discussion of this controversy.

Measurement and Statistics

Almost all types of research in the behavioral sciences require some form of measurement or quantitative assessment and the use of statistical procedures to analyze the resulting data. The two main exceptions to this requirement are clinical case studies based on interview assessments and judgmental integrative reviews of the literature, both of which are mentioned later in the chapter. Because the topics of measurement and statistical analysis are separate subjects in professional training programs, each requiring one or more courses for the attainment of even modest competence, only brief overviews are given in this section.

Most psychological measuring instruments are composed of stimuli, called items, to which the examinee responds. For many instruments, an observer or examiner observes the examinee in a standardized situation and records the response or behavior. Item scores are typically summed to generate a total (raw) score that represents the examinee's level of functioning on the dimension that the instrument purports to measure. Raw scores are converted to derived scores, such as percentiles, by using normative tables, thus locating the examinee's relative position in a representative population of individuals. Before scores on an instrument can be used for any practical purpose, they must possess two essential characteristics, reliability and validity.

Scores are reliable if they are consistent (i.e., if an examinee achieves about the same level of performance on two independent administrations of the instrument, or on two separate, equivalent parts of the test). Four major strategies for assessing instrument reliability are test–retest, alternate forms, split-half, and Kuder–Richardson (KR) reliability. Test–retest reliability is obtained by administering the same test to the same group at two different times, usually 1 or 2 weeks apart, and correlating the two sets of scores (Thorndike, 1987).

In contrast, alternate forms reliability requires two administrations of different forms of the same test. To obtain this reliability coefficient, one form of a test is administered, and a short time later another form of the same test is administered to the same group. The two sets of scores are then correlated.

A third type of reliability, split-half reliability, is based on one administration of a test. To determine split-half reliability, test items are divided into two equivalent parts, and the scores for each part are correlated. Because reliability is directly related to test length, the split-half correlation is too low a reliability estimate for the whole test. The Spearman–Brown formula is used to adjust the split-half correlation upward (Guilford & Fruchter, 1978).

Finally, KR reliability provides an index of the consistency of responses to all items in a test. A test composed of items that measure the same content would be expected to have a high KR reliability coefficient. KR reliability is based on one administration of a test (Thorndike, 1987).

Validity, the single most important quality of a test, refers to a determination of whether a test measures the characteristic, trait, or construct that it was designed to measure. If an instrument purports to measure employment potential, counselor competence, or attitudes toward disability, evidence for the validity of the claim must be presented. There are three types of validity (Betz & Weiss, 1987):

1. *Content validity* involves determining whether the test items cover all relevant material. Test authors frequently build content validity into their test by

writing items that are representative of all aspects of the behavioral domain being measured. For instance, a test of job satisfaction might be expected to contain items evaluating pay, working conditions, opportunity for advancement, and so forth.

2. *Criterion-related validity* is the correlation between the scores on a test and a criterion of performance. If the test and the criterion measure are gathered at about the same time, their correlation is referred to as concurrent validity. When the test scores are gathered first and the criterion measure is obtained later, their correlation is called a predictive validity coefficient.

3. *Construct validity* refers to the extent to which the traits or characteristics measured by a test vary according to theoretical expectations. For example, research to determine whether clients who received high scores on a test of job readiness were more successful in obtaining employment than low-scoring clients would provide evidence concerning construct validity.

Because it is impossible to cover these topics adequately in a few paragraphs, interested readers are referred to the first three chapters of the *Handbook of Measurement and Evaluation in Rehabilitation* (Bolton, 1987) or to the textbook by Cronbach (1984) for further details.

More than two dozen psychometric instruments have been developed for use specifically in rehabilitation counseling, and hundreds of standardized tests in psychology and education are also applicable in rehabilitation settings. The rehabilitation instruments can be classified into five major groups: vocational adjustment scales, psychosocial adjustment scales, rehabilitation counselor performance scales, attitudes toward disability scales, and client outcome measures. A representative instrument from each of the five categories of scales is described next.

The *Becker Work Adjustment Profile* (Becker, 1989; see Bolton, 1991a) is an observer rating instrument consisting of 63 items that are scored on four subscales (Work Habits/Attitudes, Interpersonal Relations, Cognitive Skills, and Work Performance Skills) and a global scale called broad work adjustment. The primary purpose of the profile is to identify deficits in clients' work behavior that can be remediated in vocational adjustment facilities.

The *Acceptance of Disability Scale* (Linkowski, 1987; see Bolton, 1994) is composed of 50 statements that reflect various attitude and value changes that may occur in individuals with physical disabilities who have accepted their losses. The respondent indicates extent of agreement or disagreement with the 50 items using a standard 6-point anchored format. The 50 item scores are summed to provide an estimate of the respondent's degree of acceptance of disability.

The *Rehabilitation Job Satisfaction Inventory* (G. N. Wright & Terrian, 1987) consists of 94 items that measure rehabilitation professionals' satisfaction with work in eight areas: Present Job, Work Activities, Work Role, Coworkers, Work Environment, Supervisor, Administrative Practices, and Organizational Policies and Rules. The resulting diagnostic profile of practitioner satisfaction or (collectively) organizational morale has implications for addressing job stress, burnout, and dissatisfaction in rehabilitation agencies.

The *Disability Factor Scales–General Form* (Siller, 1970; see Bolton, 1991b) contains 69 statements about people with disabilities and personal reactions to disability that individuals respond to using a 6-point scale of agreement. The item responses are scored on seven components of attitudes toward people with disabilities (Interaction Strain, Rejection of Intimacy, Inferred Emotional Consequences, Imputed Functional Limitations, etc.).

The *Minnesota Satisfactoriness Scales* (Gibson, Weiss, Dawis, & Lofquist, 1970; see Bolton, 1986) consists of 28 items that are completed by a client's supervisor and scored on four subscales (Performance, Conformance, Personal Adjustment, and Dependability), as well as general satisfactoriness. Normative comparisons may be derived using a workers-in-general norm group that is representative of the U.S. labor force.

Details about the technical characteristics, supporting research, assessment applications, and associated resource materials for these and other rehabilitation instruments are available in Bolton and Brookings (1993). Additional information and references concerning the use of psychological and vocational instruments in client assessment and service planning are contained in Chapter 12 in this text.

This section concludes with a short introduction to the complex subject of statistical methods. It may be helpful to begin with a definition. Statistical methods are techniques for transforming numerical data into a probability value that enables the investigator to reach a conclusion about a research hypothesis. As pointed out in the previous section, all research studies are conducted to test hypotheses. Whereas research hypotheses are statements of what the investigator expects to find, statistical hypotheses are almost always stated in null form (i.e., they are formal statements of no difference or no relationship that the investigator, in fact, expects to reject).

After the collected data are analyzed using the appropriate technique (e.g., analysis of variance or chi-square contingency analysis), the resulting test statistic is evaluated with reference to the corresponding theoretical statistical distribution. If the test statistic falls in the critical region (i.e., the associated probability value is very small, say less than 5 in 100 or even less than 1 in 100), then the null hypothesis of no difference or no relationship is rejected and the investigator's research hypothesis is declared to be supported by the data. In summary, the logic of statistical hypothesis testing starts with a proposition (the null hypothesis) that is contrary to what the investigator expects to find; if the evidence is determined to be highly improbable under this assumption, the null hypothesis is rejected in favor of the investigator's stated research hypothesis.

In addition to the primary purpose of all statistical analyses discussed above (i.e., establishing a basis for deciding about the research hypothesis), statistical methods also organize and reduce data to comprehensible summary indices. The standard descriptive statistics include

1. Indices of central tendency, for example, the arithmetic mean (or average) and the median (or middle score), which are values that best represent all scores in a group

2. Indices of variability or dispersion, for instance, the range and the standard deviation, which indicate the spread of scores around the average value

3. Indices of covariation or correlation, for example, the contingency coefficient, Spearman's rank-order correlation coefficient, and the product–moment correlation coefficient, all of which quantify the degree of association or relationship between two variables

4. Indices of multivariate relationship, for example, the multiple correlation, partial correlation, canonical correlation, and factor-loading coefficient, all of which summarize the relationships among three or more variables

This very brief overview of the purposes and logic of statistical analysis can do no more than introduce the reader to the rudiments of statistics. Persons interested in pursuing the topics further are referred to textbooks by Guilford and Fruchter (1978) and Hays (1981).

Principles of Research Design

Scarr (1985) presented a broad perspective of the role of research in theory development and defining reality. Her views, which she refers to as constructivist, suggest that reality is "constrained only by imagination and a few precious rules of the scientific game" (p. 512). Furthermore, Scarr stated,

> The psychological world in which we conduct research is, in my view, a cloud of correlated event to which we as human observers give meaning. In the swirling cloud of interacting organisms and environments, most events nearly co-occur. As investigators, we construct a story (often called a theory) about relations among events. We select a few elements and put them into a study. By doing so we necessarily eliminate other variables a priori from possible analysis, and we preconstrue causal relations among the events. One cannot avoid either the theoretical preconceptions or the selection of variables to study, but one can avoid exaggerated claims for the causal status of one's favorite model. (p. 502)

Variables

The "cloud of events" referred to by Scarr (1985) that researchers attempt to investigate might also have been described as a "swarm of variables." The term *variable* refers to characteristics of persons or things that can take on two or more values. For example, demographic variables include such traits as sex (which can take on two values, male or female) and age (which can take on values ranging from 0 to over 100 years). Variables may be directly observable (e.g., eye color) or nonobservable (e.g., intelligence). The social and behavioral sciences differ from the natural sciences in that many of the variables of interest to social and behavioral scientists are not directly observable. As a result, these scientists must rely heavily upon indirect means of measurement. For instance, rehabilitation clients' level of acceptance of disability cannot be directly observed—it must be inferred from indirect sources of information. Instruments such as *The Acceptance of Disability Scale* (Linkowski, 1987), described previously, may be used to obtain the desired information.

Several types of variables are critical to research design. One type of variable, the independent variable (IV), is a variable that the experimenter manipulates in a study. Another type, the dependent variable (DV), is referred to as the measured variable in the study. The IV is presumed to influence the DV. Below are a number of synonyms that will serve to further define the IV and DV:

Independent Variable	Dependent Variable
manipulated	measured
cause	effect
antecedent	consequent
predictor	criterion
process	outcome
treatment	response

It is of particular importance to be able to identify the IV and DV in planning a prospective study or evaluating a completed piece of research. The identification of these variables is facilitated when the title or purpose of a study is stated or can be translated into the following format: the effects of X on Y. X is the IV and Y is the DV. Thus, the title "Burnout and Job Satisfaction of Rehabilitation Counselors" could be translated into "The Effects of Burnout on Job Satisfaction of Rehabilitation Counselors." Clearly, the IV is burnout and the DV is job satisfaction.

In addition to demographic, independent, and dependent variables, another class of variables is crucial to understanding the research process. This class of variables, variously referred to as extraneous, contaminating, or confounding variables, contains the sources of error that call into question the results of research. Clearly, if error is not minimized, the results of a study are likely to be questionable or invalid. Consequently, it is in the best interest of researchers to make every effort to control all potential sources of error in conducting a study. Controlling extraneous variables results in heightened validity of a study.

Validity of Research

Research designs may be judged on four criteria: internal, external, statistical conclusion, and construct validity (T. Cook & Campbell, 1979, 1983). Internal validity refers to the degree to which extraneous (error) variance is controlled. Experimental control is typically achieved through one or more of the following techniques:

1. Random assignment of subjects to treatment and control groups
2. Holding extraneous variables constant or restricting their range
3. Including contaminating variables in the design and measuring their effects
4. Employing methods of statistical control
5. Matching subjects in treatment and control groups on contaminating variables

Random assignment equates (within the limits of sampling fluctuation) the treatment and control groups on all variables except the independent variable. Therefore, if the treatment group differs from the control group after the treatment is administered, the difference must be due to the treatment (IV) and not some other variable. Random assignment is the most effective and preferable form of experimental control.

The next most preferred method of control is holding extraneous variables constant. For example, if researchers have reason to suspect that gender is a potentially extraneous or contaminating variable in a study, they might study only females. Not allowing a variable to vary eliminates its influence. When this method of control is not feasible, researchers might consider including the contaminating variable in the design. In the previous example, where gender was a suspected contaminant, the researchers could include sex as a variable in the design. This inclusion would allow not only testing for differences between the treatment and control groups, but also for differences between the sexes and for interactions between sex and the treatment variable (IV).

Statistical control involves complex manipulations of the data in an attempt to reduce extraneous or error variance. Partial correlation, analysis of covariance, and multivariate strategies (e.g., regression analysis, discriminant analysis, canonical correlation analysis) may be used for this purpose. Multivariate strategies are considered in greater detail later in this chapter.

The final and most problematic method of control is matching subjects on potentially contaminating variables. Matching is most effective when several criteria are met: (a) the researcher knows in advance which variables may contaminate the results; (b) the number of confounding variables is small (three or four); and (c) each member of the treatment group is matched with a member of the control group, as opposed to matching whole groups at a time. Because these conditions are rarely met in practice, matching is not recommended to attain internal validity.

Threats to the Validity of Research

Research designs may be judged by four criteria, namely internal, external, statistical conclusion, and construct validity (T. Cook & Campbell, 1979, 1983; T. Cook,

Campbell, & Peracchio, 1990; Parker, 1990, 1993). The following paragraphs provide definitions of each type of research validity and present selected threats to research validity.[1]

Internal validity, the *most important* type of research validity, refers to the extent to which extraneous or contaminating variables are controlled. Failure to control extraneous variables prevents the researcher from concluding that differences in the observed outcomes are due to the independent or predictor variable(s). Failure to use adequate methods to control error variance results in several possible threats to the internal validity of the research. Threats to internal validity, for example, include the following:

> *History.* History refers to an extraneous event that correlates with the dependent variable and occurs during the study. Such an event could mask or enhance the outcome variable. History, for example, would threaten the validity of a study on the relationship of stressful instructions to test anxiety if several experimental group participants received Internal Revenue Service audit notices just before the posttest was administered. Their heightened anxiety might spuriously raise the experimental group's test anxiety scores, leading to a questionable conclusion that the instructions alone raised test anxiety levels.
>
> *Instrumentation.* This threat is due to deterioration or changes in the accuracy of instruments, devices, or observers used to measure the dependent (outcome) variable. Examples of instrumentation include observers forgetting their training and beginning to record observations inaccurately and surveys mailed to one geographical area becoming wrinkled and rain soaked in transit, affecting both legibility of the surveys and accuracy of the responses.
>
> *Selection.* This threat occurs when participants volunteer for a treatment or are assigned to treatment and control groups based on their preferences. This assignment results in the groups being different on many variables. Consider the example of a study conducted to identify client characteristics associated with positive outcomes in individual versus group counseling. If participants were allowed to choose the counseling approach, volunteers who "self-selected" into individual counseling may differ from those who selected group counseling in ways that affect the outcome measure.
>
> *Mortality.* This threat refers to the loss of participants and their data during the course of a study due to illness, forgetfulness, death, and so on. When the treatment itself causes participants to drop out of the study, the treatment group posttest mean would be contaminated because only the *survivors'* scores would be available.

External validity refers to the degree to which research findings can be generalized across persons, times, and settings. Generalizing across persons requires

---

[1]The threats to research validity are from "Editorial Threats to the Validity of Research," by R. Parker, 1993, *Rehabilitation Counseling Bulletin, 36*(3), pp. 130–138. Copyright 1993 by American Counseling Association. Reprinted with permission.

research samples to be representative of the population of interest. Generalizing across times and settings typically requires systematically administering the experimental procedures at different times and in different settings. Failing to obtain a sample that is representative of a population, of a variety of settings, and of times results in the inability to generalize the findings of the study beyond the persons, setting, and time employed in the research. Such failures pose serious threats to external validity. Examples of specific threats to external validity include the following:

Interaction of Testing with Treatment. A pretest may increase or decrease the participants' sensitivity to the treatment. As a consequence the results may not be generalizable to the nonpretested population from which the treatment group was selected.

Interaction of Selection with Treatment. This threat occurs when research participants are volunteers, that is, individuals who are prone to seek out research participation. Such persons may have traits that tend to enhance or diminish the effects of the treatment. Thus, the results are not generalizable to a population that includes nonvolunteers.

Interaction of Setting with Treatment. Treatments demonstrated in one environment, for example, the laboratory, may not "work" in other settings, for example, the classroom. Therefore, this threat to external validity refers to whether effects demonstrated in one setting are generalizable to other settings.

Interaction of History with Treatment. The effects observed in a study may be due to special circumstances. For instance, teachers participating in a study showed a substantial lowering of anxiety after a stress reduction program. However, during the study a tornado warning was sounded and shortly thereafter cancelled. The observed effect may not be generalizable to other, more normal circumstances.

Statistical conclusion validity is concerned with the appropriate use of statistics to arrive at accurate decisions about accepting or rejecting statistical hypotheses. Consider a study in which the treatment and control groups' performances are being compared on an outcome variable. The null hypothesis states that there is no difference between group means on the outcome variable. In this situation a *Type I error* refers to *falsely rejecting* the null hypothesis, that is, finding a statistically significant *difference* when the means come from the *same* population. The probability of committing a Type I error is called alpha (α). On the other hand, the Type II error is *failing to reject a false null hypothesis,* that is, finding *no statistically significant difference* when the means come from *different* populations. The probability of committing a Type II error is called beta (β). Threats to statistical conclusion validity include the following:

Low Statistical Power. Statistical power is equal to the quantity, 1.0 – β, or the probability of rejecting a false null hypothesis, that is, *finding a statistically significant difference* when the sample means, in fact, come from *different populations.* Power is a function of alpha (α), sample size (N), and the effect size (**ES**). Effect size (**ES**) refers to the amount of common variance between the independent variable (IV) and the dependent variable (DV), or the degree to which changes in the IV result in changes in the DV. Increasing the alpha level, sample size, and the effect size, singly or in combination, increases statistical power. According to Cohen (1988), power ideally should be about .80. That is, researchers should design their studies so that they have 8 in 10 chances of obtaining a statistically significant result in the sample data when one actually exists in the population data. However, surveys of research indicate most studies have much lower power (Cohen, 1962; Lipsey, 1990). Through conducting power analyses while designing a study and systematically varying α, N, and ES, the researcher can approximate the desired level of power in the resultant research (Szymanski & Parker, 1992).

Fishing and the Error Rate Problem. Running many statistical tests on one data set is called *fishing*. Fishing produces Type I error rates that are higher than the preset alpha. Running one statistical test on a data set results in a Type I error rate equal to preset alpha (usually .05). However, running two or more statistical tests may inflate alpha above the predetermined rate. Various corrections for alpha inflation are possible including Scheffe's, Tukey's, and similar multiple comparison tests as part of an ANOVA [analysis of variance] or ANCOVA [analysis of covariance] design. A more general procedure is called the Bonferroni correction, which is accomplished by setting alpha equal to the desired alpha (e.g., .05) divided by the number of tests run for *all hypotheses* or, alternatively, the number of tests for a *logically related subset of hypotheses* (see Parker & Szymanski, 1992).

Low Reliability of Measures. Measures with low reliability increase error variance and reduce the power of statistical tests. For instance, decreased reliability often occurs when simple gain scores (posttest minus pretest scores) are used as a measure of change on the dependent variable. Change scores are notoriously unreliable because by subtracting the pretest from the posttest, one is left with less true variance and relatively more error variance. Residual gain scores (posttest scores with pretest covariance partialled out) frequently are preferable to simple gain scores. In general, the reliability of measures may be enhanced by adding more items with high internal consistency, decreasing the intervals between pretests and posttests, and using corrections for unreliability (e.g., correction for attenuation).

Low Reliability of Treatment Implementation. This threat is due to the lack of standardization of procedures used to administer the treatment. Using different individuals and different occasions to implement the treatment increases this threat, as does the failure to adequately train individuals administering the treatment.

The *construct validity* of a variable refers to whether the variable is adequately defined and accurately measured by the instruments, procedures, manipulations, and methods employed in the study. A valid construct must have a unique theoretical definition. When a construct is suggested as a cause or effect, it is valid only when other constructs cannot be construed as being the cause or the effect. Threats to construct validity include the following:

Inadequate Pre-Operational Explication of Constructs. When constructs are poorly defined initially, the instruments, procedures, manipulations, and methods used in the study cannot be adequately specified and may bear little relationship to the constructs being studied. Consequently, the results of the study cannot be accurately attributed to the constructs of interest.

Mono-Operation Bias. Construct validity is limited when a construct is defined by only one measure or operation. Multiple operationalized variables tend to be more valid than single operations because single operations under-represent constructs and contain irrelevancies. Alternative measures of a target allow one to triangulate on the construct.

Mono-Method Bias. This threat occurs when all the manipulations and measures use the same means of presenting the treatments or recording the results. For example, because many leadership studies have employed single, paper and pencil measures, it has been suggested that leadership theories predict paper and pencil behavior better than actual leadership behaviors (Campbell, Daft, & Hulin, 1982).

Compensatory Rivalry. When participants' membership in experimental or control groups is made public, competitive motivations may result. Saretsky (1972) noted that the performance of students taught by control group teachers in a performance contracting experiment was higher than in previous years. Apparently, performance contracting was perceived by the teachers as a threat to their job security, causing them to redouble their teaching efforts. Saretsky called this the "John Henry effect," comparing the control group's extra efforts to those of John Henry, a folk song character who competed with a machine in laying rail for the railroad.

Hypothesis-Guessing Within Experimental Conditions. Research participants receiving a treatment may attempt to guess the purpose of the study and alter their outcome behavior accordingly. The well-known *Hawthorne effect* is the result of hypothesis guessing by experimental subjects. Hypothesis-guessing may be avoided by making hypotheses difficult to guess, by reducing the reactivity and obtrusiveness of the study, and by purposefully giving different bogus hypotheses to different participants. The latter action, however, may lead to ethical violations.

Experimenter Expectancies. Research suggests that experimenter expectations may influence participants' behavior and the outcome data. This effect may be avoided by selecting objective individuals who do not know the purposes of the study to administer the treatments and record the data.

The interested reader is referred to T. Cook et al. (1990) and Parker (1993) for a complete list and explanation of threats to the validity of research.

Experimental Designs

One category of research designs, true experimental designs, maximizes internal validity. There are three basic layouts for experimental designs, each of which employs random assignment of subjects to treatment and control groups. In fact, random assignment is the essential ingredient, the *sine qua non,* of true experimental designs (Campbell & Stanley, 1966; T. Cook & Campbell, 1979). The three basic design prototypes are the pretest–posttest control group design, posttest-only design, and the Solomon four-group design.

To demonstrate the pretest–posttest control group design, let us formulate a specific research question and hypothesis. Suppose we wished to study the effects of supported employment on consumer job satisfaction. The research question is, Are consumers who receive supported employment more satisfied with their jobs than consumers who do not receive supported employment? The hypothesis, stated as a null hypothesis, is, There is no difference in job satisfaction between consumers who receive supported employment services and consumers who do not. In this example the IV, or treatment variable, would be supported employment and the DV would be job satisfaction.

The pretest–posttest control group design specifies that both treatment and control groups are measured on the DV at two different times, pretest and posttest. At pretest an instrument measuring the DV, job satisfaction, would be administered to all consumers. Next, the consumers would be randomly assigned to the treatment or control group. The treatment group would receive supported employment, while the control group would receive no treatment. Following the training period the DV measure would again be given to all consumers.

Using R to indicate random assignment, O (for observation) to represent pretest and posttest, and X to designate the treatment, the pretest–posttest control group design is diagrammed as follows:

Treatment Group:	R	O_1 X	O_2
Control Group:	R	O_3	O_4

To evaluate the null hypothesis that the treatment group was no different from the control group on job satisfaction at posttest, a statistical test would be computed comparing the mean posttest score of the treatment group at O_2 with the mean posttest score of the control group at O_4. If the mean at O_2 was found to be statistically significantly higher than the mean at O_4, the researcher would conclude that supported employment increased job satisfaction. If the mean was statistically significantly lower, the conclusion would be that supported employment reduced job satisfaction. Finally, if the difference was not statistically significant, the researcher would conclude that the study revealed no evidence to support the notion that supported employment affected job satisfaction.

An ethical dilemma is inherent in most experimental designs. Administering a treatment that might be harmful or failing to give a treatment that might be helpful would be unethical. Researchers must ensure the protection of individuals involved in research and obtain their informed consent prior to participation in the study (see Patterson, Chapter 6, this text). If the treatment is potentially beneficial and unlikely to be harmful, a modification may be made whereby the control group receives the treatment after the posttest is given.

Notice that in the pretest–posttest control group design, the pretest scores at O_1 and O_3 are not used to test the null hypothesis; this is generally true, except in designs that test for differences in the amount of change from pretest to posttest. The next design omits pretests.

The posttest-only design, as its name suggests, requires no pretesting, and is diagrammed as follows:

Treatment Group:	R	X	O_1	
Control Group:	R		O_2	

The only difference between the pretest–posttest control group design and the posttest-only design is the absence of pretests in the latter design. In most cases, the posttest-only design is preferred over the pretest–posttest design for several reasons, including its simplicity (see Campbell & Stanley, 1966).

The third true experimental design, the Solomon four-group design, is simply a combination of the previous two designs, as is obvious from the following diagram:

Treatment Group 1:	R	O_1	X	O_2
Control Group 1:	R	O_3		O_4
Treatment Group 2:	R		X	O_5
Control Group 2:	R			O_6

This design not only allows the evaluation of the effect of the treatment by comparing the treatment groups (O_2 and O_5) with the control groups (O_4 and O_6), but also allows the researcher to determine whether pretested groups respond differently from nonpretested groups by comparing O_2 with O_5 and O_4 with O_6. In some instances, the pretest may sensitize subjects so that they respond differently to the posttest. This sensitization is referred to as the reactive effects of pretesting. The ability of the Solomon design to detect this effect sets it apart from the other two experimental designs. Because the Solomon design incorporates both the pretest–posttest control group design and the posttest-only design, an example of the Solomon design from the rehabilitation literature is presented next to demonstrate true experimental designs.

Matkin, Hafer, Wright, and Lutzker (1983) conducted a study to compare the effects of two movies (*A Different Approach* and *Like Other People*) on *Attitudes Toward Disabled Persons* (ATDP) scores (Yuker, Block, & Younng, 1970) using a modified version of the Solomon four-group design. Forty-four subjects were randomly assigned to one of four groups. Two groups received a pretest. One pretested group later saw *A Different Approach;* the other pretested group saw *Like Other People.* The other two groups were not pretested; each of these two groups saw one of the above movies. All four groups were given one posttest immediately after viewing the films and a second posttest 6 weeks later. The pretest and posttest for all groups were different forms of the ATDP.

Matkin et al. used the Solomon four-group design to find out whether one movie had a greater impact on attitudes than the other movie and to determine whether pretested students performed differently from nonpretested students on the posttest. Researchers have long been concerned with the effect of pretesting. Subjects taking achievement and intelligence tests a second time usually score higher than those taking the test for the first time. Similar changes have been noted for personality, attitude, and other tests (see Campbell & Stanley, 1966). As previously mentioned, the capacity to test for differences between pretested and nonpretested subjects is a unique characteristic of the Solomon design.

Although the researchers found no differences between the two movies in their effects on the students' attitudes, the participants who were not pretested and who viewed *A Different Approach* demonstrated more positive attitudes toward persons with disabilities than did the other groups. However, pretested groups, taken together, did not differ from nonpretested groups on posttest scores, indicating that the ATDP pretest did not consistently affect posttest scores.

Subject dropout rate (called experimental mortality) was a possible confounding factor, however. Pretested subjects had the highest dropout rate (10 of 22) at the first posttest compared with those not pretested (0 of 22). At the second posttest, an additional 3 pretested subjects and 8 nonpretested subjects dropped out. This level of experimental mortality (21 of 44 subjects) is a serious threat to the study's internal validity.

Quasi-Experimental Designs

Although the Matkin et al. (1983) study had the one noted weakness, research using experimental designs is generally the least vulnerable to internal validity problems. Quasi-experimental designs, on the other hand, are more susceptible to internal validity problems because random assignment of subjects to treatment and control groups is not used. These designs, however, effectively employ one of the other methods of control mentioned earlier (e.g., statistical control). Using a quasi-experimental design is the best strategy when random assignment of subjects to treatment and control groups is not possible. Two of the four quasi-experimental designs presented by Campbell and Stanley (1966) are often used in rehabilitation research: the nonequivalent control group design and the time-series design.

The nonequivalent control group design is diagrammed as follows:

Treatment Group:	O_1	X	O_2
Control Group:	O_3		O_4

The dotted line signifies that the treatment and control groups are not assigned randomly. To qualify as this design, statistical controls must be employed. Typically, the technique used is analysis of covariance with the pretest as the covariate and the posttest as the dependent variable. In all other respects, this design resembles the pretest–posttest control group design.

The time-series design may be diagrammed as follows:

$$O_1 \quad O_2 \quad O_3 \quad O_4 \quad X \quad O_5 \quad O_6 \quad O_7 \quad O_8$$

In the time-series design, several observations (often many more than the four shown in the diagram) are initially made. These observations are referred to as the baseline. A treatment is then given to the subjects, and another series of observations is made. If a statistically significant difference exists between the baseline observations and the posttreatment observations, it is concluded that the treatment had an effect. Subjects usually range in number from 1 to 20. Time-series research, however, is frequently carried out with $N = 1$, where N refers to the number of subjects in the study. This design is discussed further in the section on single-subject research.

An example of a quasi-experimental design was presented by Szymanski and Parker (1989). This study explored the relationship between rehabilitation counselors' education and their performance in rehabilitating clients with severe disabilities. Specifically, the investigators studied performance measures of 235 rehabilitation counselors employed by the New York State Office of Vocational Rehabilitation. Of the counselors, 121 had master's degrees from rehabilitation counseling programs, and the remaining 114 possessed other master's degrees or had bachelor's degrees. The clients were 8,806 individuals who had been identified as having severe disabilities and had been rehabilitated during the period of April 1, 1986, to March 31, 1987.

The dependent variable was the competitive closure rate (CCR). CCR is the number of competitive "26" closures (i.e., clients closed in competitive employment) divided by the total number of closures. The independent variable was counselor training, which consisted of two groups: counselors with master's degrees in rehabilitation counseling (MRC) and those with all other degrees (OD). A single control variable, number of years of rehabilitation counseling experience, was also utilized.

Szymanski and Parker employed an aptitude treatment interaction (ATI) analysis because the data did not meet the assumptions necessary for conducting an analysis of covariance (Szymanski, Parker, & Borich, 1990). Specifically, an interaction was found between the independent and control variables, preventing a valid analysis of covariance. ATI was developed to examine such interactions.

The analysis revealed that the MRCs' performance was significantly higher than the ODs' for those with 6 or fewer years of relevant work experience. Among counselors with 7 or more years of experience, there was no difference on CCR between MRCs and ODs. The results suggest that clients with severe disabilities achieve more successful outcomes when served by MRCs or when served by ODs with 7 or more years experience. The authors noted that their research possessed limited internal validity (because many possible contaminating variables were not controlled) and limited external validity (because the sample was restricted to New York).

Ex Post Facto Designs

The most frequent type of design used in rehabilitation counseling research is the ex post facto design. The Latin phrase *ex post facto* literally means "after the fact" and refers to the nature of the treatment (independent variable). In this design, the treatment occurred at some time in the past and is not under the control of the researcher; the effects of the treatment are studied after the fact.

Many phenomena of interest to rehabilitation researchers are not and cannot be under the control of the researcher. For instance, a study of the effects of the severity of disability on clients' employability can be conducted only using an ex post facto design. The independent variable, severity of disability, cannot be manipulated by the researcher because of ethical, legal, and moral considerations. In other words, the researcher cannot randomly inflict varying levels of disability on a group of subjects; the effects of severity of disability can be studied only after the disability has occurred.

In ex post facto studies, it is not possible to detect causal relationships or even simple, direct relationships because of the multitude of uncontrolled, extraneous variables operating on the dependent variable. Many authorities, such as Campbell and Stanley (1966), are critical of these designs because of the lack of control over contaminating variables. Failure to control extraneous variation leads to low levels of internal validity. Furthermore, a lack of internal validity (control) restricts one from drawing firm conclusions regarding the results of statistical tests. As exploratory hypothesis-generating heuristic studies, however, ex post facto research has an important role to play in many areas of applied behavioral science, including rehabilitation counseling (T. Cook & Campbell, 1979).

Multivariate Strategies

One widely voiced criticism of much counseling research that was mentioned earlier is that typically only a few variables of interest are studied in highly artificial situations. Critics reasonably question the generalizability of findings from such research to settings in which client and counselor behavior occurs naturally, interacting with numerous other psychological and sociological variables. There are two interrelated strategies for addressing this legitimate criticism of the conduct of rehabilitation research.

The first strategy encompasses the class of analytic procedures called multivariate statistical techniques. These include multiple regression analysis, multiple discriminant analysis, canonical correlation analysis, factor analysis, cluster analysis, multidimensional scaling, and a variety of specialized versions of these procedures (see Cattell, 1978; Draper & Smith, 1981; Harris, 1985; Morrison, 1990). Multivariate methods can be divided into two groups of procedures, analyses of dependence and analyses of interdependence. If the research design involves both independent variables (IVs) and dependent variables (DVs), then analysis of dependence is appropriate. If the distinction between IVs and DVs is not relevant, then analysis of interdependence is called for.

Multivariate techniques for analyzing dependence examine the relationship between two or more IVs and one or more DVs. Multiple regression analysis determines the optimal combination of a set of IVs for predicting a single DV, called the criterion. The coefficients that weight each IV (named beta weights) indicate the contribution of each IV to the predictive equation. Multiple discriminant analysis applies the same logic to the situation where the criterion variable is categorical in nature (e.g., type of disability or occupational group at closure). Canonical correlation analysis is an extension of multiple regression procedures to the design that includes multiple DVs as well as multiple IVs.

When the research hypothesis concerns the structural relationships among a set of variables that are either all IVs or (more likely) all DVs, then techniques that analyze interdependence are appropriate. The most often used of these analytic procedures is factor analysis. In general terms, a matrix of correlations among the variables is reorganized into a smaller number of composite dimensions that meaningfully summarize the measured domain. The objectives of factor analysis, then, are parsimony or simplicity of description and identification of generalizable psychometric constructs. Cluster analysis and multidimensional scaling are related techniques that operate on matrices of indices of association and require different statistical functions to accomplish the same goal as factor analysis.

The second strategy is embodied in the multivariate experimental approach to research design in psychology. The fundamental principle of multivariate experimental psychology is that causal inferences may be extrapolated from naturally occurring covariation if all critical variables are measured in longitudinal designs and appropriate analytic techniques are employed to isolate the sequential relationships among hypothesized primary variables while statistically controlling the contextual variables. It should be obvious that many key variables in rehabilitation, such as the effects of chronic illness and disablement, can be studied (ethically) only using a nonmanipulative strategy. In carefully designed investigations, the multivariate experimental strategy provides quantitative precision without sacrificing representativeness and generalizability to the natural environment (see Bolton, 1988).

There are many excellent examples of the application of multivariate statistical techniques in rehabilitation research, but, as of this writing, no illustrations of multivariate experimental design utilizing repeated psychometric assessments over substantial periods of time have been reported in the literature. Consequently, this section concludes with two examples of multivariate statistical analysis in rehabilitation counseling research.

During the past two decades, nine major studies of job functions of rehabilitation counselors have been carried out. Such an intensive phase of self-study is an essential aspect of the transformation of an occupational specialty into a legitimate profession. Professions are essentially self-regulating, with prescribed training curricula offered by accredited universities or professional schools and a legally sanctioned process for certifying or licensing graduates to practice. However, before the codification of entrance requirements can occur, the profession must define and operationalize its unique service role. Studies of counselor functions or competencies have accomplished this fundamental step for rehabilitation counseling.

In the most recent investigation of rehabilitation counselors' job functions, Szymanski and her colleagues (Leahy, Szymanski, & Linkowski, 1993; Szymanski,

Leahy, & Linkowski, 1993; Szymanski, Linkowski, Leahy, Diamond, & Thoreson, 1993) conducted a series of three studies of knowledge importance, preparedness, and training needs for a large sample of certified rehabilitation counselors (CRCs). The general purpose of the investigation was to provide an empirical basis for reviewing and updating national certification and accreditation standards for rehabilitation counseling, including examination content and curriculum requirements for rehabilitation education programs.

The research sample consisted of 1,535 certified rehabilitation counselors who had applied for certification renewal. All had been practicing rehabilitation counselors for a minimum of 5 years. The instrument listed 58 specific rehabilitation counseling knowledge areas (some examples are included in the results below) that were derived from previous curriculum standards and examination content areas. Each of the 58 areas was judged by the respondents using two 5-point scales, one measuring perceived importance of the knowledge area in rehabilitation counseling and the other indicating the respondent's estimated degree of preparedness in the knowledge area.

Three sets of data were analyzed: importance ratings, preparedness ratings, and training needs scores, which were calculated by subtracting preparedness ratings from importance ratings. To determine the dimensional structure of the three domains (knowledge, preparedness, and training needs), the intercorrelation matrices of the 58 variables were independently analyzed by a procedure called principal components reduction followed by varimax rotation of the significant components. This is a standard strategy that is described in textbooks by Cattell (1978) and Gorsuch (1983).

The independent dimensional analyses of the three domains produced highly similar results. The 10 components or facets of knowledge in rehabilitation counseling are briefly summarized:

1. Vocational counseling and consultation services (e.g., vocational implications of various disabilities, job and employer development)

2. Medical and psychosocial aspects of disability (e.g., medical aspects and implications, psychosocial and cultural impact of disability)

3. Individual and group counseling (e.g., individual counseling theories, behavior and personality theory)

4. Program evaluation and research (e.g., rehabilitation research literature, basic research methods)

5. Case management and service coordination (e.g., community resources and services, planning for independent living services)

6. Family, gender, and multicultural issues (e.g., multicultural counseling issues, family counseling practices)

7. Foundations of rehabilitation (e.g., ethical standards for rehabilitation counselors, philosophical foundations of rehabilitation)

8. Workers' compensation (e.g., workers' compensation law and practices, expert testimony)

9. Environmental and attitudinal barriers (e.g., attitudinal barriers for individuals with disabilities, environmental barriers for individuals with disabilities)

10. Assessment (e.g., interpretation of assessment results, test and evaluation techniques for assessment)

The results of the dimensional analyses for preparedness and training needs were only slightly different. The two major changes were that individual counseling and group counseling separated in the preparedness and training needs structures, whereas environmental and attitudinal barriers merged with multicultural issues.

The final phase of the investigation involved comparisons among respondents who differed in education, job level, employment setting, job title, and years of experience on the 10 dimensions of knowledge, preparedness, and training needs. Of particular interest were the findings on preparedness for subgroups of respondents with different levels of education. Respondents with master's degrees from accredited training programs perceived themselves to be better prepared in 6 of the 10 rehabilitation counseling knowledge areas, supporting the value of specialized training in rehabilitation counseling.

Latent structure modeling or path analysis is a statistical strategy for examining causal relationships in multivariate investigations (Bentler, 1980). The most popular procedure for causal modeling, linear structural relations (LISREL) (Jöreskog & Sörbom, 1984), requires the traditional distinction between independent and dependent variables, as well as coefficients of association among the variables that represent the latent constructs hypothesized to constitute the system. Most predictive modeling studies of vocational rehabilitation (VR) client outcome have been limited to multiple regression and multiple discriminant analysis. The investigation by Lewis and Bolton (1986) illustrates the application of LISREL to the employment outcomes of VR clients.

The first step in the LISREL analysis of occupational attainment of VR clients was to postulate a model that organized measured variables in terms of hypothesized employability constructs. The constructs (with measured variables in parentheses) were opportunity structure (represented by four demographic characteristics), work values (represented by five scales), educational achievement (represented by IQ and highest grade completed), and occupational attainment (represented by work status, earnings, and occupation at closure). Data analysis for the research sample of 380 former rehabilitation clients began with a structural model that postulated three independent constructs (opportunity structure, work values, and educational achievement) and one dependent construct (occupational attainment).

The LISREL program provides an evaluation of the goodness of fit of the model to the data and statistical output that can be used to modify the model.

The initial model of VR clients' occupational attainment did not yield an acceptable fit. The analysis indicated that the opportunity structure variables did not have a significant determining effect on employment outcomes. A subsequent analysis of the revised model (opportunity structure eliminated) suggested that one of the work values scales should also be deleted.

The final modified model of VR clients' employment outcomes was highly statistically significant. Educational achievement was the major determinant of occupational attainment, with work values providing a smaller but useful independent contribution. This finding suggests that vocational rehabilitation efforts should include strategies for evaluating clients' educational potential and enhancing clients' educational development.

Single-Subject Research

The case study, which refers to the intensive investigation of the psychological functioning of a single person, is the oldest research strategy for the study of human behavior. Investigators as varied as Ebbinghaus, Freud, Piaget, and Wolpe relied on careful study of individual subjects as the basis for their classical formulations. Still, with increasing emphasis on rigorous adherence to scientific methodology in psychology and related areas, especially in the 1940s and 1950s, the case study approach fell into disrepute. Only in the last 15 to 20 years has interest in single-subject research been renewed.

It is important to distinguish between two different approaches to studies of individuals: the traditional clinical case study, which depends almost exclusively on the therapeutic interview as the source of data, and various quantitative approaches to the investigation of individual behavior. The latter can be further divided into two broad classes: (a) nonmanipulative, longitudinal, psychometric studies that require repeated assessments over lengthy periods of time, and (b) intervention designs that use fairly simple measures of change, such as counting the frequency of target behaviors that occur. The reader interested in in-depth treatments of the topic of single-subject research is referred to Chassan (1979), Kazdin (1982), and Kratochwill (1978). A popular design in rehabilitation, called the multiple-baseline strategy, is discussed and illustrated by Godley and Cuvo (1981), Godley, Hafer, Vieceli, and Godley (1984), Hinman and Marr (1984), and Pancsofar and Bates (1984).

An important advantage of single-subject research is that its findings are usually directly applicable in counseling practice. Case study reports, in particular, provide results that are perceived by practitioners to be relevant and possess high generalizability. Although methodologists may doubt the generalizability of conclusions derived from case studies, they should recognize that the individual case report is a useful device for communicating research findings to counseling practitioners.

Heinemann and Shontz (1984, 1985) described and illustrated a strategy for single-subject research called the representative case method. This research approach investigates the complex psychological functioning of the whole person. The goal is achieved by collecting extensive data on a few individuals who are representative of the adjustment process being studied, rather than collecting limited information on a large sample of subjects.

The authors intensively studied two individuals with quadriplegia who had substantially different courses of adjustment to disability. The contrasts between the two persons provided a basis for examining the applicability of several explanations of adjustment to spinal cord injury (SCI). These included the following: (a) adjustment to SCI proceeds through a series of stages; (b) adjustment is a function of the individual's predisability personality; (c) emotional experience is inhibited by SCI; (d) depression or mourning after SCI is important to future adjustment; and (e) acceptance of personal responsibility for the injury enhances subsequent adjustment.

The two participants in the investigation were university graduate students. Craig was injured in a hang glider accident, whereas Diedre was injured in an automobile accident. Craig's active, risk-taking lifestyle was a factor in his injury; Diedre was a passive victim. Eight months after his accident, Craig attempted suicide but subsequently made a satisfactory adjustment; Diedre enrolled in rehabilitation studies with a career goal of helping persons with disabilities.

To provide a framework for studying the various hypothesized stages or phases of adjustment to SCI, each participant identified four critical episodes in his or her life:

1. An event typical of life before injury

2. An event that occurred shortly after hospitalization

3. An event when life seemed to lack purpose

4. An event when hope for the future was high

For each critical life episode, Craig and Diedre completed a depression inventory; an acceptance of disability questionnaire; a measure requiring judgments about 12 personal attributes (e.g., copes well with adversity, values physique, experiences emotion intensely); and a measure of self-perception that used items reflective of shock, defensive retreat, acknowledgment, and adaptation to change.

Analysis of the data located numerous differences between the participants: Diedre proceeded through the hypothesized stages (although not in the expected order), whereas Craig did not; Diedre engaged in a process of mourning her lost abilities, whereas Craig never admitted mourning his loss or engaging in defensive retreat; and Craig's personal constructs focused on achievement and physical performance, whereas Diedre's constructs reflected psychological sensitivity. Some of the authors' conclusions were that (a) integration of loss may be more complete when the individual proceeds through the stages of adjustment; (b) mourning of loss may not be essential to behavioral adjustment to SCI; (c) depression appears to be a normal early reaction to SCI; and (d) styles of adjustment to SCI tend to parallel preinjury styles of coping with life crises. Heinemann and Shontz's intensive study of two persons with quadriplegia did not demonstrate any one of the theories to be superior to the others in explaining adjustment to SCI. On the contrary, the various explanatory mechanisms were viewed as having equivalent applicability in understanding the adjustment process in individual cases. Readers interested in the complementary results of a traditional approach to studying the life adjustment of vocational rehabilitation clients with SCI are referred to D. W. Cook, Bolton, and Taperek (1981).

Integrative Reviews

Several hundred empirical studies are reported in the various journals in rehabilitation and related areas of counseling practice every year. Over a period of 5 to 10 years, the number of studies runs into the thousands. It is inevitable (and desirable) that there is substantial duplication of effort in that the same topic is independently researched by two or more investigators. When two or more studies address the same topic using similar research procedures, the independent studies are called replications. The reason why replication is desirable in research is that professionals can have much greater confidence in conclusions that are based on the convergent findings of independent investigations.

It is not unusual to locate 20, 30, or even 50 studies of the same topic in the general psychological literature. In their comprehensive review of counseling and psychotherapy outcome studies, Smith, Glass, and Miller (1980) examined 1,766 comparisons between treatment and control groups derived from 475 separate investigations. These researchers concluded that the typical client receiving counseling or psychotherapy was better off than 80% of the control subjects. Readers will also be interested in the results of Spokane and Oliver's (1983) analysis of 52 studies of vocational counseling interventions: The average client receiving some type of vocational intervention exceeded 80% of untreated subjects on the criterion measure.

In general, there are two strategies for synthesizing the results of a large number of independent investigations. The first, which may be called the judgmental procedure, relies on the reviewer's ability to appraise the relative merits of a set of studies and judgmentally integrate the findings into a series of general conclusions (e.g., Bolton, 1981). The second, known as meta-analysis, requires that the results of each investigation be reduced to a common metric; these data are then subjected to various statistical analyses (see Glass, McGaw, & Smith, 1981; Hunter & Schmidt, 1990; Light & Pillemer, 1984). Meta-analysis is a quantitative procedure that is used to summarize the results of many independently conducted studies that address the same research issue. The final product of a meta-analytic review is an overall estimate of the efficacy of a particular intervention strategy. The primary feature of the effect size estimate generated is that it is a highly reliable and broadly generalizable indicator of treatment benefit for a specified client population.

The limitations of the meta-analytic approach to research synthesis are directly related to the fundamental assumptions made. For a meta-analysis to produce valid conclusions, the constituent studies must focus on the same client population, involve a common intervention strategy, and measure target variables that reflect a defined domain of outcomes.

Numerous examples of quantitative meta-analyses are reported in the counseling and psychological literature, including a second-order meta-analysis of 302 meta-analytic investigations (Lipsey & Wilson, 1993). Only one meta-analysis has been reported in the rehabilitation literature. This study is summarized below. The reason for the virtual absence of meta-analyses in rehabilitation is that the number of studies published in the specialized rehabilitation journals is not large enough to provide a sufficient database to warrant the use of quantitative integrative procedures.

Bolton and Akridge (1995) conducted a meta-analysis to summarize the results of 15 experimental studies of 10 small-group skills training interventions that were developed for use with vocational rehabilitation clients. The focus of the 10 skills training programs is on career-related issues and preparation for employment (e.g., Life Career Skills, Occupational Choice Strategy, Peer Counseling Training, and Relationship Skills). The training process consists of lectures, demonstrations, and practice in simulated career situations. Primary teaching techniques are verbal instruction, modeling, behavioral rehearsal, coaching, response feedback, and homework assignments.

All 15 investigations were true experiments with participants randomly assigned to experimental and control groups. Nine of the investigations entailed pretest and posttest measurement of the participants, whereas six of the studies used a posttest-only design. The research population of participants was the same for all 15 investigations and could be accurately characterized as "difficult" or "high risk" clients. The 61 outcome measures used were of three types: behavioral performance measures, self-report instruments, and observer judgments.

The meta-analysis of the 15 experimental studies of small-group skills training interventions was carried out following the steps described by Glass et al. (1981) and Hunter and Schmidt (1990):

1. Effect sizes were calculated for all 61 variables measured in the 15 studies. An effect size is computed by dividing the difference between the experimental and control group means by the standard deviation (i.e., a standard score).

2. Average effect sizes were calculated for each of the 15 studies.

3. The overall effect size for all 15 studies, weighted by the study sample sizes, was computed. The weighted mean effect size was +.82 standard deviations.

4. The weighted mean effect size was corrected for unreliability of the outcome measures. The correction for attenuation produced an estimated true population effect size of +.93.

The straightforward interpretation of this effect size is that the average participant in the skills training programs exceeded 82% of the control subjects on the outcome measures.

It is important to appreciate the scope of the research foundation for this conclusion. Two hundred and twenty vocational rehabilitation clients received a total of 6,420 hours of skills training and were measured on 61 outcome variables while participating in 10 different skills intervention programs that were evaluated in 15 experimental studies. Even in this relatively small meta-analysis, the estimate of overall benefit was based on a large set of data.

It can be concluded from the results of this meta-analysis that the typical vocational rehabilitation client benefits substantially from participation in one of the small-group skills intervention programs. The clear implication is that skills training interventions should be implemented more widely with "difficult" clients. Also, students in rehabilitation education programs should be trained in the theory and application of skills training programs with clients with more severe disabilities.

Research Utilization

Research in rehabilitation is funded and conducted for the purpose of discovering new knowledge or developing applications of existing knowledge that will improve the effectiveness of medical, vocational, and psychosocial services for persons with disabilities. It is obvious that research results must be delivered to service providers in a usable form if any benefit is to be realized. The discipline of research utilization (RU) emerged in the last 30 years to address this critical linkage between researchers and research consumers.

The goal of RU efforts is simple: to get new knowledge and research-based techniques to practitioners using modes of communication and dissemination that maximize applications in rehabilitation service systems. Rehabilitation was the first human service profession to attack the problem of poor research utilization some 25 years ago. The innovative RU strategies that were developed and evaluated during the first decade of activity were described by Bolton (1975). All the early strategies were successful in enhancing the use of research by practitioners and could be profitably implemented today by VR agencies, facilities, or professional associations. A detailed, systematic review of information service provision in rehabilitation was given by Senkevitch and Roth (1981).

An important emerging strategy for enhancing research utilization in rehabilitation is to involve consumers in the research process (Childers & Rice, 1992). People with disabilities, members of families of people with disabilities, and rehabilitation service providers must be included in all phases of research sponsored by the National Institute on Disability and Rehabilitation Research (NIDRR; Graves, 1992). The NIDRR policy, which is referred to as Constituency-Oriented

Research and Dissemination (CORD), requires that consumers participate actively at key stages in the research process, including problem definition, project implementation, interpretation of results, and dissemination of findings (Fenton, Batavia, & Roody, 1993). In the CORD model, researchers are viewed as technical specialists who need input from constituents to ensure that projects are relevant to the concerns and problems of the target populations.

The underlying principles of consumer involvement in rehabilitation research are inclusion and meaningful participation in the research enterprise. The specific impetus for constituent participation in research was the perception that rehabilitation research was not addressing and solving problems faced by people with disabilities, their family members, and service providers. More generally, consumer participation in research evolved out of the disability rights movement that was initiated in the early 1970s and culminated in the Americans with Disabilities Act of 1990 and the Rehabilitation Act Amendments of 1992. This legislation guaranteed equal access in the public sector and presumptive eligibility for vocational rehabilitation services for people with severe disabilities, and also established the foundation for full participation in service delivery and research by people with disabilities and other constituents.

The immediate effect of consumer participation in the development and conduct of rehabilitation research will be shared responsibility for the research process and project outcomes. Constituents will increasingly serve as expert information sources, members of advisory boards, advocates for projects, collaborators in the conduct of studies, and promoters of system change based on the results of research. Ultimately, the full participation of people with disabilities and other constituents will bring individuals with direct life experience with disability into the research planning process and will enhance the applicability and utility of research outcomes (Menz, 1995).

In the concluding section of this chapter, the major sources of research-based knowledge for use by rehabilitation counselors and related practitioners are briefly described, and a model for individual RU is outlined. Almost all RU programs in the United States are funded by the National Institute on Disability and Rehabilitation Research (NIDRR) in Washington, D.C. Exceptions are the various professional and academic journals published by nonprofit professional organizations. The five primary sources of rehabilitation research information are as follows:

1. Research and training (R&T) centers. Presently, 42 R&T centers conduct applied research and sponsor short-term training programs for rehabilitation practitioners. Half of the R&T centers focus on medical conditions, such as spinal cord injury, cardiac disease, arthritis, and diseases of elderly persons, and half of the centers address vocational or psychosocial topics, such as employment and independent living, or focus on specific populations, such as persons with mental retardation and visual impairments. In addition to disseminating research find-

ings through their short-term training programs and research monographs, R&T centers use the remaining four sources to reach practitioners.

2. *Rehabilitation BRIEFs.* Twelve issues of the *BRIEFs* (Bringing Research Into Effective Focus) are published each year. *BRIEFs* are four-page topical summaries, written in a highly readable style, that emphasize examples, illustrations, and straightforward suggestions. Published on heavy paper that is conveniently punched for storage in a three-hole notebook, recent topics have included information systems, enhancing employability, independent living research, and community integration of individuals with traumatic brain injury.

3. Resource centers. More than 20 resource centers for research information in rehabilitation are currently operating. Three of these serve the professional information needs of rehabilitation counselors, vocational evaluators, and administrators. The National Clearinghouse of Rehabilitation Training Materials at Oklahoma State University in Stillwater, Oklahoma, serves as a national repository for rehabilitation training materials and related information. The National Rehabilitation Information Center (NARIC) located in Silver Spring, Maryland, houses a complete collection of reports generated by NIDRR grants and contracts. NARIC also prepares annotated bibliographies on requested topics. The Rehabilitation Resource at Stout State University in Menominie, Wisconsin, is the national center for information on vocational evaluation and work adjustment.

4. Institute on Rehabilitation Issues. The Institute on Rehabilitation Issues (IRI) is a cooperative project sponsored by state VR agencies, three research and training centers, and consumer organizations. Every year since 1973, three prime study groups have focused on three topics of critical concern to the rehabilitation community. The objectives of the IRI study groups are to investigate an issue or problem thoroughly and to develop a professional training resource publication. The resource publications are practical manuals that can be used as self-study guides or as text materials for in-service training and staff development. Examples of recent IRI topics are employer strategies in vocational rehabilitation, cultural diversity in rehabilitation, and consumer involvement in rehabilitation research and practice.

5. Professional rehabilitation journals. Probably the most accessible and most often used resources for practitioners are the professional journals. These are typically quarterly publications of the main professional associations in rehabilitation, and contain a variety of articles ranging from theoretical to empirical to practical suggestions on subjects directly relevant to rehabilitation service provision. The refereed journals in rehabilitation counseling are *Journal of Applied Rehabilitation Counseling, Journal of Rehabilitation, Journal of Rehabilitation Administration, Psychosocial Rehabilitation Journal, Rehabilitation Counseling Bulletin, Journal of Disability Policy Studies, Rehabilitation Psychology,* and *Vocational Evaluation and Work Adjustment Bulletin.* Numerous other journals in counseling, psychology, and social work also are relevant to the professional concerns of rehabilitation counselors.

These five sources of information about rehabilitation research can provide the practitioner with a full range of useful knowledge and practical techniques. How can rehabilitation professionals actually use research information to improve the delivery of services to persons with disabilities? This chapter concludes with five steps that the practitioner can follow (based on Backer, 1980):

1. *Diagnosis.* RU begins with the diagnosis of a professional problem, which means identifying and clearly describing the problem and then deciding that new information is required to address the problem.

2. *Information search.* This step obviously involves going to one or more of the sources of information listed above to locate knowledge or techniques that may apply to the problem. Because personal contact has been demonstrated to increase RU, practitioners may want to call one of the resource centers to discuss the problem with an information expert.

3. *Information evaluation.* Once relevant information is located, it is necessary to make a professional judgment regarding the chances of successful application (i.e., the practitioner should be reasonably confident that the new information can contribute to the solution of the problem). At this stage, it is a good idea to prepare a written implementation plan and to obtain comments and suggestions from supervisors and colleagues about the plan's feasibility.

4. *Implementation.* After the plan is appropriately modified using input from others, it is ready to be implemented. If the problem is limited to one aspect of an individual's counseling or case management activity, implementation is straightforward. However, if a new program is being installed in an agency or facility, implementation may be a major operation. In this case, the collaborating participants must be prepared to make the inevitable adjustments and revisions that accompany any planned change.

5. *Evaluation.* To know whether the new knowledge or technique had a beneficial effect on the problem, it is necessary to conduct some type of evaluation. The evaluation may involve the collection of pertinent data before and after implementation of the plan, or it may simply rely on the individual practitioner's personal satisfaction with the modification that was tried. But to complete the RU cycle, some evaluation of the degree of problem solution accomplished should be made.

Considering that the ultimate objective of all rehabilitation endeavors is the rehabilitation of individuals with disabilities, one might reasonably inquire about the role of RU within these endeavors. RU is clearly intended to advance both the science and the art of rehabilitation counseling through a diversity of research efforts. Unquestionably, effective research utilization by rehabilitation practitioners is the primary means by which the results of research can be translated into practical benefits for rehabilitation clients.

References

Americans with Disabilities Act of 1990, 42 U.S.C. § 12101 *et seq.*

Babbie, E. (1979). *The practice of social research* (2nd ed.). Belmont, CA: Wadsworth.

Backer, T. E. (1980). Putting research to use: Some guidelines for rehabilitation professionals. In D. Dew, R. Sadler, & A. Casey (Eds.), *Proceedings of the workshop: Putting research to use in rehabilitation* (pp. 15–25). Washington, DC: George Washington University Rehabilitation Research and Training Center.

Becker, R. L. (1989). *Evaluator's manual for the Becker Work Adjustment Profile.* Columbus, OH: Elbern.

Bentler, P. M. (1980). Multivariate analysis with latent variables: Causal modeling. *Annual Review of Psychology, 31,* 419–456.

Betz, N., & Weiss, D. J. (1987). Validity. In B. Bolton (Ed.), *Handbook of measurement and evaluation in rehabilitation* (2nd ed., pp. 37–55). Baltimore: Brookes.

Bolton, B. (Ed.). (1975). Research utilization in rehabilitation [Special issue]. *Rehabilitation Counseling Bulletin, 19.*

Bolton, B. (1981). Follow-up studies in vocational rehabilitation. *Annual Review of Rehabilitation, 2,* 58–82.

Bolton, B. (1986). Minnesota Satisfactoriness Scales. In D. J. Keyer & R. C. Sweetland (Eds.), *Test critiques* (Vol. 4, pp. 434–439). Kansas City, MO: Test Corporation of America.

Bolton, B. (Ed.). (1987). *Handbook of measurement and evaluation in rehabilitation* (2nd ed.). Baltimore: Brookes.

Bolton, B. (1988). Multivariate approaches to human learning. In J. N. Nesselroade & R. B. Cattell (Eds.), *Handbook of multivariate experimental psychology* (2nd ed., pp. 789–819). New York: Plenum.

Bolton, B. (1991a). Becker Work Adjustment Profile. In J. J. Kramer & J. C. Conoley (Eds.), *The eleventh mental measurements yearbook* (pp. 83–84). Lincoln, NE: Buros Institute of Mental Measurements.

Bolton, B. (1991b). Disability Factor Scales. In D. J. Keyser & R. C. Sweetland (Eds.), *Test critiques* (Vol. 9, pp. 184–192). Kansas City, MO: Test Corporation of America.

Bolton, B. (1994). Acceptance of Disability Scale. In D. J. Keyser & R. C. Sweetland (Eds.), *Test critiques* (Vol. 10, pp. 8–12). Kansas City, MO: Test Corporation of America.

Bolton, B., & Akridge, R. L. (1995). A meta-analysis of skills training programs for rehabilitation clients. *Rehabilitation Counseling Bulletin, 38,* 262–273.

Bolton, B., & Brookings, J. (1993). Appraising the psychometric adequacy of rehabilitation assessment instruments. In R. L. Glueckhauf, L. B. Sechrest, G. R. Bond, & E. C. McDonel (Eds.), *Improving assessment in rehabilitation and health* (pp. 109–132). Newbury Park, CA: Sage.

Campbell, J., Daft, R., & Hulin, C. (1982). *What to study: Generating and developing research questions.* Beverly Hills, CA: Sage.

Campbell, D., & Stanley, J. (1966). *Experimental and quasi-experimental designs for research.* Chicago: Rand McNally.

Cattell, R. B. (1978). *The scientific use of factor analysis in behavioral and life sciences.* New York: Plenum.

Chassan, J. B. (1979). *Research design in clinical psychology and psychiatry* (2nd ed.). New York: Irvington.

Childers, D., & Rice, B. D. (1992). *Consumer involvement in rehabilitation research and practice.* Hot Springs: Arkansas Research and Training Center in Vocational Rehabilitation.

Christensen, L. (1988). *Experimental methodology* (4th ed.). Boston: Allyn & Bacon.

Cohen, J. (1962). The statistical power of abnormal–social psychological research: A review. *Journal of Abnormal and Social Psychology, 65,* 145-153.

Cohen, J. (1988). *Statistical power analysis for the behavioral sciences* (3rd ed.). New York: Academic Press.

Cook, D. W., Bolton, B., & Taperek, P. (1981). Rehabilitation of the spinal cord injured: Life status at follow-up. *Rehabilitation Counseling Bulletin, 25,* 110-122.

Cook, T., & Campbell, D. (1979). *Quasi-experimentation: Design and analysis issues for field settings.* Chicago: Rand McNally.

Cook, T., & Campbell, D. (1983). The design and conduct of quasi-experiments and true experiments in field settings. In M. Dunnette (Ed.), *Handbook of industrial and organizational psychology* (pp. 223-326). Chicago: Rand McNally.

Cook, T., Campbell, D., & Peracchio, L. (1990). Quasi experimentation. In M. Dunnette & L. Hough (Eds.), *Handbook of industrial and organizational psychology* (2nd ed., Vol. 1, pp. 491-576). Palo Alto, CA: Consulting Psychologists.

Cronbach, L. J. (1984). *Essentials of psychological testing* (4th ed.). New York: Harper & Row.

De Charms, R. (1968). *Personal causation.* New York: Academic Press.

Draper, N., & Smith, H. (1981). *Applied regression analysis* (2nd ed.). New York: Wiley.

Fenton, J., Batavia, A., & Roody, D. S. (1993). *Constituency-oriented research and dissemination (CORD).* Washington, DC: National Institute on Disability and Rehabilitation Research.

Gelso, C. J. (1985). Rigor, relevance, and counseling research: On the need to maintain our course between Scylla and Charyodis. *Journal of Counseling and Development, 63,* 551-553.

Gibson, D. L., Weiss, D. J., Dawis, R. V., & Lofquist, L. H. (1970). *Manual for the Minnesota Satisfactoriness Scales* (Minnesota Studies in Vocational Rehabilitation, No. 27). Minneapolis: University of Minnesota, Vocational Psychology Research.

Glass, G. V., McGaw, B., & Smith, M. L. (1981). *Meta-analysis in social research.* Beverly Hills, CA: Sage.

Godley, S. H., & Cuvo, A. J. (1981). Single-subject experimental designs: Applications to rehabilitation administration. *Journal of Rehabilitation Administration, 5,* 14-22.

Godley, S. H., Hafer, M. D., Vieceli, L., & Godley, M. D. (1984). Evaluation of short-term training in rehabilitation: A neglected necessity. *Rehabilitation Counseling Bulletin, 27,* 291-301.

Gorsuch, R. (1983). *Factor analysis* (2nd ed.). Philadelphia: Saunders.

Graves, W. H. (1992). Participatory research: A partnership among individuals with disabilities, rehabilitation professionals, and rehabilitation researchers. *Rehabilitation Education, 6,* 221-224.

Guilford, J., & Fruchter, B. (1978). *Fundamental statistics in psychology and education* (6th ed.). New York: McGraw-Hill.

Harris, R. J. (1985). *A primer of multivariate analysis* (2nd ed.). New York: Academic Press.

Hays, W. (1981). *Statistics* (3rd ed.). New York: Holt, Rinehart & Winston.

Heinemann, A. W., & Shontz, F. C. (1984). Adjustment following disability: Representative case studies. *Rehabilitation Counseling Bulletin, 58,* 3–14.

Heinemann, A. W., & Shontz, F. C. (1985). Methods of studying persons. *Counseling Psychologist, 13,* 111–125.

Hinman, S., & Marr, J. N. (1984). Training counselors to write behavior-based client objectives. *Rehabilitation Counseling Bulletin, 27,* 291–301.

Howard, G. S. (1985). Can research in the human sciences become more relevant to practice? *Journal of Counseling and Development, 63,* 539–544.

Hunter, J. E., & Schmidt, F. L. (1990). *Methods of meta-analysis.* Newbury Park, CA: Sage.

Jøreskog, K. G., & Sørbom, D. (1984). *LISREL VI: Analysis of linear stuctural relationships by the method of maximum likelihood* (3rd ed.). Mooresville, IN: Scientific Software.

Kazdin, A. E. (1982). *Single-case research designs: Methods for clinical and applied settings.* New York: Oxford University Press.

Kerlinger, F. (1986). *Foundations of behavioral research* (3rd ed.). New York: Holt.

Kratochwill, T. R. (Ed.). (1978). *Single-subject research: Strategies for evaluating change.* New York: Academic Press.

Leahy, M. J., Szymanski, E. M., & Linkowski, D. C. (1993). Knowledge importance in rehabilitation counseling. *Rehabilitation Counseling Bulletin, 37,* 130–145.

Lewis, F. D., & Bolton, B. (1986). Latent structure modeling of occupational attainment by vocational rehabilitation clients. *Rehabilitation Counseling Bulletin, 29,* 166–172.

Light, R. J., & Pillemer, D. B. (1984). *Summing up: The science of reviewing research.* Cambridge, MA: Harvard University Press.

Linkowski, D. C. (1987). *The Acceptance of Disability Scale.* Washington, DC: Rehabilitation Research and Training Center, George Washington University Medical Center.

Lipsey, M. (1990). *Design sensitivity: Statistical power for experimental research.* Newbury Park, CA: Sage.

Lipsey, M. W., & Wilson, D. B. (1993). The efficacy of psychological, educational, and behavioral treatment. *American Psychologist, 48,* 1181–1209.

Mason, E., & Bramble, W. (1978). *Understanding and conducting research: Applications in education and the behavioral sciences.* New York: McGraw-Hill.

Matkin, R., Hafer, M., Wright, W., & Lutzker, J. (1983). Pretesting artifacts: A study of attitudes toward disability. *Rehabilitation Counseling Bulletin, 5,* 342–348.

Menz, F. E. (1995). *Constituents make the difference: Improving the value of rehabilitation research.* Menomonie, WI: Rehabilitation Research and Training Center.

Morrison, D. F. (1990). *Multivariate statistical methods* (3rd ed.). New York: McGraw-Hill.

Pancsofar, E., & Bates, P. (1984). Multiple-baseline designs for evaluating instructional effectiveness. *Rehabilitation Counseling Bulletin, 28,* 67–77.

Parker, R. (1990). Power, control, and validity in research. *Journal of Learning Disabilities, 23,* 613–620.

Parker, R. (1993). Editorial: Threats to the validity of research. *Rehabilitation Counseling Bulletin, 36,* 130–138.

Parker, R., & Szymanski, E. (1992). Editorial: Fishing and error rate problem. *Rehabilitation Counseling Bulletin, 36,* 66–69.

Rehabilitation Act Amendments of 1992, 29 U.S.C. § 701 *et seq.*

Russell, B. (1913). On the notion of cause. *Proceedings of the Aristotelian Society* (New Series), *13,* 1–26.

Rychlak, J. (1977). *The psychology of rigorous humanism.* New York: Wiley.

Saretsky, G. (1972). The OEO P.C. experiment and the John Henry effect. *Phi Delta Kappan, 53,* 579–581.

Scarr, S. (1985). Constructing psychology: Making facts and fables for our times. *American Psychologist, 40,* 499–512.

Senkevitch, J. J., & Roth, H. (1981). Organizing and delivering rehabilitation information. *Annual Review of Rehabilitation, 2,* 239–268.

Siller, J. (1970). Generality of attitudes toward the physically disabled. *Proceedings of the 78th Annual Convention of the American Psychological Association, 5,* 697–698.

Smith, M. L., Glass, G. V., & Miller, T. L. (1980). *The benefits of psychotherapy.* Baltimore: Johns Hopkins University Press.

Spokane, A. R., & Oliver, L. W. (1983). The outcomes of vocational intervention. In W. B. Walsh & S. H. Osipow (Eds.), *Handbook of vocational psychology* (Vol. 2, pp. 99–136). Hillsdale, NJ: Erlbaum.

Szymanski, E. M., Leahy, M. J., & Linkowski, D. C. (1993). Reported preparedness of certified counselors in rehabilitation counseling knowledge areas. *Rehabilitation Counseling Bulletin, 37,* 146–162.

Szymanski, E. M., Linkowski, D. C., Leahy, M. J., Diamond, E. E., & Thoreson, R. W. (1993). Human resource development: An examination of perceived training needs of certified rehabilitation counselors. *Rehabilitation Counseling Bulletin, 37,* 163–181.

Szymanski, E., & Parker, R. (1989). Competitive closure rate of rehabilitation client with severe disabilities as a function of counselor education and experience. *Rehabilitation Counseling Bulletin, 32,* 292–299.

Szymanski, E., & Parker, R. (1992). Editorial: Statistical power in rehabilitation research. *Rehabilitation Counseling Bulletin, 36,* 2–5.

Szymanski, E., Parker, R., & Borich, C. (1990). Aptitude treatment interaction designs in research on the relationship between rehabilitation counselor education and rehabilitation client outcome. *Rehabilitation Education, 4,* 85–92.

Thorndike, R. M. (1987). Reliability. In B. Bolton (Ed.), *Handbook of measurement and evaluation in rehabilitation* (2nd ed., pp. 21–36). Baltimore: Brookes.

Wright, B. A. (1983). *Physical disability: A psychosocial approach* (2nd ed.). New York: Harper & Row.

Wright, G. N., & Terrian, L. J. (1987). Rehabilitation Job Satisfaction Inventory. *Rehabilitation Counseling Bulletin, 31,* 159–176.

Yuker, H., Block, J., & Younng, J. (1970). *The measurement of attitudes toward disabled persons.* Albertson, NY: Human Resources Center.

Author Index

Subject Index

Notes

Notes

Notes

Notes